AN OVERVIEW OF METAB

DIGESTION

Proteins → Amino acids

Carbohydrates → Monosaccharides

Glycerol, Fatty acids

STORAGE AND TRANSPORT

Nitrogen Pool

Blood Sugar and Glycogen

Plasma Lipids and Triacylglycerols

Tissue Proteins

Ketogenic amino acids

Glucogenic amino acids

Gluconeogenesis

Embden-Meyerhof Pathway

ATP

β-Oxidation spiral

Fatty acid synthesis

METABOLISM

Transamination

$H_3CC(=O)-COH(=O)$
Pyruvic acid

$H_3CCH(OH)COH(=O)$
Lactic acid

CO_2

$H_3CC(=O)-SCoA$
Acetyl CoA

Urea Cycle

$H_2N-C(=O)-NH_2$
Urea

Citric Acid Cycle

CO_2

CO_2

Electron transport

Oxidative phosphorylation

ATP

O_2 → H_2O

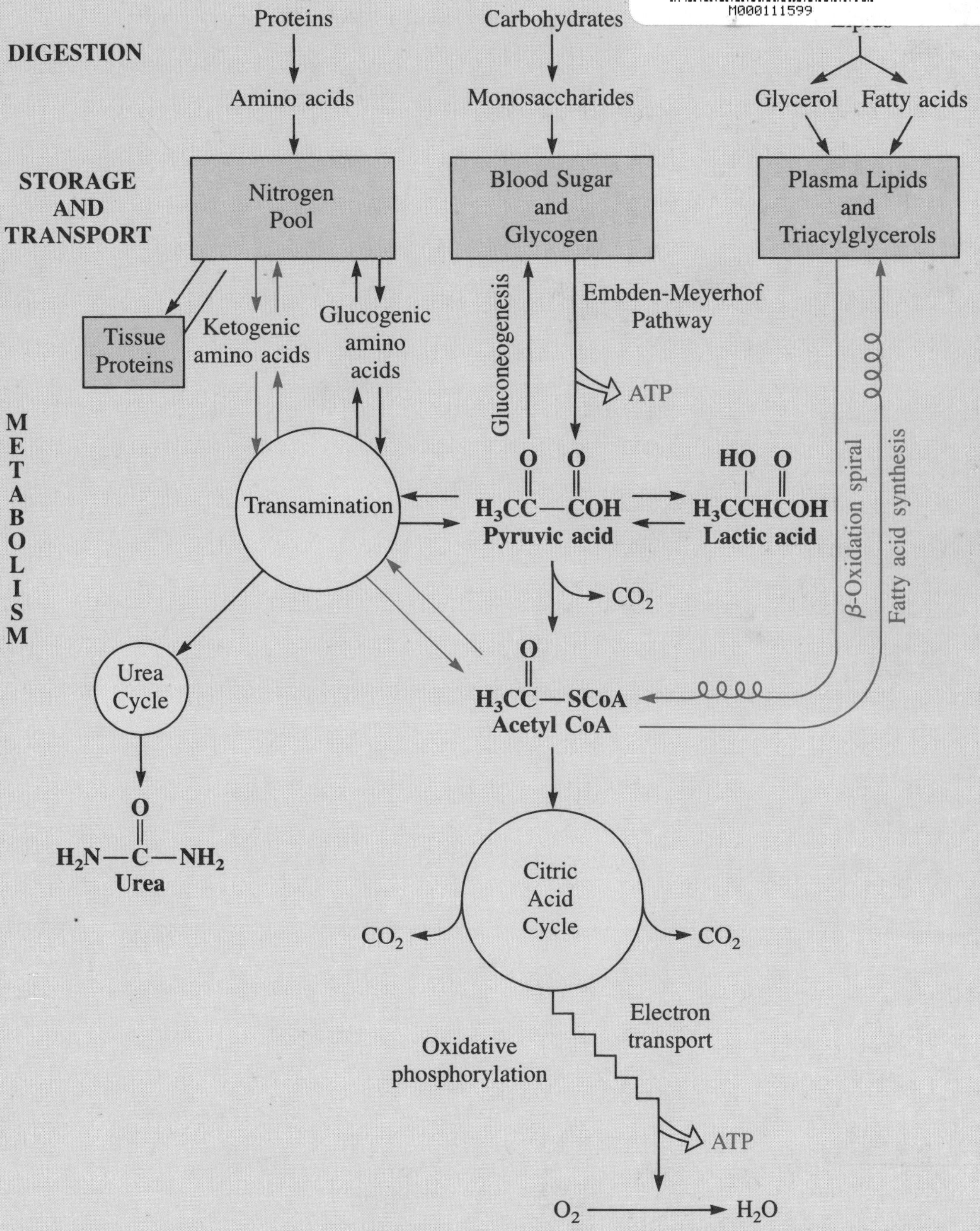

INTRODUCTION TO ORGANIC AND BIOCHEMISTRY

MORRIS HEIN

LEO R. BEST

SCOTT PATTISON

SUSAN ARENA

BROOKS/COLE PUBLISHING COMPANY
PACIFIC GROVE, CALIFORNIA

To Edna, Louise, Joan, and Frank

Brooks/Cole Publishing Company
A Division of Wadsworth, Inc.

Printed in the United States of America

10 9 8 7 6 5 4 3 2 1

Library of Congress Cataloging-in-Publication Data

Introduction to organic and biochemistry / Morris Hein ... [et al.].
p. cm.
Includes index.
ISBN 0-534-17316-0 : $42.00
1. Chemistry, Organic. 2. Biochemistry. I. Hein, Morris.
QD253.I58 1992 91-45818
547—dc20 CIP

Sponsoring Editors: Maureen A. Allaire, Harvey C. Pantzis
Editorial Assistant: Beth Wilbur
Print Buyer: Vena M. Dyer
Production: Julie Kranhold/Dianne Rhudy, Ex Libris; Joan Marsh
Manuscript Editor: Andrew Alden
Interior Design: Nancy Benedict
Interior Illustration: Nancy Benedict, Lotus Art, Pat Rogondino
Photo Researcher: Stuart Kenter
Typesetting: Polyglot Pte. Ltd. Compositors
Cover Printing: The Lehigh Press
Printing and Binding: Arcata Graphics, Hawkins County Plant
Cover Design: Vernon T. Boes
Cover Photo: Herb Charles Ohlmeyer/Fran Heyl Associates
Photo credits are listed after the index.

Preface

Many institutions require allied health students to take a two-quarter or multiple-semester chemistry sequence covering general, organic, and biochemistry. *Introduction to Organic and Biochemistry* is designed for professors who prefer to teach general chemistry from one text and organic and biochemistry from another. The contents of this book are identical to Chapters 21–37 of *College Chemistry: An Introduction to General, Organic, and Biochemistry, Fifth Edition*, published by Brooks/Cole for the complete general, organic, and biochemistry sequence. Therefore, although the title reads as if this were a first edition, the contents have been refined, reviewed, and revised through four previous editions. Those studying from this text will benefit from the countless suggestions of users and students, that have been incorporated into the text.

The material in *Introduction to Organic and Biochemistry* has been carefully selected to provide a foundation in each area that will allow the students to continue with science courses in related fields. Although some students have had experience with general chemistry prior to this course we believe a review is beneficial. Chapter 1 revisits the fundamentals of general chemistry which form the basis for a study of organic and biochemistry. Chapters 2–9 introduce topics in organic chemistry that are further integrated, developed, and applied in Chapters 10–18 on biochemistry.

Learning Aids

The use of multiple colors throughout the text highlight and identify important features and assist students in making efficient use of the book. Many full-color photos illustrate chemical principles and apply them to health-science and related fields.

- Each chapter begins with a **Chapter Preview**, listing sections covered in the chapter and an introduction that relates chemistry to aspects of modern living.
- Important **Key Terms** are set in boldfaced type where they are defined in the text, and they are also printed in color in the margin for quick review.
- Most **Examples** are followed by a **Practice Problem** (with answer) for immediate reinforcement of student learning.
- Many end-of-chapter **Exercises** have been included. Complete answers to all end-of-chapter **Exercises** are given in the *Solutions Manual*.

- A list of **Concepts in Review** is given at the end of each chapter to guide students in studying the most important concepts in the chapter.
- Most chapters feature a section called **Chemistry in Action**. The topics discussed include a variety of applications with particular emphasis in the health-science field. **Chemistry in Action** sections are designed to be supplemental to the main body of the text. However, end-of-chapter exercises do include questions relating to the **Chemistry in Action** topics.
- The Glossary/Index highlights **Key Terms** (with appropriate page reference) so that students may quickly refer back to the page where the term is defined and read the definition in context.

Supplements to Text

Materials that may be helpful to students and to their instructors have been developed to accompany the text. A short description of them follows.

Study Guide by Peter C. Scott of Linn-Benton Community College includes a self-evaluation section for students to check their understanding of each chapter's objectives, a recap section, and answers to the self-evaluation section.

Solutions Manual includes answers and solutions to all end-of-chapter questions and problems.

Instructor's Supplement includes a set of objective test questions and answers to the test questions.

College Chemistry in the Laboratory, 5th Edition, by Morris Hein, Leo R. Best, Robert L. Miner, and James M. Ritchey, includes 42 experiments for a laboratory program that may accompany the lecture course. Also included are Study Aids and Exercises.

Instructor's Manual to accompany the lab manual includes information on the management of the lab, evaluation of experiments, notes for individual experiments, a list of reagents required, and answer keys to each experiment's report form.

EXPTEST, the test generation system, Version 5.0 from Brooks/Cole for IBM PCs or compatibles.

Acknowledgments

We would like to thank the reviewers of the four previous editions of *College Chemistry*. Their contributions are incorporated into *Introduction to Organic and Biochemistry* and make it a better book. Although it is impossible to thank by name each of the many people who have been involved in the text, we are grateful for the friendship and many helpful comments from our colleagues and students who, over the years, helped to refine it.

No textbook can be completed without the untiring effort of many professionals in publishing. Special thanks to the talented staff at Brooks/Cole, especially Joan Marsh who, through her skill, knowledge, and patience, directed the production of this colorful book. Much credit also goes to Julie Kranhold of *Ex Libris* for her unfailing attention to detail and persistence in moving the book through production. We also appreciate the guidance of Harvey Pantzis, Executive Editor, and Maureen Allaire, Chemistry Editor.

M. Hein
L. Best
S. Pattison
S. Arena

CONTENTS

Chapter 11
Lipids 263

Chapter 12
Amino Acids, Polypeptides, and Proteins 286

Chapter 13
Enzymes 321

Chapter 14
Nucleic Acids and Heredity 339

Chapter 15
Nutrition 367

Chapter 16
Bioenergetics 393

Chapter 17
Carbohydrate Metabolism 414

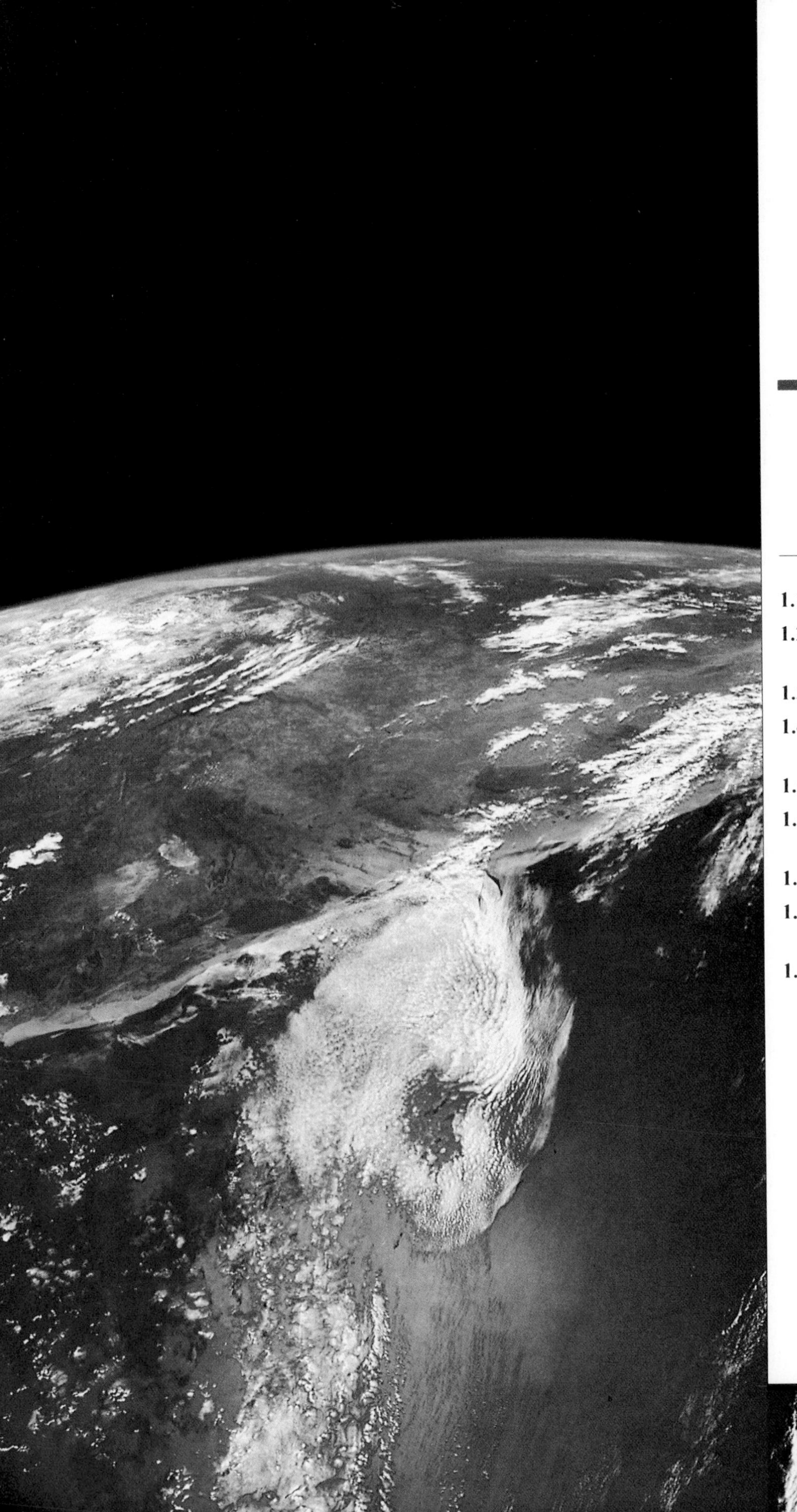

1

Chemical Fundamentals Revisited

◀ CHAPTER OPENING PHOTO: **Water on planet Earth as viewed from an Apollo spacecraft.**

Look around you. Everything you can see, hear, taste, and touch is the result of chemistry. The endless diversity and beauty of nature, from a colorful garden to a spectacular sunset, begins in chemical reactions. The myriad of common products surrounding us in our homes and offices are examples of our understanding of chemistry, especially the chemistry of carbon. To begin to study and comprehend the chemistry of carbon and its many compounds it is essential to understand the fundamentals of chemistry. In this chapter we begin by revisiting a number of important chemical principles.

1.1 ATOMIC STRUCTURE

The periodic table is an arrangement of the elements into horizontal periods and vertical groups or families of elements. The atomic structure of the elements makes this arrangement of the elements possible.

An atom is composed of a positively charged nucleus surrounded by a negatively charged cloud of electrons distributed in space around the nucleus. The nucleus consists mainly of protons and neutrons. The **atomic number** of an element is the number of protons in the nucleus. The number of electrons in a neutral atom is equal to the number of protons. The relative electrical charge of a proton is $+1$ and that of an electron is -1, accounting for the neutrality of the atom. The atomic numbers of the elements in the periodic table increase from left to right in each period (See Table 1.1).

atomic number

Electrons are located in orbitals at specified distances from the nucleus known as principal energy levels or electron shells. These shells are numbered 1, 2, 3, 4, 5, 6, and 7. Within each principal energy level electrons exist at slightly different energies in what are known as energy sublevels. There are four energy sublevels, *s*, *p*, *d*, and *f*. Each principal energy level can have at most one *s*, three *p*, five *d*, and seven *f* sublevel orbitals. Each orbital can contain two electrons. When an orbital contains two electrons, they are said to be paired.

The first electron shell contains only one orbital, the 1*s* orbital. Thus the capacity of the first shell is two electrons. The second electron shell has two kinds of orbitals, one 2*s* and three equivalent 2*p* orbitals. Each of these can contain two electrons, thus the second shell has a capacity of eight electrons. The third electron shell has three types of orbitals, one 3*s* orbital, three 3*p* orbitals, and five 3*d* orbitals, for a maximum capacity of 18 electrons. Table 1.2 shows

TABLE 1.1 Partial Periodic Table of the Elements

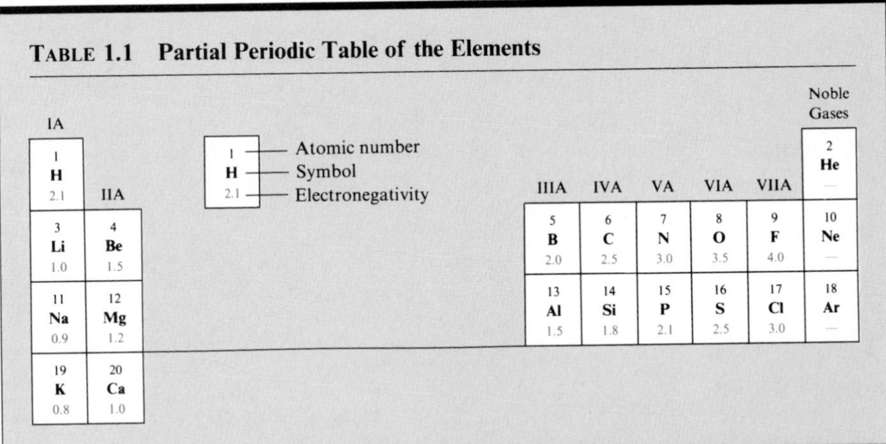

Key: 1 = Atomic number; H = Symbol; 2.1 = Electronegativity

IA	IIA	IIIA	IVA	VA	VIA	VIIA	Noble Gases
1 H 2.1							2 He —
3 Li 1.0	4 Be 1.5	5 B 2.0	6 C 2.5	7 N 3.0	8 O 3.5	9 F 4.0	10 Ne —
11 Na 0.9	12 Mg 1.2	13 Al 1.5	14 Si 1.8	15 P 2.1	16 S 2.5	17 Cl 3.0	18 Ar —
19 K 0.8	20 Ca 1.0						

TABLE 1.2 Sublevel Electron Orbitals in Each Principal Energy Level and the Maximum Number of Orbitals and Electrons in Each Energy Level

Principal energy level	Sublevel electron	Maximum number of orbitals	Maximum number of electrons
1	*s*	1	2
2	*s*, *p*	4	8
3	*s*, *p*, *d*	9	18
4	*s*, *p*, *d*, *f*	16	32
5	*s*, *p*, *d*, *f*	Incomplete[a]	(50)[a]
6	*s*, *p*, *d*	Incomplete[a]	(72)[a]
7	*s*	Incomplete[a]	(98)[a]

[a] Insufficient electrons to complete the shell.

the type of sublevel and the maximum number or orbitals in each principal energy level. Table 1.3 shows the electron structure of the first 20 elements, hydrogen to calcium.

Shells and energy sublevels are successively filled with electrons as one goes from H, atomic number 1, to He, atomic number 2, to Li, atomic number 3, and so on. In any principal energy level the order of energy sublevels is such that the *s* orbital is lower in energy than the *p* orbitals, which are lower in energy than the *d* orbitals, which are lower in energy than the *f* orbitals. Thus, in each energy level the *s* orbital is filled with electrons before the *p* orbitals, and so on. This order of filling electrons can be seen in Table 1.3.

The outermost shell of electrons is called the valence shell, and the electrons therein are known as the **valence electrons**. The atoms in the vertical groups in the periodic table contain the same number of valence electrons. Since the chemical properties of the elements depend on their valence electrons, the elements in any particular group (or family) should show some similarities in chemical

valence electrons

TABLE 1.3 Electron Structure of the First Twenty Elements

Element	Number of protons (atomic number)	Number of electrons	Electron structure
H	1	1	$1s^1$
He	2	2	$1s^2$
Li	3	3	$1s^22s^1$
Be	4	4	$1s^22s^2$
B	5	5	$1s^22s^22p^1$
C	6	6	$1s^22s^22p^2$
N	7	7	$1s^22s^22p^3$
O	8	8	$1s^22s^22p^4$
F	9	9	$1s^22s^22p^5$
Ne	10	10	$1s^22s^22p^6$
Na	11	11	$1s^22s^22p^63s^1$
Mg	12	12	$1s^22s^22p^63s^2$
Al	13	13	$1s^22s^22p^63s^23p^1$
Si	14	14	$1s^22s^22p^63s^23p^2$
P	15	15	$1s^22s^22p^63s^23p^3$
S	16	16	$1s^22s^22p^63s^23p^4$
Cl	17	17	$1s^22s^22p^63s^23p^5$
Ar	18	18	$1s^22s^22p^63s^23p^6$
K	19	19	$1s^22s^22p^63s^23p^64s^1$
Ca	20	20	$1s^22s^22p^63s^23p^64s^2$

behavior. The number of valence electrons in the representative elements, that is, the elements in Groups IA to VIIA, is the same as the group number. For example, all the elements in Group IA have one valence electron; the elements in Group IIA have two valence electrons; the elements in Group VIIA have seven valence electrons; and so forth.

Since the valence electrons are the electrons involved in chemical reactions, we can use Lewis-dot structures as a simplified method of representing the atoms. Dots are used to represent the valence electrons, and the symbol of the element represents all the rest of the atom. Thus H· is the Lewis-dot structure for a hydrogen atom, $1s^1$; $:\dot{B}$ is the Lewis-dot structure for a boron atom, $1s^22s^22p^1$; $:\ddot{\underset{\cdot\cdot}{Cl}}\cdot$ is the Lewis-dot structure for a chlorine atom, $1s^22s^22p^63s^23p^5$. Note that in each case the dots around the symbol represent only the number of electrons in the outermost energy level; one dot for hydrogen, three dots for boron, and seven dots for chlorine. The Lewis-dot structures for the first 20 elements are shown in Figure 1.1.

FIGURE 1.1 ▶ Lewis-dot diagrams of the first twenty elements. Dots represent electrons in the outermost energy level only.

H· He:

Li· Be: $:\dot{B}$ $:\dot{C}\cdot$ $:\underset{\cdot}{\dot{N}}\cdot$ $\cdot\ddot{\underset{\cdot}{O}}:$ $:\ddot{\underset{\cdot}{F}}:$ $:\ddot{\underset{\cdot\cdot}{Ne}}:$

Na· Mg: $:\dot{Al}$ $:\dot{Si}\cdot$ $:\underset{\cdot}{\dot{P}}\cdot$ $\cdot\ddot{\underset{\cdot}{S}}:$ $:\ddot{\underset{\cdot}{Cl}}:$ $:\ddot{\underset{\cdot\cdot}{Ar}}:$

K· Ca:

1.2 Principles of Chemical Bonding

The family of elements consisting of helium, neon, argon, krypton, xenon, and radon is known as the noble gases. All the noble gases except helium have eight electrons in their outermost energy level. Their electron structure is ns^2np^6 where n is a principal energy level. This electron arrangement is very stable and makes the atoms of the noble gases chemically unreactive. Recognition of the extraordinary stability of the noble gases led to the **octet rule**. Through chemical changes many of the elements tend to attain an electron structure of eight electrons in their outermost (valence) energy level, identical to that of the noble gases.

octet rule

An atom may attain a noble gas electron configuration by losing, gaining, or sharing electrons with other atoms. In so doing, chemical bonds are formed. In chemical changes the nucleus and hence the number of protons in an atom doesn't change. Thus the element, whether it loses, gains, or shares electrons, is still identified by its atomic number.

Electronegativity is the relative attractive force that an atom has for electrons in forming a chemical bond. All the atoms except the noble gases have an electronegativity value. On the Pauling electronegativity scale, metals have low values and nonmetals have high values, with fluorine having the highest value of 4.0 (See Table 1.1). The higher the electronegativity, the greater is the attraction for electrons.

electronegativity

The two main types of chemical bonds are ionic and covalent bonds. Ionic bonds are formed between atoms by the transfer of one or more electrons from one atom to another. The element that loses electrons becomes a cation (positive ion). The element that gains electrons becomes an anion (negative ion). The **ionic bond** is the attraction between the oppositely charged ions. A **covalent bond** is formed when two atoms share one or more pairs of electrons.

ionic bond

covalent bond

The Ionic Bond

The greater the difference in electronegativity between two atoms, the more likely the bond formed between them is ionic. For example, an ionic bond is formed between sodium and chlorine atoms when they form the compound sodium chloride. Sodium is in Group IA and has one valence electron. Chlorine is in Group VIIA and has seven valence electrons. By giving up its one valence electron, a sodium atom attains the electron configuration of the noble gas neon. When a chlorine atom gains one electron, it attains the electron configuration of the noble gas argon. So when one electron from a sodium atom transfers to a chlorine atom, a sodium ion (Na^+) and a chloride ion (Cl^-) are formed, and the compound NaCl is held together by an ionic bond. Each ion formed has a noble gas electron structure. Using Lewis-dot structures, the electron transfer may be shown as follows:

$$\mathrm{Na\cdot} + \mathrm{\cdot\ddot{\underset{\cdot\cdot}{Cl}}:} \longrightarrow [\mathrm{Na}]^+ + \left[\mathrm{:\ddot{\underset{\cdot\cdot}{Cl}}:}\right]^- \quad (\mathrm{NaCl})$$

Neon electron structure — Argon electron structure

Metals usually have one, two, or three valence electrons. When reacting, metals lose their valence electrons, attain a noble gas electron structure, and become cations. Nonmetals, on the other hand, are only a few electrons short of having a complete octet of valence electrons. In reacting with metals, nonmetals characteristically gain one, two, or three electrons, attain a noble gas electron structure, and become anions. Other examples of ionic bond formation are:

$$K\cdot + \cdot\overset{\cdot\cdot}{\underset{\cdot\cdot}{Br}}: \longrightarrow [K]^+ + \left[:\overset{\cdot\cdot}{\underset{\cdot\cdot}{Br}}:\right]^- \quad (KBr)$$

Argon electron structure — Krypton electron structure

$$:\overset{\cdot\cdot}{\underset{\cdot\cdot}{Cl}}\cdot + :Mg + \cdot\overset{\cdot\cdot}{\underset{\cdot\cdot}{Cl}}: \longrightarrow [Mg]^{2+} + 2\left[:\overset{\cdot\cdot}{\underset{\cdot\cdot}{Cl}}:\right]^- \quad (MgCl_2)$$

Neon electron structure — Argon electron structure

$$Na\cdot + :\overset{\cdot\cdot}{\underset{\cdot}{O}}\cdot + Na\cdot \longrightarrow 2[Na]^+ + \left[:\overset{\cdot\cdot}{\underset{\cdot\cdot}{O}}:\right]^{2-} \quad (Na_2O)$$

Neon electron structure — Neon electron structure

The Covalent Bond

The covalent bond is the most predominant bond in organic compounds. Atoms having identical or similar electronegativities form a covalent bond between them when they form compounds. For example, molecules of H_2, Cl_2, HCl, and H_2O contain covalent bonds between their atoms. Each atom may supply one of the two shared electrons, or one atom may furnish both electrons that are shared. Examples of Lewis-dot structures of molecules containing covalent bonds are:

$$H\cdot + \cdot H \longrightarrow H:H$$

$$:\overset{\cdot\cdot}{\underset{\cdot\cdot}{Cl}}\cdot + \cdot\overset{\cdot\cdot}{\underset{\cdot\cdot}{Cl}}: \longrightarrow :\overset{\cdot\cdot}{\underset{\cdot\cdot}{Cl}}:\overset{\cdot\cdot}{\underset{\cdot\cdot}{Cl}}:$$

$$H\cdot + \cdot\overset{\cdot\cdot}{\underset{\cdot\cdot}{Cl}}: \longrightarrow H:\overset{\cdot\cdot}{\underset{\cdot\cdot}{Cl}}:$$

$$H\cdot + :\overset{\cdot\cdot}{\underset{\cdot}{O}}\cdot + H\cdot \longrightarrow H:\overset{\cdot\cdot}{\underset{\underset{H}{\cdot\cdot}}{O}}:$$

The covalent bond is represented by the two dots between the atoms.

The atoms combine in such a ratio that the electron structure of each atom in the compound has an electron configuration of a noble gas. Thus, two hydrogen atoms combine to form a hydrogen molecule, in which each hydrogen atom shares two electrons and has an electron configuration of helium. In chlorine, each chlorine atom has an electron configuration of argon by sharing the central pair of electrons. In hydrogen chloride, chlorine needs one electron to complete its octet of electrons. This electron is furnished by one hydrogen atom. In water, oxygen needs two electrons to complete its octet and have a configuration of neon. Therefore, two hydrogen atoms, each with one electron, are needed to form a molecule of H_2O.

1.3 Isotopes

All atoms of the same element have the same number of protons in the nucleus, but, in most cases, do not have the same masses because some of the atoms have different numbers of neutrons in their nucleus. Atoms of an element having the same atomic number but different atomic masses are called **isotopes** of that element. Atoms of the various isotopes of an element, therefore, have the same number of protons and electrons, but different numbers of neutrons.

isotopes

Three isotopes of hydrogen are known. Each has one proton in the nucleus and one electron. The first isotope (protium) has no neutrons; it has a mass number of 1. The second isotope (deuterium), with one neutron in the nucleus, has a mass number of 2. The third isotope (tritium), with two neutrons in the nucleus, has a mass number of 3. The three isotopes of hydrogen may be represented as ${}^{1}_{1}H$, ${}^{2}_{1}H$, ${}^{3}_{1}H$, respectively. This method of representing atoms is called isotopic notation. In **isotopic notation**, the subscript (Z) is the atomic number and the superscript (A) is the mass number of the element. The **mass number** is the sum of the protons and neutrons in the nucleus of the element.

isotopic notation

mass number

Mass number (sum of protons and neutrons in the nucleus) → A

$${}^{A}_{Z}\mathbf{X}$$ ← Symbol of element

Atomic number (number of protons in the nucleus) → Z

Most of the elements occur in nature as mixtures of isotopes. However, not all isotopes are stable; some are radioactive and are continuously decomposing to form other elements. For example, of the seven known isotopes of carbon, only two, ${}^{12}_{6}C$ and ${}^{13}_{6}C$, are stable. Of the seven known isotopes of oxygen, only three, ${}^{16}_{8}O$, ${}^{17}_{8}O$, and ${}^{18}_{8}O$, are stable. Of the 15 known isotopes of arsenic, ${}^{75}_{33}As$ is the only one that is stable.

1.4 Atomic Mass (Atomic Weight)

All atoms have mass due primarily to the mass of their protons and neutrons. Elements occur in nature as mixtures of isotopes with different masses. Therefore, the **atomic mass** (or atomic weight) of an element is the average mass of the naturally occurring isotopes of that element relative to the atomic mass of the isotope ${}^{12}_{6}C$ as exactly 12.00. Units of atomic mass commonly used in chemistry are grams, but other mass units can be used.

atomic mass

A table of atomic masses is given on the inside front cover of this book and on the periodic table located on the inside back cover of the book. You do not need to memorize atomic masses. Calculations in this book use atomic masses to four figures and give results of sufficient accuracy.

1.5 The Mole and Molar Mass

A mole (abbreviated mol) is a counting unit. A mole of a substance contains 6.022×10^{23} individual particles of that substance. For example, we can have a mole of atoms, a mole of molecules, a mole of ions, and so forth. More specifically, we define a **mole** as the mass of a substance (in grams) containing the same number of formula units as there are atoms in 12.00 g of the isotope $^{12}_{6}C$ (carbon-12). There are 6.022×10^{23} atoms of $^{12}_{6}C$ in 12.00 g (1 mole) of $^{12}_{6}C$. The number 6.022×10^{23} is also known as Avogadro's number.

mole

From the above definition we can say that the atomic mass in grams of any element contains one mole of atoms. Thus, the atomic mass in grams is defined as the **molar mass** of that element. For example, one mole of sulfur contains 6.022×10^{23} atoms and has a mass of 32.06 g. The molar mass of sulfur is 32.06 g.

molar mass

1 mole of atoms = 1 molar mass (g) of an element
= Avogadro's number (6.022×10^{23}) of atoms

In a like manner, one mole of a compound contains 6.022×10^{23} molecules or formula units of that compound. Therefore, the molar mass of a compound is the mass in grams of 6.022×10^{23} molecules or formula units of that compound. For example, one mole of H_2O contains 6.022×10^{23} molecules and has a mass of 18.02 g. The molar mass of H_2O is 18.02 g. The terms molecular weight and formula weight have been used for molar mass, but molar mass is more inclusive since it can be used for all types of compounds.

If the formula of a compound is known, its molar mass may be determined by adding together the molar masses of all the atoms in the formula. When more than one atom of an element is present, its mass must be added as many times as it occurs in the formula. For example, the molar mass of H_2O is 18.02 g:

$$\begin{aligned} 1\text{ mol H} &= 1.008\text{ g} \\ 1\text{ mol H} &= 1.008\text{ g} \\ 1\text{ mol O} &= \underline{16.00\ \text{ g}} \\ 1\text{ mol } H_2O &= 18.016 \quad = 18.02\text{ g} \end{aligned}$$

Other examples follow:

$$\begin{aligned} 1\text{ mol } H_2 &= 2.016\text{ g} = 6.022 \times 10^{23}\text{ molecules} \\ 1\text{ mol NaCl} &= 58.44\text{ g} = 6.022 \times 10^{23}\text{ formula units} \\ 1\text{ mol } HNO_3 &= 63.02\text{ g} = 6.022 \times 10^{23}\text{ molecules} \\ 1\text{ mol } K_2SO_4 &= 173.3\text{ g} = 6.022 \times 10^{23}\text{ formula units} \end{aligned}$$

◀ One-mole samples of various substances. *Clockwise from lower left:* magnesium, carbon, copper(II) sulfate, copper, mercury, potassium permanganate, cadmium, and sodium chloride (*center*).

1 mole = the molar mass of a compound
$= 6.022 \times 10^{23}$ molecules or formula units

We often need to convert moles of a substance to grams, and grams of a substance to moles. The factors for these conversions are:

$$\text{grams to moles:} \quad \text{grams of substance} \times \frac{1 \text{ mole of the substance}}{\text{molar mass of the substance}}$$

$$\text{moles to grams:} \quad \text{moles of substance} \times \frac{1 \text{ molar mass of the substance}}{1 \text{ mole of the substance}}$$

1.6 Empirical and Molecular Formulas

empirical formula

molecular formula

The **empirical formula** shows the smallest possible whole-number ratio of the atoms of each element in a molecule of a compound. In contrast, the **molecular formula** is the true formula, showing the total number of atoms of each element in a molecule of a compound.

It is entirely possible that two or more substances have the same percent composition of their elements. For example, acetylene, C_2H_2, is a common gas used in welding. Benzene, C_6H_6, is an important solvent and is used in the synthesis of nylon and styrene. Both acetylene and benzene contain 92.3% C and

TABLE 1.4 Some Empirical and Molecular Formulas

Compound	Empirical formula	Molecular formula	Compound	Empirical formula	Molecular formula
Acetylene	CH	C_2H_2	Diborane	BH_3	B_2H_6
Benzene	CH	C_6H_6	Hydrazine	NH_2	N_2H_4
Ethylene	CH_2	C_2H_4	Hydrogen	H	H_2
Formaldehyde	CH_2O	CH_2O	Chlorine	Cl	Cl_2
Acetic acid	CH_2O	$C_2H_4O_2$	Bromine	Br	Br_2
Glucose	CH_2O	$C_6H_{12}O_6$	Oxygen	O	O_2
Hydrogen chloride	HCl	HCl	Nitrogen	N	N_2
Carbon dioxide	CO_2	CO_2			

7.7% H. The smallest ratio of C and H corresponding to these percents is one atom of carbon to one atom of hydrogen, CH. Therefore the empirical formula for both acetylene and benzene is CH, even though it is known that the molecular formulas are C_2H_2 and C_6H_6.

It is not uncommon for the molecular formula to be the same as the empirical formula. If the molecular formula is not the same, it will be a whole number multiple of the empirical formula. Table 1.4 shows some additional empirical and molecular formulas.

1.7 ACIDS AND BASES

acid

base

According to the Bronsted-Lowry proton transfer theory, an **acid** is a proton (H^+) donor and a **base** is a proton acceptor. Thus, when hydrogen chloride gas is dissolved in water, HCl donates a proton to form a chloride ion, and H_2O accepts the proton to form H_3O^+, a hydronium ion. Thus HCl is an acid and H_2O is a base.

$$\underset{\text{acid}}{HCl(g)} + \underset{\text{base}}{H_2O(l)} \longrightarrow \underset{\text{acid}}{H_3O^+(aq)} + \underset{\text{base}}{Cl^-(aq)}$$

Looking at the reaction in more detail, a proton cannot exist by itself in an aqueous solution. An H_2O molecule has two pairs of unbonded electrons and attracts the H^+ to form a coordinate covalent bond with one of the pairs of unbonded electrons.

$$H^+ + H:\overset{\cdot\cdot}{\underset{\cdot\cdot}{O}}: \longrightarrow \left[H:\overset{\cdot\cdot}{\underset{\cdot\cdot}{O}}:H \right]^+$$
$$\qquad\quad H \qquad\qquad\qquad H$$

A more general concept of acids and bases is the Lewis theory. This theory deals with the way an unbonded pair of electrons reacts in an acid-base type of reaction. According to the Lewis theory, a base is any species (compound or

Table 1.5 Common Acids and Bases

Acids		Bases	
Hydrochloric acid	HCl	Sodium hydroxide	$NaOH$
Sulfuric acid	H_2SO_4	Potassium hydroxide	KOH
Nitric acid	HNO_3	Calcium hydroxide	$Ca(OH)_2$
Phosphoric acid	H_3PO_4	Ammonia	NH_3 (NH_4OH)
Acetic acid	CH_3COOH		
Carbonic acid	H_2CO_3		

ion) that has an unbonded pair of electrons (electron pair donor) and an acid is a species that will bond to a pair of electrons (electron pair acceptor). In the reaction

$$\underset{\text{acid}}{H^+} + \underset{\text{base}}{H:\ddot{\underset{\cdot\cdot}{N}}:H \atop H} \longrightarrow \left[{H \atop H:\ddot{\underset{\cdot\cdot}{N}}:H \atop H} \right]^+$$

H^+ is a Lewis acid and $:NH_3$ is a Lewis base. The Lewis and Bronsted-Lowry bases are identical because, to accept a proton, a base must have an unshared pair of electrons. Table 1.5 is a list of familiar acids and bases whose formulas you should know.

1.8 Oxidation–Reduction (Redox)

Oxidation–reduction, also known as redox, is a chemical process in which the oxidation number of an element changes.

The oxidation number or oxidation state of an atom can be considered to represent the number of electrons lost, gained, or unequally shared by the atom. An oxidation number can have a zero, a positive, or a negative value. When the oxidation number of an atom is zero, the atom has the same number of electrons assigned to it as there are electrons in the free neutral atom. When the oxidation number is positive, the atom has fewer electrons assigned to it than there are in the neutral atom. When the oxidation number is negative, the atom has more electrons assigned to it than there are in the neutral atom. Oxidation numbers help us keep track of the electrons associated with each atom.

The oxidation number of an atom that has lost or gained electrons to form an ion is the same as the plus or minus charge of the ion. In the ionic compound NaCl the oxidation numbers are clearly established to be $+1$ for the Na^+ ion and -1 for the Cl^- ion. The Na^+ ion has one less electron than the neutral Na atom; and the Cl^- ion has one more electron than the neutral Cl atom. In $MgCl_2$ two electrons have transferred from the Mg atom to the Cl atoms; thus, the oxidation number of Mg is $+2$.

In covalently bonded substances, where electrons are shared between two atoms, oxidation numbers are assigned by a somewhat arbitrary system based on relative electronegativities. For symmetrical covalent molecules, such as H_2 and Cl_2, each atom is assigned an oxidation number of zero because the bonding pair of electrons is shared equally between two like atoms, neither of which is more electronegative than the other.

H:H :C̈l:C̈l:

When the covalent bond is between two unlike atoms, the bonding electrons are shared unequally because the more electronegative element has a greater attraction for them. In this case the oxidation numbers are determined by assigning both electrons to the more electronegative element.

Thus in compounds with covalent bonds, such as NH_3 and H_2O,

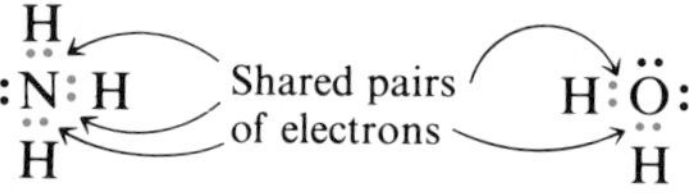

the pairs of electrons are unequally shared between the atoms and are attracted toward the more electronegative elements, N and O. This unequal sharing causes the N and O atoms to be relatively negative with respect to the H atoms. At the same time it causes the H atoms to be relatively positive with respect to the N and O atoms. In H_2O both pairs of shared electrons are assigned to the O atom, giving it two electrons more than the neutral O atom. At the same time, each H atom is assigned one electron less than the neutral H atom. Therefore, the O atom is assigned an oxidation number of -2, and each H atom is assigned an oxidation number of $+1$. In NH_3 the three pairs of shared electrons are assigned to the N atom, giving it three electrons more than the neutral N atom. At the same time, each H atom has one electron less than the neutral atom. Therefore, the N atom is assigned an oxidation number of -3, and each H atom is assigned an oxidation number of $+1$.

Rules for assigning oxidation numbers are given in Table 1.6.

TABLE 1.6 Arbitrary Rules for Assigning Oxidation Numbers

1. All elements in their free state (uncombined with other elements) have an oxidation number of zero (for example, Na, Cu, Mg, H_2, O_2, Cl_2, N_2).
2. H is $+1$, except in metal hydrides, where it is -1 (for example, NaH, CaH_2).
3. O is -2, except in peroxides, where it is -1, and in OF_2, where it is $+2$.
4. The metallic element in an ionic compound has a positive oxidation number.
5. In covalent compounds the negative oxidation number is assigned to the most electronegative atom.
6. The algebraic sum of the oxidation numbers of all the atoms in a compound is zero.
7. The algebraic sum of the oxidation numbers of all the atoms in a polyatomic ion is equal to the charge of the ion.

Oxidation occurs whenever the oxidation number of an element increases as a result of losing electrons. Conversely, **reduction** occurs whenever the oxidation number of an element decreases as a result of gaining electrons. For example, a change in oxidation number from +2 to +3 or from −1 to 0 is oxidation; a change from +5 to +2 or from −2 to −4 is reduction. Oxidation and reduction occur simultaneously in a chemical reaction; one cannot take place without the other.

oxidation

reduction

Many combination, decomposition, and single-displacement reactions involve oxidation–reduction. Let us examine the combustion of hydrogen and oxygen from this point of view:

$$2\,H_2 + O_2 \longrightarrow 2\,H_2O$$

Both reactants, hydrogen and oxygen, are elements in the free state and have an oxidation number of zero. In the product, water, hydrogen has been oxidized to +1 and oxygen reduced to −2. The substance that causes an increase in the oxidation state of another substance is called an **oxidizing agent**. The substance that causes a decrease in the oxidation state of another substance is called a **reducing agent**. In this reaction the oxidizing agent is free oxygen, and the reducing agent is free hydrogen. In the reaction

oxidizing agent

reducing agent

$$Zn(s) + H_2SO_4(aq) \longrightarrow ZnSO_4(aq) + H_2(g)$$

metallic zinc is oxidized, and hydrogen ions are reduced. Zinc is the reducing agent, and hydrogen ions, the oxidizing agent. Electrons are transferred from the zinc metal to the hydrogen ions. The reaction is better expressed as

$$Zn^0 + 2\,H^+ + SO_4^{2-} \longrightarrow Zn^{2+} + SO_4^{2-} + H_2^0(g)$$

The oxidizing agent is reduced and gains electrons. The reducing agent is oxidized and loses electrons. The transfer of electrons is characteristic of all redox reactions.

Oxidation:	**Increase in oxidation number** **Loss of electrons**
Reduction:	**Decrease in oxidation number** **Gain of electrons**

▲ **The space shuttle is powered by H_2 and O_2 reacting to H_2O.**

1.9 Hydrogen Bonding

When we compare the physical properties of water, ammonia, and hydrogen fluoride with the other hydrogen compounds in their respective families we find, for example, that their boiling points are abnormally high (See Table 1.7).

TABLE 1.7 Boiling Points of Groups VA, VIA, and VIIA Hydrogen Compounds

Compound	Boiling point (°C)	Compound	Boiling point (°C)	Compound	Boiling point (°C)
H_2O	100	NH_3	−33.4	HF	19.5
H_2S	−85.5	PH_3	−87.4	HCl	−84.9
H_2Se	−65.7	AsH_3	−55	HBr	−67.0
H_2Te	−49			HI	−50.8

FIGURE 1.2 ▶ Hydrogen bonding in H_2O, NH_3, and HF by intermolecular dipole-dipole attraction.

H—N: ····H—N: ····H—N: ····H—N:

H—F: ····H—F: ····H—F: ····H—F:

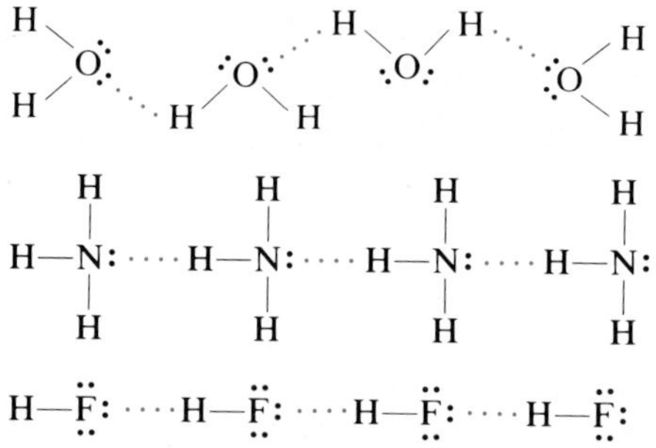

hydrogen bond

Why do H_2O, NH_3, and HF have such exceptionally high boiling points? The answer is that these molecules in the liquid state are linked together by hydrogen bonds (See Figure 1.2). A **hydrogen bond** is a chemical bond that is formed between polar molecules that contain hydrogen bonded to a small, strongly electronegative element such as oxygen, nitrogen, or fluorine (H—O, H—N, H—F). The bond is actually the dipole-dipole attraction between polar molecules containing these three types of polar bonds. The dipole-dipole attraction is particularly strong in molecules that have a hydrogen atom bonded to oxygen, nitrogen, or fluorine.

Hydrogen bonding can occur between two different atoms that are capable of forming H-bonds. Thus we may have an O····H—N or O—H····N linkage in which the hydrogen atom forming the H-bond is between oxygen and nitrogen atoms. These forms of H-bonds exist in certain types of proteins and are common in many biological systems. Hydrogen bonding can be intermolecular or intramolecular, that is, between molecules or within a molecule.

Chemistry in Action

Serendipity in Science

Discoveries in the world of chemistry are for the most part made by people who are applying the scientific method in their work. Occasionally, important discoveries are made by chance, or through serendipity. But even when serendipity is involved, a discovery is more likely to be made by someone with a good knowledge of the field. Louis Pasteur summed this up in a statement made long ago: "Chance favors the prepared mind." In chemistry serendipity often can lead to whole new fields and technology.

The Discovery of Artificial Sweeteners

Sweetener	Date	Discoverer
Saccharin	1878	I. Remsen and C. Fahlberg
Cyclamate	1937	M. Sveda
Aspartame	1965	J. Schlatter

The synthetic dye industry began in 1856 when William Perkin, an 18-year-old student at the Royal College of Chemistry in London, was attempting to synthesize quinine, a drug used to treat malaria. He reacted two chemicals, aniline sulfate and potassium dichromate, and obtained a black paste. Perkin then extracted the paste with alcohol. Upon evaporating the alcohol, violet crystals appeared which, when dissolved in water, made a beautiful purple solution. He so enjoyed the color he began investigating the solution; he then determined the purple color had a strong affinity for silk. Perkin had discovered the first synthetic aniline dye. Recognizing the commercial possibilities, he immediately left school and, with his father and an older brother, went into the dye manufacturing business. His dye, known as mauve, quickly became a success and inspired other research throughout Europe. By 1870, cloth could be purchased in more and brighter synthetic colors than were ever available with natural dyes.

Cotton dyeing plant.

A second, more recent, account of chance events in chemistry also led to a multimillion dollar industry (see table). In 1965 James Schlatter was researching anti-ulcer drugs for the pharmaceutical firm G. D. Searle. In the course of his work he accidentally ingested a small amount of his preparation and found, to his surprise, it had an extremely sweet taste. (*Note:* Tasting chemicals of any kind in the laboratory is not a safe procedure.) When purified, the sweet-tasting substance turned out to be aspartame, a molecule consisting of two amino acids joined together. Since only very small quantities are necessary to produce sweetness, it proved to be an excellent low calorie artificial sweetener. Today, under the trade names of "Equal" and "Nutrasweet," aspartame is one of the cornerstones of the artificial sweetener industry.

2

Organic Chemistry: Saturated Hydrocarbons

◀ **CHAPTER OPENING PHOTO: Saturated hydrocarbons provide the fuel for us to enjoy many of the wonders of nature.**

Many substances throughout nature contain silicon or carbon within their molecular structures. Silicon is the staple of the geologist—it combines with oxygen in a variety of ways to produce silica and a family of compounds known as the silicates. These compounds form the chemical foundation of most types of sand, rocks, and soil, the essential materials to the construction industry.

In the living world, carbon provides the basis for millions of organic compounds in combination with hydrogen, oxygen, nitrogen, and sulfur. Carbon compounds provide us with energy sources in the form of hydrocarbons and their derivatives that allow us to heat and light our homes, drive our automobiles to work, and fly off to Paris for an elegant dinner. Small substitutions in these carbon molecules can produce chlorofluorocarbons, compounds used in plastics and refrigerants. An understanding of these molecules and their effect upon our global environment is vital in the continuing search to find ways to maintain our lifestyles while preserving the planet.

2.1 ORGANIC CHEMISTRY: HISTORY AND SCOPE

During the late 18th and the early 19th centuries, chemists were baffled by the fact that compounds obtained from animal and vegetable sources defied the established rules for inorganic compounds—namely, that compound formation is due to a simple attraction between positively and negatively charged elements. In their experience with inorganic chemistry, only one, or at most a few, compounds were composed of any group of only two or three elements. However, they observed that a group of only four elements—carbon, hydrogen, oxygen, and nitrogen—gave rise to a large number of different compounds that often were remarkably stable.

Because no organic compounds had been synthesized from inorganic substances and because there was no other explanation for the complexities of organic compounds, chemists believed that organic compounds were formed by some "vital force." The **vital force theory** held that organic substances could originate only from living material. In 1828 Friedrich Wöhler (1800–1882), a German chemist, did a simple experiment that eventually proved to be the death blow to this theory. In attempting to prepare ammonium cyanate (NH_4CNO) by heating cyanic acid (HCNO) and ammonia, Wöhler obtained a white crystalline

vital force theory

substance that he identified as urea (H_2N—CO—NH_2). Wöhler knew that urea is an authentic organic substance because it is a product of metabolism that had been isolated from urine. Although Wöhler's discovery was not immediately and generally recognized, the vital force theory was overthrown by this simple experiment since *one* organic compound had been made from nonliving materials.

After the work of Wöhler, it was apparent that no vital force other than skill and knowledge was needed to make organic chemicals in the laboratory and that inorganic as well as organic substances could be used as raw materials. Today, **organic chemistry** designates the branch of chemistry that deals with carbon compounds but does not imply that these compounds must originate from some form of life. A few special kinds of carbon compounds (for example, carbon oxides, metal carbides, and metal carbonates) are often excluded from the organic classification because their chemistry is more conveniently related to that of inorganic substances.

organic chemistry

The field of organic chemistry is vast, for it includes not only the composition of all living organisms but also of a great many other materials that we use daily. Examples of organic materials are foodstuffs (fats, proteins, carbohydrates), fuels, fabrics (cotton, wool, rayon, nylon), wood and paper products, paints and varnishes, plastics, dyes, soaps and detergents, cosmetics, medicinals, rubber products, and explosives.

What makes carbon compounds special and different from the other elements in the periodic table? Carbon has the unique ability to bond to itself in long chains and rings of varying size. The greater the number of carbon atoms, the more ways there are to link these atoms in different arrangements. This flexibility in arrangement of atoms produces compounds with the same chemical composition and different structures. There is no theoretical limit on the number of organic compounds that can exist. In addition to this unique bonding property, carbon can form strong covalent bonds with a variety of elements, most often including hydrogen, nitrogen, oxygen, sulfur, phosphorus, and the halogens. These are the elements most commonly found in organic compounds.

2.2 The Carbon Atom: Bonding and Shape

The carbon atom is central to all organic compounds. The atomic number of carbon is 6, and its electron structure is $1s^2 2s^2 2p^2$. Two stable isotopes of carbon exist, ^{12}C and ^{13}C. In addition there are several radioactive isotopes; ^{14}C is the most widely known of these because of its use in radiocarbon dating. Having four electrons in its outer shell, carbon has oxidation numbers ranging from $+4$ to -4 and forms predominantly covalent bonds. Carbon occurs as the free element in diamond, graphite, coal, coke, carbon black, charcoal, and lampblack.

A carbon atom usually forms four covalent bonds, that is, bonds that result from the sharing of one or more pairs of electrons by two atoms. The number of electron pairs shared between atoms determines whether the bond is single or multiple. In a single bond only one pair of electrons is shared by the atoms, with one electron most often contributed by each atom. If both atoms have the same

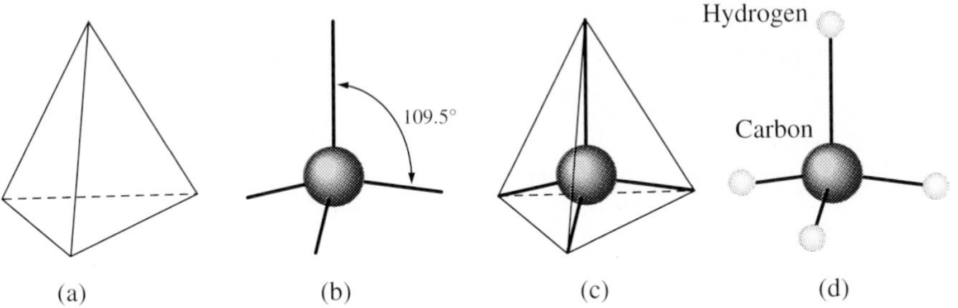

◄ **FIGURE 2.1**
Tetrahedral structure of carbon: (a) a regular tetrahedron; (b) a carbon atom with tetrahedral bonds; (c) a carbon atom within a regular tetrahedron; (d) a methane molecule, CH_4.

electronegativity, the bond is classified as nonpolar. In this type of bond there is no separation of positive and negative charge between the atoms.

Carbon can also form multiple bonds by sharing two or three pairs of electrons between two atoms. The double bond formed by sharing two electron pairs is stronger than a single bond, but not twice as strong. It is also shorter than a single bond. Similarly, a triple bond is formed by the sharing of three electron pairs and is stronger and shorter than a double bond. An organic compound is classified as **saturated** if it contains only single bonds, **unsaturated** if the molecules possess one or more multiple carbon–carbon bonds.

saturated

unsaturated

Lewis structures are useful in representing the bonding between atoms in a molecule, but these representations tell us little about the geometry of the molecules. There are a number of bonding theories that can be used to predict the shape of molecules. One of the common theories is called the valence shell electron pair repulsion (VSEPR) theory. This is a fairly simple, yet accurate method for determining the shape of a molecule.

The basis of the VSEPR theory is the concept that electron pairs repel each other since they have like charges. The electron pairs will therefore try to spread out as far as possible around an atom. In addition, unshared pairs of electrons occupy more space than shared electron pairs.

What does the VSEPR theory tell us about the shapes of carbon-containing compounds? Consider the simplest organic molecule, methane (CH_4). It contains one carbon atom with four single bonds to hydrogen atoms. The four shared pairs of electrons must be placed as far apart as possible in three dimensions. This results in the hydrogen atoms forming the corners of a tetrahedron with the carbon atom in the center (see Figure 2.1). The angle between these tetrahedral bonds is 109.5°.

Double or triple bonds have a significant effect on the shape of the molecule. The additional pairs of electrons in close proximity take up more space than those in a single bond as a result of increased repulsion between the pairs. Consider the Lewis structure for C_2H_4.

H:C::C:H
    H H

Each carbon atom has three separate regions for shared electrons. To place them as far apart as possible requires placing each atom at the corner of a triangle (see Figure 2.2). The bond angles around the carbon atoms are 120°.

H 120° H
C=C
H H

▲
FIGURE 2.2
Shape of a molecule with a carbon–carbon double bond. The hydrogens and carbon form the vertices of a triangle. The bond angles around the carbon are 120°.

In a triple bond the carbon has only two regions for shared electrons. To be placed as far apart as possible, a linear arrangement is required. The bond angle is 180°.

H:C:::C:H   H—C≡C—H (180°)

2.3 Molecular Models

Models are often used in organic chemistry to illustrate molecules. Many representations of molecules can be drawn. Each has its own advantages and disadvantages. Two common methods are: ball-and-stick models and space-filling models. Both types of models are illustrated in Figure 2.3 for the methane molecule.

In the ball-and-stick model different atoms are represented by different colored balls, and bonds are clearly shown with sticks. The space-filling model gives a more accurate representation of the actual molecule but is not as clear in representing the chemical bonds between the atoms. Since most organic molecules contain many atoms, it is often difficult or inconvenient to draw either of these types of model on paper every time we wish to represent a molecule. Chemists often translate a three-dimensional model into a two-dimensional representation (a Lewis structure or bond-line drawing). An example of all four models is shown in Figure 2.4. In both Lewis and bond-line drawings it is important to remember that the bond angle is not 90° the way it appears in the drawing. Rather it is 109.5° since the molecule is actually three-dimensional.

Formulas of organic molecules are also represented differently than those of inorganic compounds. A formula gives information about the composition of a compound. Inorganic compounds contain relatively few groups of atoms and are frequently represented by *empirical formulas*, which give only the simplest ratio of the atoms in a molecule. Larger molecules are often represented by a *molecular formula*, which gives more information. The molecular formula gives the actual number of atoms in a molecule. For inorganic compounds the

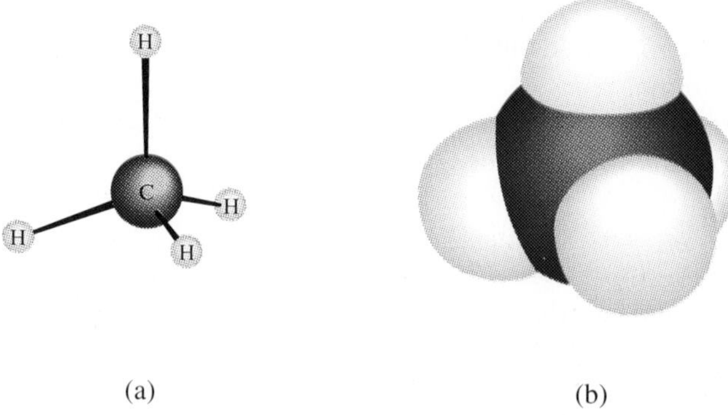

Figure 2.3 ▶ Molecular models of methane. (a) Ball-and-stick model; (b) space-filling model.

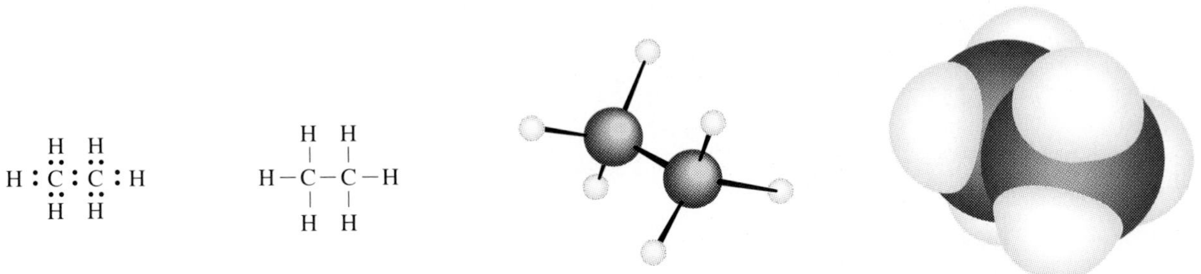

H H
H : C : C : H
H H

(a)

H H
H—C—C—H
H H

(b)

(c)

(d)

▲
FIGURE 2.4
Models of ethane. (a) Lewis structure; (b) bond-line drawing; (c) ball-and-stick model; (d) space-filling model.

empirical and molecular formulas are often the same. The models we've just been considering represent yet another even more informative type of formula. In a *structural formula* the arrangement of the atoms within the molecule is clearly shown. Organic chemists often shorten these structural formulas into a final type called *condensed structural formulas.* In these formulas each carbon is grouped with adjacent hydrogens and then written as a formula, for example CH_3CH_3 or $CH_3CH_2CH_2CH_3$. The diversity of methods for writing organic formulas is illustrated in Table 2.1, which gives examples of the four types of formulas.

2.4 Classifying Organic Compounds

It is impossible for anyone to study the properties of each of the millions of known organic compounds. Organic compounds with similar structures are grouped into classes as shown in Table 2.1. The members of each class of compounds contain a characteristic atom or group of atoms called a **functional group** shown as the colored portion of the structural formula in Table 2.1.

functional group

Organic compounds from different classes may have the same empirical and molecular formulas, but completely different chemical and physical properties. Look at the compounds in Table 2.1. Notice that the molecular formulas for diethyl ether and ethyl alcohol are C_2H_6O. Compounds that have the same molecular formula but different structural formulas are called **isomers**.

isomers

2.5 Hydrocarbons

Hydrocarbons are compounds that are composed entirely of carbon and hydrogen atoms bonded to each other by covalent bonds. Several classes of hydrocarbons are known. These include the alkanes, alkenes, alkynes, and aromatic hydrocarbons (see Figure 2.5).

hydrocarbons

Fossil fuels—natural gas, petroleum, and coal—are the principal sources of hydrocarbons. Natural gas is primarily methane with small amounts of ethane, propane, and butane. Petroleum is a mixture of hydrocarbons from which gasoline, kerosene, fuel oil, lubricating oil, paraffin wax, and petrolatum (themselves

TABLE 2.1 Classes of Organic Compounds

Class of compound	General formula[a]	Example	Empirical formula	Molecular formula	Condensed formula	Structural formula
Alkane	RH	Ethane	CH_3	C_2H_6	CH_3CH_3	H H | | H—C—C—H | | H H
Alkene	R—CH=CH$_2$	Ethylene	CH_2	C_2H_4	$H_2C{=}CH_2$	H H \\ / C=C / \\ H H
Alkyne	R—C≡C—H	Acetylene	CH	C_2H_2	HC≡CH	H—C≡C—H
Alkyl halide	RX	Ethyl chloride	C_2H_5Cl	C_2H_5Cl	CH_3CH_2Cl	H H | | H—C—C—Cl | | H H
Alcohol	ROH	Ethyl alcohol	C_2H_6O	C_2H_6O	CH_3CH_2OH	H H | | H—C—C—OH | | H H
Ether	R—O—R	Diethyl ether	C_2H_6O	C_2H_6O	CH_3OCH_3	H H | | H—C—O—C—H | | H H
Aldehyde	R—C=O | H	Acetaldehyde	C_2H_4O	C_2H_4O	CH_3CHO	H | H—C—C—H | ‖ H O
Ketone	R—C—R ‖ O	Acetone	C_3H_6O	C_3H_6O	CH_3COCH_3	H H | | H—C—C—C—H | ‖ | H O H
Carboxylic acid	R—C—OH ‖ O	Acetic acid	CH_2O	$C_2H_4O_2$	CH_3COOH	H | H—C—C—OH | ‖ H O
Ester	R—C—OR ‖ O	Methyl acetate	$C_3H_6O_2$	$C_3H_6O_2$	CH_3COOCH_3	H H | | H—C—C—O—C—H | ‖ | H O H
Amide	R—C—NH$_2$ ‖ O	Acetamide	C_2H_5ON	C_2H_5ON	CH_3CONH_2	H H | / H—C—C—N | ‖ \\ H O H
Amine	R—CH$_2$—NH$_2$	Ethylamine	C_2H_7N	C_2H_7N	$CH_3CH_2NH_2$	H H | | H—C—C—N—H | | | H H H

[a] The letter R is used to indicate any of the many possible alkyl groups.

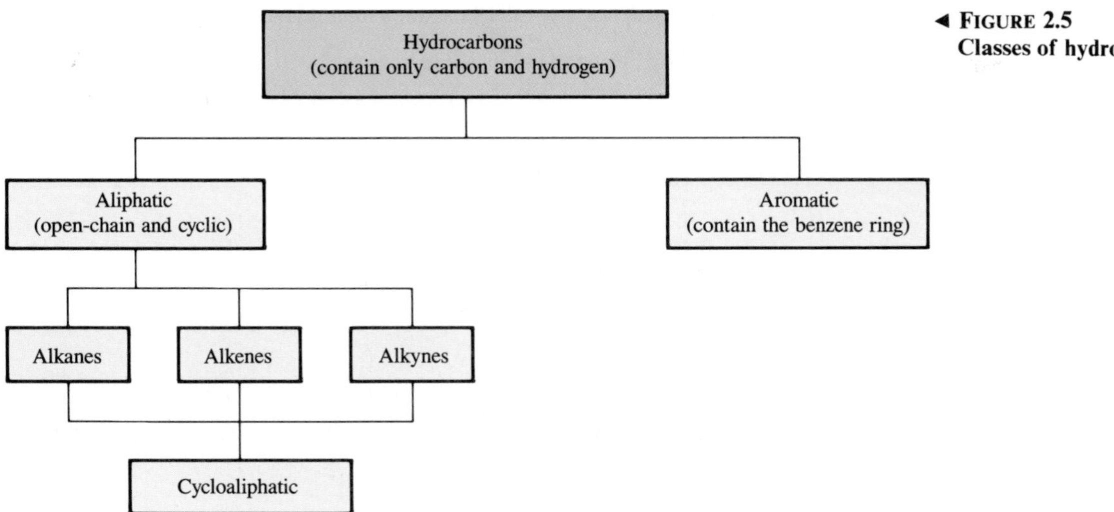

◀ **FIGURE 2.5**
Classes of hydrocarbons.

mixtures of hydrocarbons) are separated. Coal tar, a volatile by-product of the process of making coke from coal for use in the steel industry, is the source of many valuable chemicals including the aromatic hydrocarbons benzene, toluene, and naphthalene.

2.6 SATURATED HYDROCARBONS: ALKANES

alkanes

The **alkanes**, also known as *paraffins* or *saturated hydrocarbons*, are straight- or branched-chain hydrocarbons with only single covalent bonds between the carbon atoms. We shall study the alkanes in some detail because many other classes of organic compounds can be considered as derivatives of these substances. For example, it is necessary to learn the names of the first ten members of the alkane series, because these names are used as a basis for naming other classes of compounds.

Methane (CH_4) is the first member of the alkane series. Members having two, three, and four carbon atoms are ethane, propane, and butane, respectively. The names of the first four alkanes are of common or trivial origin and must be memorized; but the names beginning with the fifth member, pentane, are derived from Greek numbers and are relatively easy to recall. The names and formulas of the first ten members of the series are given in Table 2.2.

homologous series

Adjacent compounds in the alkane series differ from each other in composition by one carbon and two hydrogen atoms. When each member of a series differs from the next member by a CH_2 group, the series is called a **homologous series**. The members of a homologous series are similar in structure but have a regular difference in formula. All common classes of organic compounds exist in homologous series. Each homologous series can be represented by a general formula. For all open-chain alkanes, the general formula is C_nH_{2n+2}, where n corresponds to the number of carbon atoms in the molecule. The formula of any specific alkane is easily determined from this general formula. Thus, for pentane,

TABLE 2.2 Names, Formulas, and Physical Properties of Straight-Chain Alkanes

Name	Molecular formula C_nH_{2n+2}	Condensed structural formula	Boiling point (°C)	Melting point (°C)
Methane	CH_4	CH_4	−161	−183
Ethane	C_2H_6	CH_3CH_3	−88	−172
Propane	C_3H_8	$CH_3CH_2CH_3$	−45	−187
Butane	C_4H_{10}	$CH_3CH_2CH_2CH_3$	−0.5	−138
Pentane	C_5H_{12}	$CH_3CH_2CH_2CH_2CH_3$	36	−130
Hexane	C_6H_{14}	$CH_3CH_2CH_2CH_2CH_2CH_3$	69	−95
Heptane	C_7H_{16}	$CH_3CH_2CH_2CH_2CH_2CH_2CH_3$	98	−90
Octane	C_8H_{18}	$CH_3CH_2CH_2CH_2CH_2CH_2CH_2CH_3$	125	−57
Nonane	C_9H_{20}	$CH_3CH_2CH_2CH_2CH_2CH_2CH_2CH_2CH_3$	151	−54
Decane	$C_{10}H_{22}$	$CH_3CH_2CH_2CH_2CH_2CH_2CH_2CH_2CH_2CH_3$	174	−30

$n = 5$ and $2n + 2 = 12$, so the formula is C_5H_{12}. For hexadecane, the 16-carbon alkane, the formula is $C_{16}H_{34}$.

2.7 Carbon Bonding in Alkanes

As was pointed out in Section 2.4, a carbon atom is capable of forming single covalent bonds with one, two, three, or four other carbon atoms. To understand this remarkable bonding ability, we must look at the electron structure of carbon. The valence electrons of carbon in their ground state are $2s^2 2p_x^1 2p_y^1$. These are the electrons that enter into bonding. When a carbon atom is bonded to other atoms by single bonds (for example, to four hydrogen atoms in CH_4), it would appear at first that there should be two different types of bonds—bonds involving the 2*s* electrons and bonds involving the 2*p* electrons of the carbon atom. However, this is not the case. All four carbon–hydrogen bonds are found to be identical.

If the carbon atom is to form four equivalent bonds, its electrons in the 2*s* and 2*p* orbitals must rearrange to four equivalent orbitals. To form the four equivalent orbitals, imagine that a 2*s* electron is promoted to a 2*p* orbital, giving carbon an outer-shell electron structure of $2s^1 2p_x^1 2p_y^1 2p_z^1$. The 2*s* orbital and the three 2*p* orbitals then hybridize to form four equivalent hybrid orbitals, which are designated sp^3 orbitals. The orbitals formed (sp^3) are neither *s* orbitals nor *p* orbitals but are a hybrid of those orbitals, having one-fourth *s* orbital character and three-fourths *p* orbital character. This process is illustrated in Figure 2.6. It is these sp^3 orbitals that are directed toward the corners of a regular tetrahedron (see Figure 2.7).

A single bond is formed when one of the sp^3 orbitals overlaps an orbital of another atom. Thus each C—H bond in methane is the result of the overlapping of a carbon sp^3 orbital and a hydrogen *s* orbital [Figure 2.7, part (c)]. Once the bond is formed, the pair of bonding electrons constituting it are said to be in a

2p ↑ ↑ —   A 2s electron is promoted to a 2p orbital →   2p ↑ ↑ ↑   Hybridization → $2sp^3$ ↑ ↑ ↑ ↑

2s ↑↓   2s ↑

Four carbon electrons in their ground-state orbitals

Four equivalent sp^3 orbitals– each contains one electron

FIGURE 2.6
Schematic hybridization of $2s^2 2p_x^1 2p_y^1$ orbitals of carbon to form four sp^3 electron orbitals.

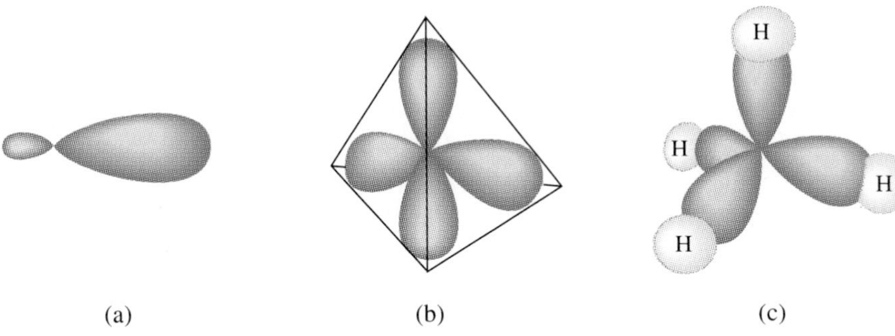

FIGURE 2.7
Tetrahedral nature of sp^3 orbitals: (a) a single sp^3 hybridized orbital; (b) four sp^3 hybridized orbitals in tetrahedral arrangement; (c) sp^3 and s orbitals overlapping to form C—H bonds in methane.

molecular orbital. In a similar way a C—C single bond results from the overlap of sp^3 orbitals between two carbon atoms. This type of bond is called a sigma (σ) bond. A **sigma bond** exists if the electron cloud formed by the pair of bonding electrons is symmetrical about a straight line drawn between the nuclei of the bonded atoms.

sigma bond

2.8 ISOMERISM

The properties of an organic substance are dependent on its molecular structure. The majority of organic compounds are made from relatively few elements—carbon, hydrogen, oxygen, nitrogen, and the halogens. The valence bonds or points of attachment may be represented in structural formulas by a corresponding number of dashes attached to each atom:

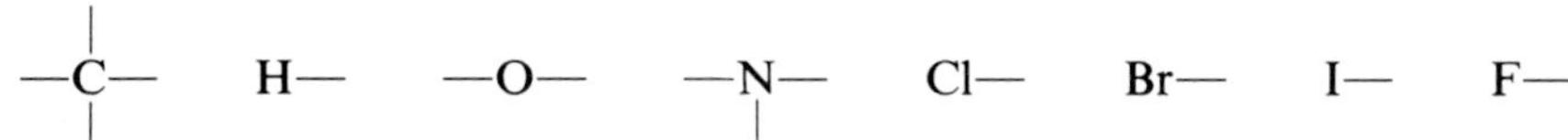

Thus carbon has four bonds to each atom, nitrogen three bonds, oxygen two bonds, and hydrogen and the halogens one bond to each atom.

In an alkane each carbon atom is joined to four other atoms by four single covalent bonds. These bonds are separated by angles of 109.5° (the angles correspond to those formed by lines drawn from the center of a regular tetrahedron to its corners). Alkane molecules contain only carbon–carbon and carbon–hydrogen bonds and are essentially nonpolar. Alkane molecules are nonpolar because (1) carbon–carbon bonds are nonpolar since they are between like atoms; (2) carbon–hydrogen bonds are only slightly polar since there is only a small difference in electronegativity between carbon and hydrogen atoms; and (3) the bonds in an alkane are symmetrically directed toward the corners of a tetrahedron. Because of their low polarity, alkane molecules have very little intermolecular attraction and therefore relatively low boiling points compared with other organic compounds of similar molar mass.

Without the use of models or perspective drawings, the three-dimensional character of atoms and molecules is difficult to portray accurately. However, concepts of structure can be conveyed to some extent by Lewis (or electron-dot) diagrams of structural formulas.

To write the correct structural formula for propane (C_3H_8) we must determine how to place each atom in the molecule. An alkane contains only single bonds. Therefore, each carbon atom must be bonded to four other atoms by either C—C or C—H bonds. Hydrogen must be bonded to only one carbon atom by a C—H bond, since C—H—C bonds do not occur, and an H—H bond would simply represent a hydrogen molecule. Applying this information, we find that the only possible structure for propane is

```
    H  H  H
    |  |  |
 H—C—C—C—H
    |  |  |
    H  H  H
```

Propane

However, it is possible to write two structural formulas corresponding to the molecular formula C_4H_{10}:

```
                                      H
                                   H  |  H
                                    \ | /
                                      C
    H  H  H  H                    H   |   H
    |  |  |  |                    |   |   |
 H—C—C—C—C—H      and      H—C—C—C—H
    |  |  |  |                    |   |   |
    H  H  H  H                    H   H   H
```

Butane and Isobutane

Two C_4H_{10} compounds with the structural formulas shown above actually exist. The butane with the unbranched carbon chain is called *butane* or *normal butane* (abbreviated *n*-butane); it boils at 0.5°C and melts at −138.3°C. The branched-chain butane is called *isobutane*; it boils at −11.7°C and melts at −159.5°C. These differences in physical properties are sufficient to establish that the two compounds, though they have the same molecular formula, are different substances. Models illustrating the structural arrangement of the atoms in methane, ethane, propane, butane, and isobutane are shown in Figure 2.8.

isomerism

isomers

This phenomenon of two or more compounds having the same molecular formula but different structural arrangements of their atoms is called **isomerism**. The various individual compounds are called **isomers**. For example, there are two isomers of butane, C_4H_{10}. Isomerism is very common among organic compounds and is another reason for the large number of known compounds. There are 3 isomers of pentane, 5 isomers of hexane, 9 isomers of heptane, 18 isomers of octane, 35 isomers of nonane, and 75 isomers of decane. The phenomenon of isomerism is a very compelling reason for the use of structural formulas.

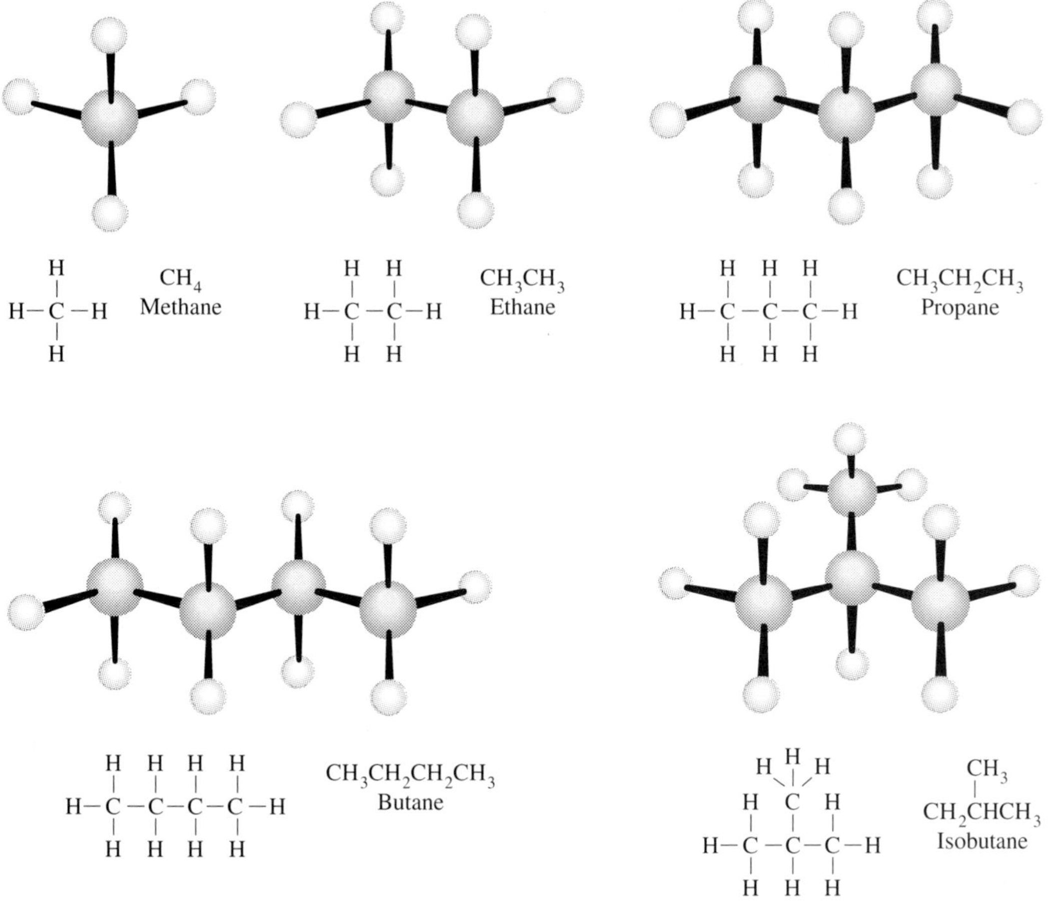

▲ **FIGURE 2.8**
Ball-and-stick models illustrating structural formulas of methane, ethane, propane, butane, and isobutane.

Isomers are compounds that have the same molecular formula but different structural formulas.

To save time and space in writing, condensed structural formulas are often used. In the condensed structural formulas, atoms and groups that are attached to a carbon atom are generally written to the right of that carbon atom.

Let us interpret the condensed structural formula for propane:

$$\overset{1}{C}H_3{-}\overset{2}{C}H_2{-}\overset{3}{C}H_3$$

Carbon number 1 has three hydrogen atoms attached to it and is bonded to carbon number 2, which has two hydrogen atoms on it and is bonded to carbon number 3, which has three hydrogen atoms bonded to it.

When structures are written as in butane, $CH_3CH_2CH_2CH_3$, the bonds (dashes) are often not shown. But when a group is shown above or below the main carbon chain, as in 2-methylpropane, a vertical dash must be used to indicate the point of attachment of the group to the main carbon chain.

EXAMPLE 2.1

There are three isomers of pentane, C_5H_{12}. Write structural formulas and condensed structural formulas for these isomers.

SOLUTION

In a problem of this kind it is best to start by writing the carbon skeleton of the compound containing the longest continuous carbon chain. In this case it is five carbon atoms:

C—C—C—C—C

Now complete the structure by attaching hydrogen atoms around each carbon atom so that each carbon atom has four bonds attached to it. The carbon atoms at each end of the chain need three hydrogen atoms. The three inner carbon atoms each need two hydrogen atoms to give them four bonds.

```
   H  H  H  H  H
   |  |  |  |  |
H—C—C—C—C—C—H      CH3CH2CH2CH2CH3
   |  |  |  |  |
   H  H  H  H  H
```

For the next isomer, start by writing a four-carbon chain and attach the fifth carbon atom to either of the middle carbon atoms—do not use the end ones.

```
       C          C
       |          |
C—C—C—C      C—C—C—C
```

Both of these structures represent the same compound.

Now add the 12 hydrogen atoms to complete the structure:

```
         H
       H\|/H
   H  H  C  H                 CH3
   |  |  |  |                  |
H—C—C—C—C—H      CH3CH2CHCH3      or      CH3CH2CH(CH3)2
   |  |  |  |
   H  H  H  H
```

For the third isomer, write a three-carbon chain, attach the other two carbon atoms to the central carbon atom, and complete the structure by adding the 12 hydrogen atoms:

```
                  H
                H\|/H
   C            H  C  H          CH3
   |            |  |  |           |
C—C—C       H—C—C—C—H      CH3CCH3      or      C(CH3)4
   |            |  |  |           |
   C            H  C  H          CH3
                H/|\H
                  H
```

Practice Write structural and condensed formulas for the isomers of hexane, C_6H_{14}.

Answer:

```
    H  H  H  H  H  H
    |  |  |  |  |  |
 H—C—C—C—C—C—C—H
    |  |  |  |  |  |
    H  H  H  H  H  H
```

$CH_3CH_2CH_2CH_2CH_2CH_3$

```
                H
                |
             H—C—H
                |
    H  H  H     |  H
    |  |  |     |  |
 H—C—C—C—C—C—H
    |  |  |  |  |
    H  H  H  H  H
```

$CH_3CH_2CH_2\overset{\displaystyle CH_3}{\overset{|}{C}}HCH_3$

```
          H
          |
       H—C—H
          |
    H  H  |  H  H
    |  |  |  |  |
 H—C—C—C—C—C—H
    |  |  |  |  |
    H  H  H  H  H
```

$CH_3CH_2\overset{\displaystyle CH_3}{\overset{|}{C}}HCH_2CH_3$

```
             H
             |
          H—C—H
             |
    H  H     |  H
    |  |     |  |
 H—C—C—C—C—H
    |  |  |  |
    H  |  H  H
       |
    H—C—H
       |
       H
```

$CH_3\underset{\displaystyle CH_3}{\underset{|}{C}}H\overset{\displaystyle CH_3}{\overset{|}{C}}HCH_3$

```
          H
          |
       H—C—H
          |
    H  H  |  H
    |  |  |  |
 H—C—C—C—C—H
    |  |  |  |
    H  H  |  H
          |
       H—C—H
          |
          H
```

$CH_3CH_2\overset{\displaystyle CH_3}{\overset{|}{\underset{\displaystyle CH_3}{\underset{|}{C}}}}—CH_3$

2.9 Naming Organic Compounds

In the early development of organic chemistry, each new compound was given a name, usually by the person who had isolated or synthesized it. Names were not systematic but often did carry some information—usually about the origin

TABLE 2.3 Names and Formulas of Selected Alkyl Groups

Formula	Name	Formula	Name
$CH_3—$	Methyl	$CH_3CH(CH_3)—$	Isopropyl
$CH_3CH_2—$	Ethyl	$CH_3CH(CH_3)CH_2—$	Isobutyl
$CH_3CH_2CH_2—$	Propyl	$CH_3CH_2CH(CH_3)—$	*sec*-Butyl (secondary butyl)
$CH_3CH_2CH_2CH_2—$	Butyl	$CH_3C(CH_3)_2—$	*tert*-Butyl or *t*-Butyl (tertiary butyl)
$CH_3(CH_2)_3CH_2—$	Pentyl		
$CH_3(CH_2)_4CH_2—$	Hexyl		
$CH_3(CH_2)_5CH_2—$	Heptyl		
$CH_3(CH_2)_6CH_2—$	Octyl		
$CH_3(CH_2)_7CH_2—$	Nonyl		
$CH_3(CH_2)_8CH_2—$	Decyl		

of the substance. Wood alcohol (methanol), for example, was so named because it was obtained by destructive distillation or pyrolysis of wood. Methane, formed during underwater decomposition of vegetable matter in marshes, was originally called *marsh gas*. A single compound was often known by several names. For example, the active ingredient in alcoholic beverages has been called *alcohol*, *ethyl alcohol*, *methyl carbinol*, *grain alcohol*, *spirit*, and *ethanol*.

Beginning with a meeting in Geneva in 1892, an international system for naming compounds was developed. In its present form the method recommended by the International Union of Pure and Applied Chemistry is systematic, generally unambiguous, and internationally accepted. It is called the **IUPAC System**. Despite the existence of the official IUPAC System, a great many well-established common, or trivial, names and abbreviations (such as TNT and DDT) are used because of their brevity and/or convenience. So it is necessary to have a knowledge of both the IUPAC System and many common names.

IUPAC System

In order to name organic compounds systematically, you must be able to recognize certain common alkyl groups. **Alkyl groups** have the general formula C_nH_{2n+1} (one less hydrogen atom than the corresponding alkane). The missing H atom can be from any carbon in the alkane. The name of the group is formed from the name of the corresponding alkane by simply dropping *-ane* and substituting a *-yl* ending. The names and formulas of selected alkyl groups up to and including four carbon atoms are given in Table 2.3. The letter R is often used in formulas to mean any of the many possible alkyl groups.

alkyl groups

$$R = C_nH_{2n+1} \quad \text{Any alkyl group}$$

The following relatively simple rules are all that are needed to name a great many alkanes according to the IUPAC System. In later sections these rules will be extended to cover other classes of compounds, but advanced texts or references must be consulted for the complete system. The IUPAC rules for naming alkanes are

1. Select the longest continuous chain of carbon atoms as the parent compound, and consider all alkyl groups attached to it as side chains that have replaced hydrogen atoms of the parent hydrocarbon. The name of the alkane consists of the name of the parent compound prefixed by the names of the side-chain alkyl groups attached to it.
2. Number the carbon atoms in the parent carbon chain starting from the end closest to the first carbon atom that has an alkyl or other group substituted for a hydrogen atom.
3. Name each side-chain alkyl group and designate its position on the parent carbon chain by a number (for example, 2-methyl means a methyl group attached to carbon number 2).
4. When the same alkyl-group side chain occurs more than once, indicate this by a prefix (*di-*, *tri-*, *tetra-*, and so forth) written in front of the alkyl-group name (for example, *dimethyl* indicates two methyl groups). The numbers indicating the positions of these alkyl groups are separated by a comma and followed by a hyphen and are placed in front of the name (for example, 2,3-dimethyl).
5. When several different alkyl groups are attached to the parent compound, list them in alphabetical order; for example, *ethyl* before *methyl* in 3-ethyl-4-methyloctane.

The compound shown below is commonly called isopentane. Consider naming it by the IUPAC System:

$$\overset{4}{CH_3}-\overset{3}{CH_2}-\overset{2}{\underset{\displaystyle CH_3}{\underset{|}{CH}}}-\overset{1}{CH_3}$$

2-Methylbutane
(Isopentane)

The longest continuous chain contains four carbon atoms. Therefore, the parent compound is butane and the compound is named as a butane. The methyl group (CH_3—) attached to carbon number 2 is named as a prefix to butane, the "2-" indicating the point of attachment of the methyl group on the butane chain.

How would we write the structural formula for 2-methylpentane? An analysis of its name gives us this information.

1. The parent compound, pentane, contains five carbons. Write and number the five-carbon skeleton of pentane:

$$\overset{5}{C}-\overset{4}{C}-\overset{3}{C}-\overset{2}{C}-\overset{1}{C}$$

2. Put a methyl group on carbon number 2 ("2-methyl" in the name gives this information):

$$\overset{5}{C}-\overset{4}{C}-\overset{3}{C}-\overset{2}{\underset{\displaystyle CH_3}{\underset{|}{C}}}-\overset{1}{C}$$

3. Add hydrogens to give each carbon four bonds. The structural formula is

$$\begin{array}{ccccccccc} CH_3 & — & CH_2 & — & CH_2 & — & CH & — & CH_3 \\ &&&&&& | && \\ &&&&&& CH_3 && \end{array}$$

2-Methylpentane

Should this compound be called 4-methylpentane? No, the IUPAC System specifically states that the parent carbon chain shall be numbered starting from the end nearest to the side or branch chain.

It is very important to understand that it is the sequence of atoms and groups that determines the name of a compound, and not the way the sequence is written. Each of the following formulas represents 2-methylpentane:

$$\begin{array}{ccccccccc} 1 && 2 && 3 && 4 && 5 \\ CH_3 & — & CH & — & CH_2 & — & CH_2 & — & CH_3 \\ && | &&&&&& \\ && CH_3 &&&&&& \end{array} \qquad \begin{array}{ccccccccc} &&&&&& CH_3 && \\ 5 && 4 && 3 && |2 && 1 \\ CH_3 & — & CH_2 & — & CH_2 & — & CH & — & CH_3 \end{array}$$

$$\begin{array}{ccccccc} && CH_3 &&&& \\ 1 && 2| && 3 && \\ CH_3 & — & CH & — & CH_2 && \\ &&&& 4| && 5 \\ &&&& CH_2 & — & CH_3 \end{array} \qquad \begin{array}{ccccc} & CH_3 &&& \\ & 2| && 4 & \\ & CH && CH_2 & \\ 1\ / && \backslash 3\ / && \backslash 5 \\ CH_3 && CH_2 && CH_3 \end{array}$$

The following formulas and names demonstrate other aspects of the official nomenclature system:

$$\begin{array}{ccccccc} 4 && 3 && 2 && 1 \\ CH_3 & — & CH & — & CH & — & CH_3 \\ && | && | && \\ && CH_3 && CH_3 && \end{array}$$

2,3-Dimethylbutane

The name of this compound is 2,3-dimethylbutane. The longest carbon atom chain is four, indicating butane; "dimethyl" indicates two methyl groups; "2,3-" means that one CH_3 is on carbon 2 and one is on carbon 3.

$$\begin{array}{ccccccc} &&&& CH_3 && \\ 4 && 3 && |2 && 1 \\ CH_3 & — & CH_2 & — & C & — & CH_3 \\ &&&& | && \\ &&&& CH_3 && \end{array}$$

2,2-Dimethylbutane

(Both methyl groups are on the same carbon atom; both numbers are required.)

$$\begin{array}{ccccccccccc} &&&&&& CH_3 &&&& \\ 1 && 2 && 3 && 4| && 5 && 6 \\ CH_3 & — & CH & — & CH_2 & — & CH & — & CH_2 & — & CH_3 \\ && | &&&&&&&& \\ && CH_3 &&&&&&&& \end{array}$$

2,4-Dimethylhexane

(The molecule is numbered from left to right.)

```
          3       4        5        6
CH3—CH—CH2—CH2—CH3
         2|
         CH2
         1|
         CH3
```

3-Methylhexane

(There are six carbons in the longest continuous chain.)

```
                                           CH2—CH3
 8           7          6          5       |4      3        2       1
CH3—CH2—CH2—CH2—C——CH—CH—CH3
                                            |         |          |
                                           CH3    Cl      CH3
```

3-Chloro-4-ethyl-2,4-dimethyloctane

The longest carbon chain is eight. The groups that are attached or substituted for H on the octane chain are named in alphabetical order.

Example 2.2

Write the formulas for

(a) 3-Ethylpentane (b) 2,2,4-Trimethylpentane

Solution

(a) The name *pentane* indicates a five-carbon chain. Write five connected carbon atoms and number them:

```
1   2   3   4   5
C—C—C—C—C
```

An ethyl group is written as CH_3CH_2—. Attach this group at the open bond to carbon number 3:

```
1   2   3   4   5
C—C—C—C—C
          |
        CH2CH3
```

Now add hydrogen atoms to give each carbon atom four bonds. Carbons 1 and 5 each need three H atoms; carbons 2 and 4 each need two H atoms; and carbon 3 needs one H atom. The formula is complete:

```
CH3CH2CHCH2CH3
          |
        CH2CH3
```

(b) Pentane indicates a five-carbon chain. Write five connected carbon atoms and number them:

```
1   2   3   4   5
C—C—C—C—C
```

There are three methyl groups (CH_3—) in the compound (*trimethyl*), two attached to carbon 2 and one attached to carbon 4. Attach these three methyl groups to their respective carbon atoms:

```
    CH3   CH3
 1  2|  3 4|  5
 C—C—C—C—C
     |
    CH3
```

Now add H atoms to give each carbon atom four bonds. Carbons 1 and 5 each need three H atoms; carbon 2 does not need any H atoms; carbon 3 needs two H atoms; and carbon 4 needs one H atom. The formula is complete:

```
      CH3 CH3
       |   |
  CH3CCH2CHCH3
       |
      CH3
```

EXAMPLE 2.3

Name the following compounds:

```
(a)               CH3      (b)               CH2CH3
                   |                          |
 CH3CH2CH2CH2CHCH3           CH3CH2CH2CHCH2CHCH3
                                                 |
                                               CH2CH3
```

SOLUTION

(a) The longest continuous carbon chain contains six carbon atoms (Rule 1). Thus the parent name of the compound is hexane. Number the carbon chain from right to left so that the methyl group attached to carbon 2 is given the lowest possible number (Rule 2). With a methyl group on carbon 2, the name of the compound is 2-methylhexane (Rule 3).

(b) The longest continuous carbon chain contains eight carbon atoms:

```
               C—C
 8  7  6  |5  4  3
 C—C—C—C—C—C—C
                  |2  1
                  C—C
```

Thus the parent name is octane. As the chain is numbered, there is a methyl group on carbon 3 and an ethyl group on carbon 5. Thus the name of the compound is 5-ethyl-3-methyloctane. Note that ethyl is named before methyl (alphabetical order) (Rule 5).

PRACTICE Write the formula for: (a) 2-methylhexane; (b) 3,4-dimethylheptane; (c) 2-chloro-3-ethylpentane

Answers:

```
                                             Cl
                                              |
(a) CH3CHCH2CH2CH2CH3          (c) CH3CHCHCH2CH3
         |                                     |
        CH3                                  CH2CH3

             CH3
              |
(b) CH3CH2CHCHCH2CH2CH3
                 |
                CH3
```

PRACTICE Name the following compounds:

(a) $CH_3CH(CH_3)CH_2CH_3$ (b) $CH_3CH_2CH(CH_3)CH_2CH(CH_2CH_3)CH_3$

Answers: (a) 2-methylbutane (b) 3,5-dimethylheptane

2.10 Reactions of Alkanes

One single type of reaction of alkanes has inspired people to explore equatorial jungles, endure the heat and sandstorms of the deserts of Africa and the Middle East, mush across the frozen Arctic, and drill holes in the earth more than 30,000 feet deep! These strenuous and expensive activities have been undertaken because alkanes, as well as other hydrocarbons, undergo combustion with oxygen with the evolution of large amounts of heat energy. Methane, for example, reacts with oxygen:

$$CH_4(g) + 2\ O_2(g) \longrightarrow CO_2(g) + 2\ H_2O(g) + 802.5\ \text{kJ}\ (191.8\ \text{kcal})$$

The thermal energy can be converted to mechanical and electrical energy. Combustion reactions overshadow all other reactions of alkanes in economic importance. But combustion reactions are not usually of great interest to organic chemists, since carbon dioxide and water are the only chemical products of complete combustion.

Aside from their combustibility, alkanes are relatively sluggish and limited in reactivity. But with proper activation, such as high temperature and/or catalysts, alkanes can be made to react in a variety of ways. Some important non-combustion reactions of alkanes are the following:

1. *Halogenation* (substitution of halogens for hydrogen). *Halogenation* is a general term. When a specific halogen such as chlorine is used, the reaction is called chlorination. RH is an alkane (alkyl group + H atom).

$$RH + X_2 \longrightarrow RX + HX \qquad (X = Cl\ \text{or}\ Br)$$

$$CH_3CH_3 + Cl_2 \longrightarrow \underset{\text{Chloroethane}}{CH_3CH_2Cl} + HCl$$

This reaction yields alkyl halides (RX), which are useful as intermediates for the manufacture of other substances.

2. *Dehydrogenation* (removal of hydrogen)

$$C_nH_{2n+2} \xrightarrow{700\text{–}900^\circ C} C_nH_{2n} + H_2$$

$$CH_3CH_2CH_3 \xrightarrow{\Delta} \underset{\text{Propene}}{CH_3CH{=}CH_2} + H_2$$

This reaction yields alkenes, which, like alkyl halides, are useful chemical intermediates. Hydrogen is a valuable by-product.

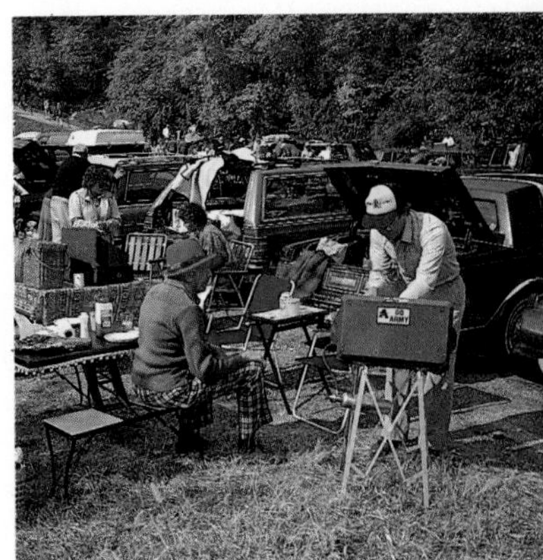

▲ The combustion of alkanes provides the energy for cars and camp stoves.

3. *Cracking* (breaking up large molecules to form smaller ones)

Example: $\underset{\text{Alkane}}{C_{16}H_{34}} \xrightarrow{\Delta} \underset{\text{Alkane}}{C_8H_{18}} + \underset{\text{Alkene}}{C_8H_{16}}$ (one of several possibilities)

4. *Isomerization* (rearrangement of molecular structures)

Example: $CH_3\text{—}CH_2\text{—}CH_2\text{—}CH_2\text{—}CH_3 \longrightarrow CH_3\text{—}CH_2\text{—}CH(CH_3)\text{—}CH_3$

Halogenation is used extensively in the manufacture of petrochemicals (chemicals derived from petroleum and used for purposes other than fuels). The other three reactions—dehydrogenation, cracking, and isomerization—singly or in combination, are of great importance in the production of motor fuels and petrochemicals.

A well-known reaction of methane and chlorine is shown by the equation

$$CH_4 + Cl_2 \longrightarrow \underset{\substack{\text{Chloromethane}\\ \text{(Methyl chloride)}}}{CH_3Cl} + HCl$$

The reaction of methane and chlorine gives a mixture of mono-, di-, tri-, and tetra-substituted chloromethanes.

$$CH_4 \xrightarrow{Cl_2} CH_3Cl \xrightarrow{Cl_2} CH_2Cl_2 \xrightarrow{Cl_2} CHCl_3 \xrightarrow{Cl_2} CCl_4 + 4\ HCl$$

However, if an excess of chlorine is used, the reaction can be controlled to give all tetrachloromethane (carbon tetrachloride). On the other hand, if a large ratio of methane to chlorine is used, the product will be predominantly chloromethane (methyl chloride). Table 2.4 shows the formulas and names for all the chloromethanes. The names for the other halogen-substituted methanes follow the same pattern as for the chloromethanes; for example, CH_3Br is bromomethane, or methyl bromide, and CHI_3 is triiodomethane, or iodoform.

monosubstitution

Chloromethane is a monosubstitution product of methane. The term **monosubstitution** refers to the fact that one hydrogen atom in an organic molecule is substituted by another atom or by a group of atoms. In hydrocarbons, for example, when we substitute one chlorine atom for a hydrogen atom, the new compound is a monosubstitution (monochlorosubstitution) product. In a like manner we can have di-, tri-, tetra-, and so on, substitution products.

TABLE 2.4 Chlorination Products of Methane

Formula	IUPAC name	Common name
CH_3Cl	Chloromethane	Methyl chloride
CH_2Cl_2	Dichloromethane	Methylene chloride
$CHCl_3$	Trichloromethane	Chloroform
CCl_4	Tetrachloromethane	Carbon tetrachloride

This kind of chlorination (or bromination) is general with alkanes. There are nine different chlorination products of ethane. See if you can write the structural formulas for all of them.

When propane is chlorinated, two isomeric monosubstitution products are obtained, because a hydrogen atom may be replaced on either the first or second carbon:

$$CH_3CH_2CH_3 + Cl_2 \xrightarrow[25^\circ C]{Light} CH_3CH_2CH_2Cl + CH_3CHClCH_3 + HCl$$

1-Chloropropane (*n*-Propyl chloride) 2-Chloropropane (Isopropyl chloride)

The letter X is commonly used to indicate a halogen atom. The formula RX indicates a halogen atom attached to an alkyl group and represents the class of compounds known as the **alkyl halides**. When R is CH_3, then CH_3X can be CH_3F, CH_3Cl, CH_3Br, or CH_3I.

alkyl halide

Alkyl halides are named systematically in the same general way as alkanes. Halogen atoms are identified as *fluoro-*, *chloro-*, *bromo-*, or *iodo-* and are named as substituents like side-chain alkyl groups. Study these examples:

$CH_3—CHCl—CH_2—CH_3$
2-Chlorobutane

$CH_2Cl—CHBr—CH_3$
2-Bromo-1-chloropropane

$$CH_3—CH_2—\underset{\displaystyle CH_3}{\underset{|}{CH}}—CHCl—CH_3$$
2-Chloro-3-methylpentane

EXAMPLE 2.4

How many monochlorosubstitution products can be obtained from pentane?

SOLUTION

First write the formula for pentane:

$$\overset{5}{C}H_3\overset{4}{C}H_2\overset{3}{C}H_2\overset{2}{C}H_2\overset{1}{C}H_3$$

Now rewrite the formula five times substituting a Cl atom for an H atom on each C atom:

I	$CH_3CH_2CH_2CH_2\overset{1}{C}H_2Cl$	Cl on carbon 1
II	$CH_3CH_2CH_2\overset{2}{C}HClCH_3$	Cl on carbon 2
III	$CH_3CH_2\overset{3}{C}HClCH_2CH_3$	Cl on carbon 3
IV	$CH_3\overset{4}{C}HClCH_2CH_2CH_3$	Cl on carbon 4
V	$\overset{5}{C}H_2ClCH_2CH_2CH_2CH_3$	Cl on carbon 5

Compounds I and V are identical. By numbering compound V from left to right, we find that both compounds (I and V) are 1-chloropentane. Compounds II and IV are identical. By numbering compound IV from left to right, we find that both compounds (II and IV) are 2-chloropentane. Thus there are three monochlorosubstitution products of pentane: 1-chloropentane, 2-chloropentane, and 3-chloropentane.

Practice How many dichlorosubstitution products can be obtained from hexane?

Answer: 12

2.11 Sources of Alkanes

The two main sources of alkanes are natural gas and petroleum. Natural gas is formed by the anaerobic decay of plants and animals. The composition of natural gas varies in different locations. Its main component is methane (80–95%), the balance being varying amounts of other hydrocarbons, hydrogen, nitrogen, carbon monoxide, carbon dioxide, and in some locations, hydrogen sulfide. Economically significant amounts of methane are now obtained by the decomposition of sewage, garbage, and other organic waste products.

Petroleum, also called *crude oil*, is a viscous black liquid consisting of a mixture of hydrocarbons with smaller amounts of nitrogen and sulfur-containing organic compounds. Petroleum is formed by the decomposition of plants and animals over millions of years. The composition of petroleum varies widely from one locality to another. Crude oil is refined into many useful products such as gasoline, kerosene, diesel fuel, jet fuel, lubricating oil, heating oil, paraffin wax, petroleum jelly (petrolatum), tars, and asphalt. Petroleum jelly is a jellylike semisolid that is used in preparing medicinal ointments and for lubrication (see Figure 2.9).

A petroleum refinery ▶ processes crude oil into the materials used to produce many consumer products.

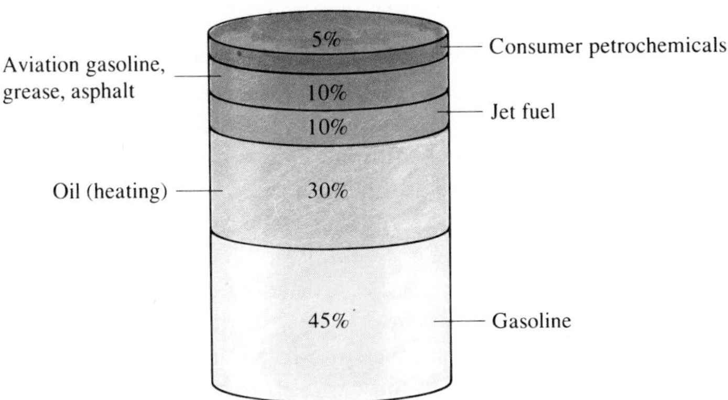

◀ **FIGURE 2.9 Uses of petroleum.**

At the rate that natural gas and petroleum are being used, these sources of hydrocarbons are destined to be in short supply and virtually exhausted in the not-too-distant future. Alternate sources of fuels must be developed.

2.12 Octane Rating of Gasoline

Gasoline, aside from the additives put into it, consists primarily of hydrocarbons. Gasoline, as it is distilled from crude oil, causes "knocking" when burned in high-compression automobile engines. Knocking, which is due to a too-rapid combustion or detonation of the air–gasoline mixture, is a severe problem in high-compression engines. The knock-resistance of gasolines, a quality that varies widely, is usually expressed in terms of *octane number*, or *octane rating*.

Isooctane (2,2,4-trimethylpentane), because of its highly branched chain structure, is a motor fuel that is resistant to knocking. Mixtures of isooctane and *n*-heptane, a straight-chain alkane that knocks badly, have been used as standards to establish octane ratings of gasolines. Isooctane is arbitrarily assigned an octane number of 100 and *n*-heptane an octane number of 0. To determine the octane rating, a gasoline is compared with mixtures of isooctane and *n*-heptane in a test engine. The octane number of the gasoline corresponds to the percentage of isooctane present in the isooctane and *n*-heptane mixture that matches the knocking characteristics of the gasoline being tested. Thus a 90 octane gasoline has knocking characteristics matching those of a mixture of 90% isooctane and 10% *n*-heptane.

When first used to establish octane numbers, isooctane was the most knock-resistant substance available. Technological advances have resulted in engines with greater power and compression ratios. Higher quality fuels were subsequently necessary. Fuels containing more highly branched hydrocarbons, unsaturated hydrocarbons, or aromatic hydrocarbons may burn more smoothly than isooctane, and have a higher octane rating than 100.

An alternative method to boost octane rating and minimize engine knocking is to add small amounts of an additive to the fuel. One such additive commonly used in gasoline was tetraethyllead, $(C_2H_5)_4Pb$. Adding only 3 mL per gallon of gasoline can increase the octane rating by 15 units. The function of the tetraethyllead is to prevent the premature explosions that constitute knocking. Use of tetraethyllead additives poses a serious environmental hazard. Lead becomes yet another air pollutant, in addition to the others (carbon monoxide, hydrocarbons, and nitrogen oxides) already produced by the automobile. Since lead is a toxic substance which accumulates in living organisms, legal restrictions are constantly being tightened on the use of tetraethyllead. In addition, most cars are now equipped with catalytic converters to reduce the emissions of pollutants into the atmosphere. These catalytic converters are deactivated by lead. These environmental problems are producing changes in the formulation of gasoline.

Major oil companies have changed the formulation of gasoline in recent years to eliminate leaded gasoline and reduce emissions into the atmosphere. Current additives in unleaded gasoline include aromatic compounds such as toluene and xylene (Chapter 3) or methyl *tert*-butyl ether (MTBE):

$$CH_3-O-\underset{\displaystyle CH_3}{\overset{\displaystyle CH_3}{\overset{|}{\underset{|}{C}}}}-CH_3$$

Chemical conversion of straight-chain alkanes into branched or cyclic compounds is also a method for "reformulating" gasoline. Fuels are also changed from season to season as well as from one region of the country to another. These seasonal and regional changes reflect variations in air pollution and environmental standards.

2.13 CYCLOALKANES

cycloalkanes

Cyclic, or closed-chain, alkanes also exist. These substances, called **cycloalkanes**, *cycloparaffins*, or *naphthenes*, have the general formula C_nH_{2n}. Note that this series of compounds has two fewer hydrogen atoms than the open-chain alkanes. The bonds for the two missing hydrogen atoms are accounted for by an additional carbon–carbon bond in forming the cyclic ring of carbon atoms. Structures for the four smallest cycloalkanes are shown in Figure 2.10.

With the exception noted below for cyclopropane and cyclobutane, cycloalkanes are generally similar to open-chain alkanes in both physical properties and chemical reactivity. Cycloalkanes are saturated hydrocarbons; they contain only single bonds between carbon atoms.

The reactivity of cyclopropane, and to a lesser degree that of cyclobutane, is greater than that of other alkanes. This greater reactivity exists because the carbon–carbon bond angles in these substances deviate substantially from the normal tetrahedral angle. The carbon atoms form a triangle in cyclopropane, and in cyclobutane they approximate a square. Cyclopropane molecules therefore have carbon–carbon bond angles of 60°, and in cyclobutane the bond angles are about 90°. In the open-chain alkanes and in larger cycloalkanes,

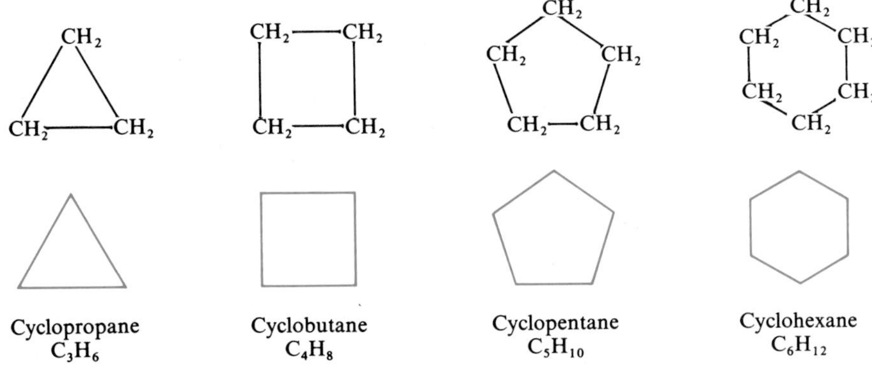

FIGURE 2.10 Cycloalkanes. In the line representations, each corner of the diagram represents a CH_2 group.

the carbon atoms are in a three-dimensional zigzag pattern in space and have normal (tetrahedral) bond angles of about 109.5°.

Bromine adds to cyclopropane readily and to cyclobutane to some extent. In this reaction the ring breaks and an open-chain dibromopropane is formed:

$$\underset{\text{Cyclopropane}}{\overset{CH_2}{CH_2{-}CH_2}} + Br_2 \longrightarrow \underset{\text{1,3-Dibromopropane}}{BrCH_2CH_2CH_2Br}$$

Cyclopropane and cyclobutane react in this way because their carbon–carbon bonds are strained and therefore weakened. Cycloalkanes with rings having more than four carbon atoms do not react in this way because their molecules take the shape of nonplanar puckered rings. These rings can be considered to be formed by simply joining the end carbon atoms of the corresponding normal alkanes. The resulting cyclic molecules are nearly strain-free, with carbon atoms arranged in space so that the bond angles are close to 109.5° (Figure 2.11).

Molecular models show that cyclohexane can assume two distinct nonplanar conformations. One form is shaped like a chair, while the other is shaped like a boat (see Figure 2.12). In the chair form the hydrogen atoms are separated as effectively as possible, so this is the more stable conformation. Six of the hydrogens in "chair" cyclohexane lie approximately in the same plane as the carbon ring. These are called **equatorial** hydrogens. The other six hydrogen atoms are approximately at right angles above or below the plane of the ring. These hydrogens are called **axial**. Substituent groups usually are found in equatorial positions where they are furthest from hydrogens and other groups. Five- and six-membered rings are a common occurrence in organic chemistry and biochemistry. These conformations and isomers are evident in carbohydrates as well as in nucleic acids.

equatorial

axial

Cyclopropane is a useful general anesthetic and, along with certain other cycloalkanes, is used as an intermediate in some chemical syntheses. The high reactivity of cyclopropane requires great care in its use as an anesthetic because it is an extreme fire and explosion hazard. The cyclopentane and cyclohexane ring structures are present in many naturally occurring molecules such as prostaglandins, steroids (for example, cholesterol and sex hormones), and some vitamins.

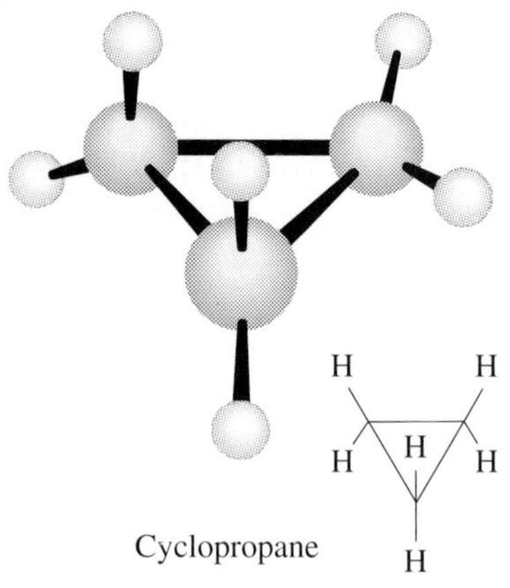

Cyclopropane

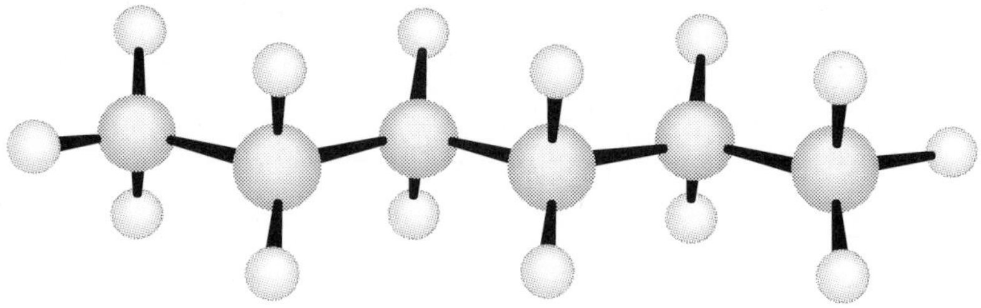

n–Hexane $CH_3CH_2CH_2CH_2CH_2CH_3$

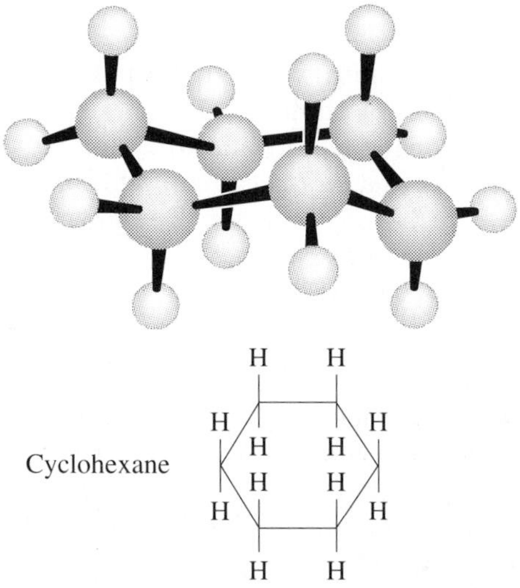

Cyclohexane

▲
FIGURE 2.11
Ball-and-stick models illustrating cyclopropane, hexane, and cyclohexane: In cyclopropane all the carbon atoms are in one plane. The angle between carbon atoms is 60°, not the usual 109.5°; therefore the cyclopropane ring is strained. In cyclohexane the carbon–carbon bonds are not strained. This is because the molecule is puckered, with carbon–carbon bond angles of 109.5°, as found in normal hexane.

FIGURE 2.12 ▶
Conformations of cyclohexane: (a) chair conformation; (b) boat conformation. Axial hydrogens are shown in color in the chair conformation.

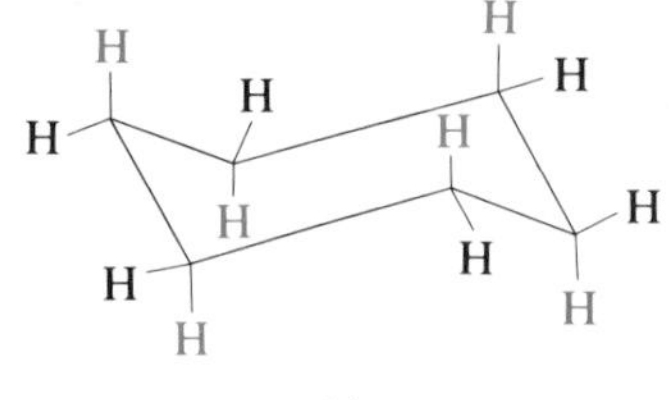

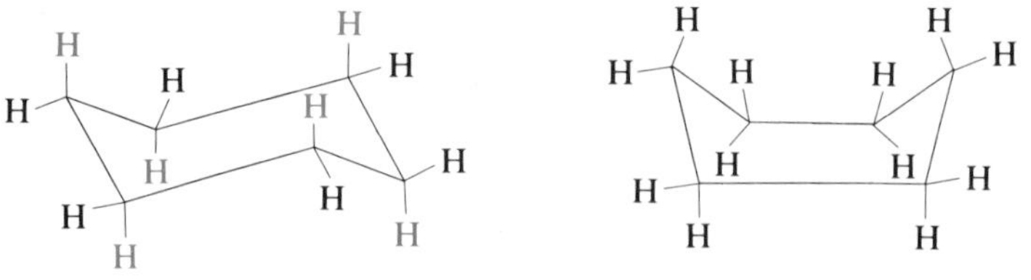

(a)

(b)

CHEMISTRY IN ACTION

MOLECULES TO COMMUNICATE, REFRIGERATE, AND SAVE LIVES

By far the major role of alkanes in our world is as a source of energy for industrial and consumer use. Hydrocarbons do not function as an energy source in the physiological world of living organisms. The compounds that supply fuel necessary for life contain oxygen as well as carbon and hydrogen.

Alkanes do find other significant uses in our lives. High-molar-mass alkanes can be used to soften or moisten the skin. Petroleum jelly and mineral oil are both mixtures of hydrocarbons used to protect the skin or as a lubricant.

Insects can use hydrocarbons (as well as other organic compounds) as chemical communication devices. These compounds, called pheromones, are secreted by an insect and recognized by other members of the species as a message. The meaning of the pheromone varies with its composition. It could be a sex attractant, an alarm, or an indication of the path to a source of food. Ants release alarm pheromones when disturbed which have been identified as undecane, $CH_3(CH_2)_9CH_3$, and tridecane, $CH_3(CH_2)_{11}CH_3$. Our growing understanding of these molecules is beginning to lead to their use in insect abatement. Commercial traps are baited with sex pheromone and the insects are captured without the use of pesticides.

Halogenated hydrocarbons serve several significant functions in society. Tetrachloroethylene, C_2Cl_4, and carbon tetrachloride, CCl_4, are both good solvents for nonpolar molecules and have been used as cleaning solvents. Carbon tetrâchloride exposure can lead to kidney and liver damage. Both compounds are carcinogens. The dry-cleaning industry is eliminating the use of these compounds.

Freons and other chlorofluorocarbons (CFCs) are useful because they are nontoxic, nonflammable, and noncorrosive. Many of these compounds have low boiling points and make excellent refrigerants. They have also been used as propellants in aerosol sprays, and in the production of some fast food containers. Unfortunately the use of CFCs is a major factor in the destruction of the ozone layer. Use of these compounds is currently being discontinued by major industries in an effort to protect our atmosphere.

Some fluorinated hydrocarbons are used as blood substitutes. All the hydrogens in the hydrocarbon are replaced with fluorine, producing a compound known as a fluorocarbon. Dispersions of these compounds in water can absorb nearly 3 times the oxygen per unit as whole blood. Organisms receiving blood substitutes continue to produce whole blood. The substitute permits the tissues to absorb oxygen while it remains chemically inert and is excreted over a period of time.

CONCEPTS IN REVIEW

1. Describe the tetrahedral nature of the carbon atom.
2. Explain why the concept of hybridization is used to describe the bonding of carbon in simple compounds such as methane.
3. Explain the bonding in alkanes.
4. Write the Lewis structures for alkanes and halogenated alkanes.

5. Write the names and formulas for the first ten normal alkanes.
6. Understand the concept of isomerization.
7. Write structural formulas and IUPAC names for the isomers of an alkane or a halogenated alkane.
8. Give the IUPAC name of a hydrocarbon or a halogenated hydrocarbon when given the structural formula and vice versa.
9. Write equations for the halogenation of an alkane, giving all possible monohalosubstitution products.
10. Write structural formulas and names for simple cycloalkanes.
11. Draw the two major conformations for cyclohexane.
12. Understand the octane number rating system for gasoline and discuss methods for increasing the octane number.
13. Indicate several biological uses of alkanes.

Exercises

1. What are the major reasons for the large number of organic compounds?
2. Why is it believed that a carbon atom must form hybrid electron orbitals when it bonds to hydrogen atoms to form methane?
3. Write Lewis structures for:
   (a) CCl_4 (b) C_2Cl_6 (c) $CH_3CH_2CH_3$
4. Write the names and formulas for the first ten normal alkanes.
5. The name of the compound of formula $C_{11}H_{24}$ is undecane. What is the formula for dodecane, the next higher homologue in the alkane series?
6. How many sigma bonds are in a molecule of
   (a) Ethane (b) Butane (c) Isobutane
7. Which of these formulas represent isomers?
   (a) $CH_3CH_2CH_2CH_3$
   (b) $CH_3CH_2CH_2CH_2CH_3$
   (c) CH_3CHCH_3 (with CH_3CH_2 on the middle C)
   (d) $CH_3CH_2CH_2CH_2CH_2CH_3$
   (e) $(CH_3)_2CH{-}CH(CH_3)_2$

       CH₃   CH₃
          \   /
          CH—CH
          /   \
       CH₃   CH₃

   (f) $CH_2{-}CH_2$, CH_2 CH_2, CH_2
   (g) $CH_3CHCH_2CH_2CH_3$ (with CH_3 on C-2)
   (h) cyclopropane ring CH_2, CH_2, $CHCH_2CH_3$
   (i) CH_3CH_2 bonded to CH_2CH_3
8. (a) How many methyl groups are in each formula in Question 7?
   (b) How many ethyl groups?
9. Which of these formulas represent the same compound?
   (a) $CH_3CHCH_2CHCH_3$ (with CH_3 on C-2 and CH_3 on C-4)
   (b) $CH_2CHCH_2CHCH_3$ (with CH_3 on C-1, CH_3 on C-2, and CH_3 on C-4)
   (c) $CH_3CHCH_2CH_2CHCH_3$ (with CH_3 on C-2 and CH_3 on C-5)
   (d) $CH_3CHCHCH_2CH_2$ (with CH_3 on C-2, CH_3 on C-3, and CH_3 on C-5)
   (e) CH_3 bonded to CH_3CHCH_2, whose CH_2 is bonded to the CH of $CH_3CH_2CHCH_3$
   (f) CH_3 bonded to CH_3CH, bonded to CH_2CHCH_3, whose CH bears CH_2CH_3

10. Draw structural formulas for all the isomers of
(a) CH_3Br (d) C_3H_7Br (g) C_3H_6BrCl
(b) CH_2Cl_2 (e) C_4H_9I (h) $C_4H_8Cl_2$
(c) C_2H_5Cl (f) $C_3H_6Cl_2$

11. What is the molar mass of an alkane that contains 30 carbon atoms?

12. Write condensed structural formulas for:
(a) The five isomers of hexane
(b) The nine isomers of heptane

13. Give common and IUPAC names for the following:
(a) CH_3CH_2Cl (d) $CH_3CH_2CH_2Cl$
(b) $CH_3CHClCH_3$ (e) $(CH_3)_3CCl$
(c) $(CH_3)_2CHCH_2Cl$ (f) $CH_3CHClCH_2CH_3$

14. The following names are incorrect. Tell why the name is wrong and give the correct name.
(a) 3-Methylbutane
(b) 2-Ethylbutane
(c) 2-Dimethylpentane
(d) 3-Methyl-5-ethyloctane
(e) 3,5,5-Triethylhexane

15. Draw structural formulas of the following compounds:
(a) 2,4-Dimethylpentane
(b) 2,2-Dimethylpentane
(c) 3-Isopropyloctane
(d) 4-Ethyl-2-methylhexane
(e) 4-*t*-Butylheptane
(f) 4-Ethyl-7-isopropyl-2,4,8-trimethyldecane

16. Give the IUPAC name for each of the following compounds:

(a) $CH_3CH_2CHCH_3$ with CH_3 attached below the third carbon (the CH)

(b) $(CH_3)_2CHCH_2CH(CH_3)_2$

(c) 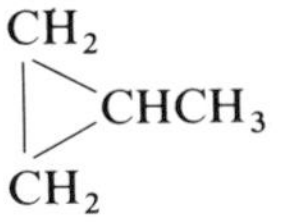 three-membered ring: CH_2, CH_2, $CHCH_3$

(d) $CH_3CH_2CH_2CHCH_3$ with CH_3CHCH_3 attached above the fourth carbon (the CH)

17. Complete the equations for (a) the monochlorination and (b) complete combustion of butane.

(a) $CH_3CH_2CH_2CH_3 + Cl_2 \xrightarrow{hv}$

(b) $CH_3CH_2CH_2CH_3 + O_2 \xrightarrow{\Delta}$

18. The structure for hexane is

$CH_3CH_2CH_2CH_2CH_2CH_3$

Draw structural formulas for all the monochlorohexanes, $C_6H_{13}Cl$, that have the same carbon structures as hexane.

19. Draw structures for the ten dichlorosubstituted isomers ($C_5H_{10}Cl_2$) of 2-methylbutane.

20. A hydrocarbon sample of formula C_4H_{10} was brominated, and four different monobromo compounds of formula C_4H_9Br were isolated. Was the sample a pure compound or a mixture of compounds? Explain your answer.

21. There are two cycloalkanes that have the formula C_4H_8. Draw their structures and name them.

22. Which of these statements are correct? Rewrite the incorrect statements to make them correct.
(a) Alkane hydrocarbons are essentially nonpolar.
(b) The C—H sigma bond in methane is made from an overlap of an *s* electron orbital and an sp^3 electron orbital.
(c) The valence electrons of every carbon atom in an alkane are in sp^3-hybridized orbitals.
(d) The four carbon–hydrogen bonds in methane are equivalent.
(e) Hydrocarbons are composed of carbon and water.
(f) In the alkane homologous series, the formula of each member differs from its preceding member by CH_3.
(g) Carbon atoms can form single, double, and triple bonds with other carbon atoms.
(h) The name for the alkane C_5H_{12} is propane.
(i) There are eight carbon atoms in a molecule of 2,3,3-trimethylpentane.
(j) The general formula for an alkyl halide is RX.
(k) The IUPAC name for $CH_3CH_2CH_2CHClCH_3$ is 4-chloropentane.
(l) Isopropyl chloride is also called 2-chloropropane.
(m) The molecular formula for chlorocyclohexane is $C_6H_{11}Cl$.
(n) Chlorocyclohexane and 1-chlorohexane are isomers.
(o) The products of complete combustion of a hydrocarbon are carbon monoxide and water.
(p) When pentane is chlorinated, three monochlorosubstitution products can be obtained.
(q) Isobutane, 2-methylpropane, and 1,1-dimethylethane are all correct names for the same compound.
(r) Only one monochloro-substituted product results from the chlorination of butane.
(s) Cycloalkanes have the general formula C_nH_{2n}.

3

Unsaturated Hydrocarbons

◄ **CHAPTER OPENING PHOTO: The brilliant dyes used in the textile industry are unsaturated organic compounds.**

Think of the many images a particular fragrance can evoke. A favorite perfume may provide memories of a romantic evening, the aroma of a light-bodied red wine may remind us of a favorite restaurant, while the smell of cloves forces us to remember the dentist's office. The molecules associated with the essential oils in plants often contain multiple bonds between carbon atoms. These oils are widely used in cosmetics, medicines, flavorings, and perfumes.

Many of these molecules are necessary to enhance our lives. Vitamin A prevents night blindness and maintains the integrity of the eyes. Unsaturated molecules can also link together to form polymers. These large molecules find many uses, such as polypropylene in plastic bottles and carpet fibers, polystyrene in foam cups, Teflon, plastic wrap, and Orlon fiber in clothing.

Hydrocarbons also often form into rings. These ring molecules are the basis for many consumer products such as detergents, insecticides, and dyes. Some aromatic carbon compounds are also found in living organisms.

3.1 BONDING IN UNSATURATED HYDROCARBONS

The unsaturated hydrocarbons consist of three families of homologous compounds which contain multiple bonds between carbon atoms. In each family the compounds contain fewer hydrogens than the corresponding alkanes. One family of compounds contains carbon–carbon double bonds. These compounds are called **alkenes** or olefins. The family of compounds containing carbon–carbon triple bonds is called **alkynes** or acetylenes. The third family of hydrocarbons contains the benzene ring and is known as the **aromatic compounds**.

alkenes

alkynes

aromatic compounds

The double bonds in alkenes are different from the sp^3 hybrid bonds found in the alkanes. The alkene hybridization may be visualized in the following way. One of the 2*s* electrons of carbon is promoted to a 2*p* orbital forming the four half-filled orbitals, $2s^1 2p_x^1 2p_y^1 2p_z^1$. Three of these orbitals ($2s^1 2p_x^1 2p_y^1$) hybridize, forming three equivalent orbitals designated as sp^2. Thus the four orbitals available for bonding are three sp^2 orbitals and one *p* orbital. This process is illustrated in Figure 3.1.

The three sp^2 hybrid orbitals form angles of 120° with each other and lie in a single plane. The remaining 2*p* orbital is oriented perpendicular to this plane,

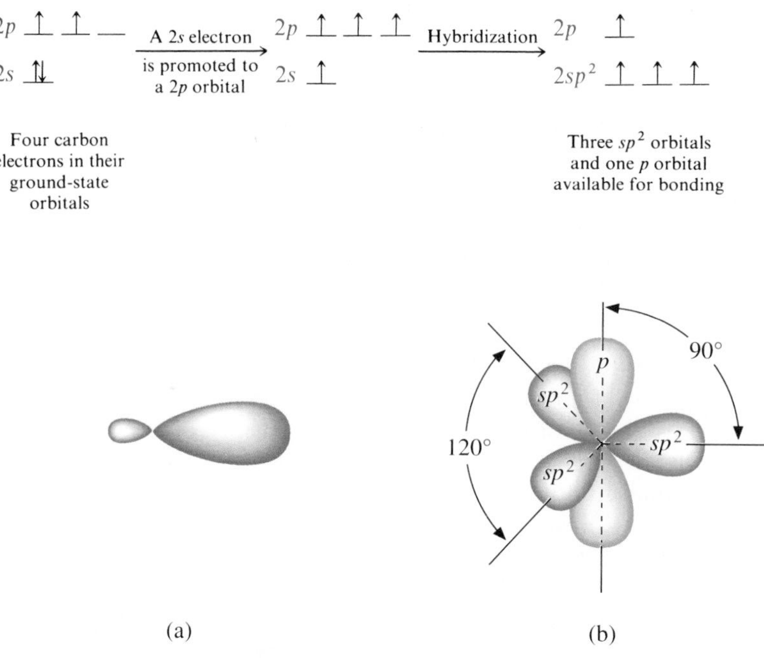

FIGURE 3.1 ▶ **Schematic hybridization of $2s^22p_x^12p_y^1$ orbitals of carbon to form three sp^2 electron orbitals and one p electron orbital.**

FIGURE 3.2 ▶ **(a) A single sp^2 electron orbital and (b) a side view of three sp^2 orbitals all lying in the same plane with a p orbital perpendicular to the three sp^2 orbitals.**

with one lobe above and one lobe below the plane (see Figure 3.2). In the formation of a double bond, an sp^2 orbital of one carbon atom overlaps an identical sp^2 orbital of another carbon to form a sigma bond. At the same time the two perpendicular p orbitals (one on each carbon atom) overlap to form a **pi (π) bond** between the two carbon atoms. This pi bond consists of two electron clouds, one above and one below the sigma bond (see Figure 3.3). The $H_2C{=}CH_2$ molecule is completed as the remaining sp^2 orbitals (two on each carbon atom) overlap hydrogen s orbitals to form sigma bonds between the carbon and hydrogen atoms. Thus there are five sigma bonds and one pi bond in an ethylene molecule.

pi bond

In the formula commonly used to represent ethylene ($CH_2{=}CH_2$), no distinction is made between the sigma bond and the pi bond in the carbon–carbon double bond. Each bond is represented by a dash. However, these bonds are actually very different from each other. The sigma bond is formed by the overlap of sp^2 orbitals; the pi bond is formed by the overlap of p orbitals. The sigma bond electron cloud is distributed about a line joining the carbon nuclei, but the pi bond electron cloud is distributed above and below the sigma bond region (see Figure 3.3). The carbon–carbon pi bond is much weaker and, as a consequence, much more reactive than the carbon–carbon sigma bond.

The formation of a triple bond between carbon atoms, as in acetylene, $HC{\equiv}CH$, may be visualized as follows:

1. A carbon atom $2s$ electron is promoted to a $2p$ orbital ($2s^12p_x^12p_y^12p_z^1$).
2. The $2s$ orbital hybridizes with one of the $2p$ orbitals to form two equivalent orbitals known as sp orbitals. These two hybrid orbitals lie on a straight line that passes through the center of the carbon atom. The re-

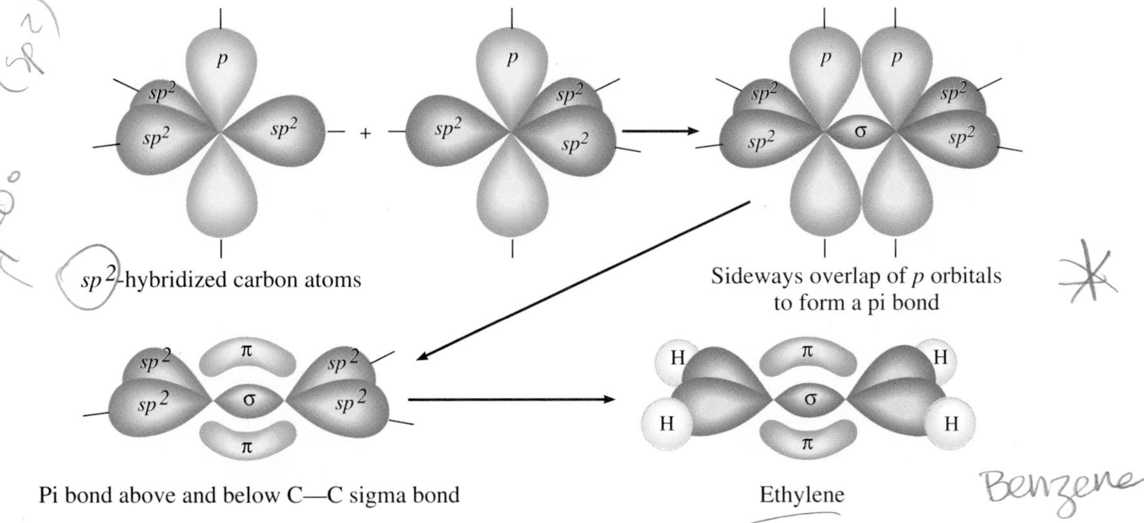

▲
FIGURE 3.3
Pi (π) and sigma (σ) bonding in ethylene.

maining two unhybridized 2*p* orbitals are oriented at right angles to these *sp* orbitals and to each other.

3. In forming carbon–carbon bonds, one carbon *sp* orbital overlaps an identical *sp* orbital on another carbon atom to establish a sigma bond between the two carbon atoms.
4. The remaining *sp* orbitals (one on each carbon atom) overlap *s* orbitals on hydrogens to form sigma bonds and establish the H—C—C—H bond sequence. Because all the atoms forming this sequence lie in a straight line, the acetylene molecule is linear.
5. Simultaneously the two 2*p* orbitals on each carbon overlap to form two pi bonds. These two pi bond orbitals occupy sufficient space that they overlap each other to form a continuous tubelike electron cloud surrounding the sigma bond between the carbon atoms (Figure 3.4). These pi bond electrons (as in ethylene) are not as tightly held by the carbon nuclei as are the sigma bond electrons. Acetylene, consequently, is a very reactive substance.

3.2 Nomenclature of Alkenes

The names of alkenes are derived from the names of corresponding alkanes. To name an alkene by the IUPAC System:

1. Select the longest carbon–carbon chain that contains the double bond.
2. Name this parent compound as you would an alkane but change the *-ane* ending to *-ene*; for example, propane is changed to propene.

$CH_3CH_2CH_3$	$CH_3CH{=}CH_2$
Propane	Propene

FIGURE 3.4 ▶ Pi (π) and sigma (σ) bonding in acetylene.

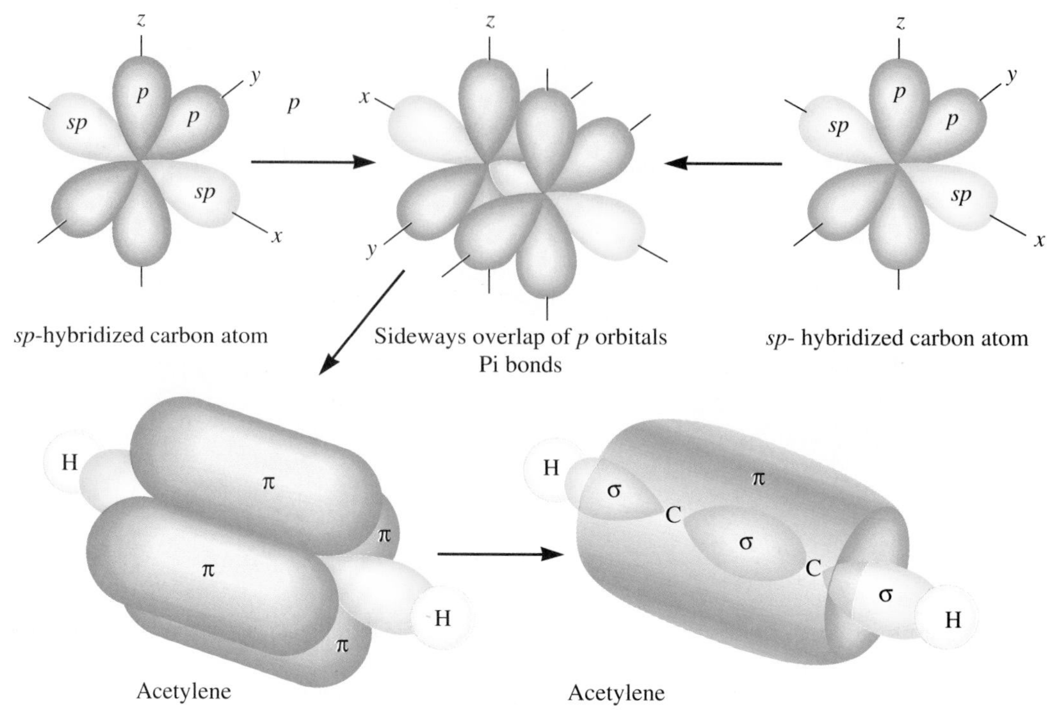

3. Number the carbon chain of the parent compound starting with the end nearer to the double bond. Use the smaller of the two numbers on the double-bonded carbon atoms to indicate the position of the double bond. Place this number in front of the alkene name; for example, 2-butene means that the carbon–carbon double bond is between carbon numbers 2 and 3.
4. Side chains and other groups are treated as in naming alkanes, by numbering and assigning them to the carbon atom to which they are bonded.

Study the following examples of named alkenes:

$$\overset{4}{C}H_3\overset{3}{C}H_2\overset{2}{C}H{=}\overset{1}{C}H_2$$
1-Butene

$$\overset{1}{C}H_3\overset{2}{C}H{=}\overset{3}{C}H\overset{4}{C}H_3$$
2-Butene

$$\overset{4}{C}H_3\overset{3}{\underset{}{C}}(CH_3)H\overset{2}{C}H{=}\overset{1}{C}H_2$$
3-Methyl-1-butene

$$(\overset{6}{C}H_3\overset{5}{C}H_2\overset{4}{C}H_2)(CH_3CH_2CH_2)\overset{3}{C}H\overset{2}{C}H{=}\overset{1}{C}H_2$$
3-Propyl-1-hexene

To write a structural formula from a systematic name, the naming process is reversed. For example, how would we write the structural formula for 4-methyl-2-pentene? The name indicates:

1. Five carbons in the longest chain

2. A double bond between carbons 2 and 3
3. A methyl group on carbon 4

Write five carbon atoms in a row. Place a double bond between carbons 2 and 3, and place a methyl group on carbon 4:

```
1   2   3   4   5
C—C=C—C—C
            |
           CH3
```

Carbon skeleton

Now add hydrogen atoms to give each carbon atom four bonds. Carbons 1 and 5 each need three H atoms; carbons 2, 3, and 4 each need one H atom. The complete formula is

```
CH3CH=CHCHCH3
           |
          CH3
```

4-Methyl-2-pentene

EXAMPLE 3.1

Write structural formulas for (a) 2-pentene and (b) 7-methyl-2-octene.

SOLUTION

(a) The stem *pent-* indicates a five-carbon chain; the suffix *-ene* indicates a carbon–carbon double bond; the number 2 locates the double bond between carbons 2 and 3. Write five carbon atoms in a row and place a double bond between carbons 2 and 3:

```
1   2   3   4   5
C—C=C—C—C
```

Add hydrogen atoms to give each carbon atom four bonds. Carbons 1 and 5 each need three H atoms; carbons 2 and 3 each need one H atom; carbon 4 needs two H atoms. The complete formula is

$CH_3CH{=}CHCH_2CH_3$

2-Pentene

(b) Octene, like octane, indicates an eight-carbon chain. The chain contains a double bond between carbons 2 and 3 and a methyl group on carbon 7. Write eight carbon atoms in a row, place a double bond between carbons 2 and 3, and place a methyl group on carbon 7:

```
1   2   3   4   5   6   7   8
C—C=C—C—C—C—C—C
                        |
                       CH3
```

Now add hydrogen atoms to give each carbon atom four bonds. The complete formula is

```
CH3CH=CHCH2CH2CH2CHCH3
                   |
                  CH3
```

7-Methyl-2-octene

EXAMPLE 3.2

Name this compound:

$$\mathrm{CH_3CH_2\underset{\underset{\displaystyle CH_2}{\|}}{C}CH_2CH_2CH_3}$$

SOLUTION

The longest carbon chain contains six carbons. However, since the compound is an alkene, we must include the double bond in the chain. The longest carbon chain containing the double bond has five carbons. Therefore, the compound is named as a pentene.

$$\mathrm{CH_3\overset{4}{C}H_2\overset{3}{\underset{\underset{\displaystyle {}^{1}CH_2}{\|}}{C}}\overset{2}{C}H_2\overset{5}{C}H_2CH_3}$$

(Printed numbering above the chain: 2 3 4 5; $^1CH_2$ below.)

Attached to carbon 2 is an ethyl group. The name is 2-ethyl-1-pentene.

PRACTICE Write structural formulas for (a) 3-hexene, (b) 4-ethyl-2-heptene, and (c) 3,4-dimethyl-2-pentene.

Answers: (a) $\mathrm{CH_3CH_2CH{=}CHCH_2CH_3}$

(b) $\mathrm{CH_3CH{=}CH\underset{\underset{\displaystyle CH_2CH_3}{|}}{C}HCH_2CH_2CH_3}$

(c) $\mathrm{CH_3CH{=}\overset{\overset{\displaystyle CH_3}{|}}{\underset{\underset{\displaystyle CH_3}{|}}{C}}CHCH_3}$

PRACTICE Name these compounds.

(a) $\mathrm{CH_3\underset{\underset{\displaystyle CH_2CH_3}{|}}{C}{=}CHCH_3}$ (b) $\mathrm{CH_3\underset{\underset{\displaystyle CH_3}{|}}{C}{=}CH\underset{\underset{\displaystyle CH_3}{|}}{C}HCH_3}$

Answers: (a) 3-methyl-2-pentene (b) 2,4-dimethyl-2-pentene

3.3 GEOMETRIC ISOMERISM IN ALKENES

There are only two dichloroethanes: 1,1-dichloroethane ($CHCl_2CH_3$) and 1,2-dichloroethane (CH_2ClCH_2Cl). But surprisingly there are three dichloroethenes—namely, 1,1-dichloroethene ($CCl_2{=}CH_2$) and *two* isomers of 1,2-dichloroethene ($CHCl{=}CHCl$). There is only one 1,2-dichloroethane because carbon atoms can rotate freely about a single bond. Thus, the structural formulas I and II that follow represent the same compound. The chlorine atoms are simply shown in different relative positions in the two formulas due to rotation of the CH_2Cl group about the carbon–carbon single bond.

```
Cl  Cl            Cl  H
 |   |             |  |
H—C—C—H         H—C—C—H
 |   |             |  |
 H   H             H  Cl
   I                II
```

1,2-Dichloroethane

Compounds containing a carbon–carbon double bond have restricted rotation about that double bond. Restricted rotation in a molecule gives rise to a type of isomerism known as *geometric isomerism.* Isomers that differ from each other only in the geometry of the molecules and not in the order of their atoms are known as **geometric isomers**. They are also called cis–trans isomers. Two isomers of 1,2-dichloroethene exist because of geometric isomerism.

geometric isomers

For a further explanation, let us look at the geometry of an ethylene molecule. This molecule is planar, or flat, with all six atoms lying in a single plane as in a rectangle:

```
H       H
 \     /
  C═C
 /     \
H       H
```

Because the hydrogen atoms are identical, only one structural arrangement is possible for ethylene. But if one hydrogen atom on each carbon atom is replaced by chlorine, for example, two different geometric isomers are possible:

```
Cl       Cl              H        Cl
  \     /                 \      /
   C═C          and        C═C
  /     \                 /      \
H        H              Cl        H
```

cis-1,2-Dichloroethene (bp = 60.1°C) *trans*-1,2-Dichloroethene (bp = 48.4°C)

Both of these isomers are known and have been isolated. The fact that they have different boiling points as well as other different physical properties is proof that they are not the same compound. Note that, in naming these geometric isomers, the prefix *cis-* is used to designate the isomer having the substituent groups (chlorine atoms) on the same side of the double bond, and the prefix *trans-* is used to designate the isomer having the substituent groups on opposite sides of the double bond.

Molecules of *cis-* and *trans*-1,2-dichloroethene are not superimposable. That is, we cannot pick up one molecule and place it over the other in such a way that all the atoms in each molecule occupy the same relative positions in space. Nonsuperimposability is a general test for isomerism that all kinds of isomers must meet.

An alkene shows cis–trans isomerism when each of the carbon atoms of the double bond has two different kinds of groups attached to it.

```
a       a        a       b
 \     /          \     /
  C═C              C═C
 /     \          /     \
b       b        b       a
```

cis isomer trans isomer

An alkene does not show cis–trans isomerism if one of the carbon atoms of the double bond has two identical groups attached to it. Thus there are no geometric isomers of ethene or propene.

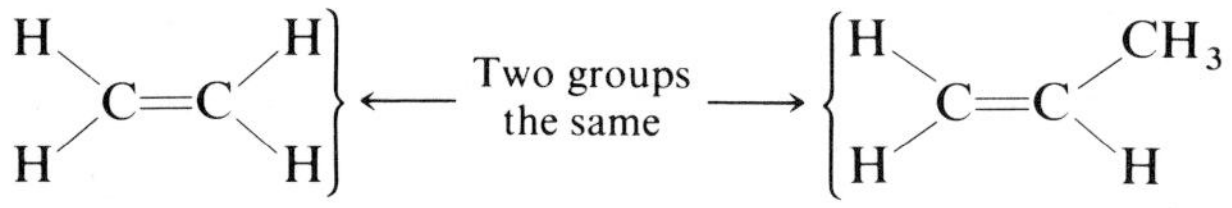

H, H C=C H, H ← Two groups the same → H, H C=C CH_3, H

Four structural isomers of butene (C_4H_8) are known. Two of these, 1-butene and 2-methylpropene, do not show geometric isomerism.

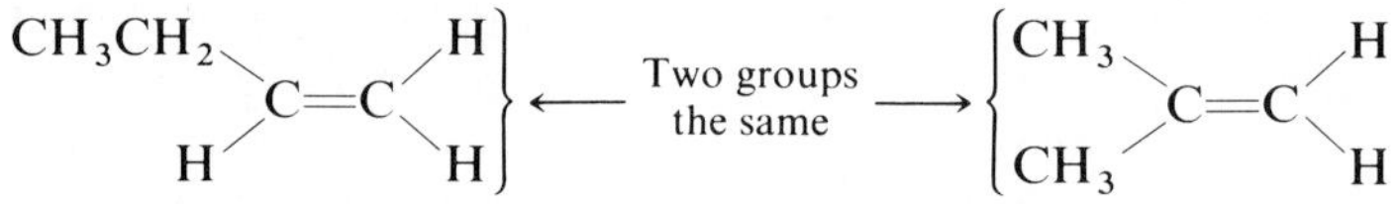

CH_3CH_2, H C=C H, H ← Two groups the same → CH_3, CH_3 C=C H, H

1-Butene 2-Methylpropene

The other two butenes are the cis–trans isomers shown below.

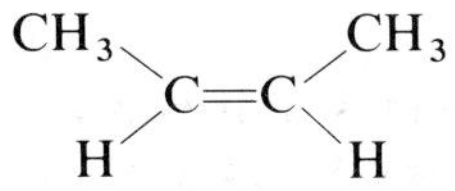

CH_3, H C=C CH_3, H and CH_3, H C=C H, CH_3

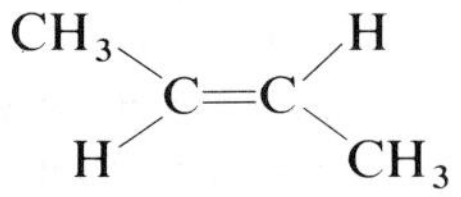

cis-2-Butene *trans*-2-Butene

EXAMPLE 3.3

Draw structures for (a) *trans*-3-heptene and (b) *cis*-5-chloro-2-hexene.

SOLUTION

(a) The compound contains seven carbon atoms with a double bond between C 3 and C 4. First draw a C=C double bond in a planar arrangement:

C=C

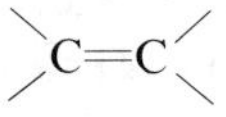

In the trans positions attach a two-carbon chain to one carbon atom and a three-carbon chain to the other carbon atom:

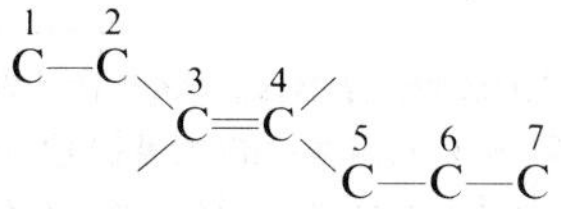

C—C (1, 2) C=C (3, 4) C—C—C (5, 6, 7)

Now attach hydrogen atoms to give each carbon atom four bonds. C 3 and C 4 need only one hydrogen atom apiece; these two hydrogen atoms are also trans to each other. The structure is

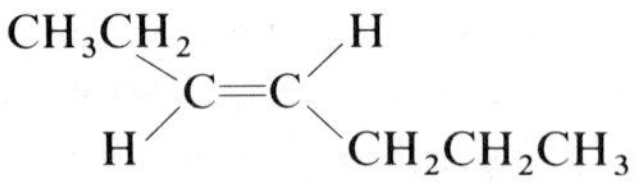

CH_3CH_2, H C=C H, $CH_2CH_2CH_3$

(b) The compound contains six carbons, a double bond between C 2 and C 3, and a Cl atom on C 5. Draw a C=C double bond in a planar arrangement:

C=C

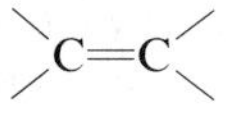

In the cis positions attach a $—CH_3$ to one carbon and a three-carbon chain to the other carbon. Place a Cl on C 5.

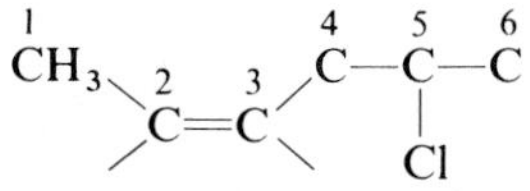

$$\overset{1}{CH_3}\diagdown\overset{2}{C}=\overset{3}{C}\diagup\overset{4}{C}-\underset{Cl}{\overset{5}{C}}-\overset{6}{C}$$

Now add H atoms to give each carbon four bonds. C 2, C 3, and C 5 each need only one H atom. The structure is

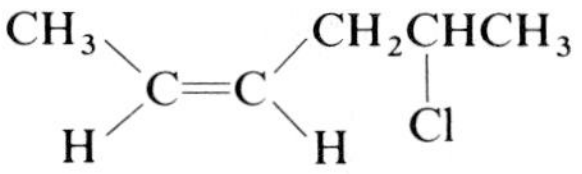

$$\begin{array}{c} CH_3 \diagdown \quad \diagup CH_2\underset{|}{C}HCH_3 \\ C=C \quad\quad\; \\ H \diagup \quad \diagdown H \quad Cl \end{array}$$

EXAMPLE 3.4

Draw structural formulas and names for all the isomers of pentene, C_5H_{10}. Identify all geometric isomers.

SOLUTION

Start by drawing the isomers of the five-carbon chain, placing the C=C in all possible positions (there are two possible isomers). Then proceed to the four-carbon chains with a methyl-group side chain. Locate the C=C and the CH_3 group in all possible positions. Check for duplications from the names of the compounds.

$CH_2=CHCH_2CH_2CH_3$
1-Pentene

$CH_3CH=CHCH_2CH_3$
2-Pentene

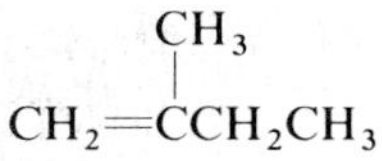

$CH_2=\overset{CH_3}{\overset{|}{C}}CH_2CH_3$
2-Methyl-1-butene

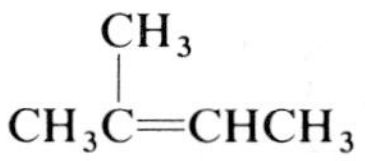

$CH_3\overset{CH_3}{\overset{|}{C}}=CHCH_3$
2-Methyl-2-butene

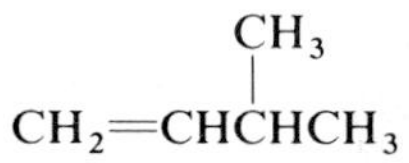

$CH_2=CH\overset{CH_3}{\overset{|}{C}}HCH_3$
3-Methyl-1-butene

Of these five compounds, only 2-pentene can have cis–trans isomers. All of the others have two identical groups on one of the carbon atoms of the double bond. Draw the cis–trans isomers.

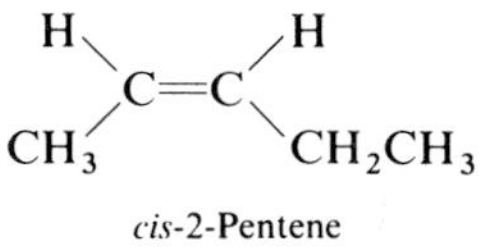

$$\begin{array}{c} H \diagdown \quad \diagup H \\ C=C \\ CH_3 \diagup \quad \diagdown CH_2CH_3 \end{array}$$
cis-2-Pentene

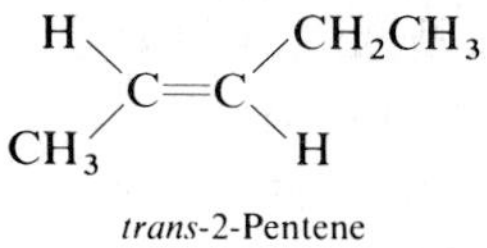

$$\begin{array}{c} H \diagdown \quad \diagup CH_2CH_3 \\ C=C \\ CH_3 \diagup \quad \diagdown H \end{array}$$
trans-2-Pentene

EXAMPLE 3.5

Is the compound below the cis or the trans isomer?

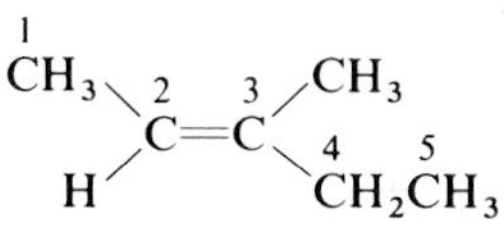

$$\begin{array}{c} \overset{1}{CH_3} \diagdown \quad \diagup CH_3 \\ \overset{2}{C}=\overset{3}{C} \\ H \diagup \quad \diagdown \overset{4}{C}H_2\overset{5}{C}H_3 \end{array}$$

SOLUTION

In branched-chain alkenes, the cis–trans designation ordinarily is given to the structure containing the longest carbon chain that includes the carbon–carbon double bond. In this case the longest chain is the 2-pentene, in which the methyl group on carbon 2 and the ethyl group on carbon 3 are trans to each other. Thus the name of the compound shown is *trans*-3-methyl-2-pentene. The cis isomer is

$$\begin{array}{ccc} CH_3 & & CH_2CH_3 \\ & C{=}C & \\ H & & CH_3 \end{array}$$

PRACTICE Draw structures for (a) *cis*-2-methyl-2-pentene and (b) *trans*-2-bromo-2-pentene.

Answers: (a) $\begin{array}{ccc} CH_3CH_2 & & H \\ & C{=}C & \\ CH_3 & & CH_3 \end{array}$ (b) $\begin{array}{ccc} Br & & CH_2CH_3 \\ & C{=}C & \\ CH_3 & & H \end{array}$

PRACTICE Determine whether geometric isomers exist for the following compounds. Draw structures for the *cis* and *trans* isomers.

(a) 1-chloro-2-methyl-2-butene (b) 3-hexene (c) 2,3-dimethyl-2-pentene

Answers: (a) Yes $\begin{array}{ccc} CH_3 & & CH_3 \\ & C{=}C & \\ CH_2Cl & & H \end{array}$ trans $\begin{array}{ccc} CH_3 & & H \\ & C{=}C & \\ CH_2Cl & & CH_3 \end{array}$ cis

(b) Yes $\begin{array}{ccc} CH_3CH_2 & & CH_2CH_3 \\ & C{=}C & \\ H & & H \end{array}$ cis $\begin{array}{ccc} H & & CH_2CH_3 \\ & C{=}C & \\ CH_3CH_2 & & H \end{array}$ trans

(c) No

PRACTICE Identify each of the following as the cis or trans isomer.

(a) $\begin{array}{ccc} H & & CH_3 \\ & C{=}C & \\ CH_3CH_2 & & Cl \end{array}$ (b) $\begin{array}{ccc} CH_3CH_2 & & CH_2CH_3 \\ & C{=}C & \\ CH_3 & & Br \end{array}$

Answers: (a) trans (b) cis

Enzymes (biological catalysts) test molecules for superimposability. In order to react with an enzyme, a molecule must twist and turn in solution until it achieves a specific shape. If this specific shape cannot be attained, the molecule won't react. For example, our bodies commonly use the cis isomer of unsaturated fatty acids but not the trans isomer in building more complex fats. That is why the great majority of unsaturated fatty acids in most cells are cis isomers.

$$\begin{array}{ccc} H & & CH_2CH_2CH_2CH_2CH_2CH_2CH_2COOH \\ & C & \\ & \| & \\ & C & \\ H & & CH_2CH_2CH_2CH_2CH_2CH_2CH_2CH_3 \end{array}$$

cis isomer

$$CH_3CH_2CH_2CH_2CH_2CH_2CH_2CH_2\diagdown \quad \diagup H$$
$$C$$
$$\|$$
$$C$$
$$H \diagup \quad \diagdown CH_2CH_2CH_2CH_2CH_2CH_2CH_2COOH$$

trans isomer

Enzymes differentiate between the "hairpin" shape of the cis isomer and the more linear trans form. Although these molecules are constantly tumbling and vibrating in solution, they cannot normally attain the same shape due to restricted rotation about the carbon–carbon double bond. Because the two shapes cannot be superimposed, the two isomers are treated differently by the body's enzymes.

3.4 CYCLOALKENES

As the name implies, **cycloalkenes** are cyclic compounds that contain a carbon–carbon double bond in the ring. The two most common cycloalkenes are cyclopentene and cyclohexene. The double bond may be placed between any two carbon atoms in cyclopentene and cyclohexene. cycloalkenes

Cyclopentene (C_5H_8)

Cyclohexene (C_6H_{10})

In cycloalkenes the carbons of the double bond are assigned numbers 1 and 2. Thus the positions of the double bond need not be indicated in the name of the compound. Other substituents on the ring are named in the usual manner, and their positions on the ring is indicated with the smallest possible numbers.

In the examples below note that a Cl or a CH_3 has replaced one H atom in the molecule. The ring is numbered either clockwise or counterclockwise starting with the carbon–carbon double bond so that the substituted group(s) have the smallest possible numbers.

3-Chlorocyclohexene (C_6H_9Cl)

1-Methylcyclopentene ($C_5H_7CH_3$)

1,3-Dimethylcyclohexene [$C_6H_8(CH_3)_2$]

No cis–trans designation is necessary for cycloalkenes containing up to seven carbon atoms in the ring. Cyclooctene has been shown to exist in both cis and trans forms.

3.5 Preparation and Physical Properties of Alkenes

Cracking

cracking

Ethylene can be produced by the cracking of petroleum. **Cracking**, or pyrolysis, is the process in which saturated hydrocarbons are heated to very high temperatures in the presence of a catalyst (usually silica-alumina). This results in the breaking of large molecules into smaller ones, with the elimination of hydrogen, forming alkenes and small hydrocarbons like methane and ethane. Unfortunately, cracking always results in mixtures of products and is therefore not used often in the laboratory.

Dehydration of Alcohols

dehydration

Dehydration involves the elimination of a molecule of water from a reactant molecule. Dehydration reactions are very common in organic chemistry as well as in biochemistry.

To produce an alkene by dehydration, an alcohol is heated in the presence of concentrated sulfuric acid.

$$CH_3\underset{\substack{|\\H}}{\overset{\substack{H\\|}}{C}}-\underset{\substack{|\\OH}}{\overset{\substack{H\\|}}{C}}CH_3 \xrightarrow[\Delta]{\text{con } H_2SO_4} CH_3\overset{\substack{H\\|}}{C}=\overset{\substack{H\\|}}{C}CH_3 + H_2O$$

Physical Properties

Alkenes have physical properties very similar to the corresponding alkanes. This is not surprising since the difference between an alkane and an alkene is simply two hydrogen atoms.

General formula for alkanes	C_nH_{2n+2}
General formula for alkenes	C_nH_{2n}

Since alkenes have a slightly smaller molar mass, their boiling points are slightly lower than the corresponding alkanes. The smaller alkenes (to 5 carbons) are gases at room temperature. As the chain lengthens (5–17 carbons) the alkenes are liquid, and above 17 carbons they are solid. The alkenes are nonpolar, like the other hydrocarbons, and so are insoluble in water but are soluble in organic solvents. The densities of most alkenes are much less than water. Table 3.1 shows the properties of some alkenes. Notice that isomers (C_4H_8) have similar boiling points although they differ significantly in melting points. The different shapes of the isomers fit into crystals in significantly different ways.

Table 3.1 Physical Properties of Alkenes

Molecular formula	Structural formula	IUPAC name	Density (g/mL)	Melting point (°C)	Boiling point (°C)
C_2H_4	$CH_2{=}CH_2$	Ethene	—	−169	−104
C_3H_6	$CH_3CH{=}CH_2$	Propene	—	−185	−47
C_4H_8	$CH_3CH_2CH{=}CH_2$	1-Butene	0.595	−130	−6
C_4H_8	$(CH_3)_2C{=}CH_2$	2-Methylpropene	0.594	−14	−7
C_5H_{10}	$CH_3(CH_2)_2CH{=}CH_2$	1-Pentene	0.641	−138	30

3.6 Chemical Properties of Alkenes

The alkenes are much more reactive than the corresponding alkanes. This greater reactivity is due to the carbon–carbon double bonds.

Addition

A reaction in which two substances join together to produce one compound is called an **addition reaction**. Addition at the carbon–carbon double bond is the most common reaction of alkenes. Hydrogen, halogens (Cl_2 or Br_2), hydrogen halides, sulfuric acid, and water are some of the reagents that can be added to unsaturated hydrocarbons. Ethylene (ethene), for example, reacts in the presence of a platinum catalyst in this fashion:

addition reaction

$$\underset{\text{Ethylene}}{CH_2{=}CH_2} + H_2 \xrightarrow[\text{1 atm}]{\text{Pt, 25°C}} \underset{\text{Ethane}}{CH_3{-}CH_3}$$

$$CH_2{=}CH_2 + Br{-}Br \longrightarrow \underset{\text{1,2-Dibromoethane}}{CH_2Br{-}CH_2Br}$$

The product in the foregoing reaction is colorless. Therefore the disappearance of the reddish-brown bromine color provides visible evidence of reaction. Other reactions of ethylene follow.

$$CH_2{=}CH_2 + HCl \longrightarrow \underset{\substack{\text{Chloroethane} \\ \text{(Ethyl chloride)}}}{CH_3CH_2Cl}$$

$$CH_2{=}CH_2 + \underset{\text{Sulfuric acid}}{HOSO_3H(\textit{conc.})} \longrightarrow \underset{\text{Ethyl hydrogen sulfate}}{CH_3CH_2OSO_3H}$$

$$CH_2{=}CH_2 + HOH \xrightarrow{H^+} \underset{\substack{\text{Ethanol} \\ \text{(Ethyl alcohol)}}}{CH_3CH_2OH}$$

The H^+ indicates that the reaction is carried out under acidic conditions.

Note that the double bond is broken and the unsaturated alkene molecules become saturated by an addition reaction.

The preceding examples dealt with ethylene, but reactions of this kind can be made to occur on almost any molecule that contains a carbon–carbon double bond. If a symmetrical molecule such as Cl_2 is added to propene, only one product, 1,2-dichloropropane, is formed:

$$CH_2{=}CH{-}CH_3 + Cl_2 \longrightarrow \underset{\text{1,2-Dichloropropane}}{CH_2Cl{-}CHCl{-}CH_3}$$

But if an unsymmetrical molecule such as HCl is added to propene, two products are theoretically possible, depending upon which carbon atom adds the hydrogen. The two possible products are 1-chloropropane and 2-chloropropane. Experimentally we find that 2-chloropropane is formed almost exclusively:

$$CH_3{-}CH{=}CH_2 + HCl \longrightarrow \underset{\text{(About 100\%)}}{CH_3CHClCH_3} \qquad CH_3{-}CH{=}CH_2 + HCl \not\longrightarrow \underset{\text{(Trace)}}{CH_3CH_2CH_2Cl}$$

A single product is obtained because the reaction proceeds stepwise according to the following mechanism:

1. A proton (H^+) from HCl bonds to the number 1 carbon of propene utilizing the pi bond electrons. The intermediate formed is a positively charged alkyl group, or carbocation. The positive charge is localized on the number 2 carbon atom of this carbocation.

$$CH_2{=}CH{-}CH_3 + HCl \longrightarrow \underset{\text{Isopropyl carbocation}}{CH_3{-}\overset{+}{C}H{-}CH_3} + Cl^-$$

2. The chloride ion then adds to the positively charged carbon atom to form a molecule of 2-chloropropane:

$$CH_3{-}\overset{+}{C}H{-}CH_3 + Cl^- \longrightarrow \underset{\text{2-Chloropropane}}{CH_3{-}CHCl{-}CH_3}$$

carbocation

An ion in which a carbon atom has a positive charge is known as a **carbocation**. There are four types of carbocations: methyl, primary (1°), secondary (2°), and tertiary (3°). Examples of these four types follow:

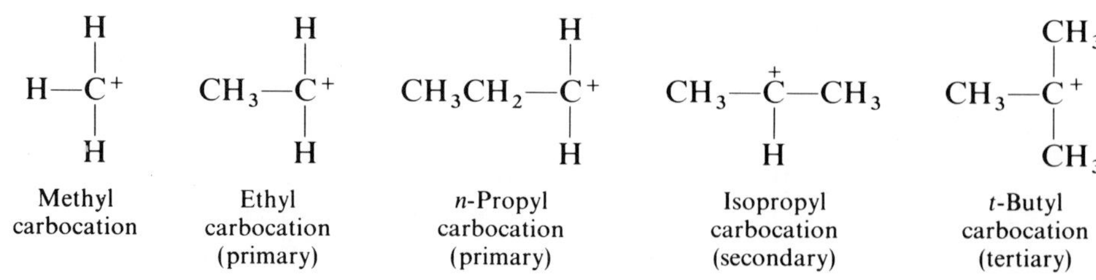

Methyl carbocation | Ethyl carbocation (primary) | *n*-Propyl carbocation (primary) | Isopropyl carbocation (secondary) | *t*-Butyl carbocation (tertiary)

A carbon atom is designated as primary if it is bonded to one carbon atom, secondary if it is bonded to two carbon atoms, and tertiary if it is bonded to three carbon atoms. In a primary carbocation the positive carbon atom is bonded to only one carbon atom. In a secondary carbocation the positive carbon atom is bonded to two carbon atoms. In a tertiary carbocation the positive carbon atom is bonded to three carbon atoms.

The order of stability of carbocations and hence the ease with which they are formed is tertiary > secondary > primary. Thus, in the reaction of propene and HCl, isopropyl carbocation (secondary) is formed as an intermediate in preference to *n*-propyl carbocation (primary).

Stability of carbocations: $3^\circ > 2^\circ > 1^\circ > \overset{+}{C}H_3$

In the middle of the 19th century, a Russian chemist, V. Markovnikov, observed reactions of this kind, and in 1869 he formulated a useful generalization now known as **Markovnikov's rule**. This rule in essence states:

Markovnikov's rule

When an unsymmetrical molecule such as HX(HCl) adds to a carbon–carbon double bond, the hydrogen from HX goes to the carbon atom that has the greater number of hydrogen atoms.

As you can see, the addition of HCl to propene, discussed above, follows Markovnikov's rule. The addition of HI to 2-methylpropene (isobutylene) is another example illustrating this rule:

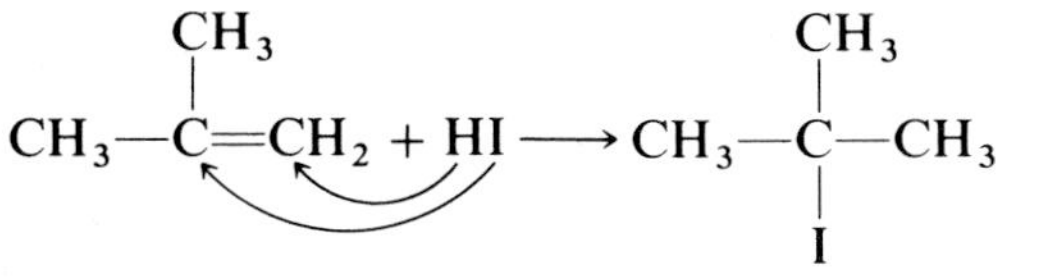

$$CH_3-\underset{}{\overset{CH_3}{\overset{|}{C}}}=CH_2 + HI \longrightarrow CH_3-\underset{\underset{I}{|}}{\overset{CH_3}{\overset{|}{C}}}-CH_3$$

2-Iodo-2-methylpropane
(*tert*-Butyl iodide)

General rules of this kind are useful in predicting the products of reactions. However, exceptions are known for most such rules.

EXAMPLE 3.6

Write formulas for the organic products formed when 2-methyl-1-butene reacts with (a) H_2, Pt/25°C; (b) Cl_2; (c) HCl; (d) H_2O, H^+.

SOLUTION

First write the formula for 2-methyl-1-butene:

$$\overset{1}{C}H_2=\overset{2}{\overset{CH_3}{\overset{|}{C}}}-\overset{3}{C}H_2-\overset{4}{C}H_3$$

(a) The double bond is broken when a hydrogen molecule adds. One H atom adds to each carbon atom of the double bond. Platinum, Pt, is a necessary catalyst

in this reaction. The product is

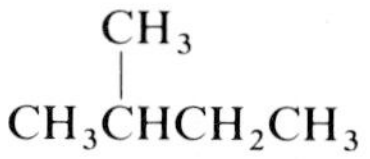

$$\begin{array}{c} \quad CH_3 \\ \quad | \\ CH_3CHCH_2CH_3 \end{array}$$

2-Methylbutane

(b) The Cl_2 molecule adds to the carbons of the double bond. One Cl atom adds to each carbon atom of the double bond. The product is

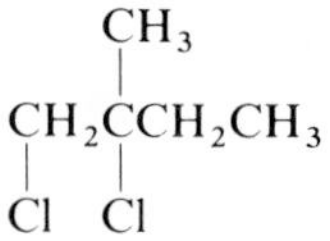

$$\begin{array}{l} \quad\;\; CH_3 \\ \quad\;\;\; | \\ CH_2CCH_2CH_3 \\ \;| \quad\; | \\ Cl \;\; Cl \end{array}$$

1,2-Dichloro-2-methylbutane

(c) HCl adds to the double bond according to Markovnikov's rule. The H^+ goes to C 1 (the more stable 3° carbocation is formed as an intermediate product), and the Cl^- goes to C 2. The product is

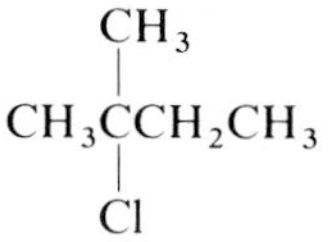

$$\begin{array}{l} \quad\;\; CH_3 \\ \quad\;\;\; | \\ CH_3CCH_2CH_3 \\ \quad\;\;\; | \\ \quad\;\; Cl \end{array}$$

2-Chloro-2-methylbutane

(d) The net result of this reaction is a molecule of water added across the double bond. The H adds to C 1 (the carbon with the greater number of hydrogen atoms), and the OH adds to C 2 (the carbon of the double bond with the lesser number of hydrogen atoms). The product is

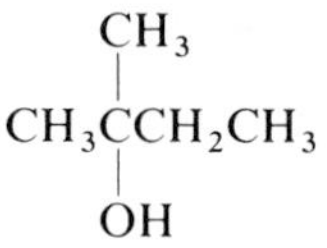

$$\begin{array}{l} \quad\;\; CH_3 \\ \quad\;\;\; | \\ CH_3CCH_2CH_3 \\ \quad\;\;\; | \\ \quad\;\; OH \end{array}$$

2-Methyl-2-butanol
(an alcohol)

EXAMPLE 3.7

Write equations for the addition of HCl to (a) 1-pentene and (b) 2-pentene.

SOLUTION

(a) In the case of 1-pentene, $CH_3CH_2CH_2CH{=}CH_2$, the proton from HCl adds to carbon 1 to give the more stable secondary carbocation, followed by the addition of Cl^- to give the product 2-chloropentane. The addition is directly in accordance with Markovnikov's rule.

$$CH_3CH_2CH_2CH{=}CH_2 + HCl \longrightarrow CH_3CH_2CH_2CHClCH_3$$

2-Chloropentane

(b) In 2-pentene, $CH_3CH_2CH{=}CHCH_3$, each carbon of the double bond has one hydrogen atom, and the addition of a proton to either one forms a secondary carbocation. After the addition of Cl^-, the result is two isomeric products that are formed in almost equal quantities:

$$CH_3CH_2CH{=}CHCH_3 + HCl \longrightarrow \underset{\text{2-Chloropentane}}{CH_3CH_2CH_2CHClCH_3} + \underset{\text{3-Chloropentane}}{CH_3CH_2CHClCH_2CH_3}$$

PRACTICE Write formulas for the organic products formed when 3-methyl-2-pentene reacts with (a) H_2/Pt, (b) Br_2, (c) HCl, and (d) H_2O, H^+.

Answers:

(a) $CH_3CH_2\underset{\displaystyle CH_3}{\underset{|}{C}}HCH_2CH_3$ (c) $CH_3CH_2\overset{\displaystyle CH_3}{\overset{|}{\underset{\displaystyle Cl}{\underset{|}{C}}}}CH_2CH_3$

(b) $CH_3\underset{\displaystyle Br}{\underset{|}{C}}H\overset{\displaystyle CH_3}{\overset{|}{\underset{\displaystyle Br}{\underset{|}{C}}}}CH_2CH_3$ (d) $CH_3CH_2\overset{\displaystyle CH_3}{\overset{|}{\underset{\displaystyle OH}{\underset{|}{C}}}}CH_2CH_3$

PRACTICE Write equations for (a) addition of water to 1-methylcyclopentene and (b) addition of HI to 2-methyl-2-butene.

Answers:

(a) 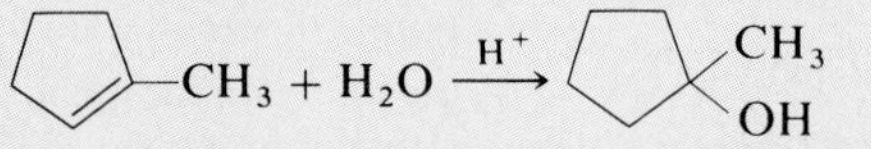 1-methylcyclopentene (ring)—$CH_3 + H_2O \xrightarrow{H^+}$ cyclopentane ring bearing CH_3 and OH on the same carbon

(b) $\underset{CH_3}{\overset{H}{}}\!\!>C{=}C<\!\!\underset{CH_3}{\overset{CH_3}{}} + HI \longrightarrow CH_3CH_2\overset{\displaystyle CH_3}{\overset{|}{\underset{\displaystyle I}{\underset{|}{C}}}}CH_3$

Oxidation

Another typical reaction of alkenes is oxidation at the double bond. For example, when shaken with a cold, dilute solution of potassium permanganate ($KMnO_4$), an alkene is converted to a glycol (glycols are dihydroxy alcohols). Ethylene reacts in this manner:

$$\underset{\text{Ethylene}}{CH_2{=}CH_2} + \underset{\text{(Purple)}}{KMnO_4(aq)} + H_2O \longrightarrow \underset{\text{Ethylene glycol}}{\underset{\displaystyle OH\quad OH}{CH_2{-}CH_2}} + \underset{\text{(Brown)}}{MnO_2} + KOH$$

The *Baeyer test* makes use of this reaction to detect or confirm the presence of double (or triple) bonds in hydrocarbons. Evidence of reaction (positive Baeyer test) is the disappearance of the purple color of permanganate ions. The Baeyer test is not specific for detecting unsaturation in hydrocarbons, since other classes of compounds may also give a positive Baeyer test.

CHEMISTRY IN ACTION

MOLECULES OF SIGHT AND SMELL

Complex alkenes containing multiple double bonds occur throughout nature. Many of these molecules are built from the molecule isoprene:

$$CH_2{=}\underset{}{\overset{CH_3}{\overset{|}{C}}}{-}CH{=}CH_2$$

Isoprene
(2-Methyl-1,3-butadiene)

Isoprene is a conjugated diene, a molecule in which two double bonds are separated by a single bond. Conjugated double bonds are very stable and so occur in many biochemical molecules. In general isoprene molecules do not appear alone in nature. Compounds generally contain several isoprene units.

Essential oils, substances which give plants their pleasant odors, are frequently extracted from the plant and used in cosmetics, flavorings and perfumes. They are all part of a class of compounds known as the terpenes. These molecules are combinations of isoprene and therefore contain a multiple of 5 carbons.

▲ **Scanning electron microscope of rods and cones in the human eye.**

Two of the larger terpene molecules are β-carotene and vitamin A, illustrated below.

β-Carotene is responsible for the color of carrots and tomatoes. The carotenes are an important intermediate in the formation of vitamin A. In animals vitamin A is produced by the splitting of β-carotene in the small intestine. Vitamin A is a precursor to 11-*cis*-retinal, a compound essential to vision.

The retina of the eye contains colored compounds called the visual pigments in a receptor known as a rod. In the dark these pigments are rose-colored, hence their name rhodopsin (Greek). The color fades on exposure to light. Rhodopsin is a compound composed of a protein (opsin) linked to 11-*cis*-retinal. The 11-*cis*-retinal has a shape that fits perfectly into a cavity on the surface of the opsin. When light energy is absorbed by the rod cells, the cis bond at the 11-carbon atom is broken and reformed as the trans isomer. Since the shape of the molecule is now different, it no longer fits into the cavity on the opsin. The 11-*trans*-retinal is now cleaved from the opsin protein. During this process enzymes are activated that cause a change in electrical character of the rod and generate a nerve impulse, which is perceived as light by the brain. The 11-*trans*-retinal is reconverted to 11-*cis*-retinal, which can then recombine with the opsin. The process is summarized in the figure on the facing page.

(ring with CH_3 CH_3 and CH_3)$-CH{=}CH{-}\underset{CH_3}{C}{=}CH{-}CH{=}CH{-}\underset{CH_3}{C}{=}CH{-}CH_2OH$

Vitamin A

(ring with CH_3 CH_3 and CH_3)$-CH{=}CH{-}\overset{CH_3}{C}{=}CHCH{=}CH{-}\overset{CH_3}{C}{=}CHCH{=}CHCH{=}\underset{CH_3}{C}{-}CH{=}CHCH{=}\underset{CH_3}{C}{-}CH{=}CH-$(ring with CH_3 CH_3 and CH_3)

β-Carotene

▲ **Structure of vitamin A and β-carotene. The colored lines indicate the isoprene units in each molecule.**

(*continued*)

(continued)

◄ **Chemistry and vision.**

Isomerization

11-*cis*-retinal

Bonding reaction

H_2N-

Opsin (a protein)

all-*trans*-retinal +

Opsin

$-H_2O$

(11-*cis*)

$CH=N-$

RHODOPSIN

Light

(all-*trans*)

Cleavage reaction

H_2O

Nerve impulse

Carbon–carbon double bonds are found in many different kinds of molecules. Most of these substances react with potassium permanganate and undergo somewhat similar reactions with other oxidizing agents including oxygen in the air and, especially, with ozone. Such reactions are frequently troublesome. For example, premature aging and cracking of tires in smoggy atmospheres occur because ozone attacks the double bonds in rubber molecules. Cooking oils and fats sometimes develop disagreeable odors and flavors because the oxygen of the air reacts with the double bonds present in these materials. Potato chips, because of their large surface area, are especially subject to flavor damage caused by oxidation of the unsaturated cooking oils that they contain.

▲ **The cracking on this automobile tire is the result of ozone attacking the rubber molecules.**

3.7 Alkynes: Nomenclature and Preparation

Nomenclature

The procedure for naming alkynes is the same as that for alkenes, but the ending used is *-yne* to indicate the presence of a triple bond. The smaller members of the series are often referred to by their common names. Table 3.2 lists names and formulas for some common alkynes.

TABLE 3.2 Nomenclature for Some Common Alkynes

Molecular formula	Structural formula	Common name	IUPAC name
C_2H_2	$H—C{\equiv}C—H$	Acetylene	Ethyne
C_3H_4	$CH_3—C{\equiv}C—H$	Methylacetylene	Propyne
C_4H_6	$CH_3CH_2—C{\equiv}C—H$	Ethylacetylene	1-Butyne
C_4H_6	$CH_3—C{\equiv}C—CH_3$	Dimethylacetylene	2-Butyne

Preparation

Although triple bonds are very reactive it is relatively easy to synthesize alkynes. Acetylene can be prepared inexpensively from calcium carbide and water.

$$CaC_2 + 2\,H_2O \longrightarrow HC{\equiv}CH + Ca(OH)_2$$

Acetylene is also prepared by the cracking of methane in an electric arc.

$$2\,CH_4 \xrightarrow{1500^\circ C} HC{\equiv}CH + 3\,H_2$$

3.8 Physical and Chemical Properties of Alkynes

Physical Properties

Acetylene is a colorless gas, with little odor when pure. Its common disagreeable odor is the result of impurities (usually PH_3). Acetylene is insoluble in water and a gas at normal temperature and pressure (bp = $-84^\circ C$). As a liquid acetylene is very sensitive and may decompose violently (explode) spontaneously or from a slight shock.

$$HC{\equiv}CH \longrightarrow H_2 + 2\,C + 227\text{ kJ (54.3 kcal)}$$

To eliminate the danger of explosions, acetylene is dissolved under pressure in acetone and is packed in cylinders that contain a porous inert material.

Chemical Properties

Acetylene is used mainly (1) as fuel for oxyacetylene cutting and welding torches and (2) as an intermediate in the manufacture of other substances. Both uses are dependent upon the great reactivity of acetylene. Acetylene and oxygen mixtures produce flame temperatures of about 2800°C. Acetylene readily undergoes addition reactions rather similar to those of ethylene. It reacts with chlorine and bromine and decolorizes a permanganate solution (Baeyer's test). Either one or two molecules of bromine or chlorine can be added:

$$HC{\equiv}CH + Br_2 \longrightarrow \underset{\text{1,2-Dibromoethene}}{CHBr{=}CHBr}$$

or

$$HC{\equiv}CH + 2\ Br_2 \longrightarrow CHBr_2{-}CHBr_2$$

1,1,2,2-Tetrabromoethane

It is apparent that either unsaturated or saturated compounds can be obtained as addition products of acetylene. Often, unsaturated compounds capable of undergoing further reactions are made from acetylene. For example, vinyl chloride, which is used to make the plastic polyvinyl chloride (PVC), can be made by simple addition of HCl to acetylene:

$$CH{\equiv}CH + HCl \longrightarrow CH_2{=}CHCl$$

Chloroethene
(Vinyl chloride)

(*Note:* The common name for the $CH_2{=}CH{-}$group is *vinyl.*) If the reaction is not properly controlled, another HCl adds to the chloroethene:

$$CH_2{=}CHCl + HCl \longrightarrow CH_3CHCl_2$$

1,1-Dichloroethane

Hydrogen chloride reacts with other alkynes in a similar fashion to form substituted alkenes. The addition follows Markovnikov's rule. Alkynes can react with 1 or 2 moles of HCl. Consider the reaction of propyne with HCl:

$$CH_3C{\equiv}CH + HCl \longrightarrow CH_3CCl{=}CH_2$$

2-Chloropropene

$$CH_3CCl{=}CH_2 + HCl \longrightarrow CH_3CCl_2CH_3$$

2,2-Dichloropropane

There are certain unique reactions for the alkynes. They are capable of reacting at times when alkenes will not. Acetylene, with certain catalysts, reacts with HCN to form cyanoethylene ($CH_2{=}CHCN$). This chemical is used industrially to manufacture Orlon, a polymer commonly found in clothing. It is also used to form the superabsorbants, which are capable of retaining up to 2000 times their mass of distilled water. These superabsorbants are found in disposable diapers as well as in soil additives to retain water.

The reactions of other alkynes are similar to those of acetylene. Although many other alkynes are known, acetylene is by far the most important industrially.

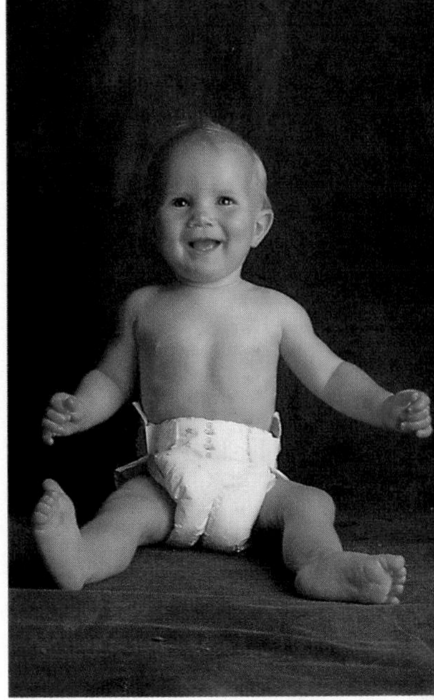

▲ **Superabsorbants are used in disposable diapers to increase the amount of liquid the diaper will absorb without leaking.**

3.9 Aromatic Hydrocarbons: Structure

Benzene and all substances that have structures and chemical properties resembling benzene are classified as **aromatic compounds**. The word *aromatic* originally referred to the rather pleasant odor possessed by many of these substances, but this meaning has been dropped. Benzene, the parent substance of the aromatic hydrocarbons, was first isolated by Michael Faraday in 1825; its correct molecular formula, C_6H_6, was established a few years later. The establishment

aromatic compounds

of a reasonable structural formula that would account for the properties of benzene was a very difficult problem for chemists in the mid-19th century.

Finally, in 1865, August Kekulé proposed that the carbon atoms in a benzene molecule are arranged in a six-membered ring with one hydrogen atom bonded to each carbon atom and with three carbon–carbon double bonds, as shown in the following formula:

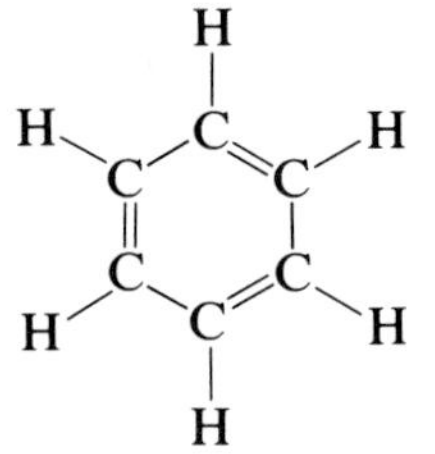

Kekulé soon realized that there should be two dibromobenzenes, based on double- and single-bond positions relative to the two bromine atoms:

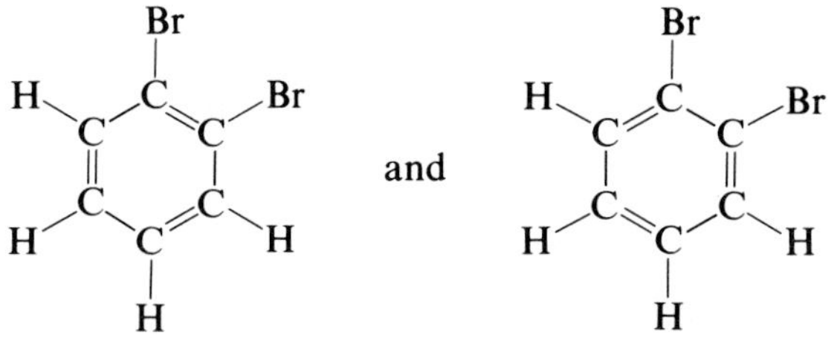

and

Since only one dibromobenzene (with bromine atoms on adjacent carbons) could be produced, Kekulé suggested that the double bonds are in rapid oscillation within the molecule. He therefore proposed that the structure of benzene could be represented in this fashion:

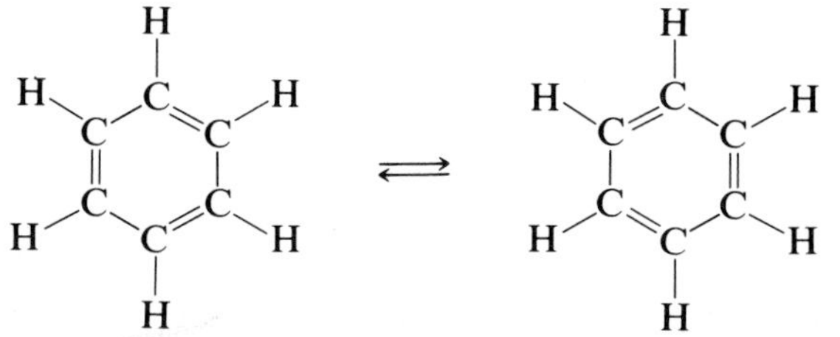

$\rightleftharpoons$

Kekulé's concepts are a landmark in the history of chemistry. They are the basis of the best representation of the benzene molecule devised in the 19th century, and they mark the beginning of our understanding of structure in aromatic compounds.

Kekulé's formulas have one serious shortcoming: They represent benzene and related substances as highly unsaturated compounds. Yet benzene does not react like a typical alkene (olefin); it does not decolorize bromine solutions rapidly, nor does it destroy the purple color of permanganate ions (Baeyer's test). Instead, the chemical behavior of benzene resembles that of an alkane. Its typical reactions are the substitution type, wherein a hydrogen atom is replaced

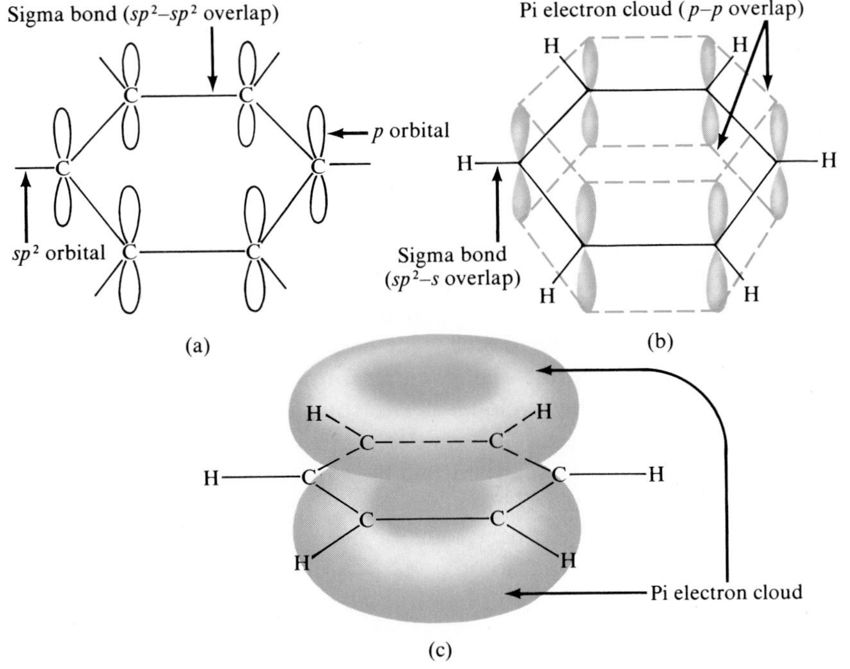

◀ FIGURE 3.5
Bonding in a benzene molecule: (a) sp^2–sp^2 orbital overlap to form the carbon ring structure; (b) carbon–hydrogen bonds formed by sp^2–s orbital overlap and overlapping of p orbitals; (c) pi electron clouds above and below the plane of the carbon ring.

by some other group; for example,

$$C_6H_6 + Cl_2 \xrightarrow{Fe} C_6H_5Cl + HCl$$

This problem was not fully resolved until the technique of X-ray diffraction, developed in the years following 1912, permitted us to determine the actual distances between the nuclei of carbon atoms in molecules. The center-to-center distances between carbon atoms in different kinds of hydrocarbon molecules are

Ethane (single bond)	0.154 nm
Ethylene (double bond)	0.134 nm
Benzene	0.139 nm

Because only one carbon–carbon distance (bond length) is found in benzene, it is apparent that alternating single and double bonds do not exist in the benzene molecule.

Modern theory accounts for the structure of the benzene molecule in this way: The orbital hybridization of the carbon atoms is sp^2 (see structure of ethylene in Section 3.2). A planar hexagonal ring is formed by the overlapping of two sp^2 orbitals on each of six carbon atoms. The other sp^2 orbital on each carbon atom overlaps an s orbital of a hydrogen atom, bonding the carbon to the hydrogen by a sigma bond. The remaining six p orbitals, one on each carbon atom, overlap each other and form doughnut-shaped pi electron clouds above and below the plane of the ring (see Figure 3.5). The electrons composing these clouds are not attached to particular carbon atoms but are delocalized and associated with the entire molecule. This electronic structure imparts unusual stability to benzene and is responsible for many of the characteristic properties of aromatic compounds.

For convenience present-day chemists usually write the structure of benzene as one or the other of these abbreviated forms:

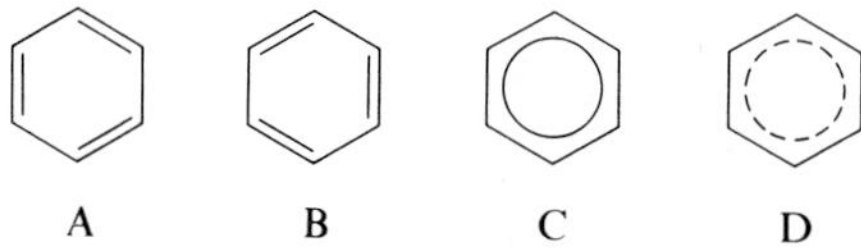

A B C D

In all of these representations, it is understood that there is a carbon atom and a hydrogen atom at each corner of the hexagon. The classical Kekulé structures are represented by formulas A and B. However, neither of these Kekulé structures actually exists. The real benzene molecule is a hybrid of these structures and is commonly represented by either formula C or D. The circle or the dotted circle represents the pi cloud of electrons, as shown in Figure 3.5. We will use the hexagon with the solid circle to represent a benzene ring.

Hexagons are used in representing the structural formulas of benzene derivatives—that is, substances in which one or more hydrogen atoms in the ring have been replaced by other atoms or groups. Chlorobenzene (C_6H_5Cl), for example, is written in this fashion:

Cl

Chlorobenzene, C_6H_5Cl

This notation indicates that the chlorine atom has replaced a hydrogen atom and is bonded directly to a carbon atom in the ring. Thus, the correct formula for chlorobenzene is C_6H_5Cl, not C_6H_6Cl.

3.10 Naming Aromatic Compounds

A substituted benzene is derived by replacing one or more hydrogen atoms of benzene by another atom or group of atoms. Thus, a monosubstituted benzene has the formula C_6H_5G, where G is the group replacing a hydrogen atom.

Monosubstituted Benzenes

Some monosubstituted benzenes are named by adding the name of the substituent group as a prefix to the word *benzene*. The name is written as one word. Note that the position of the substituent is not important here as all the positions in the hexagon are equivalent. Several examples follow:

O_2N CH_2CH_3 Cl Br

Nitrobenzene Ethylbenzene Chlorobenzene Bromobenzene

Certain monosubstituted benzenes have special names. These are used as parent names for further substituted compounds, so they should be learned.

refer to p. 128

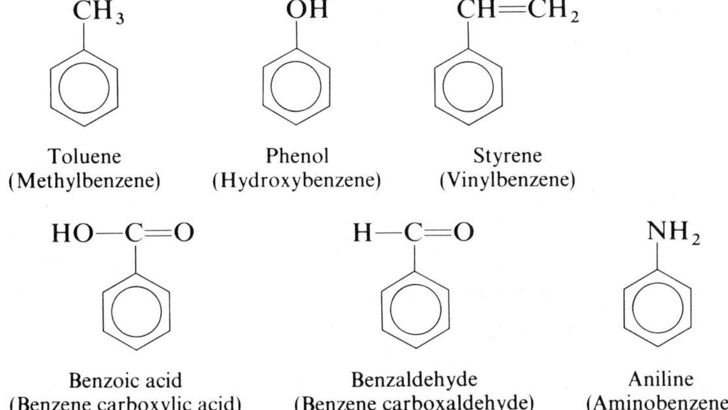

Toluene (Methylbenzene) Phenol (Hydroxybenzene) Styrene (Vinylbenzene)

Benzoic acid (Benzene carboxylic acid) Benzaldehyde (Benzene carboxaldehyde) Aniline (Aminobenzene)

The C_6H_5— group is known as the phenyl group, and the name *phenyl* is used to name compounds that cannot easily be named as benzene derivatives. For example, the following compounds are named as derivatives of alkanes:

1 CH_3, 2 3 4 5 C_6H_5—$CHCHClCH_2CH_3$

3-Chloro-2-phenylpentane

C_6H_5—CH_2—C_6H_5

Diphenylmethane

Disubstituted Benzenes

When two substituent groups replace two hydrogen atoms in a benzene molecule, three different isomeric compounds are possible. The prefixes *ortho-*, *meta-*, and *para-* (abbreviated *o-*, *m-*, and *p-*) are used to name these disubstituted benzenes in one nomenclature system. Ortho designates 1,2 disubstitution, meta represents 1,3 disubstitution, and para designates 1,4 disubstitution.

Consider the dichlorobenzenes, $C_6H_4Cl_2$. Note that the three isomers have different physical properties, indicating that they are truly different substances:

Cl, Cl (1,2) — Cl, Cl (1,3) — Cl, Cl (1,4)

ortho-Dichlorobenzene (1,2-Dichlorobenzene) (mp −17.2°C, bp 180.4°C)

meta-Dichlorobenzene (1,3-Dichlorobenzene) (mp −24.8°C, bp 172°C)

para-Dichlorobenzene (1,4-Dichlorobenzene) (mp 53.1°C, bp 174.4°C)

When the two substituents are different and neither is part of a compound with a special name, the names of the two substituents are given in alphabetical order, followed by the word *benzene*. For example,

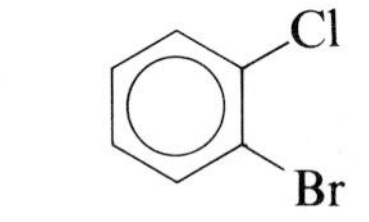

o-Bromochlorobenzene 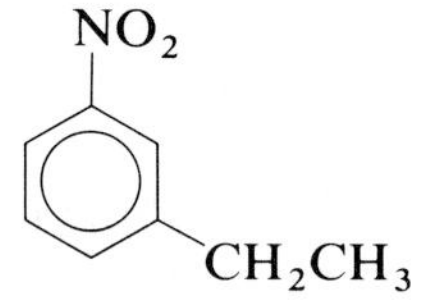 *m*-Ethylnitrobenzene

The dimethylbenzenes have the special name *xylene*.

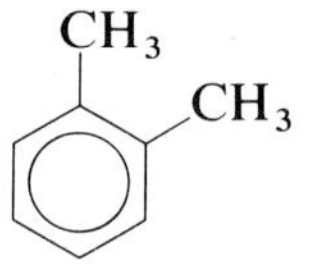

ortho-Xylene 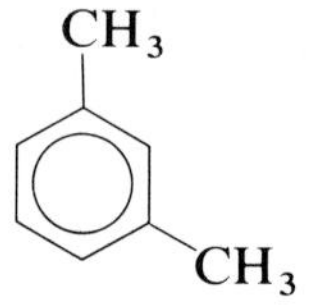 *meta*-Xylene 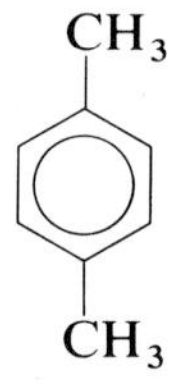 *para*-Xylene

When one of the substituents corresponds to a monosubstituted benzene that has a special name, the disubstituted compound is named as a derivative of that parent compound. In the following examples the parent compounds are phenol, aniline, and toluene:

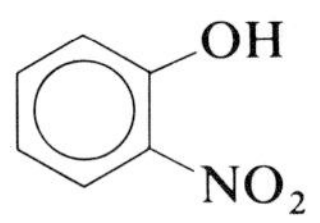

o-Nitrophenol 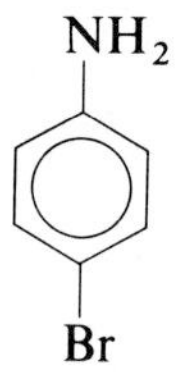 *p*-Bromoaniline 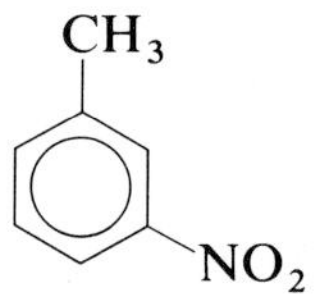 *m*-Nitrotoluene

The numbering system as described under polysubstituted benzenes is also used to name disubstituted benzenes.

Polysubstituted Benzenes

When there are more than two substituents on a benzene ring, the carbon atoms in the ring are numbered starting at one of the substituted groups. Numbering may be either clockwise or counterclockwise but must be done in the direction that gives the lowest possible numbers to the substituent groups. When the compound is named as a derivative of one of the special parent compounds, the substituent of the parent compound is considered to be on carbon 1 of the ring (the CH_3 group is on C 1 in 2,4,6-trinitrotoluene). The following examples illustrate this system:

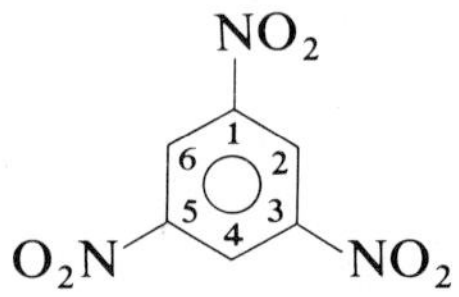

1,3,5-Trinitrobenzene 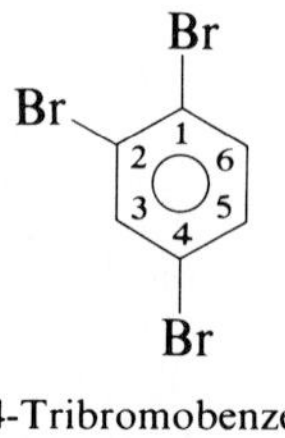 1,2,4-Tribromobenzene (not 1,4,6-) 2,4,6-Trinitrotoluene (TNT) 5-Bromo-2-chlorophenol

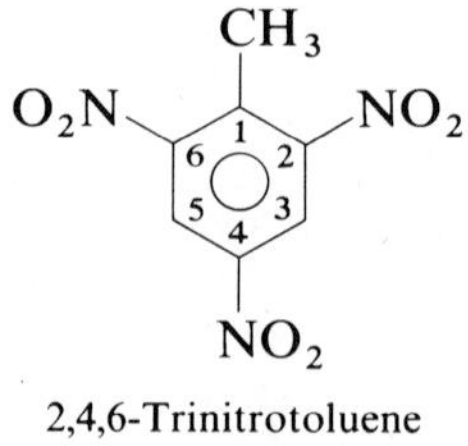

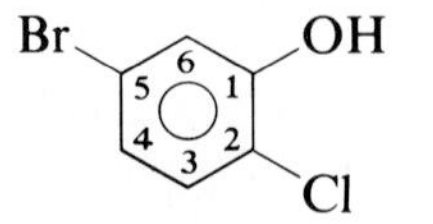

EXAMPLE 3.8

Write formulas and names for all the possible isomers of (a) chloronitrobenzene, $C_6H_4Cl(NO_2)$, and (b) tribromobenzene, $C_6H_3Br_3$.

SOLUTION

(a) The name and formula indicate a chloro group (Cl) and a nitro group (NO_2) attached to a benzene ring. There are six positions in which to place these two groups. They can be ortho, meta, or para to each other.

o-Chloronitrobenzene *m*-Chloronitrobenzene *p*-Chloronitrobenzene

(b) For tribromobenzene start by placing the three bromo groups in the 1-, 2-, and 3-positions; then the 1-, 2-, and 4-positions; and so on until all the possible isomers are formed. The name of each isomer will allow you to check that no duplication of formulas has been written.

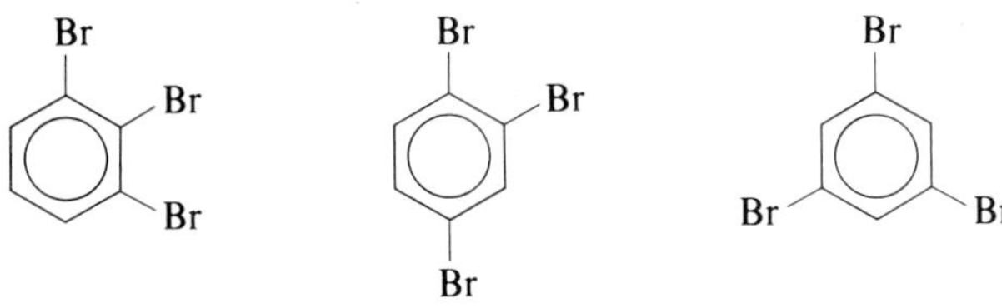

1,2,3-Tribromobenzene 1,2,4-Tribromobenzene 1,3,5-Tribromobenzene

There are only three isomers of tribromobenzene. If one erroneously writes the 1,2,5- compound, a further check will show that, by numbering the rings as indicated, it is in reality the 1,2,4- isomer:

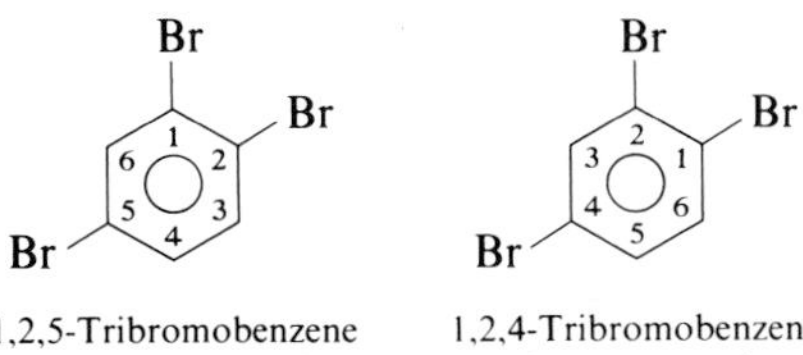

1,2,5-Tribromobenzene (erroneous name) 1,2,4-Tribromobenzene (correct name)

PRACTICE Write formulas and names for all possible isomers of chlorophenol.

Answer:

o-Chlorophenol *m*-Chlorophenol *p*-Chlorophenol

3.11 Polycyclic Aromatic Compounds

polycyclic or fused aromatic ring systems

There are many other aromatic ring systems besides benzene. Their structures consist of two or more rings in which two carbon atoms are common to two rings. These compounds are known as **polycyclic or fused aromatic ring systems**. Three of the most common hydrocarbons in this category are naphthalene, anthracene, and phenanthrene. One hydrogen is attached to each carbon atom except at the carbons that are common to two rings.

Naphthalene, $C_{10}H_8$

Anthracene, $C_{14}H_{10}$

Phenanthrene, $C_{14}H_{10}$

All three of these substances may be obtained from coal tar. Naphthalene is known as moth balls and has been used as a moth repellant for many years. A number of the polycyclic aromatic hydrocarbons (and benzene) have been shown to be carcinogenic (cancer-producing). Formulas for some of the more notable ones, found in coal tar, tar from cigarette smoke, and soot in urban environments follow.

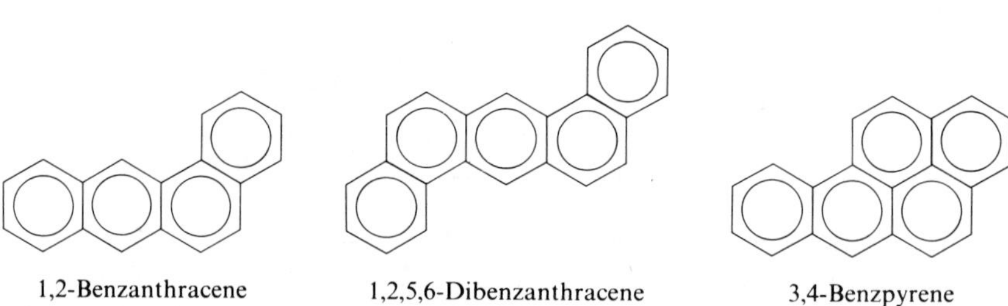

1,2-Benzanthracene

1,2,5,6-Dibenzanthracene

3,4-Benzpyrene

The mechanism by which these compounds cause cancer has not yet been determined. One hypothesis is that the polycyclic hydrocarbons are not active carcinogens; rather, the metabolites (products of chemical transformations in living cells) of these hydrocarbons are currently thought to be the active carcinogens. These fused ring hydrocarbons are formed when organic molecules are heated to high temperatures as they are in the burning of cigarettes.

3.12 Sources and Physical Properties of Aromatic Hydrocarbons

When coal is heated to high temperatures (450–1200°C) in the absence of air to produce coke (C), coal gas and a complex mixture of condensable substances called *coal tar* are driven off:

$$\text{Coal} \xrightarrow{\Delta} \text{Coke} + \text{Coal gas} + \text{Coal tar}$$

The aromatic hydrocarbons, such as benzene, toluene, xylene, naphthalene, and anthracene, were first obtained in quantity from coal tar. Since coal tar itself is a by-product of the manufacture of coke, the total amount of aromatics that can be obtained from this source is limited. The demand for aromatic hydrocarbons, which are used in the production of a vast number of materials such as drugs, dyes, detergents, explosives, insecticides, plastics, and synthetic rubber, became too great to be obtained from coal tar alone. Processes were devised to make aromatic hydrocarbons from the relatively inexpensive alkanes found in petroleum. Currently, about one-third of our benzene supply, and the greater portion of our toluene and xylene supplies, are obtained from petroleum.

Aromatic hydrocarbons are essentially nonpolar substances, insoluble in water but soluble in many organic solvents. They are liquids or solids and usually have densities less than that of water. Aromatic hydrocarbons burn readily, usually with smoky yellow flames as a result of incomplete carbon combustion. Some are good motor fuels with excellent antiknock properties.

3.13 Chemical Properties of Aromatic Hydrocarbons

The most characteristic reactions of aromatic hydrocarbons involve the substitution of some group for a hydrogen on one of the ring carbons. The following are examples of typical aromatic substitution reactions. In each of these reactions, a functional group is substituted for a hydrogen atom.

1. *Halogenation* (chlorination or bromination) When benzene reacts with chlorine or bromine in the presence of a catalyst such as iron(III) chloride or iron(III) bromide, a Cl or a Br atom replaces an H atom to form the products.

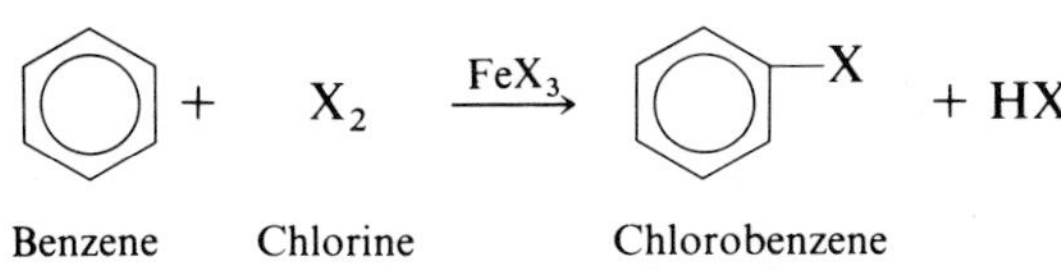

Benzene Chlorine or bromine Chlorobenzene or bromobenzene

2. *Nitration* When benzene reacts with a mixture of concentrated nitric acid and concentrated sulfuric acid at about 50°C, nitrobenzene is formed. In this reaction a nitro group, $-NO_2$, is substituted for an H atom of benzene.

$$C_6H_6 + HO-NO_2 \xrightarrow{H_2SO_4} C_6H_5-NO_2 + H_2O$$

Benzene   Nitric acid   Nitrobenzene

3. *Alkylation* (Friedel–Crafts reaction) There are many variations of the Friedel–Crafts reaction. In this type the alkyl group from an alkyl halide (RX), in the presence of $AlCl_3$ catalyst, substitutes for an H atom on the benzene ring.

$$C_6H_6 + CH_3CH_2Cl \xrightarrow{AlCl_3} C_6H_5-CH_2CH_3 + HCl$$

Benzene   Chloroethane   Ethylbenzene

From about 1860 onward, especially in Germany, a great variety of useful substances such as dyes, explosives, and drugs were synthesized from aromatic hydrocarbons by reactions of the types just described. These early syntheses were developed by trial-and-error methods. A good picture of the reaction mechanism, or step-by-step sequence of intermediate stages in the overall reaction, was not obtained until about 1940.

It is now recognized that aromatic substitution reactions usually proceed by a mechanism called *electrophilic substitution*. Three steps are involved: (1) the formation of an electrophile (electron-seeking group), (2) the attachment of the electrophile to the benzene ring forming a positively charged carbocation intermediate, and finally (3) the loss of a hydrogen ion from the carbocation to form the product. This reaction mechanism is illustrated in the chlorination of benzene catalyzed by iron(III) chloride.

Step 1 $FeCl_3 + Cl_2 \longrightarrow FeCl_4^- + Cl^+$

Iron(III) chloride   Chloronium ion

Step 2 $C_6H_6 + Cl^+ \longrightarrow [C_6H_6Cl]^+$ (ring carbon bearing H and Cl)

A carbocation

Step 3 $[C_6H_6Cl]^+ + FeCl_4^- \longrightarrow C_6H_5Cl + FeCl_3 + HCl$

Chlorobenzene

In Step 1 the electrophile (chloronium ion) is formed. In Step 2 the chloronium ion adds to benzene to form an intermediate carbocation, which loses a

Chemistry in Action

Aromatic Hydrocarbons

Benzene is the starting material for the production of many consumer products. Detergents, insecticides, plastics, dyes, and a multitude of drugs are all synthesized from benzene. It was once widely used as an organic solvent, but now benzene has been classified as a hazardous substance. Prolonged inhalation of benzene can cause nausea and death from cardiac or respiratory failure. Repeated exposure to benzene can result in aplastic anemia, a condition in which both the red and white blood cells decrease. Most laboratories have greatly reduced the use of benzene as a solvent, often substituting toluene or another aromatic compound. Toluene is used in the production of dyes, drugs, lacquers, and in explosives. It can be used to increase the octane rating of fuels and to preserve specimens of urine.

Substances containing the benzene ring are commonly found in living organisms. Plants synthesize benzene rings from carbon dioxide, water, and inorganic materials. Animals are not capable of this synthesis and so must ingest aromatic compounds to survive. Important aromatic compounds necessary to animals include some amino acids and vitamins.

proton (H^+) in Step 3 to form the products, C_6H_5Cl and HCl. The catalyst, $FeCl_3$, is regenerated in Step 3.

This same mechanism is used by living organisms when aromatic rings gain or lose substituents. For example, the thyroxines (thyroid gland hormones) contain aromatic rings that are iodinated by following an electrophilic substitution mechanism. Iodination is a key step in producing these potent hormones. In general, scientists find that most of life's reactions follow mechanisms that have been elucidated in the organic chemist's laboratory.

4. *Oxidation of side chains* Carbon chains attached to an aromatic ring are fairly easy to oxidize. Reagents most commonly used to accomplish this in the laboratory are $KMnO_4$ or $K_2Cr_2O_7 + H_2SO_4$. No matter how long the side chain is, the carbon atom attached to the aromatic ring is oxidized to a carboxylic acid group, —COOH. For example, toluene, ethylbenzene, and propylbenzene are all oxidized to benzoic acid:

$$C_6H_5\text{—}CH_3 \xrightarrow[\Delta]{KMnO_4/H_2O} C_6H_5\text{—}COOH$$

Toluene Benzoic acid

$$C_6H_5\text{—}CH_2CH_3 \xrightarrow[\Delta]{K_2Cr_2O_7/H_2SO_4} C_6H_5\text{—}COOH + CO_2$$

Ethylbenzene

$$C_6H_5\text{—}CH_2CH_2CH_3 \xrightarrow[\Delta]{K_2Cr_2O_7/H_2SO_4} C_6H_5\text{—}COOH + CH_3COOH$$

Propylbenzene

Concepts in Review

1. Explain the sp^2 and sp hybridization of carbon atoms.
2. Explain the formation of a pi bond.
3. Explain the formation of double and triple bonds.
4. Distinguish, by formulas, the difference between saturated and unsaturated hydrocarbons.
5. Name and write structural formulas of alkenes, alkynes, cycloalkenes, and aromatic compounds.
6. Determine from structural formulas whether a compound can exist as geometric isomers.
7. Name geometric isomers by the cis–trans method.
8. Write equations for the addition reactions of alkenes and alkynes.
9. Explain the formation of carbocations and the role they play in chemical reactions.
10. Apply Markovnikov's rule to the addition of HCl, HBr, HI, and H_2O/H^+ to alkenes and alkynes.
11. Explain the Baeyer test for unsaturation.
12. Distinguish, using simple chemical tests, among alkanes, alkenes, and alkynes.
13. Describe the nature of benzene and how its properties differ from open-chain unsaturated compounds.
14. Explain the role of geometric isomers in vision.
15. Name monosubstituted, disubstituted, and polysubstituted benzene compounds.
16. Draw structural formulas of substituted benzene compounds.
17. Recognize the more common fused aromatic ring compounds.
18. Write equations for the following reactions of benzene and substituted benzenes: halogenation (chlorination or bromination), nitration, alkylation (Friedel–Crafts reaction), and side-chain oxidation.
19. Describe and write equations for the mechanism by which benzene compounds are brominated in the presence of $FeBr_3$ or chlorinated in the presence of $FeCl_3$.

Equations in Review

Alkenes and Alkynes

Addition Reactions

Hydrogenation: $RCH{=}CHR + H_2 \longrightarrow RCH_2CH_2R$

Halogenation: $RCH{=}CHR + X_2 \longrightarrow RCHX{-}CHXR$

Hydrogen halide: $RCH{=}CH_2 + HX \longrightarrow \underset{\displaystyle X}{\underset{|}{RCH}}{-}CH_3$

Water: $RCH{=}CH_2 + H_2O \xrightarrow{H^+} \underset{\displaystyle OH}{\underset{|}{RCH}}{-}CH_3$

Oxidation

$$RCH{=}CH_2 \xrightarrow[H_2O]{KMnO_4} \underset{\displaystyle OH}{\underset{|}{RCH}}{-}\underset{\displaystyle OH}{\underset{|}{CH_2}}$$

Alkynes

Same types as alkenes

Aromatic hydrocarbons

Halogenation:

$$C_6H_6 + X_2 \xrightarrow{FeX_3} C_6H_5X + HX$$

Nitration:

$$C_6H_6 + HNO_3 \xrightarrow{H_2SO_4} C_6H_5NO_2 + H_2O$$

Alkylation:

$$C_6H_6 + R{-}Cl \xrightarrow{AlCl_3} C_6H_5R + HCl$$

Oxidation of side chains:

$$C_6H_5CH_2CH_3 \xrightarrow{KMnO_4/H_2O} C_6H_5{-}COOH + CO_2$$

Exercises

1. The double bond in ethylene (C_2H_4) is made up of a sigma bond and a pi bond. Explain how the pi bond differs from the sigma bond.
2. Draw Lewis structures to represent the following molecules:
   (a) Ethane (b) Ethene (c) Ethyne
3. (a) Draw structural formulas for the four isomeric chloropropenes, C_3H_5Cl.
   (b) There is another compound with this same molecular formula. What is its structure?
4. There are 17 possible isomeric hexenes including geometric isomers.
   (a) Write the structural formula for each isomer.
   (b) Name each isomer and include the prefix *cis-* or *trans-* where appropriate.

5. Draw structural formulas for the following:
   (a) 2,5-Dimethyl-3-hexene
   (b) 2-Ethyl-3-methyl-1-pentene
   (c) *cis*-4-Methyl-2-pentene
   (d) *cis*-1,2-Diphenylethene
   (e) 3-Pentene-1-yne
   (f) 3-Phenyl-1-butyne
   (g) Vinyl bromide
   (h) Cyclopentene
   (i) *trans*-3-Hexene
   (j) 1-Methylcyclohexene
   (k) 3-Methyl-1-pentyne
   (l) 3-Isopropylcyclopentene
   (m) 3-Methyl-2-phenylhexane
6. Name the following compounds:
   (a) 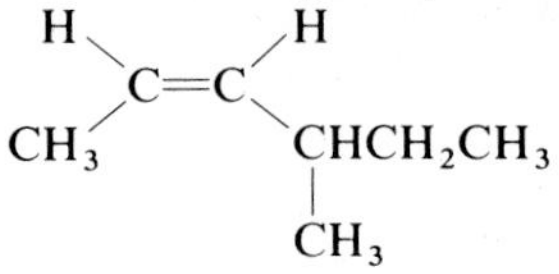 $(H)(CH_3)C{=}C(H)(CHCH_2CH_3)$, with CH_3 on the CH of the $CHCH_2CH_3$ group

   H   H
   C=C
   CH_3 $CHCH_2CH_3$
   |
   CH_3

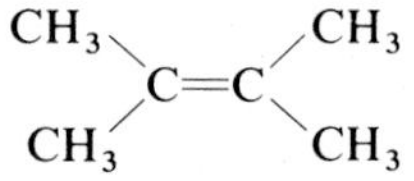

   (b) $(CH_3)_2C{=}C(CH_3)_2$

   CH_3 CH_3
   C=C
   CH_3 CH_3

   (c) $CH_3CH_2CHCH{=}CH_2$, with $CH(CH_3)_2$ on the CH

   $CH_3CH_2\underset{|}{C}HCH{=}CH_2$
   CH
   CH_3 CH_3

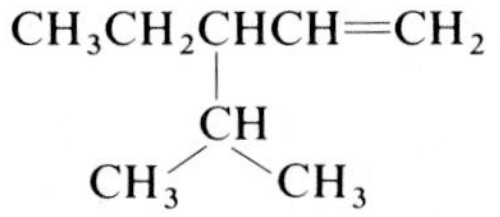

   (d) 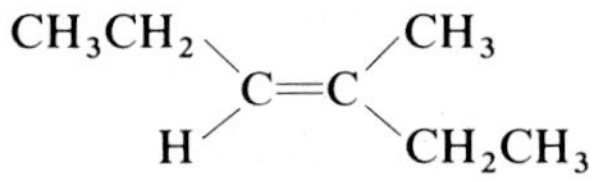 CH_3CH_2 and H on one carbon, CH_3 and CH_2CH_3 on the other

   CH_3CH_2 CH_3
   C=C
   H CH_2CH_3

   (e) 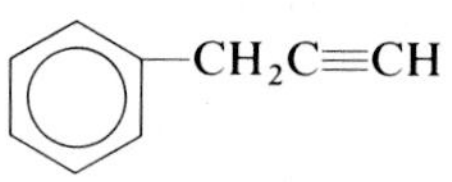 C_6H_5–$CH_2C{\equiv}CH$ (benzene ring)–$CH_2C{\equiv}CH$
   (f) $CH_3CHBrCHBrC{\equiv}CCH_3$
7. Write the structural formulas and IUPAC names for all the (a) pentynes and (b) hexynes.
8. Why is it possible to obtain cis and trans isomers of 1,2-dichloroethene but not of 1,2-dichloroethane?
9. Which of the following molecules have structural formulas that permit cis–trans isomers to exist?
   (a) $(CH_3)_2C{=}CHCH_3$
   (b) $CH_2{=}CHCl$
   (c) $CH_3CH_2C{\equiv}CCH_3$
   (d) $CH_3CH{=}CHCl$
   (e) $CCl_2{=}CBr_2$
   (f) $CH_2ClCH{=}CHCH_2Cl$
10. The following names are incorrect. Tell why each name is wrong and give the correct name.
   (a) 3-Methyl-3-butene
   (b) 3-Pentene
   (c) *cis*-2-Methyl-2-pentene
   (d) 3-Ethyl-1-butene
   (e) 2-Chlorocyclohexene
11. Complete the following equations:
   (a) $CH_3CH_2CH_2CH{=}CH_2 + Br_2 \longrightarrow$
   (b) $CH_3CH_2CH_2CH{=}CH_2 + HCl \longrightarrow$
   (c) 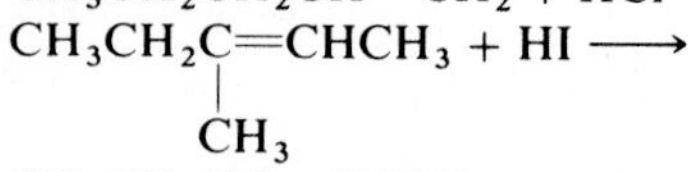 $CH_3CH_2\underset{\displaystyle CH_3}{\underset{|}{C}}{=}CHCH_3 + HI \longrightarrow$
   (d) $CH_3CH_2CH{=}CHCH_3 + HBr \longrightarrow$
   (e) $CH_3CH_2CH{=}CH_2 + H_2O \xrightarrow{H^+}$
   (f) 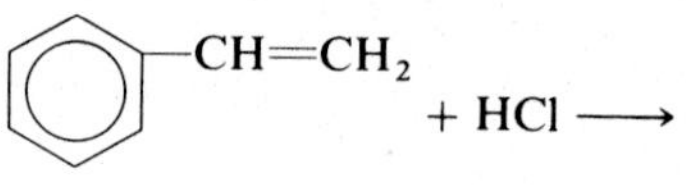 (benzene ring)–$CH{=}CH_2$ $+ HCl \longrightarrow$
   (g) 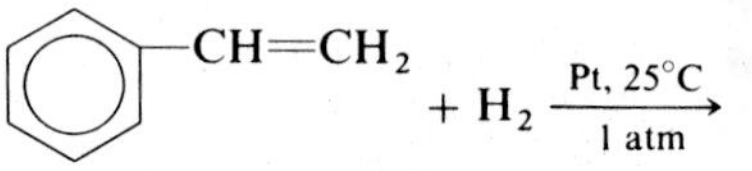 (benzene ring)–$CH{=}CH_2$ $+ H_2 \xrightarrow[\text{1 atm}]{\text{Pt, 25°C}}$
   (h) $CH_2{=}CHCl + HBr \longrightarrow$
   (i) $CH_3CH{=}CHCH_3 + KMnO_4 \xrightarrow[\text{Cold}]{H_2O}$
12. Complete the following equations:
   (a) $CH_3C{\equiv}CH + 2\,H_2 \xrightarrow[\text{1 atm}]{\text{Pt, 25°C}}$
   (b) $CH_3C{\equiv}CCH_3 + Br_2\ (1\ \text{mol}) \longrightarrow$
   (c) $CH_3C{\equiv}CCH_3 + Br_2\ (2\ \text{mol}) \longrightarrow$
   (d) The two-step reaction
   $CH{\equiv}CH + HCl \longrightarrow \quad \xrightarrow{HCl}$
   (e) The two-step reaction
   $CH_3C{\equiv}CH + HCl \longrightarrow \quad \xrightarrow{HCl}$
13. Write the formula and name for the product when cyclohexene reacts with
   (a) Br_2 (c) H_2O, H^+
   (b) HI (d) $KMnO_4(aq)$(cold)
14. Write equations to show how 2-butyne can be converted to:
   (a) 2,3-Dibromobutane
   (b) 2,2-Dibromobutane
   (c) 2,2,3,3-Tetrabromobutane
15. Two alkyl bromides are possible when 2-methyl-1-pentene is reacted with HBr. Which one will predominate? Why?
16. Cyclohexane and 2-hexene both have the formula C_6H_{12}. How could you readily distinguish one from the other by chemical tests?
17. Why do many rubber products deteriorate rapidly in smog-ridden areas?
18. Explain the two different kinds of explosion hazards present when acetylene is being handled.
19. Write structural formulas for
   (a) Benzene (f) Phenol
   (b) Toluene (g) *o*-Bromochlorobenzene
   (c) *p*-Xylene (h) 1,3-Dichloro-5-nitrobenzene
   (d) Styrene (i) *m*-Dinitrobenzene
   (e) Aniline

20. Write structural formulas for
(a) Ethylbenzene
(b) Benzoic acid
(c) 1,3,5-Tribromobenzene
(d) Naphthalene
(e) Anthracene
(f) *tert*-Butylbenzene
(g) 1,1-Diphenylethane

21. Write structural formulas and names for all the isomers of:
(a) Trichlorobenzene ($C_6H_3Cl_3$)
(b) Dichlorobromobenzene ($C_6H_3Cl_2Br$)
(c) The benzene derivatives of formula C_8H_{10}

22. (a) Write the structures for all the isomers that can be written by substituting a third chlorine atom in *o*-dichlorobenzene.
(b) Write the structures for all the isomers that can be written by substituting an additional chlorine atom in *o*-chlorobromobenzene.

23. Name the following compounds:
(a)  CH_2CH_3 … Cl
(b) 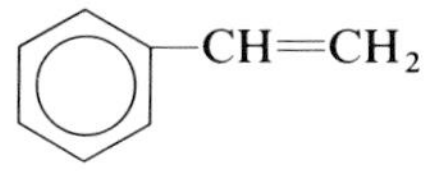 —CH=CH$_2$
(c) 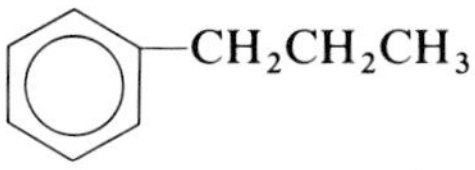 —$CH_2CH_2CH_3$
(d) 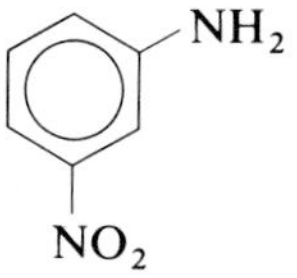 NH_2 … NO_2
(e) 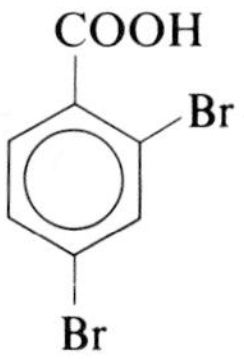 COOH … Br … Br
(f) 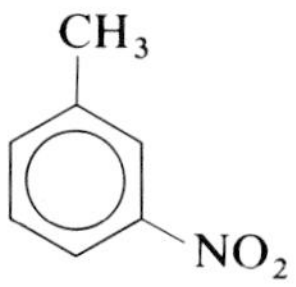 CH_3 … NO_2
(g) 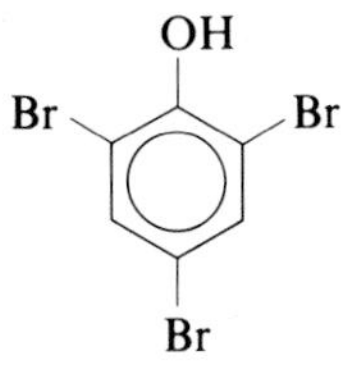 OH … Br … Br … Br
(h) 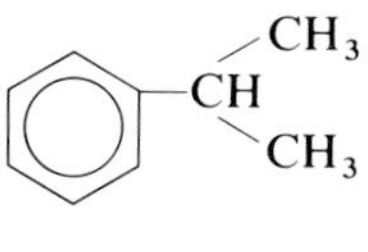 —CH(CH_3)(CH_3)
(i) 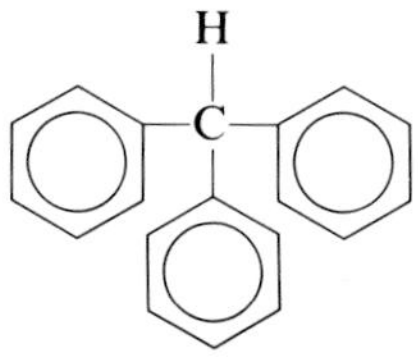 H—C—

24. Explain how the reactions of benzene provide evidence that its structure does not include double bonds like those found in alkenes.

25. Complete the following equations and name the organic products:

(a) 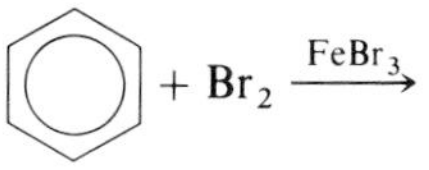 + Br_2 $\xrightarrow{FeBr_3}$

(b) 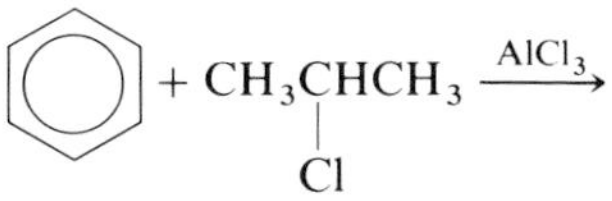 + CH_3CHCH_3 (with Cl on the central C) 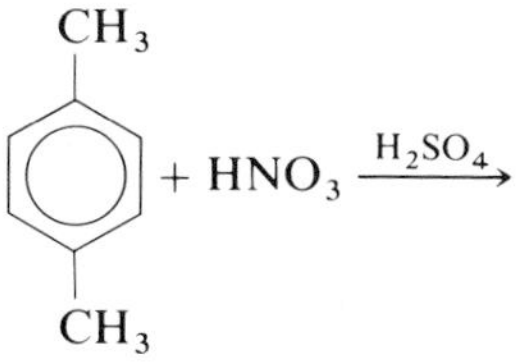 $\xrightarrow{AlCl_3}$

(c) CH_3 … CH_3 + HNO_3 $\xrightarrow{H_2SO_4}$

(d) 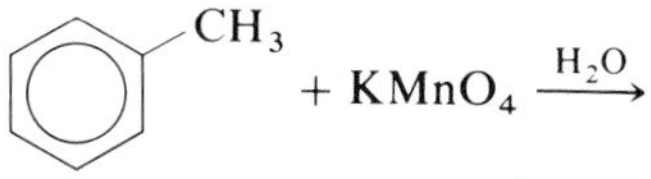 CH_3 + $KMnO_4$ $\xrightarrow{H_2O}$

26. Describe the reaction mechanism by which benzene is brominated in the presence of $FeBr_3$ [Question 25, part (a)]. Show equations.

27. In terms of historical events, why did the major source of aromatic hydrocarbons shift from coal tar to petroleum during the 10-year period 1935–1945?

28. Which of the following statements are correct? Rewrite the incorrect statements to make them correct.
(a) The compound with the formula C_5H_{10} can be either an alkene or a cycloalkane.
(b) If C_8H_{10} is an open-chain compound with multiple double bonds, it needs an additional ten hydrogen atoms to become a saturated hydrocarbon.
(c) Propene and propane are isomers.
(d) The pi bond is formed from two sp^2 electron orbitals.
(e) A double bond consists of two equivalent bonds called pi bonds.
(f) A triple bond consists of one sigma bond and two pi bonds.
(g) The hybridized electron structure of a carbon atom in alkynes is *sp, sp, p, p*.
(h) The acetylene molecule is linear.
(i) A molecule of 2,3-dimethyl-1-pentene contains seven carbon atoms.
(j) When an alkene is reacted with cold $KMnO_4$, a glycol is formed.
(k) The compound C_6H_{10} can have in its structure: two carbon–carbon double bonds, or

one carbon–carbon triple bond, or one cyclic ring and one carbon–carbon double bond.

(l) The disappearance of the purple color when $KMnO_4$ reacts with an alkene is known as the Markovnikov test for unsaturation.

(m) $CH_3CH_2CH_2^+$ is a primary carbocation.

(n) A secondary carbocation is more stable than a primary carbocation and less stable than a tertiary carbocation.

(o) After bromine has added to an alkene, the product is no longer unsaturated.

(p) Alkynes have the general formula C_nH_{2n-4}.

(q) Cis–trans isomerism occurs in alkenes and alkynes.

(r) Geometric isomers are superimposable on each other.

(s) All six hydrogen atoms in benzene are equivalent.

(t) The chemical behavior of benzene is similar to that of alkenes.

(u) Toluene and benzene are isomers.

(v) Two substituents on a benzene ring that are in the 1,2-position are ortho to each other.

(w) 1,4-Dichlorobenzene and *p*-dichlorobenzene are different names for the same compound.

(x) The oxidation of toluene with hot $KMnO_4$ yields benzoic acid.

(y) The oxidation of ethylbenzene with hot $KMnO_4$ yields benzoic acid.

(z) Toluene and benzene are homologues.

4

Alcohols, Ethers, Phenols, and Thiols

◄ **CHAPTER OPENING PHOTO: The fermentation of grapes into ethyl alcohol has been known for centuries.**

In today's active society we often play as strenuously as we work. A vacation getaway might include an initial car voyage, followed by some vigorous physical activity (hiking, cycling, skiing, or swimming). After a hard day of fun, friends gather to relax and commiserate over sore muscles. During these activities, organic molecules containing an —OH group play a significant role. Ethylene glycol acts as a coolant in the radiator of the car, sugar and carbohydrates provide the biochemical energy for our sport activity, ethyl alcohol is a component in any alcoholic beverage consumed, and phenolic compounds are an active ingredient in the muscle rubs and analgesics that relieve our sore muscles.

Just what changes does the addition of an OH group produce in the physical and chemical properties of an organic molecule? In this chapter we begin to examine the effect of various functional groups on organic molecules.

4.1 FUNCTIONAL GROUPS

Organic compounds were obtained originally from plants and animals, which, even today, are still the direct sources of many important chemicals. As a case in point, millions of tons of sucrose (table sugar) are obtained from sugar cane and sugar beet juices each year. As chemical knowledge developed, many naturally occurring compounds were synthesized, often at far less cost than the natural products. Of even greater significance than the cheaper manufacture of natural substances was the synthesis of new substances totally unlike any natural product. The synthesis of new substances was aided greatly by the realization that organic chemicals can be divided into a relatively small number of classes and studied on the basis of similar chemical properties (Table 2.1). The various classes of compounds are identified by the presence of certain characteristic groups called functional groups. For example, if a hydroxyl group (—OH) is substituted for a hydrogen atom in an alkane molecule, the resulting compound is an **alcohol**. Thus alcohols are a class of compounds in which the functional group is the hydroxyl group.

alcohol

Through the chemical reactions of functional groups, it is possible to create or synthesize new substances. The synthesis of new and possibly useful compounds or the more economical synthesis of known compounds is a main concern of modern organic chemistry. Most chemicals used today do not occur in nature but are synthesized from naturally occurring materials. The chemical and physical properties of an organic compound depend on (1) the kinds and number of functional groups present and (2) the shape and size of the molecule.

The structures of alcohols, ethers, and phenols may be derived from water by replacing the hydrogen atoms of water with alkyl groups (R) or aromatic rings:

H–O–H	R–O–H	R–O–R	C_6H_5–O–H
Water	Alcohol	Ether	Phenol

The R— groups in ethers can be the same or different and can be alkyl groups or aromatic rings.

4.2 Classification of Alcohols

Structurally, an alcohol is derived from a nonaromatic hydrocarbon by the replacement of at least one hydrogen atom with a hydroxyl group (—OH). Alcohols are represented by the general formula ROH, with methanol (CH_3OH) being the first member of the homologous series. R represents an alkyl or substituted alkyl group. Models illustrating the structural arrangements of the atoms in methanol and ethanol are shown in Figure 4.1.

primary alcohol

secondary alcohol

tertiary alcohol

Alcohols are classified as **primary** (1°), **secondary** (2°), or **tertiary** (3°), depending on whether the carbon atom to which the —OH group is attached is directly bonded to one, two, or three other carbon atoms, respectively. Generalized formulas for 1°, 2°, and 3° alcohols follow.

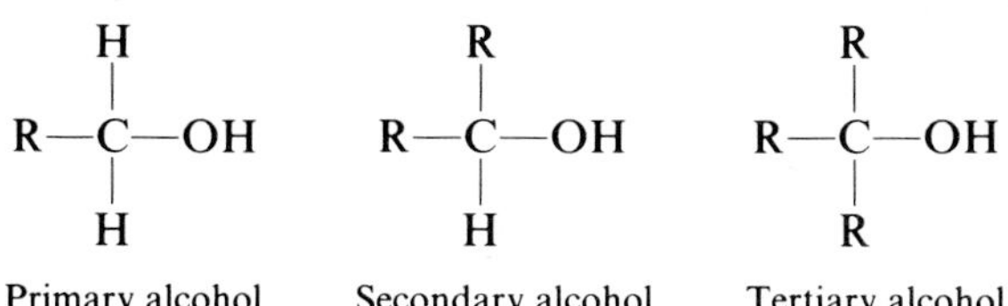

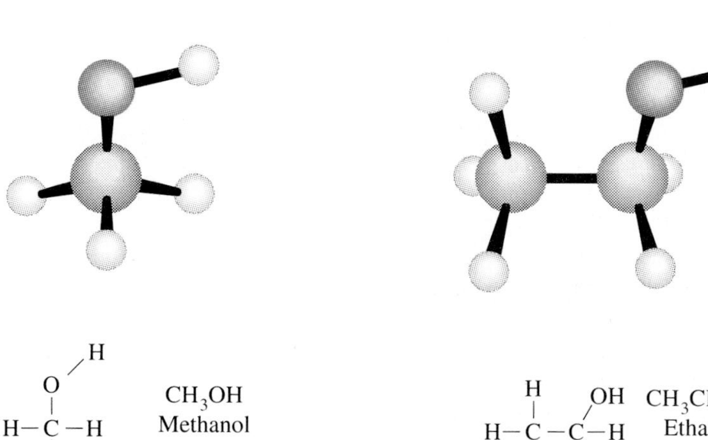

◀ **Figure 4.1**
Ball-and-stick models illustrating structural formulas of methanol and ethanol.

TABLE 4.1 Names and Classification of Alcohols

Class	Formula	IUPAC name	Common name[a]	Boiling point (°C)
Primary	CH_3OH	Methanol	Methyl alcohol	65.0
Primary	CH_3CH_2OH	Ethanol	Ethyl alcohol	78.5
Primary	$CH_3CH_2CH_2OH$	1-Propanol	*n*-Propyl alcohol	97.4
Primary	$CH_3CH_2CH_2CH_2OH$	1-Butanol	*n*-Butyl alcohol	118
Primary	$CH_3(CH_2)_3CH_2OH$	1-Pentanol	*n*-Amyl or *n*-pentyl alcohol	138
Primary	$CH_3(CH_2)_6CH_2OH$	1-Octanol	*n*-Octyl alcohol	195
Primary	CH_3CHCH_2OH | CH_3	2-Methyl-1-propanol	Isobutyl alcohol	108
Secondary	CH_3CHCH_3 | OH	2-Propanol	Isopropyl alcohol	82.5
Secondary	$CH_3CH_2CHCH_3$ | OH	2-Butanol	*sec*-Butyl alcohol	91.5
Tertiary	CH_3 | $CH_3—C—OH$ | CH_3	2-Methyl-2-propanol	*t*-Butyl alcohol	82.9
Dihydroxy	$HOCH_2CH_2OH$	1,2-Ethanediol	Ethylene glycol	197
Trihydroxy	$HOCH_2CHCH_2OH$ | OH	1,2,3-Propanetriol	Glycerol or glycerine	290

[a] The abbreviations *n*, *sec*, and *t* stand for normal, secondary, and tertiary, respectively.

Formulas of specific examples of these classes of alcohols are shown in Table 4.1. Methanol (CH_3OH) is grouped with the primary alcohols.

Molecular structures with more than one —OH group attached to a single carbon atom are generally not stable. But an alcohol molecule can contain two or more —OH groups if each —OH is attached to a different carbon atom. Accordingly, alcohols are also classified as monohydroxy, dihydroxy, trihydroxy, and so on, on the basis of the number of hydroxyl groups per molecule. **Polyhydroxy alcohols** and *polyols* are general terms for alcohols that have more than one —OH group per molecule. Polyhydroxy compounds are very important molecules in living cells as they include the carbohydrate class of biochemicals.

polyhydroxy alcohol

An alcohol such as 2-butanol can be written in a single-line formula by putting the —OH group in parentheses and placing it after the carbon to which it is bonded. For example, the following two formulas represent the same compound:

$$\underset{\displaystyle OH}{CH_3CH_2\overset{}{C}HCH_3} \qquad CH_3CH_2CH(OH)CH_3$$

4.3 NAMING ALCOHOLS

If you know how to name alkanes, it is easy to name alcohols by the IUPAC System. Unfortunately, several of the alcohols are generally known by common or nonsystematic names, so it is often necessary to know more than one name for a given alcohol. The common name is usually formed from the name of the alkyl group that is attached to the —OH group, followed by the word *alcohol.* See examples given below and in Table 4.1. To name an alcohol by the IUPAC System:

1. Select the longest continuous chain of carbon atoms containing the hydroxyl group.
2. Number the carbon atoms in this chain so that the one bearing the —OH group has the lowest possible number.
3. Form the parent alcohol name by replacing the final *e* of the corresponding alkane name by *ol.* When isomers are possible, locate the position of the —OH by placing the number (hyphenated) of the carbon atom to which the —OH is bonded immediately before the parent alcohol name.
4. Name each alkyl side chain (or other group) and designate its position by number.

For example, let us go through the steps above to name the alcohol $CH_3CH_2CH_2CH_2OH$.

Step 1 The longest carbon chain containing the —OH group has four carbons.

Step 2 Number the carbon atoms, giving the carbon bonded to the —OH the number 1.

$$\overset{4}{C}—\overset{3}{C}—\overset{2}{C}—\overset{1}{C}—OH$$

Step 3 The name of the four-carbon alkane is butane. Replace the final *e* in butane with *ol*, forming the name *butanol.* Since the —OH is on carbon 1, place a *1* before butanol to give the complete alcohol name 1-butanol.

Step 4 No groups of atoms other than hydrogen are attached to the butanol chain, so the name of this alcohol is 1-butanol.

Study the application of this naming system to these examples and to those shown in Table 4.1.

$$\overset{3}{CH_3}—\overset{2}{CH_2}—\overset{1}{CH_2OH}$$

1-Propanol
(*n*-Propyl alcohol)

$$\overset{1}{CH_3}—\underset{\displaystyle OH}{\overset{2}{CH}}—\overset{3}{CH_3}$$

2-Propanol
(Isopropyl alcohol)

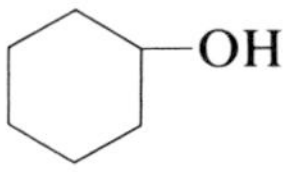

(cyclohexane ring)—OH

Cyclohexanol

$$\begin{array}{ccccccc} 4 & & 3 & & 2 & & 1 \\ CH_3 & - & CH & - & CH_2 & - & CH_2OH \\ & & | & & & & \\ & & CH_3 & & & & \end{array}$$

3-Methyl-1-butanol
(Isoamyl alcohol or
isopentyl alcohol)

$$\begin{array}{ccc} 2 & & 1 \\ HOCH_2 & - & CH_2OH \end{array}$$

1,2-Ethanediol
(Ethylene glycol)

EXAMPLE 4.1

Name this alcohol by the IUPAC method.

$$\begin{array}{l} CH_3CH_2\underset{\displaystyle CH_3}{\underset{|}{C}}HCH_2\underset{\displaystyle OH}{\underset{|}{C}}HCH_3 \end{array}$$

SOLUTION

Step 1 The longest continuous carbon chain containing the —OH group has six carbon atoms.

Step 2 This carbon chain is numbered from right to left so that the —OH group has the smallest possible number:

$$\begin{array}{ccccccccccc} 6 & & 5 & & 4 & & 3 & & 2 & & 1 \\ C & - & C & - & C & - & C & - & C & - & C \\ & & & & | & & & & | & & \\ & & & & CH_3 & & & & OH & & \end{array}$$

In this case, the —OH is on carbon 2.

Step 3 The name of the six-carbon alkane is hexane. Replace the final *e* in hexane by *ol*, forming the name *hexanol*. Since the —OH is on carbon 2, place a *2* before hexanol to give the parent alcohol name 2-hexanol.

Step 4 A methyl group (—CH_3) is located on carbon 4. Therefore the full name of the compound is 4-methyl-2-hexanol.

EXAMPLE 4.2

Write the structural formula of 3,3-dimethyl-2-hexanol.

SOLUTION

Step 1 The "2-hexanol" refers to a six-carbon chain with an —OH group on carbon 2. Write the skeleton structure as follows:

$$\begin{array}{ccccccccccc} 1 & & 2 & & 3 & & 4 & & 5 & & 6 \\ C & - & C & - & C & - & C & - & C & - & C \\ & & | & & & & & & & & \\ & & OH & & & & & & & & \end{array}$$

Step 2 Place the two methyl groups ("3,3-dimethyl") on carbon 3:

$$\begin{array}{ccccccccccc} & & & & CH_3 & & & & & & \\ & & & & | & & & & & & \\ 1 & & 2 & & 3 & & 4 & & 5 & & 6 \\ C & - & C & - & C & - & C & - & C & - & C \\ & & | & & | & & & & & & \\ & & HO & & CH_3 & & & & & & \end{array}$$

Step 3 Finally, add H atoms to give each carbon atom four bonds:

$$\begin{array}{ccccc} & & CH_3 & & \\ & & | & & \\ CH_3CH & - & C & - & CH_2CH_2CH_3 \\ | & & | & & \\ OH & & CH_3 & & \end{array}$$

3,3-Dimethyl-2-hexanol

Practice Write the correct IUPAC name for each of the following:

(a) $CH_3CH_2\underset{\displaystyle CH_2OH}{\underset{|}{C}}HCH_2CH_2CH_3$ (b) $CH_3CH_2\underset{\displaystyle OH}{\underset{|}{C}}HCH_2\overset{\displaystyle Br}{\overset{|}{\underset{\displaystyle CH_3}{\underset{|}{C}}}}CH_3$

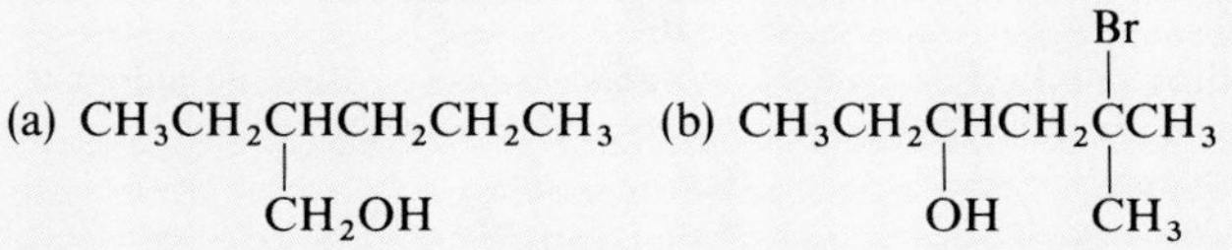

Answers: (a) 2-ethyl-1-pentanol (b) 5-bromo-5-methyl-3-hexanol

Practice Write the structural formula for each of the following:
(a) 3-methylcyclohexanol (b) 4-ethyl-2-methyl-3-heptanol

Answers: (a) cyclohexane ring with OH on C-1 and CH_3 on C-3 (OH, CH_3)

(b) $CH_3\overset{\displaystyle CH_3}{\overset{|}{C}}H\underset{\displaystyle OH}{\underset{|}{C}}H\overset{\displaystyle CH_2CH_3}{\overset{|}{C}}HCH_2CH_2CH_3$

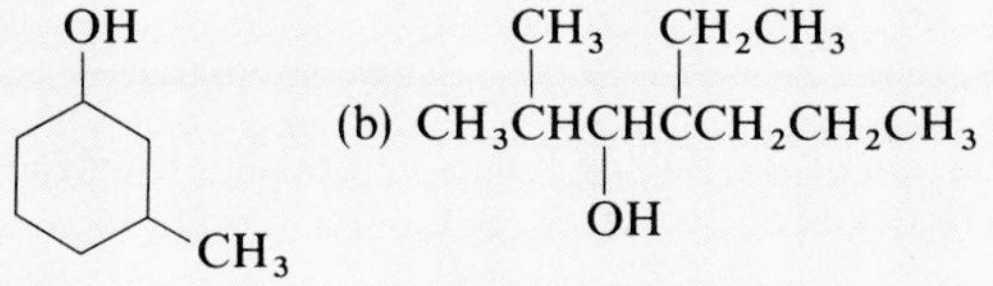

4.4 Physical Properties of Alcohols

The physical properties of alcohols are related to those of both water and alkane hydrocarbons. This is easily understandable if we recall certain facts about water and the alkanes. Water molecules are quite polar. The properties of water, such as its high boiling point and its ability to dissolve many polar substances, are largely due to the polarity of its molecules. Alkane molecules possess almost no polarity. The properties of the alkanes reflect this lack of polarity—for example, their relatively low boiling points and inability to dissolve water and other polar substances. An alcohol molecule is made up of a water-like hydroxyl group joined to a hydrocarbon-like alkyl group.

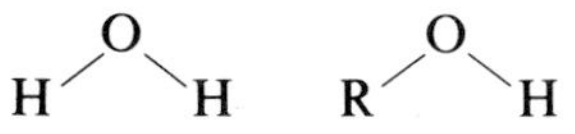

$$\underset{\text{Water}}{H{-}O{-}H} \qquad \underset{\text{Alcohol}}{R{-}O{-}H}$$

One striking property of alcohols is their relatively high boiling points. The simplest alcohol, methanol, boils at 65°C. But methane, the simplest hydrocarbon, boils at −162°C. The boiling points of the normal alcohols increase in a regular fashion with increasing number of carbon atoms. Branched-chain alcohols have lower boiling points than the corresponding straight-chain alcohols (see Table 4.1).

Alcohols containing up to three carbon atoms are infinitely soluble in water. With one exception (*t*-butyl alcohol), alcohols with four or more carbon atoms have limited solubility in water. In contrast, all hydrocarbons are essentially insoluble in water.

The hydroxyl group on the alcohol molecule is responsible for both the water solubility and the relatively high boiling points of the low molecular-mass alcohols. Hydrogen bonding between water and alcohol molecules accounts for

Table 4.2 Boiling Points of Alkanes and Monohydroxy Alcohols

Name	Boiling point (°C)	Name	Boiling point (°C)
Hexane	69	1-Hexanol	156
Octane	126	1-Octanol	195
Decane	174	1-Decanol	228

Table 4.3 Comparison of the Boiling Points of Ethanol, Ethylene Glycol, and 1-Propanol

Name	Formula	Molar mass	Boiling point (°C)
Ethanol	CH_3CH_2OH	46	78
Ethylene glycol	$CH_2(OH)CH_2OH$	62	197
1-Propanol	$CH_3CH_2CH_2OH$	60	97

the solubility, and hydrogen bonding between alcohol molecules accounts for their high boiling points.

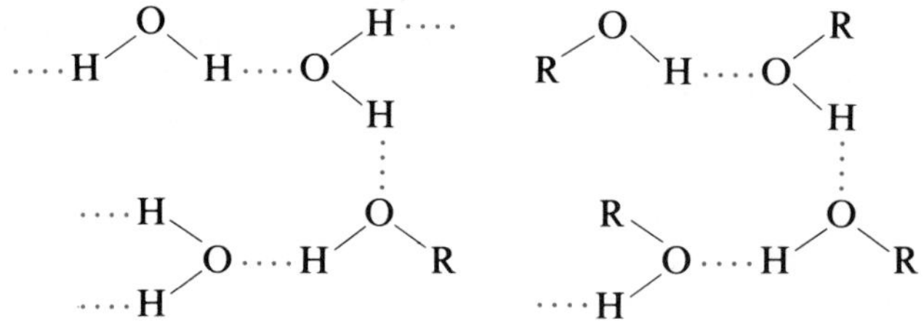

Water–Alcohol

Alcohol–Alcohol

As the length of the hydrocarbon chain increases, the effect of the hydroxyl group becomes relatively less important. Alcohols with 5 to 11 carbons are oily liquids of slight water solubility, and in physical behavior they resemble the corresponding alkane hydrocarbons. However, the effect of the —OH group is still noticeable in that their boiling points are higher than those of alkanes with similar molar masses (see Table 4.2). Alcohols containing 12 or more carbons are waxlike solids that resemble solid alkanes in physical appearance.

In alcohols with two or more hydroxyl groups, the effect of the hydroxyl groups on intermolecular attractive forces is, as we might suspect, even more striking than in monohydroxy alcohols. Ethanol, CH_3CH_2OH, boils at 78°C, but the boiling point of ethylene glycol, or 1,2-ethanediol, $CH_2(OH)CH_2OH$, is 197°C. Comparison of the boiling points of ethanol, 1-propanol, and ethylene glycol shows that increased molar mass does not account for the high boiling point of ethylene glycol (see Table 4.3). The higher boiling point is primarily a result of additional hydrogen bonding due to the two —OH groups in the ethylene glycol molecule.

EXAMPLE 4.3

Glucose is one of the most important carbohydrates in biochemistry. It has six carbons and five alcohol groups (molar mass = 180.2 g). How would you predict the water solubility of glucose will differ from that of hexanol?

SOLUTION

Each polar alcohol group attracts water molecules and increases the solubility of organic compounds in water. Because glucose contains five —OH groups whereas hexanol contains only one, glucose should dissolve to a much greater extent than hexanol. In fact, only about 0.6 g of hexanol will dissolve in 100 g of water (at 20°C). In contrast, about 95 g of glucose will dissolve in 100 g of water. The high water solubility of glucose is important because this molecule is transported in a water solution to the body's cells.

4.5 Chemical Properties of Alcohols

Acidic and Basic Properties

Aliphatic alcohols are similar to water in their acid/basic properties. If an alcohol is placed in a strong acid it will accept a proton (act as a Brønsted–Lowry base) to form a protonated alcohol or **oxonium ion**.

oxonium ion

$$CH_3-\ddot{\underset{\cdot\cdot}{O}}H + H_2SO_4 \longrightarrow CH_3-\overset{+}{\ddot{O}}(H)_2 + HSO_4^-$$

Methanol and ethanol are approximately the same strength as water as an acid, while the larger alcohols are weaker acids than water. Both water and alcohols react with alkali metals to release hydrogen gas and an anion.

$$2\,H_2O + 2\,Na \longrightarrow \underset{\text{Sodium hydroxide}}{2\,Na^+\,{}^-OH} + H_2\uparrow$$

$$2\,CH_3CH_2OH + 2\,Na \longrightarrow \underset{\text{Sodium ethoxide}}{2\,Na^+\,{}^-OCH_2CH_3} + H_2\uparrow$$

The resulting anion in the alcohol reaction is known as an **alkoxide ion** (RO^-). Alkoxides are strong bases (stronger than hydroxide) and so are used in organic chemistry when a strong base is required in a nonaqueous solution.

alkoxide ion

The order of reactivity of alcohols with sodium or potassium is primary > secondary > tertiary. Alcohols do not react with sodium as vigorously as water. Reactivity decreases with increasing molar mass since the —OH group becomes a relatively smaller, less significant part of the molecule.

Oxidation

We will consider only a few of the many reactions that alcohols are known to undergo. One important reaction is oxidation. We saw in Chapter 18 that the oxidation number of an element increases as a result of oxidation. Carbon can exist in several oxidation states, ranging from −4 to +4. In the −4 oxidation state, such as in methane, the carbon atom is considered to be completely reduced. In carbon dioxide the carbon atom is completely oxidized; that is, it is

TABLE 4.4 Oxidation States of Carbon in One-Carbon Compounds

	Compound	Number of C—O bonds	Oxidation state
CH_4	Methane	0	−4
CH_3OH	Methanol	1	−2
$H_2C{=}O$	Methanal (formaldehyde)	2	0
$HC(=O)OH$	Methanoic acid (formic acid)	3	+2
$O{=}C{=}O$	Carbon dioxide	4	+4

(+4). In many cases, oxidation reactions in organic and biochemistry can be considered in a simple manner without the use of oxidation numbers. Oxidation is the loss of hydrogen or the gain of bonds to oxygen by the organic reactant. Table 4.4 illustrates the progression of oxidation states for various compounds containing one carbon atom.

Carbon atoms exist in progressively higher stages of oxidation in different functional-group compounds:

$$\text{Alkanes} \longrightarrow \text{Alcohols} \longrightarrow \begin{Bmatrix}\text{Aldehydes}\\ \text{Ketones}\end{Bmatrix} \longrightarrow \text{Carboxylic acids} \longrightarrow \text{Carbon dioxide}$$

Increasing oxidation state ⟶

The different stages shown do not necessarily indicate direct methods of synthesis. For example, some, but not all alcohols can be converted to aldehydes by oxidation; but it is not practical to convert alkanes directly to alcohols. The following equations represent generalized oxidation reactions in which the oxidizing agent is represented by [O].

$$\underset{\text{Primary alcohol}}{R{-}CH_2{-}OH} \xrightarrow{[O]} \underset{\text{Aldehyde}}{R{-}\overset{O}{\overset{\|}{C}}{-}H} + H_2O \xrightarrow{[O]} \underset{\text{Carboxylic acid}}{R{-}\overset{O}{\overset{\|}{C}}{-}OH}$$

$$\underset{\text{Secondary alcohol}}{R{-}CH(OH){-}R} \xrightarrow{[O]} \underset{\text{Ketone}}{R{-}\overset{O}{\overset{\|}{C}}{-}R} + H_2O$$

$$R_3C{-}OH \xrightarrow{[O]} \text{No reaction}$$

Tertiary alcohols do not have a hydrogen on the —OH carbon and so cannot react with oxidizing agents except by such drastic procedures as combustion. Both primary and secondary alcohols are oxidized as shown in the equations by the loss of the colored hydrogen atoms.

Some common oxidizing agents used for specific reactions are potassium permanganate ($KMnO_4$) in an alkaline solution, potassium dichromate ($K_2Cr_2O_7$) in an acid solution, or oxygen of the air. A complete equation for an alcohol oxidation may be fairly complex. Since our main interest is in the changes that occur in the functional groups, we can convey this information in abbreviated form:

$$\underset{\text{Ethanol}}{CH_3CH_2OH} \xrightarrow[\Delta]{K_2Cr_2O_7/H_2SO_4} \underset{\text{Ethanal}}{CH_3\overset{\overset{\displaystyle O}{\|}}{C}-H} + H_2O$$

Although the abbreviated equation lacks some of the details, it does show the overall reaction involving the organic compounds. Additional information is provided by notations above and below the arrow, which indicate that this reaction is carried out in heated potassium dichromate–sulfuric acid solution. Abbreviated equations of this kind will be used frequently in the remainder of this book.

EXAMPLE 4.4

What are the products when (a) 1-propanol, (b) 2-propanol, and (c) cyclohexanol are oxidized with $K_2Cr_2O_7/H_2SO_4$?

SOLUTION

(a) The formula for 1-propanol is $CH_3CH_2CH_2OH$. Since it is a primary alcohol, it can be oxidized to an aldehyde or a carboxylic acid. The oxidation occurs at the carbon bonded to the —OH group, and this carbon atom becomes an aldehyde or a carboxylic acid. The rest of the molecule remains the same.

$$CH_3CH_2CH_2OH \nearrow \underset{\text{Propanal}}{CH_3CH_2\overset{\overset{\displaystyle H}{|}}{C}=O}$$

$$CH_3CH_2CH_2OH \searrow \underset{\text{Propanoic acid}}{CH_3CH_2COOH}$$

(b) 2-Propanol is a secondary alcohol and is oxidized to a ketone. Ketones resist further oxidation. The oxidation occurs at the carbon bonded to the —OH group.

$$CH_3\underset{\underset{\displaystyle OH}{|}}{C}HCH_3 \longrightarrow \underset{\text{Propanone (Acetone)}}{CH_3\underset{\underset{\displaystyle O}{\|}}{C}CH_3}$$

(c) Cyclohexanol is also a secondary alcohol and is oxidized to cyclohexanone, a ketone.

$$C_6H_{11}OH \longrightarrow \underset{\text{Cyclohexanone}}{C_6H_{10}O}$$

PRACTICE Write the structure for the products of the oxidation of these alcohols with $K_2Cr_2O_7$ and H_2SO_4:
(a) 1-Butanol (b) 2-Methyl-2-butanol (c) Cyclopentanol

Answers:

(a) $CH_3CH_2CH_2C(=O)-H \xrightarrow{[O]} CH_3CH_2C(=O)-OH$

(b) No reaction (2-methyl-2-butanol is a tertiary alcohol)

(c) O

Dehydration

The term dehydration implies the elimination of water. Alcohols can be dehydrated to form alkenes (Section 3.5) or ethers. One of the more effective dehydrating agents is sulfuric acid. Whether an ether or an alkene is formed depends on the ratio of alcohol to sulfuric acid, the reaction temperature, and the type of alcohol.

Alkenes: Intramolecular Dehydration The formation of alkenes from an alcohol molecule requires a relatively high temperature. Water is removed from within a *single* alcohol molecule and a new carbon–carbon double bond forms as shown below:

$$H-\underset{H}{\overset{H}{C}}-\underset{OH}{\overset{H}{C}}-H \xrightarrow[180^\circ C]{96\%\ H_2SO_4} CH_2{=}CH_2 + H_2O$$

For many alcohols there are a number of ways to remove water. Therefore the double bond can be located in different positions. The major product in these cases is the compound in which the double bond has the greatest number of alkyl substituents (or lesser number of hydrogens).

$$\underset{\text{2-Butanol}}{CH_3CH_2\underset{OH}{CH}CH_3} \xrightarrow[100^\circ C]{60\%\ H_2SO_4} \underset{\text{2-Butene (major product)}}{CH_3CH{=}CHCH_3} + \underset{\text{1-Butene}}{CH_3CH_2CH{=}CH_2} + H_2O$$

To predict the major product in an intramolecular dehydration, follow these steps: (1) Remove H and OH from adjacent carbons forming a carbon–carbon double bond; (2) if there are choices (multiple hydrogen containing neighboring carbon atoms adjacent to the —OH carbon), remove the hydrogen from the carbon with fewer hydrogens. This is known as **Saytzeff's rule**.

Saytzeff's rule

Ethers: Intermolecular Dehydration A dehydration reaction can take place between two alcohol molecules to produce an ether. However, the dehydration of ether is only useful for primary alcohols since secondary and tertiary alcohols predominantly yield alkenes.

$$\begin{matrix} CH_3CH_2O\boxed{H} \\ CH_3CH_2\boxed{OH} \end{matrix} \xrightarrow[140^\circ C]{96\%\ H_2SO_4} \underset{\text{Diethyl ether}}{CH_3CH_2OCH_2CH_3} + H_2O$$

A reaction in which *two* molecules are combined by removing a small molecule is known as a **condensation** reaction. There are many examples of other condensation reactions in the formation of biochemical molecules.

condensation

The type of dehydration which occurs depends on the temperature and the number of reactant molecules. Lower temperatures and *two* alcohol molecules produce ethers while higher temperatures and a *single* alcohol produce alkenes.

Dehydration reactions are often used in industry to make relatively expensive ethers from lower priced alcohols. Alkenes are less expensive than alcohols and so are not produced industrially by this method.

Esterification (Conversion of Alcohols to Esters)

An alcohol can react with a carboxylic acid to form an ester and water. The reaction is represented as follows:

$$\underset{\text{Carboxylic acid}}{R{-}\overset{\overset{\displaystyle O}{\|}}{C}{-}OH} + \underset{\text{Alcohol}}{H{-}OR'} \xrightleftharpoons{H^+} \underset{\text{Ester}}{R\overset{\overset{\displaystyle O}{\|}}{C}{-}OR'} + HOH$$

$$\underset{\text{Acetic acid}}{CH_3\overset{\overset{\displaystyle O}{\|}}{C}{-}OH} + \underset{\text{Ethanol}}{HOCH_2CH_3} \xrightleftharpoons{H^+} \underset{\text{Ethyl acetate}}{CH_3\overset{\overset{\displaystyle O}{\|}}{C}{-}OCH_2CH_3} + HOH$$

Esterification is an important reaction of alcohols and is discussed in greater detail in Chapter 6.

4.6 Common Alcohols

Three general methods for making alcohols are

1. *Hydrolysis of an ester*

$$\underset{\text{Ester}}{R\overset{\overset{\displaystyle O}{\|}}{C}{-}OR'} + HOH \xrightarrow[\Delta]{H^+} \underset{\text{Carboxylic acid}}{R\overset{\overset{\displaystyle O}{\|}}{C}{-}OH} + \underset{\text{Alcohol}}{R'OH}$$

2. *Alkaline hydrolysis of an alkyl halide* (1° and 2° alcohols only)

$$\underset{\text{Alkyl halide}}{RX} + NaOH(aq) \longrightarrow \underset{\text{Alcohol}}{ROH} + NaX$$

$$CH_3CH_2Cl + NaOH(aq) \longrightarrow CH_3CH_2OH + NaCl$$

see also p. 106

Hydrolysis is a reaction of water with another species in which the water molecule is split. The hydrolysis of an ester is the reverse reaction of esterification. A carboxylic acid and an alcohol are formed as products. The reaction can be conducted in an acid or an alkaline medium.

3. *Catalytic reduction of aldehydes and ketones* to produce primary and secondary alcohols. These reactions are discussed in Chapter 5.

In theory, these general methods provide a way to make almost any desired alcohol, but they may not be practical for a specific alcohol because the necessary starting material—ester, alkyl halide, aldehyde, or ketone—cannot be obtained at a reasonable cost. Hence, for economic reasons most of the widely used alcohols are made on an industrial scale by special methods that have been developed for specific alcohols. The preparation and properties of several of these alcohols are described in the following paragraphs.

Methanol

When wood is heated to a high temperature in an atmosphere lacking oxygen, methanol (wood alcohol) and other products are formed and driven off. The process is called *destructive distillation*, and until about 1925 nearly all methanol was obtained in this way. In the early 1920s the synthesis of methanol by high-pressure catalytic hydrogenation of carbon monoxide was developed in Germany. The reaction is

$$CO + 2\,H_2 \xrightarrow[300\text{–}400^\circ C,\ 200\ atm]{ZnO\text{–}Cr_2O_3} CH_3OH$$

Nearly all methanol is now manufactured by this method.

Methanol is a volatile (bp 65°C), highly flammable liquid. It is poisonous and capable of causing blindness or death if taken internally. Exposure to methanol vapors for even short periods of time is dangerous. Despite this danger, over 3.6×10^9 kg (7.9×10^9 lb) annually is manufactured and used for

1. Conversion to formaldehyde (methanal) primarily for use in the manufacture of polymers
2. Manufacture of other chemicals, especially various kinds of esters
3. Denaturing ethyl alcohol (rendering it unfit as a beverage)
4. An industrial solvent
5. An inexpensive and temporary antifreeze for radiators (it is not a satisfactory permanent antifreeze, because its boiling point is lower than that of water)

The experimental use of 5–30% methanol or ethanol in gasoline (*gasohol*) has shown promising results in reducing the amount of air pollutants emitted in automobile exhausts. Another benefit of using methanol in gasoline is that methanol can be made from nonpetroleum sources. The most economical nonpetroleum source of carbon monoxide for making methanol is coal. In addition to coal, burnable materials such as wood, agricultural wastes, and sewage sludge also are potential sources of methanol.

Ethanol

Ethanol is without doubt the earliest and most widely known alcohol. It is or has been known by a variety of names such as ethyl alcohol, "alcohol," grain alcohol, and spirit. Huge quantities of this substance are prepared by fermentation. Starch and sugar are the raw materials. Starch is first converted to sugar by enzyme- or acid-catalyzed hydrolysis. (An enzyme is a biological catalyst, as discussed in Chapter 13.) Conversion of simple sugars to ethanol is accomplished by yeast:

$$\underset{\text{Glucose}}{C_6H_{12}O_6} \xrightarrow{\text{Yeast}} \underset{\text{Ethanol}}{2\,CH_3CH_2OH} + 2\,CO_2$$

For legal use in beverages, ethanol is made by fermentation; but a large part of the alcohol for industrial uses (5.9×10^8 kg [about 1.3×10^9 lb] annually) is made from petroleum-derived ethylene. Ethylene is passed into an aqueous acid solution to form ethanol:

$$CH_2{=}CH_2 + H_2O \xrightarrow{H^+} CH_3CH_2OH$$

Some of the economically significant uses of ethanol are the following:

1. Intermediate in the manufacture of other chemicals such as acetaldehyde, acetic acid, ethyl acetate, and diethyl ether
2. Solvent for many organic substances
3. Compounding ingredient for pharmaceuticals, perfumes, flavorings, and so on
4. Essential ingredient of alcoholic beverages

Ethanol acts physiologically as a food, as a drug, and as a poison. It is a food in the limited sense that the body is able to metabolize it to carbon dioxide and water with the production of energy. As a drug, ethanol is often mistakenly considered to be a stimulant, but it is in fact a depressant. In moderate quantities ethanol causes drowsiness and depresses brain functions so that activities requiring skill and judgment (such as automobile driving) are impaired. In larger quantities ethanol causes nausea, vomiting, impaired perception, and incoordination. If a very large amount is consumed, unconsciousness and ultimately death may occur.

Authorities maintain that the effects of ethanol on automobile drivers are a factor in about half of all fatal traffic accidents in the United States. The gravity of this problem can be grasped when you realize that traffic accidents are responsible for about 50,000 deaths each year in the United States.

Heavy taxes are imposed on alcohol in beverages. A gallon of pure alcohol costs only a few dollars to produce, but in a distilled beverage it bears a tax of about 20 dollars or more.

Ethanol for industrial use is often denatured (rendered unfit for drinking) and, thus, is not taxed. Denaturing is done by adding small amounts of methanol and other denaturants that are extremely difficult to remove. Denaturing is required by the federal government to protect the beverage-alcohol tax source. Special tax-free use permits are issued to scientific and industrial users who require pure ethanol for nonbeverage uses.

Isopropyl Alcohol (2-Propanol)

Isopropyl alcohol (2-propanol) is made from propene derived from petroleum. This synthesis is analogous to that used for making ethanol from ethylene:

$$\underset{\text{Propene}}{CH_3CH{=}CH_2} + H_2O \xrightarrow{H^+} \underset{\text{Isopropyl alcohol (2-Propanol)}}{CH_3\underset{\displaystyle OH}{\underset{|}{C}}HCH_3}$$

Note that 2-propanol, not 1-propanol, is produced. This is because, in the first step of the reaction, an H^+ adds to carbon 1 of propene according to Markovnikov's rule (Section 3.6). The —OH group then ends up on carbon 2 to give the final product.

Isopropyl alcohol is a relatively low-cost alcohol that is manufactured in large quantities, about 7.3×10^8 kg (1.6×10^9 lb) annually. It is not a potable alcohol, and even breathing large quantities of the vapor may cause dizziness, headache, nausea, vomiting, mental depression, and coma. Isopropyl alcohol is used (1) to manufacture other chemicals (expecially acetone), (2) as an industrial solvent, and (3) as the principal ingredient in rubbing alcohol formulations.

Ethylene Glycol (1,2-Ethanediol)

Ethylene glycol is the simplest alcohol containing two —OH groups. Like most other relatively cheap, low-molar-mass alcohols, it is commercially derived from petroleum. One industrial synthesis is from ethylene via ethylene oxide (oxirane).

$$2\,\underset{\text{Ethylene}}{CH_2{=}CH_2} + O_2 \xrightarrow[200\text{–}300^\circ C]{\text{Ag catalyst}} 2\,\underset{\substack{\text{Oxirane}\\ \text{(Ethylene oxide)}}}{CH_2\overset{O}{—}CH_2}$$

$$CH_2\overset{O}{—}CH_2 + H_2O \xrightarrow{H^+} \underset{\substack{\text{1,2-Ethanediol}\\ \text{(Ethylene glycol)}}}{HOCH_2CH_2OH}$$

Major uses of ethylene glycol are (1) in the preparation of the synthetic polyester fibers (Dacron) and film (Mylar), (2) as a major ingredient in "permanent type" antifreeze for cooling systems, (3) as a solvent in the paint and plastics industries, and (4) in the formulations of printing ink and ink for ballpoint pens.

The low molar mass, complete water solubility, low freezing point, and high boiling point make ethylene glycol a nearly ideal antifreeze. A 58% by mass aqueous solution of ethylene glycol freezes at $-48^\circ C$. Its high boiling point and high heat of vaporization prevent it from being boiled away and permit higher, and therefore more efficient, engine operating temperatures than are possible with water alone. The U.S. production of ethylene glycol amounts to about 1.8×10^8 kg (4.0×10^8 lb) annually. Ethylene glycol is extremely toxic when ingested.

Glycerol

Glycerol, also known as *glycerine* or 1,2,3-propanetriol, is an important trihydroxy alcohol. Glycerol is a syrupy liquid with a sweet, warm taste. It is about 0.6 times as sweet as cane sugar. It is obtained as a by-product of processing animal and vegetable fats to make soap and other products, and it is also synthesized commercially from propene. The major uses of glycerol are (1) as a raw material in the manufacture of polymers and explosives, (2) as an emollient in cosmetics, (3) as a humectant in tobacco products, and (4) as a sweetener. Each use is directly related to the three —OH groups on glycerol.

The —OH groups provide sites through which the glycerol unit may be bonded to other molecules to form a polymer (Chapter 8). The explosive nitroglycerine or glyceryltrinitrate, is made by reacting the —OH groups with nitric acid:

$$\begin{array}{l} CH_2OH \\ | \\ CHOH \\ | \\ CH_2OH \end{array} + \underset{\text{Nitric acid}}{3\,HONO_2} \longrightarrow \begin{array}{l} CH_2ONO_2 \\ | \\ CHONO_2 \\ | \\ CH_2ONO_2 \end{array} + 3\,H_2O$$

Glycerol — Glyceryltrinitrate (Nitroglycerine)

The three polar —OH groups on the glycerol molecule are able to hold water molecules by hydrogen bonding. Consequently, glycerol is a hygroscopic substance; that is, it has the ability to take up water vapor from the air. It is therefore used as a skin moisturizer in cosmetic preparations. Glycerol is also used as an additive in tobacco products; by taking up moisture from the air, it prevents the tobacco from becoming excessively dry and crumbly.

4.7 Phenols

phenol

The term **phenol** is used for the class of compounds that have a hydroxy group attached to an aromatic ring. The parent compound is called *phenol* (C_6H_5OH) and is also known as carbolic acid.

Naming Phenols

Many phenols are named as derivatives of the parent compound using the general methods for naming aromatic compounds. For example,

OH | OH, Br | OH, NH_2 | OH, O_2N, NO_2, NO_2

Phenol (Carbolic acid) — *m*-Bromophenol — *p*-Aminophenol — 2,4,6-Trinitrophenol (Picric acid)

The *ortho*-, *meta*-, and *para*-dihydroxybenzenes have the special names catechol, resorcinol, and hydroquinone, respectively. The catechol structure occurs in many natural substances; and hydroquinone, a manufactured product, is commonly used as a photographic reducer and developer.

OH, OH | OH, OH | OH, OH

Catechol (1,2-Dihydroxybenzene) — Resorcinol (1,3-Dihydroxybenzene) — Hydroquinone (1,4-Dihydroxybenzene)

Chemistry in Action

Common Phenols

Many well-known natural substances have phenolic groups in their structures. The formulas and brief descriptions of several examples follow.

Vanillin is the principal odorous component of the vanilla bean. It is one of the most widely used flavorings and is also used for masking undesirable odors in many products such as paints.

Eugenol is the essence of oil of cloves. Two of its uses are as a dental analgesic and for the manufacture of synthetic vanillin. Thymol occurs in the oil of thyme. It has a pleasant odor and flavor and is used as an antiseptic in preparations such as mouthwashes. Thymol is the starting material for the synthesis of menthol, the main constituent of oil of peppermint. Thymol is a widely used flavoring and pharmaceutical.

Butylated hydroxytoluene (BHT) is used in small amounts as an antioxidant preservative for food, synthetic rubber, vegetable oils, soap, and some plastics.

The active irritants in poison ivy and poison oak are called urushiols. They are catechol derivatives with an unbranched 15-carbon side chain in position 3 on the phenol ring.

The widely discussed active principle of marijuana is tetrahydrocannabinol. It is obtained from the dried leaves and flowering tops of the hemp plant and has been used since antiquity for its physiological effects. The common acid–base indicator phenolphthalein is a phenol derivative. Phenolphthalein is also used as a medical cathartic. Epinephrine (adrenalin) is secreted by the adrenal gland in response to stress, fear, anger, or other heightened emotional states. It stimulates the conversion of glycogen to glucose in the body. Phenol is the starting material for the manufacture of aspirin, one of the most widely used drugs for self-medication.

OH, OCH_3, H—C=O

Vanillin

OH, OCH_3, $CH_2CH{=}CH_2$

Eugenol

OH, OH, $C_{15}H_{25-31}$

Urushiols

CH_3, OH, CH, CH_3 CH_3

Thymol

OH, $(CH_3)_3C$, $C(CH_3)_3$, CH_3

2,6-di-*t*-Butyl-4-methylphenol (Butylated hydroxytoluene, BHT)

CH_3, OH, CH_3, O, CH_3, $n\text{-}C_5H_{11}$

Tetrahydrocannabinol (from Marijuana)

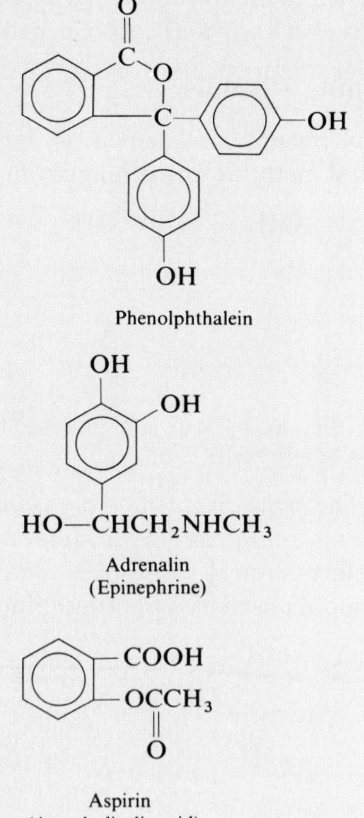

The *ortho-*, *meta-*, and *para-*methylphenols are present in coal tar and are known as cresols. They are all useful disinfectants.

OH, CH_3	OH, CH_3	OH, CH_3
o-Cresol (*o*-Methylphenol)	*m*-Cresol (*m*-Methylphenol)	*p*-Cresol (*p*-Methylphenol)

4.8 Properties of Phenols

In the pure state, phenol is a colorless crystalline solid with a melting point at about 41°C and a characteristic odor. Phenol is highly poisonous. Ingestion of even small amounts of it may cause nausea, vomiting, circulatory collapse, and death from respiratory failure.

Phenol is a weak acid; it is more acidic than alcohols and water but less acidic than acetic and carbonic acids. The pH values are as follows: 0.1 *M* acetic acid, 2.87; water, 7.0; 0.1 *M* phenol, 5.5. Thus, phenol reacts with sodium hydroxide solution to form a salt but does not react with sodium bicarbonate. The salt formed is called sodium phenoxide or sodium phenolate. Sodium hydroxide does not remove a hydrogen atom from an alcohol because alcohols are weaker acids than water.

$$C_6H_5OH + NaOH \longrightarrow C_6H_5ONa + H_2O$$

Sodium phenoxide (Sodium phenolate)

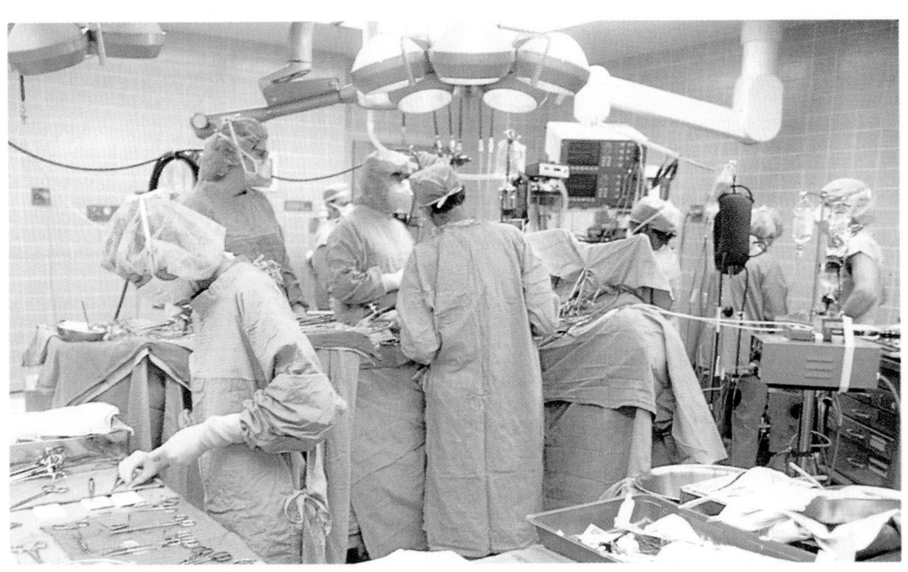

◀ **Phenols were among the first antiseptics to be used in operating rooms to prevent the spread of bacteria. Today other antiseptics such as iodine solutions and germicidal soaps have replaced phenols.**

In general the phenols are toxic to microorganisms. They are widely used as antiseptics and disinfectants. Phenol was the first compound to be used extensively as an operating room disinfectant. Joseph Lister (1827–1912) first used phenol for this purpose in 1867. The antiseptic power of phenols is increased by substituting alkyl groups (up to six carbons) in the benzene ring. For example, 4-hexylresorcinol is used as an antiseptic in numerous pharmaceuticals.

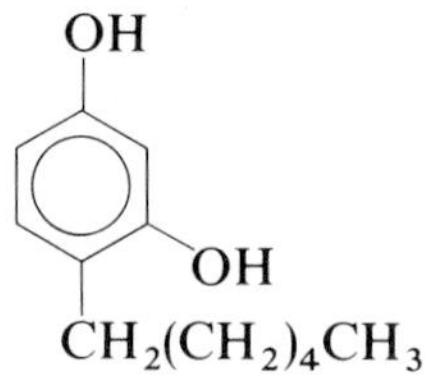

OH

OH

$CH_2(CH_2)_4CH_3$

4-Hexylresorcinol

4.9 Production of Phenol

Phenol is obtained from coal tar. In addition, there are several commercial methods used to produce phenol synthetically. The most economical of these methods starts with benzene and propylene, which react to form cumene (isopropylbenzene). Cumene is then oxidized by air to cumene hydroperoxide, which is treated with dilute sulfuric acid to obtain phenol and acetone. The economic feasibility of the process is due to the fact that two important commercial products are produced. The equations for the reactions are

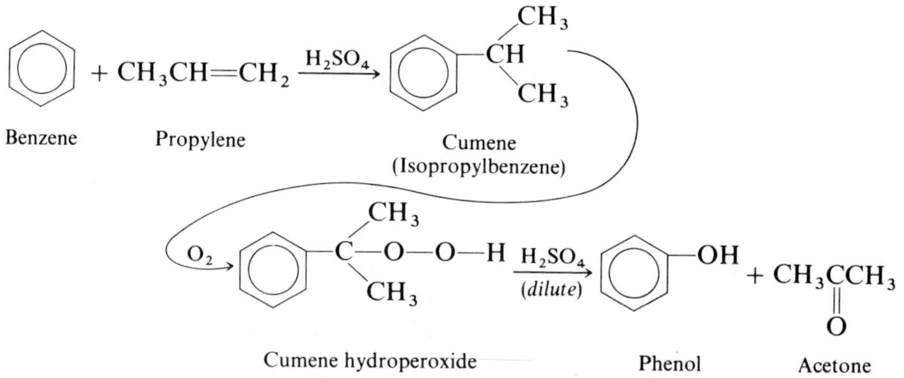

$$C_6H_6 + CH_3CH{=}CH_2 \xrightarrow{H_2SO_4} C_6H_5{-}CH(CH_3)_2$$

Benzene — Propylene — Cumene (Isopropylbenzene)

$$\xrightarrow{O_2} C_6H_5{-}C(CH_3)_2{-}O{-}O{-}H \xrightarrow[\textit{(dilute)}]{H_2SO_4} C_6H_5{-}OH + CH_3\overset{\displaystyle O}{\overset{\|}{C}}CH_3$$

Cumene hydroperoxide — Phenol — Acetone

Over 1.1×10^9 kg (2.4×10^9 lb) of synthetic phenol is produced annually in the United States. The chief use of phenol is for the manufacture of phenol–formaldehyde resins and plastics (see Chapter 8).

4.10 Ethers

ether

Ethers have the general formula ROR′. The groups R and R′ can be derived from saturated, unsaturated, or aromatic hydrocarbons; and, for a given ether, R and R′ may be alike or different. Cyclic ethers are formed by joining the ends

TABLE 4.5 Names and Structural Formulas of Ethers

Name[a]	Formula	Boiling point (°C)
Dimethyl ether (Methoxymethane)	$CH_3—O—CH_3$	−25
Methyl ethyl ether (Methoxyethane)	$CH_3CH_2—O—CH_3$	8
Diethyl ether (Ethoxyethane)	$CH_3CH_2—O—CH_2CH_3$	35
Ethyl isopropyl ether (2-Ethoxypropane)	$CH_3CH_2—O—CH(CH_3)CH_3$	54
Divinyl ether	$CH_2{=}CH—O—CH{=}CH_2$	39
Anisole (Methoxybenzene) Methyl phenyl ether	$C_6H_5—OCH_3$	154
Diphenyl ether	$C_6H_5—O—C_6H_5$	259
Tetrahydrofuran (THF)	$CH_2—CH_2$, CH_2 CH_2, O (ring)	66

[a] The IUPAC name is in parentheses when given.

of a single hydrocarbon chain through an oxygen atom to form a ring structure. Table 4.5 shows structural formulas and names for some of the different kinds of ethers.

Naming Ethers

Individual ethers, like alcohols, may be known by several names. The ether having the formula $CH_3CH_2—O—CH_2CH_3$ and formerly widely used as an anesthetic is called diethyl ether, ethyl ether, ethoxyethane, or simply ether. Common names of ethers are formed from the names of the groups attached to the oxygen atom, followed by the word *ether*.

$$\underset{\text{Methyl}}{CH_3}—\underset{\text{Ether}}{\boxed{O}}—\underset{\text{Methyl}}{CH_3} \qquad \underset{\text{Methyl}}{CH_3}—\underset{\text{Ether}}{\boxed{O}}—\underset{\text{Ethyl}}{CH_2CH_3}$$

Dimethyl ether — Methyl ethyl ether

In the IUPAC System, ethers are named as alkoxy (RO—) derivatives of the alkane corresponding to the longest carbon–carbon chain in the molecule. To name an ether by this system:

1. Select the longest carbon–carbon chain and label it with the name of the corresponding alkane.

2. Change the *yl* ending of the other hydrocarbon group to *oxy* to obtain the alkoxy group name. For example, $CH_3O—$ is called *methoxy*.
3. Combine the two names from Steps 1 and 2, giving the alkoxy name first, to form the ether name.

$CH_3—O—CH_2CH_3$

This is the longest C—C chain, so call it *ethane*.

$CH_3O—$ is the other group; modify its name from *methyl* to *methoxy* and combine with *ethane* to obtain the name of the ether, methoxyethane. Thus

$CH_3CH_2—O—CH_2CH_3$ is ethoxyethane

$CH_3CH_2CH_2—O—CH_2CH_2CH_2CH_3$ is propoxybutane

Additional examples named by both methods are found in Table 4.5.

4.11 Structures and Properties of Ethers

An oxygen atom linking together two carbon atoms is the key structural feature of an ether molecule. This oxygen atom causes ether molecules to have a bent shape somewhat like that of water and alcohol molecules:

H—Ö—H (Water) R—Ö—H (Alcohol) R—Ö—R (Ether)

Ethers are somewhat more polar than alkanes, because alkanes lack the oxygen atom with its exposed, nonbonded electrons. But ethers are much less polar than alcohols, since no hydrogen is attached to the oxygen atom in an ether. The solubility and boiling point (vapor pressure) characteristics of ethers are related to the C—O—C structure. Alkanes have virtually no solubility in water or acid. But about 7.5 g of diethyl ether will dissolve in 100 g of water at 20°C. Diethyl ether also dissolves in sulfuric acid. Hydrogen bonding between ether and water molecules and between ether and acid molecules is responsible for this solubility.

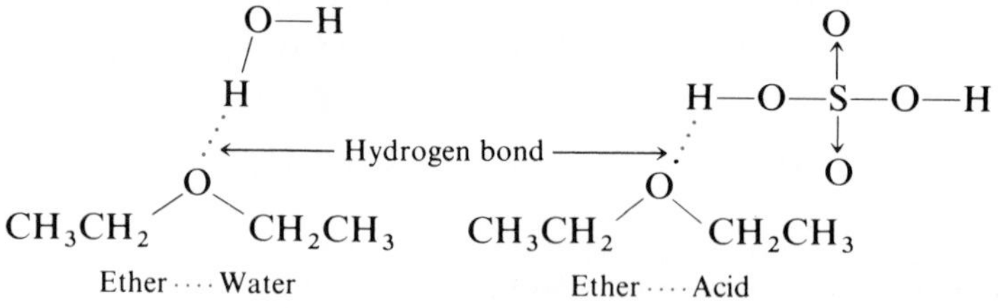

O—H / H ···· O(CH_3CH_2)(CH_2CH_3) — Ether····Water

H—O—S(→O)(→O)—O—H ···· O(CH_3CH_2)(CH_2CH_3) — Ether····Acid

← Hydrogen bond →

Because no —OH group is present, hydrogen bonding does not occur between ether molecules. This lack of hydrogen bonding can be seen by comparing the boiling points of a hydrocarbon, an ether, and an alcohol of similar molecular mass, as in Table 4.6. The boiling point of the ether is somewhat above that of the hydrocarbon but much lower than that of the more polar alcohol.

Table 4.6 Boiling Points of Ethers, Alkanes, and Alcohols

Name	Formula	Molar mass	Boiling point (°C)
Dimethyl ether	CH_3OCH_3	46	−24
Propane	$CH_3CH_2CH_3$	44	−42
Ethanol	CH_3CH_2OH	46	78
Methoxyethane	$CH_3OCH_2CH_3$	60	8
Butane	$CH_3CH_2CH_2CH_3$	58	−0.6
1-Propanol	$CH_3CH_2CH_2OH$	60	97
2-Propanol	$CH_3CH(OH)CH_3$	60	83

Ethers, especially diethyl ether, are exceptionally good solvents for organic compounds. Many polar compounds, including water, acids, alcohols, and other oxygenated organic compounds, dissolve, at least to some extent, in ethers. This solubility is a result of intermolecular attractions between the slightly polar ether molecules and the molecules of the other polar substance. Nonpolar compounds such as hydrocarbons and alkyl halides also dissolve in ethers. These substances dissolve because the ether molecules are not very polar and therefore are not strongly attracted either to one another or to the other kinds of molecules. Thus, ether molecules are able to intermingle freely with the molecules of a nonpolar substance and form a solution by simple mixing.

In summary, ethers are polar enough to dissolve some polar substances; but their polarity is so slight that they act as nonpolar solvents for a great many nonpolar substances.

Ethers have little chemical reactivity, but because a great many organic substances dissolve readily in ethers, they are often used as solvents in laboratory and manufacturing operations. Their use may be dangerous, since low-molar-mass ethers are volatile, and their highly flammable vapors form explosive mixtures with air. Another hazard of ethers is that, despite their generally low chemical reactivity, oxygen of the air slowly reacts with them to form unstable peroxides that are subject to explosive decomposition:

$$CH_3CH_2{-}O{-}CH_2CH_3 + O_2 \longrightarrow \underset{\displaystyle |\atop \displaystyle O{-}O{-}H}{CH_3CH}{-}O{-}CH_2CH_3$$

Diethyl ether hydroperoxide

4.12 Preparation of Ethers

We have seen that ethers can be made by intermolecular dehydration of alcohols by heating in the presence of an acid (see Section 4.5). Ethers are also made from sodium alkoxides or sodium phenoxides and alkyl halides, a reaction called the *Williamson synthesis*.

CHEMISTRY IN ACTION

ETHERS

The most widely known use of ethyl ether has been as a general anesthetic for surgery. The introduction of ether for this purpose is one of the great landmarks of medicine. Two Americans, Crawford W. Long and William T. Morton, played important roles in this development. Long, a physician, used ether in a surgical operation as early as 1842 but did not publish his discovery until 1849. Morton, a dentist, used ether as an anesthetic for dental work in 1846. He publicly demonstrated its effectiveness by administering ether to a patient undergoing surgery at the Massachusetts General Hospital on October 16, 1846.

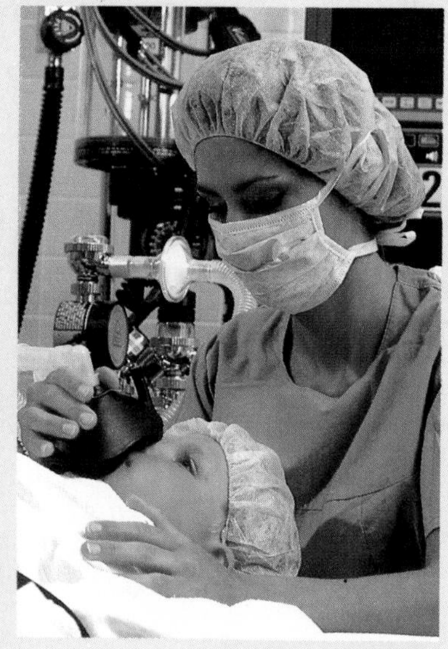

The word *anesthesia* is from the Greek, meaning insensibility, and was suggested to Morton by the poet and physician Oliver Wendell Holmes. A *general anesthetic* is a substance or combination of substances that produces both unconsciousness and insensitivity to pain. Many other substances, including other ethers such as divinyl ether (Vinethene) and methoxyflurane (Penthrane), are general inhalation anesthetics. These substances are superior in some respects, and in recent years have replaced ethyl ether as a general anesthetic.

$$CH_2{=}CH{-}O{-}CH{=}CH_2$$

Divinyl ether

$$CHCl_2CF_2{-}O{-}CH_3$$

Methoxyflurane

Ether produces unconsciousness by depressing the activity of the central nervous system. The major disadvantages of ether include flammability, irritation of respiratory passages, and occurrence of nausea and vomiting after its use. These hazards have resulted in a change toward the use of other substances (such as nitrous oxide, N_2O, or halogenated compounds like halothane, $CF_3CHClBr$) as general anesthetics. These substitute compounds also pose hazards and must be used with caution.

A number of theories explaining the biochemical activity of anesthetics have been proposed. All are based on the nonpolar nature of the compounds. This property leads to high solubility in fats and membranes. One theory suggests that anesthetics interfere with electrical activity in nerve impulses by dissolving in brain cells.

Ether also serves as an excellent extracting medium. It acts as a good solvent for separating lipids (ether soluble) from carbohydrates and proteins (ether insoluble). Ether is the solvent of choice for cocaine users as well. The technique known as "free-basing" involves the separation of cocaine from other substances by extracting it into ether. One method used to capture cocaine manufacturers involves tracking large ether shipments.

$$\underset{\text{Sodium alkoxide}}{RONa} + \underset{\text{Alkyl halide}}{R'X} \longrightarrow \underset{\text{Ether}}{ROR'} + \underset{\text{Sodium halide}}{NaX}$$

The Williamson synthesis is especially useful in the preparation of mixed ethers (where $R \neq R'$) and aromatic ethers:

$$\underset{\text{Sodium ethoxide}}{CH_3CH_2ONa} + \underset{\text{Bromomethane}}{CH_3Br} \longrightarrow \underset{\substack{\text{Methoxyethane}\\ \text{(Methyl ethyl ether)}}}{CH_3CH_2{-}O{-}CH_3} + NaBr$$

$$C_6H_5ONa + CH_3Br \longrightarrow C_6H_5OCH_3 + NaBr$$

Sodium phenoxide — Bromomethane — Methyl phenyl ether (Anisole)

It is interesting to note that organic chemistry is replete with "name reactions," such as the Williamson synthesis, named after the scientists who invented the reactions.

4.13 Thiols

Sulfur and oxygen are found next to each other in the same family on the periodic table. This indicates some similarity in the formulas of their compounds. Organic compounds which contain the —SH group are analogs of alcohols. The —SH-containing compounds are known as **thiols**, or mercaptans. Examples include:

thiols

CH_3SH — Methanethiol (Methyl mercaptan)

$CH_3CH_2CH(SH)CH_3$ — 2-Butanethiol (*sec*-Butyl mercaptan)

Thiols have a higher molar mass than corresponding alcohols, but boil at lower temperatures (ethanol 78°C, ethanethiol 36°C). The reason for this discrepancy lies in the fact that alcohols form hydrogen bonds while thiols do not.

The major important properties of thiols are summarized below:

1. Foul odors: some of these compounds smell so awful that companies make special labels to warn consumers. The odor given off by a frightened skunk has thiols as the active ingredient. Natural gas is odorized to be detectable by adding small amounts of methanethiol.
2. Oxidation to disulfides

$$2\ RSH \xrightarrow{[O]} R—S—S—R$$

Thiol — Disulfide

This reaction can be accomplished using many oxidizing agents. The sulfur is being oxidized just as the carbon was being oxidized in alcohols. The conversion between thiols and disulfides is important in proteins. When oxidation occurs one part of a protein chain is linked to another, giving the protein a characteristic three-dimensional shape as shown in Figure 4.2.

Coenzyme A (CoA or CoASH) is a complex coenzyme (Chapter 13) which plays a central role in the metabolism of carbohydrates, lipids, and proteins. The acetyl derivative of CoA, called acetyl CoA, occurs in all living organisms. The link between the acetyl group and the coenzyme is a high-energy bond. Acetyl CoA is very reactive and therefore functions as a carrier for acetyl groups in the cell. The biochemical synthesis of acetyl CoA is complex, involving many steps, but may be described overall as a thioesterification.

$$\underset{\text{Acetic acid}}{CH_3\overset{\overset{\displaystyle O}{\|}}{C}{-}OH} + \underset{\text{Coenzyme A}}{H{-}S{-}CoA} \longrightarrow \underset{\text{Acetyl CoA}}{CH_3{-}\overset{\overset{\displaystyle O}{\|}}{C}{-}S{-}CoA} + H_2O$$

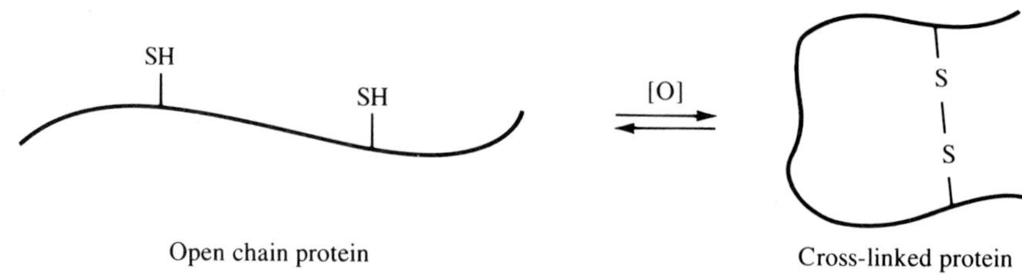

FIGURE 4.2 ▶ Oxidation of thiols to disulfides.

CONCEPTS IN REVIEW

1. Name alcohols by common and IUPAC methods.
2. Write the structural formula when given the name of an alcohol.
3. Write the structural formulas for all the isomeric alcohols of a given molecular formula.
4. Recognize and identify primary, secondary, and tertiary alcohols.
5. Compare and explain the relative solubilities of alcohols and ethers in water.
6. Indicate a class of biochemicals that has many of the same properties as the polyhydroxy alcohols.
7. Summarize the acid/base properties of alcohols and alkoxides.
8. Write equations for the oxidation of alcohols.
9. Write equations for the dehydration of alcohols to ethers and alkenes.
10. Differentiate between intramolecular and intermolecular dehydration, indicating proper conditions for each.
11. Write equations for the synthesis of alcohols from alkyl halides and from alkenes.
12. Explain the relative reactivities of primary, secondary, and tertiary alcohols.
13. Understand the common methods of preparing methyl alcohol, ethyl alcohol, isopropyl alcohol, ethylene glycol, and glycerol.
14. Name phenols and write their formulas.
15. Understand the differences in properties of the hydroxyl group when bonded to an aromatic ring (a phenol) and to an aliphatic group (an alcohol).
16. Be familiar with the general properties of phenols.
17. Name ethers and write their formulas.
18. Write equations for preparing ethers by the Williamson synthesis.
19. List major properties for thiols.
20. Discuss relative boiling points and water solubilities of comparable hydrocarbons, alcohols, dihydroxy alcohols, ethers, and thiols.
21. Discuss the hazards of using ethers in the laboratory.

Equations in Review

Alcohols

Oxidation reactions

$$R{-}CH_2{-}OH \xrightarrow{[O]} R{-}\overset{\overset{\displaystyle O}{\|}}{C}{-}H + H_2O \xrightarrow{[O]} R{-}\overset{\overset{\displaystyle O}{\|}}{C}{-}OH$$

Primary alcohol — Aldehyde — Carboxylic acid

$$R{-}\underset{\underset{\displaystyle OH}{|}}{\overset{\overset{\displaystyle H}{|}}{C}}{-}R \xrightarrow{[O]} R{-}\overset{\overset{\displaystyle O}{\|}}{C}{-}R + H_2O$$

Secondary alcohol — Ketone

$$R{-}\underset{\underset{\displaystyle OH}{|}}{\overset{\overset{\displaystyle R}{|}}{C}}{-}R \xrightarrow{[O]} \text{No reaction}$$

Tertiary alcohol

Dehydration reactions

Intramolecular

$$H{-}\underset{\underset{\displaystyle H}{|}}{\overset{\overset{\displaystyle H}{|}}{C}}{-}\underset{\underset{\displaystyle OH}{|}}{\overset{\overset{\displaystyle H}{|}}{C}}{-}H \xrightarrow[180^\circ C]{H_2SO_4} CH_2{=}CH_2 + H_2O$$

Intermolecular

$$\begin{matrix} CH_3CH_2OH \\ CH_3CH_2OH \end{matrix} \xrightarrow[140^\circ C]{H_2SO_4} CH_3CH_2OCH_2CH_3 + H_2O$$

Esterification

$$R{-}\overset{\overset{\displaystyle O}{\|}}{C}{-}OH + H{-}OR' \xrightarrow{H^+} R{-}\overset{\overset{\displaystyle O}{\|}}{C}{-}OR' + H_2O$$

Ethers

Williamson synthesis

$$RO^- \, {}^+Na + R'X \longrightarrow ROR' + NaX$$

Thiols

Oxidation to disulfides

$$RSH \xrightarrow{[O]} R{-}S{-}S{-}R$$

EXERCISES

1. Write structural formulas for and give an example of
   (a) An alkyl halide (e) A ketone
   (b) A phenol (f) A carboxylic acid
   (c) An ether (g) An ester
   (d) An aldehyde (h) A thiol
2. Although it is possible to make alkenes from alcohols, alkenes are seldom, if ever, made in this way on an industrial scale. Why not?
3. Isopropyl alcohol is usually used in rubbing alcohol formulations. Why is this alcohol used in preference to normal propyl alcohol?
4. What classes of compounds can be formed by the oxidation of primary alcohols? Cite examples.
5. What is the molar mass of myricyl alcohol, an open-chain saturated alcohol containing 30 carbon atoms? Myricyl alcohol is present in beeswax as an ester.
6. Why is ethylene glycol (1,2-ethanediol) superior to methyl alcohol (methanol) as an antifreeze for automobile radiators?
7. Briefly outline the physiological effects of
   (a) Methanol (b) Ethanol
8. Explain, in terms of molecular structure, why ethanol (CH_3CH_2OH, molar mass = 46) is a liquid at room temperature and dimethyl ether (CH_3OCH_3, molar mass = 46) is a gas.
9. Write structural formulas for
   (a) Methanol
   (b) 2-Butanol
   (c) 3-Methyl-1-hexanol
   (d) 2-Methyl-2-butanol
   (e) Propylene glycol
   (f) Isopropyl alcohol
   (g) 1-Phenylethanol
   (h) Cyclopentanol
   (i) 2,3-Butanediol
   (j) *sec*-Butyl alcohol
   (k) 2-Propanethiol
   (l) *n*-Pentyl mercaptan
10. Write structures for all the isomers (alcohols and ethers) with the formula
    (a) C_3H_8O
    (b) $C_4H_{10}O$
11. There are eight open-chain isomeric alcohols that have the formula $C_5H_{11}OH$. Write the structural formula and the IUPAC name for each of these alcohols.
12. Which of the isomers in Question 11 are
    (a) Primary alcohols?
    (b) Secondary alcohols?
    (c) Tertiary alcohols?
13. Write the structural formula of a glycol that is both a primary and a secondary alcohol.
14. Name the following compounds:
    (a) CH_3CH_2OH
    (b) $CH_3CH(OH)CH_3$
    (c) 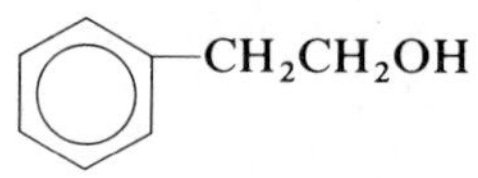 (benzene ring)—CH_2CH_2OH
    (d) $CH_3CH_2CH(OH)CH_2CH_3$
    (e) $CH_3\overset{CH_2CH_3}{\underset{OH}{C}}CH_2CH_3$
    (f) 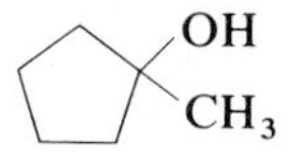 (cyclopentane ring) with OH and CH_3 on the same carbon
    (g) 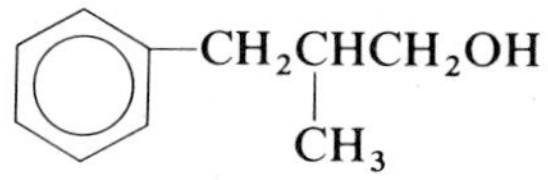 (benzene ring)—$CH_2\underset{CH_3}{CH}CH_2OH$
    (h) CH_2—CH_2 joined through O
    (i) $CH_3\underset{OH}{CH}$—$\underset{OH}{CH_2}$
    (j) $HOCH_2\overset{CH_3}{CH}$—$\overset{CH_3}{CH}CH_2OH$
15. Cyclic glycols show cis–trans isomerism because of restricted rotation about the carbon–carbon bonds in the ring. Draw and label the structures for *cis*- and *trans*-cyclopentane-1,2-diol.
16. Write the formula and the name of the chief product when the following alcohols are dehydrated to alkenes:
    (a) $CH_3\underset{OH}{CH}\overset{CH_3}{CH}CH_3$
    (b) $CH_3\underset{OH}{CH}CH_2CH_2CH_3$
    (c) 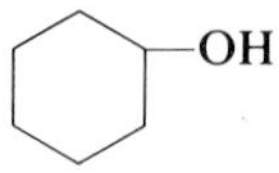 (cyclohexane ring)—OH
17. When 1-butanol is dehydrated to an alkene, it yields mainly 2-butene rather than 1-butene. This indicates that the dehydration process is at least a two-step reaction. Suggest a mechanism to explain the reaction. (*Hint: n*-Butyl carbocation is formed initially.)

18. Alcohols can be made by reacting alkyl halides with aqueous sodium hydroxide, as follows:

$$RX + NaOH(aq) \longrightarrow ROH + NaX(aq)$$

Give the names and formulas of the alkyl bromides (RBr) needed to prepare the following alcohols by this method:
(a) Isopropyl alcohol (c) Cyclohexanol
(b) 3-Methyl-1-butanol
Write the equation for the preparation of each alcohol.

19. Write the equation for the preparation of an alcohol by reacting each of the following alkenes with sulfuric acid and water:
(a) Propene (d) 1-Pentene
(b) 1-Butene (e) 2-Methyl-2-butene
(c) 2-Butene

20. Write equations to show how each of the following transformations can be accomplished. Some conversions may require more than one step, and some reactions studied in previous chapters may be needed.

(a) $CH_3\underset{\displaystyle |\atop OH}{C}HCH_3 \longrightarrow CH_3\underset{\displaystyle \|\atop O}{C}CH_3$

(b) $CH_3CH_2CH_2CH{=}CH_2 \longrightarrow CH_3CH_2CH_2\underset{\displaystyle |\atop OH}{C}HCH_3$

(c) $CH_3CH_2OH \longrightarrow CH_3CH_2O^- Na^+$

(d) $CH_3CH_2CH{=}CH_2 \longrightarrow CH_3CH_2\underset{\displaystyle \|\atop O}{C}CH_3$

(e) $CH_3CH_2CH_2CH_2OH \longrightarrow CH_3CH_2\underset{\displaystyle |\atop Cl}{C}HCH_3$

(f) $CH_3CH_2CH_2Cl \longrightarrow CH_3CH_2\underset{\displaystyle |\atop H}{C}{=}O$

21. Complete the following equations and name the principal organic product formed in each case:

(a) $2\ CH_3CH_2OH \xrightarrow[140^\circ C]{96\%\ H_2SO_4}$

(b) $CH_3CH_2CH_2OH \xrightarrow[180^\circ C]{96\%\ H_2SO_4}$

(c) $CH_3CH(OH)CH_2CH_3 \xrightarrow[\Delta]{K_2Cr_2O_7/H_2SO_4}$

(d) $CH_3CH_2\overset{\displaystyle O\atop \|}{C}{-}OCH_2CH_3 + H_2O \xrightarrow{H^+}$

22. Benzyl alcohol ($C_6H_5CH_2OH$) is a primary alcohol. Write the formulas of two different organic compounds that can be obtained by oxidizing benzyl alcohol.

23. Name the following compounds:

(a) OH

(d) OH, Br, NO_2

(b) OH, OH

(e) OH, OH, $CH_2(CH_2)_4CH_3$

(c) OH, CH_3

(f) OH, NO_2, NO_2

24. Write structural formulas for each of the following:
(a) *o*-Cresol
(b) *p*-Nitrophenol
(c) Resorcinol
(d) 2,6-Dimethylphenol
(e) 4-Hydroxy-3-methoxybenzaldehyde (vanillin)

25. Summarize the general properties of phenols.

26. Write equations for the cumene hydroperoxide synthesis of phenol and acetone.

27. Which of the following compounds would you expect to react with (a) sodium metal and (b) sodium hydroxide solution? Write equations for those that react.

(a) OH

(c) O

(b) CH_2OH

28. Starting with *p*-cresol and ethane, show equations for the synthesis of ethyl-*p*-methylphenyl ether (p-$CH_3C_6H_4OCH_2CH_3$).

29. What two hazards may be present when working with low-molar-mass ethers?

30. Arrange the following substances in order of increasing solubility in water:
(a) $CH_3CH_2{-}O{-}CH_2CH_2CH_3$
(b) $CH_3CH(OH)CH_2CH_2CH_3$
(c) $CH_3CH_2CH_2CH_2CH_3$
(d) $CH_3CH(OH)CH(OH)CH_2CH_3$

31. Arrange these three compounds in order of increasing acidity:

C_6H_5—CH_2OH (benzyl alcohol)   OH-substituted benzene with CH_3 (m-cresol) H_2O

32. There are six isomeric saturated ethers that have the formula $C_5H_{12}O$. Write the structural formula and name for each of these ethers.

33. Write the balanced chemical equation for the complete combustion of diethyl ether,

$CH_3CH_2—O—CH_2CH_3$

34. Write the formulas of all the possible combinations of RONa and RCl for making each of these ethers by the Williamson synthesis:
(a) $CH_3CH_2—O—CH_3$
(b) $CH_3CH_2CH_2—O—CH_2CH_2CH_3$
(c) $C_6H_5—CH_2—O—CH_2CH_3$
(d) $HC(CH_3)_2—O—CH_2CH_2CH_3$

35. Write equations for the following transformations. Name each of the products.

(a) $C_6H_5—CH_2OH \longrightarrow C_6H_5—CH_2—O—CH_2CH_3$

(b) cyclopentyl—Br $\longrightarrow$ cyclopentyl—O—cyclopentyl

36. Give a simple chemical test that will distinguish between the compounds in each of the following pairs:
(a) Ethanol and dimethyl ether
(b) 1-Pentanol and 1-pentene
(c) *p*-Cresol and methyl phenyl ether

37. Complete the following equations giving only the major organic products:
(a) $CH_3CH_2OH + Na \longrightarrow$

(b) $CH_3CH_2CH_2CH_2OH \xrightarrow[H_2SO_4]{K_2Cr_2O_7}$

(c) $CH_3CH_2OCH_2CH_3 + Na \longrightarrow$

(d) cyclopentyl—$CH{=}CH_2 \xrightarrow{H_2SO_4/H_2O}$

(e) $CH_3CH_2CH_2OH + NaOH \longrightarrow$

38. Which of the following statements are correct? Rewrite the incorrect statements to make them correct.
(a) Another name for isopropyl alcohol is 2-propanol.
(b) Ethanol and dimethyl ether are isomers.
(c) Alcohols and phenols are more acidic than water.
(d) Sodium ethoxide can be prepared by reacting ethyl alcohol and sodium hydroxide solution.
(e) Methyl alcohol is a very poisonous substance that can lead to blindness if ingested.
(f) Tertiary alcohols are easier to oxidize than primary alcohols.
(g) A correct name for $CH_3CH_2CH(OH)CH_3$ is *sec*-butyl alcohol.
(h) $(CH_3)_3CCH_2OH$ is a primary alcohol.
(i) When a secondary alcohol is oxidized, a ketone is formed.
(j) Alcohols have higher boiling points than ethers with comparable molecular masses due to hydrogen bonding between the alcohol molecules.
(k) The product formed when a molecule of water is split out between an alcohol and a carboxylic acid is called an ether.
(l) When 1-butene is reacted with dilute H_2SO_4, the alcohol formed is 1-butanol.
(m) Ethanol used for industrial purposes and rendered unfit for use in beverages is said to be denatured.
(n) The common name for 1,2,3-propanetriol is ethylene glycol.
(o) Although ethyl alcohol is used in beverages, it is still classified physiologically as a depressant and a poison.
(p) Cyclohexanol is a primary alcohol.
(q) Dihydroxy alcohols are more soluble in water than monohydroxy alcohols.
(r) Aldehydes and ketones may be prepared by the oxidation of primary alcohols.
(s) Thiols have a higher molar mass and lower boiling point than alcohols containing an equal number of carbons.
(t) Coenzyme A is an alcohol that has a central role in metabolism.

5 Aldehydes and Ketones

◀ **CHAPTER OPENING PHOTO: Many plastic products begin with molecules known as aldehydes.**

Many organic molecules contain a carbon atom that is connected to oxygen with a double bond. This particular grouping of atoms is particularly reactive and is present in both aldehydes and ketones. Formaldehyde is by far the most common aldehyde molecule. It finds commercial uses as a preservative for animal specimens and in the formation of formaldehyde polymers. These polymers are often used to form plastics, such as Formica and Melmac, and as adhesives in the manufacture of plywood and fiberboard. Other aldehydes are found in nature as spices.

Acetone is the simplest and most common ketone in our lives. It is used in nail polish remover, paints, varnishes, and resins. Acetone is also produced in the body during lipid metabolism. It generally is metabolized, but in diabetic patients more is formed than can be oxidized. The presence of acetone in a urine sample or on the breath is a positive indicator of diabetes. An understanding of aldehydes and ketones forms the basis for a discussion of many of the important organic and biochemical reactions.

5.1 STRUCTURE OF ALDEHYDES AND KETONES

carbonyl group

aldehydes

ketones

The aldehydes and ketones are closely related classes of compounds. Their structures contain the **carbonyl group**, $>C{=}O$, a carbon–oxygen double bond. **Aldehydes** have at least one hydrogen atom bonded to the carbonyl group, whereas **ketones** have only alkyl or aryl (aromatic, denoted Ar) groups bonded to the carbonyl group.

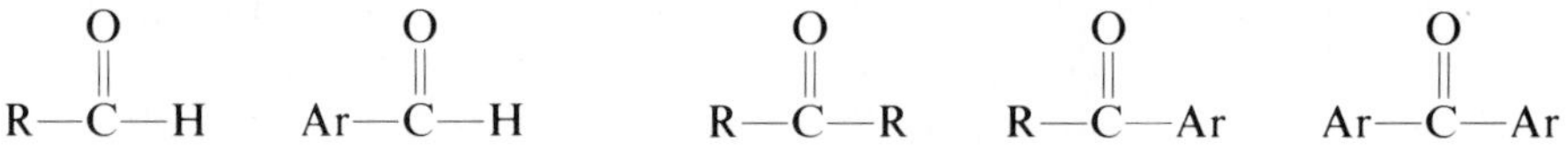

$$\underbrace{R-\overset{\overset{\large O}{\|}}{C}-H \qquad Ar-\overset{\overset{\large O}{\|}}{C}-H}_{\text{Aldehydes}} \qquad \underbrace{R-\overset{\overset{\large O}{\|}}{C}-R \qquad R-\overset{\overset{\large O}{\|}}{C}-Ar \qquad Ar-\overset{\overset{\large O}{\|}}{C}-Ar}_{\text{Ketones}}$$

In a linear expression, the aldehyde group is often written as CHO. For example,

$$CH_3CHO \qquad \text{is equivalent to} \qquad CH_3\overset{\overset{\large O}{\|}}{C}-H$$

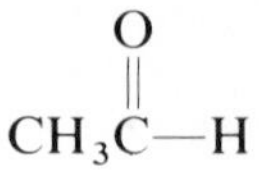

In the linear expression of a ketone, the carbonyl group is written as CO; for example,

$$CH_3COCH_3 \quad \text{is equivalent to} \quad CH_3\overset{\overset{\displaystyle O}{\|}}{C}CH_3$$

The general formula for the saturated homologous series of aldehydes and ketones is $C_nH_{2n}O$.

5.2 Naming Aldehydes and Ketones

Aldehydes

The IUPAC names of aliphatic aldehydes are obtained by dropping the final *e* and adding *al* to the name of the parent hydrocarbon (that is, the longest carbon–carbon chain carrying the —CHO group). The aldehyde carbon is always at the beginning of the carbon chain, is understood to be carbon number 1, and does not need to be numbered. The first member of the homologous series, $H_2C{=}O$, is methanal. The name *methanal* is derived from the hydrocarbon methane, which contains one carbon atom. The second member of the series is ethanal; the third member of the series is propanal; and so on.

CH_4	$H{-}\overset{\overset{\displaystyle O}{\|}}{C}{-}H$	CH_3CH_3	$CH_3\overset{\overset{\displaystyle O}{\|}}{C}{-}H$
Methane	Methanal (from methan~~e~~ + *al*)	Ethane	Ethanal (from ethan~~e~~ + *al*)

The longest carbon chain containing the aldehyde group is the parent compound. Other groups attached to this chain are numbered and named as we have done previously. For example,

$$CH_3CH_2\overset{\overset{\displaystyle CH_3}{|}}{C}HCH_2CH_2\overset{\overset{\displaystyle O}{\|}}{C}{-}H$$

4-Methylhexanal

Common names for some aldehydes are widely used. The common names for the aliphatic aldehydes are derived from the common names of the carboxylic acids (see Table 6.1). The *-ic acid* or *-oic acid* ending of the acid name is dropped and is replaced with the suffix *-aldehyde*. Thus, the name of the one-carbon acid, formic acid, becomes formaldehyde for the one-carbon aldehyde.

$H{-}\overset{\overset{\displaystyle O}{\|}}{C}{-}OH$	$H{-}\overset{\overset{\displaystyle O}{\|}}{C}{-}H$
Formic acid	Formaldehyde

Naming aldehydes by both methods is illustrated in Table 5.1.

TABLE 5.1 IUPAC and Common Names of Selected Aldehydes

Formula	IUPAC name	Common name
$H-\overset{O}{\overset{\|}{C}}-H$	Methanal	Formaldehyde
$CH_3\overset{O}{\overset{\|}{C}}-H$	Ethanal	Acetaldehyde
$CH_3CH_2\overset{O}{\overset{\|}{C}}-H$	Propanal	Propionaldehyde
$CH_3CH_2CH_2\overset{O}{\overset{\|}{C}}-H$	Butanal	Butyraldehyde
$CH_3\underset{CH_3}{\underset{\|}{C}}H\overset{O}{\overset{\|}{C}}-H$	2-Methylpropanal	Isobutyraldehyde

Aromatic aldehydes contain an aldehyde group bonded to an aromatic ring. They are also named after the corresponding carboxylic acids. Thus the name benzaldehyde is derived from benzoic acid, and the name *p*-tolualdehyde is from *p*-toluic acid.

$C_6H_5-\overset{O}{\overset{\|}{C}}-H$ Benzaldehyde

$C_6H_5-\overset{O}{\overset{\|}{C}}-OH$ Benzoic acid

$CH_3-C_6H_4-\overset{O}{\overset{\|}{C}}-H$ *p*-Tolualdehyde

$CH_3-C_6H_4-COOH$ *p*-Toluic acid

In dialdehydes the suffix *dial* is added to the corresponding hydrocarbon name; for example,

$$H-\overset{O}{\overset{\|}{C}}CH_2CH_2\overset{O}{\overset{\|}{C}}-H$$

is named butanedial.

Ketones

The IUPAC name of a ketone is derived from the name of the alkane corresponding to the longest carbon chain that contains the ketone carbonyl group.

The parent name is formed by changing the *e* ending of the alkane to *one*. If the chain is longer than four carbons, it is numbered so that the carbonyl carbon has the smallest number possible, and this number is prefixed to the name of the ketone. Other groups bonded to the parent chain are named and numbered as previously indicated for hydrocarbons and alcohols. See the following examples:

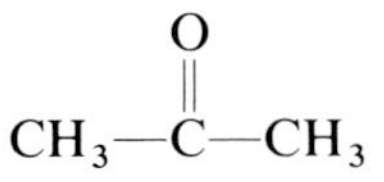

$$CH_3-\overset{\overset{\displaystyle O}{\|}}{C}-CH_3$$

Propanone

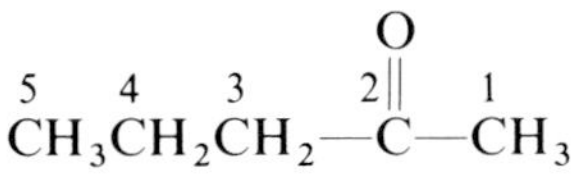

$$\overset{5}{C}H_3\overset{4}{C}H_2\overset{3}{C}H_2-\overset{\overset{\displaystyle O}{\|}}{\overset{2}{C}}-\overset{1}{C}H_3$$

2-Pentanone

$$\overset{1}{C}H_3\overset{2}{C}H_2-\overset{\overset{\displaystyle O}{\|}}{\overset{3}{C}}-\underset{\underset{\displaystyle CH_3}{|}}{\overset{4}{C}H}\overset{5}{C}H_2\overset{6}{C}H_3$$

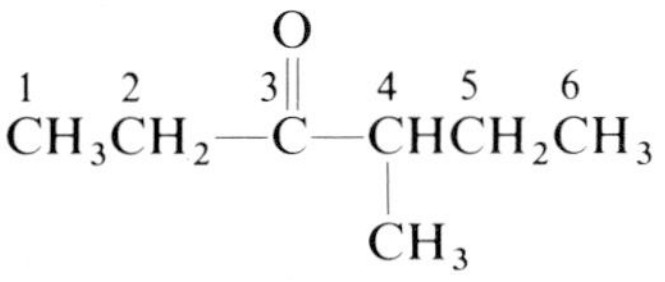

4-Methyl-3-hexanone

Note that in 4-methyl-3-hexanone the carbon chain is numbered from left to right to give the ketone group the lowest possible number.

An alternate non-IUPAC method commonly used to name simple ketones is to list the names of the alkyl or aromatic groups attached to the carbonyl carbon together with the word *ketone*. Thus, butanone ($CH_3COCH_2CH_3$) is methyl ethyl ketone:

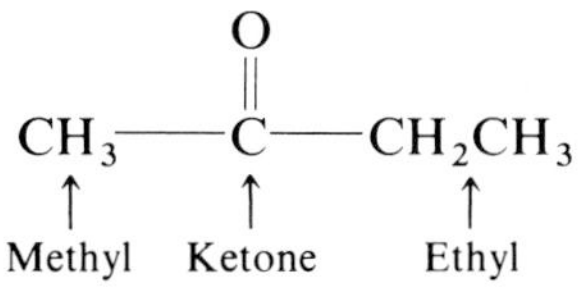

$$\underset{\underset{\text{Methyl}}{\uparrow}}{CH_3}-\underset{\underset{\text{Ketone}}{\uparrow}}{\overset{\overset{\displaystyle O}{\|}}{C}}-\underset{\underset{\text{Ethyl}}{\uparrow}}{CH_2CH_3}$$

Two of the most widely used ketones have special common names: Propanone is called acetone, and butanone is known as methyl ethyl ketone, or MEK.

Aromatic ketones are named in a fashion similar to that for aliphatic ketones and often have special names as well.

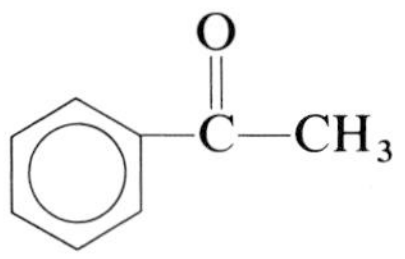

$$C_6H_5-\overset{\overset{\displaystyle O}{\|}}{C}-CH_3$$

Methyl phenyl ketone
Acetophenone
1-Phenylethanone

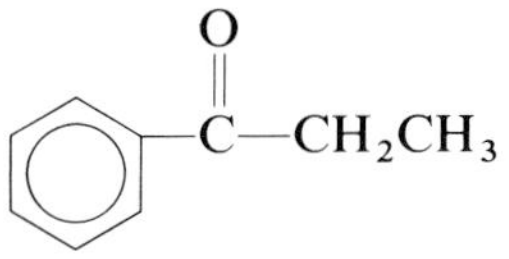

$$C_6H_5-\overset{\overset{\displaystyle O}{\|}}{C}-CH_2CH_3$$

Ethyl phenyl ketone
Propiophenone
1-Phenylpropanone

EXAMPLE 5.1

Write the formulas and the names for the straight-chain five- and six-carbon aldehydes.

SOLUTION

The IUPAC names are based on the five- and six-carbon alkanes. Drop the *e* of the alkane name and add the suffix *al*. Pentane (C_5) becomes pentanal and hexane (C_6) becomes hexanal. (The aldehyde group does not need to be renumbered; it is understood to be on carbon 1.) The common names are derived from valeric acid and caproic acid, respectively.

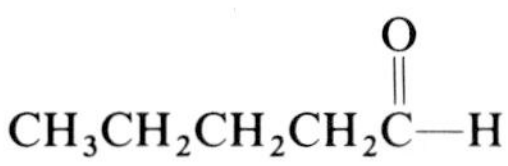

$$CH_3CH_2CH_2CH_2\overset{\overset{\displaystyle O}{\|}}{C}-H$$

Pentanal (Valeraldehyde)

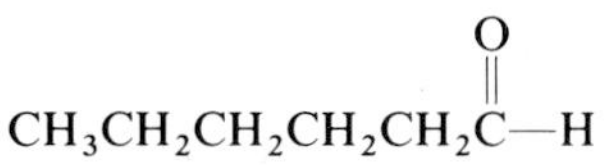

$$CH_3CH_2CH_2CH_2CH_2\overset{\overset{\displaystyle O}{\|}}{C}-H$$

Hexanal (Caproaldehyde)

EXAMPLE 5.2

Give two names for each of the following ketones:

$$\text{(a) } CH_3CH_2\overset{\overset{\displaystyle O}{\|}}{C}CH_2\underset{}{\overset{\overset{\displaystyle CH_3}{|}}{C}}HCH_3 \qquad \text{(b) } CH_3CH_2CH_2\overset{\overset{\displaystyle O}{\|}}{C}-C_6H_5$$

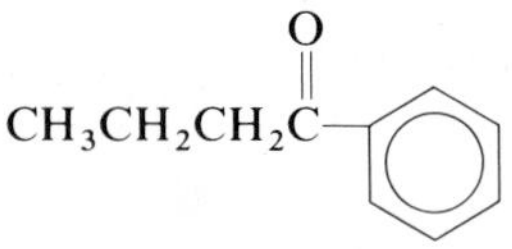

SOLUTION

(a) The parent carbon chain that contains the carbonyl group has six carbons. Number this chain from the end nearer to the carbonyl group. The ketone group is on carbon 3, and a methyl group is on carbon 5. The six-carbon alkane is hexane. Drop the *e* from hexane and add *one* to give the parent name, hexanone. Prefix the name hexanone with a 3- to locate the ketone group and with 5-methyl- to locate the methyl group. The name is 5-methyl-3-hexanone. The common name is ethyl isobutyl ketone since the C═O has an ethyl group and an isobutyl group bonded to it.

(b) The longest aliphatic chain has four carbons. The parent ketone name is butanone, derived by dropping the *e* of butane and adding *one*. The butanone has a phenyl group attached to carbon 1. The IUPAC name is therefore 1-phenyl-1-butanone. The common name for this compound is phenyl *n*-propyl ketone, since the C═O group has a phenyl and an *n*-propyl group bonded to it.

PRACTICE Write structures for the following carbonyl compounds:

(a) 4-Bromo-5-hydrohexanal (c) 3-Buten-2-one
(b) Phenylethanal (d) Diphenylmethanone (diphenyl ketone)

Answers:

$$\text{(a) } CH_3\overset{\overset{\displaystyle OH}{|}}{C}H\underset{\underset{\displaystyle Br}{|}}{C}HCH_2CH_2\overset{\overset{\displaystyle O}{\|}}{C}-H \qquad \text{(c) } CH_3\overset{\overset{\displaystyle O}{\|}}{C}CH{=}CH_2$$

$$\text{(b) } C_6H_5-CH_2\overset{\overset{\displaystyle O}{\|}}{C}-H \qquad \text{(d) } C_6H_5-\overset{\overset{\displaystyle O}{\|}}{C}-C_6H_5$$

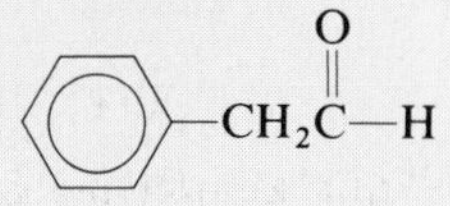

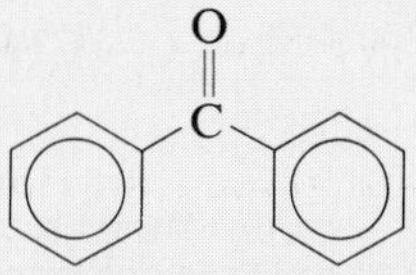

PRACTICE Name each of the following compounds using the IUPAC system:

$$\text{(a) cyclohexane ring}{=}O \qquad \text{(c) } CH_3\underset{\underset{\displaystyle CH_3}{|}}{C}HCH_2\overset{\overset{\displaystyle O}{\|}}{C}-H$$

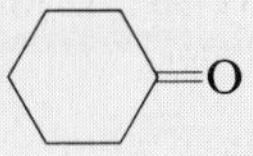

$$\text{(b) } ClCH_2CH_2\overset{\overset{\displaystyle O}{\|}}{C}-CH_3 \qquad \text{(d) } \underset{\underset{\displaystyle C_6H_5}{|}}{C}H{=}CH-\overset{\overset{\displaystyle O}{\|}}{C}-H$$

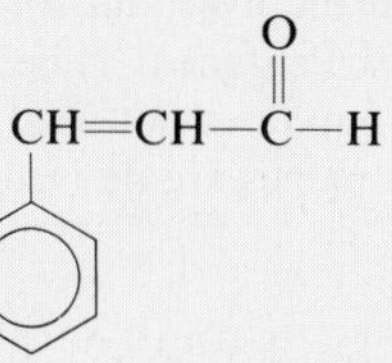

Answers: (a) Cyclohexanone (c) 3-Methylbutanal
(b) 4-Chloro-2-butanone (d) 3-Phenyl-2-propenal

5.3 Bonding and Physical Properties

The carbon atom of the carbonyl group is sp^2 hybridized and is joined to three other atoms by sigma bonds. The fourth bond is made by overlapping *p* electrons of carbon and oxygen to form a pi bond between the carbon and oxygen atoms.

Because the oxygen atom is considerably more electronegative than carbon, the carbonyl group is polar, with the electrons shifted toward the oxygen atom. This makes the oxygen atom partially negative (δ^-) and leaves the carbon atom partially positive (δ^+). Many of the chemical reactions of aldehydes and ketones are due to this polarity.

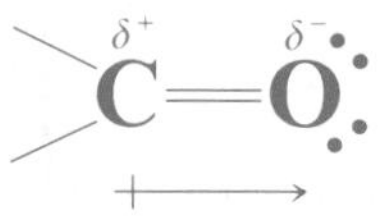

$$\overset{\delta^+}{C}=\overset{\delta^-}{\ddot{O}}\!:$$

Polarity

Unlike alcohols, aldehydes and ketones cannot interact with themselves through hydrogen bonding, because there is no hydrogen atom attached to the oxygen atom of the carbonyl group. Aldehydes and ketones, therefore, have lower boiling points than alcohols of comparable molar mass (Table 5.2).

Low molar mass aldehydes and ketones are soluble in water, but for five or more carbons, the solubility decreases markedly. Ketones are very efficient organic solvents.

The lower molar mass aldehydes have a penetrating, disagreeable odor and are partially responsible for the taste of some rancid and stale foods. As the molar mass increases, the odor of both aldehydes and ketones, especially the aromatic ones, becomes more fragrant. Some are even used in flavorings and perfumes. A few of these and other selected aldehydes and ketones are shown in Figure 5.1.

Table 5.2 Boiling Points of Selected Aldehydes and Ketones and Corresponding Alcohols

Name	Molar mass	Boiling point (°C)
1-Propanol	60	97
Propanal	58	49
Propanone	58	56
1-Butanol	74	118
Butanal	72	76
Butanone	72	80
1-Pentanol	86	138
Pentanal	84	103
2-Pentanone	84	102

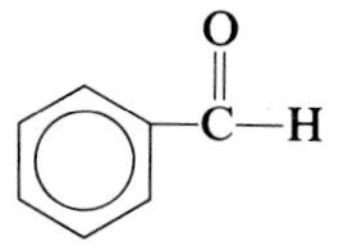

Benzaldehyde
(oil of bitter almonds)

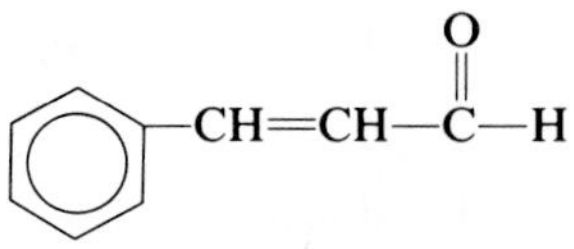

Cinnamaldehyde
(oil of cinnamon)

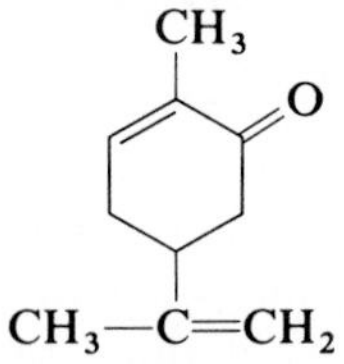

Carvone
(chief component of spearmint oil)

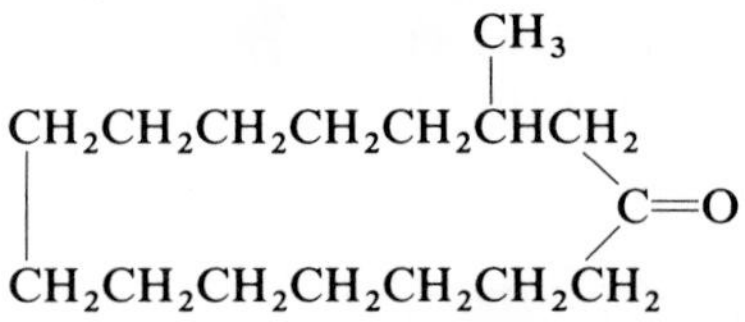

Muscone
(gland of male musk deer, used in perfume)

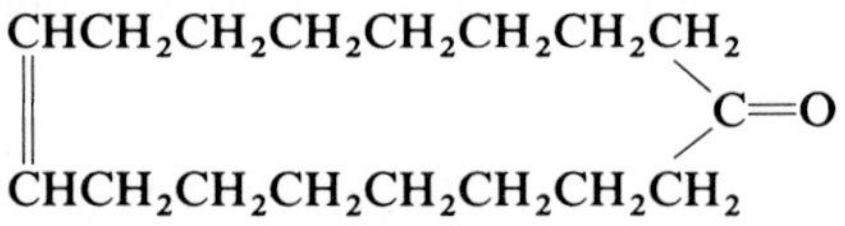

Civetone
(secretion of the civet cat, used in perfume)

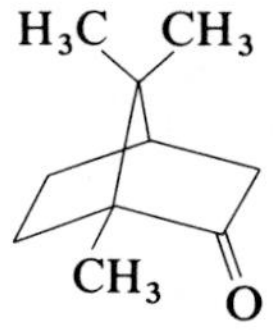

Camphor
(from the camphor tree)

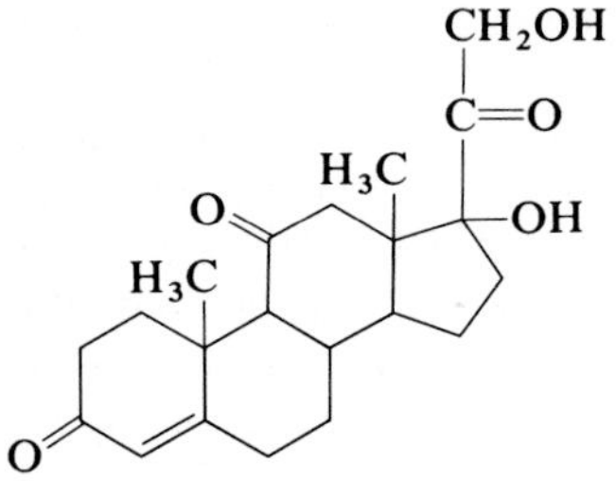

Cortisone
(hormone; regulation of carbohydrate and protein metabolism; used to reduce inflammation)

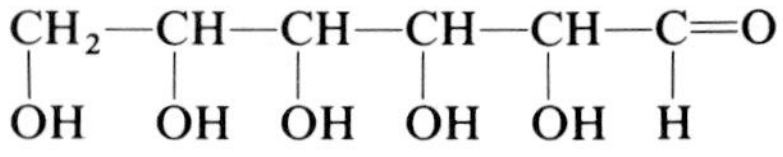

Glucose
(sugar)

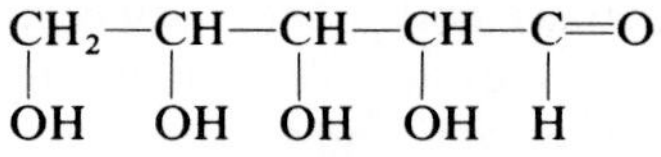

Ribose
(sugar)

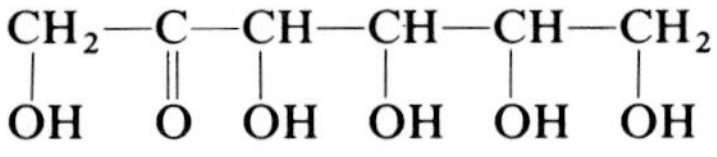

Fructose
(sugar)

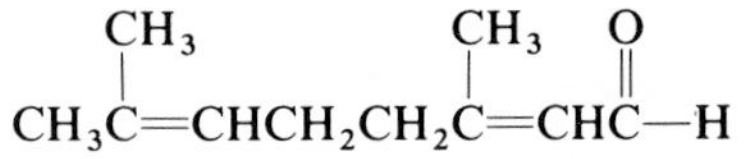

Citral
(oil of lemon)

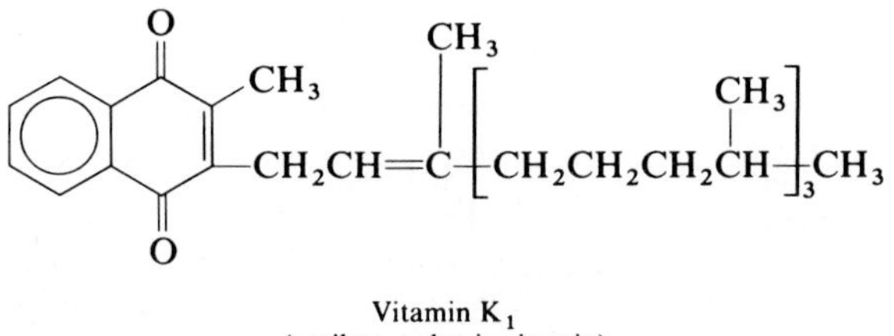

Vitamin K_1
(antihemorrhagic vitamin)

▲
FIGURE 5.1
Selected naturally occurring aldehydes and ketones.

5.4 Chemical Properties of Aldehydes and Ketones

The carbonyl group undergoes a great variety of reactions. Although there are differences, aldehydes and ketones undergo many similar reactions. However, ketones are generally less reactive than aldehydes. Some typical reactions follow.

Oxidation

Aldehydes are easily oxidized to carboxylic acids by a variety of oxidizing agents, including (under some conditions) oxygen of the air. Oxidation is the reaction in which aldehydes differ most from ketones. In fact, aldehydes and ketones may be separated into classes by their relative susceptibilities to oxidation. Aldehydes are easily oxidized to carboxylic acids by $K_2Cr_2O_7 + H_2SO_4$ and by mild oxidizing agents such as Ag^+ and Cu^{2+} ions; ketones are unaffected by such reagents. Ketones can be oxidized under drastic conditions—for example, by treatment with hot potassium permanganate solution. However, under these conditions carbon–carbon bonds are broken, and a variety of products are formed. Equations for the oxidation of aldehydes by dichromate are

$$3\,R\overset{\overset{\displaystyle O}{\|}}{C}\!-\!H + Cr_2O_7^{2-} + 8\,H^+ \longrightarrow 3\,\underset{\text{Carboxylic acid}}{R\overset{\overset{\displaystyle O}{\|}}{C}\!-\!OH} + 2\,Cr^{3+} + 4\,H_2O$$

$$3\,CH_3\overset{\overset{\displaystyle O}{\|}}{C}\!-\!H + Cr_2O_7^{2-} + 8\,H^+ \longrightarrow 3\,\underset{\text{Acetic acid}}{CH_3\overset{\overset{\displaystyle O}{\|}}{C}\!-\!OH} + 2\,Cr^{3+} + 4\,H_2O$$

Tollens test

The **Tollens test** (silver-mirror test) for aldehydes is based on the ability of silver ions to oxidize aldehydes. The Ag^+ ions are thereby reduced to metallic silver. In practice a little of the suspected aldehyde is added to a solution of silver nitrate and ammonia in a clean test tube. The appearance of a silver mirror on the inner wall of the tube is a positive test for the aldehyde group. The abbreviated equation is

$$R\overset{\overset{\displaystyle O}{\|}}{C}\!-\!H + 2\,Ag^+ \xrightarrow[H_2O]{NH_3} R\overset{\overset{\displaystyle O}{\|}}{C}\!-\!O^-\,NH_4^+ + 2\,Ag(s) \qquad \text{(general reaction)}$$

$$CH_3\overset{\overset{\displaystyle O}{\|}}{C}\!-\!H + 2\,Ag^+ \xrightarrow[H_2O]{NH_3} CH_3COO^-\,NH_4^+ + 2\,Ag(s)$$

Fehling and Benedict tests

Fehling's and Benedict's solutions contain Cu^{2+} ions in an alkaline medium. In the **Fehling and the Benedict tests**, the aldehyde group is oxidized to an acid by Cu^{2+} ions. The blue Cu^{2+} ions are reduced and form brick-red copper(I) oxide (Cu_2O), which precipitates during the reaction. These tests can be used for detecting carbohydrates that have an available aldehyde group. The abbreviated equation is

$$\underset{}{\mathrm{R\overset{\overset{\large O}{\|}}{C}{-}H}} + \underset{\text{(blue)}}{2\,Cu^{2+}} \xrightarrow[H_2O]{NaOH} RCOO^-\,Na^+ + \underset{\text{(brick-red)}}{Cu_2O(s)}$$

Most ketones do not give a positive test with Tollens', Fehling's, or Benedict's solutions. These tests are used to distinguish between aldehydes and ketones.

$$\mathrm{R{-}\overset{\overset{\large O}{\|}}{C}{-}R} + Ag^+ \xrightarrow[H_2O]{NH_3} \text{No reaction}$$

$$\mathrm{R{-}\overset{\overset{\large O}{\|}}{C}{-}R} + Cu^{2+} \xrightarrow[H_2O]{OH^-} \text{No reaction}$$

Aldehydes and ketones are highly combustible, yielding carbon dioxide and water when completely burned. Their vapors, like those of nearly all volatile organic substances, form explosive mixtures with air. Adequate safety precautions must be taken to guard against fire and explosions when working with aldehydes and ketones or other volatile organic compounds, especially hydrocarbons, alcohols, and ethers.

The oxidation of aldehydes is a very important reaction in biochemistry. When our cells "burn" carbohydrates, they take advantage of the aldehyde reactivity. The aldehyde group is oxidized to a carboxylic acid and is eventually converted to carbon dioxide, which is then exhaled. This stepwise oxidation provides some of the energy necessary to sustain life.

Reduction

Aldehydes and ketones are easily reduced to alcohols, either by elemental hydrogen in the presence of a catalyst or by chemical reducing agents such as lithium aluminum hydride ($LiAlH_4$) or sodium borohydride ($NaBH_4$). Aldehydes yield primary alcohols; ketones yield secondary alcohols:

$$\mathrm{R{-}\overset{\overset{\large O}{\|}}{C}{-}H} \xrightarrow[\Delta]{H_2/Ni} \underset{1^\circ\ \text{alcohol}}{RCH_2OH} \qquad \text{(general reaction)}$$

$$\mathrm{R{-}\overset{\overset{\large O}{\|}}{C}{-}R} \xrightarrow[\Delta]{H_2/Ni} \underset{2^\circ\ \text{alcohol}}{\mathrm{R{-}\overset{\overset{\large OH}{|}}{C}H{-}R}} \qquad \text{(general reaction)}$$

$$\mathrm{CH_3\overset{\overset{\large O}{\|}}{C}{-}H} \xrightarrow[\Delta]{H_2/Ni} CH_3CH_2OH$$

$$\mathrm{CH_3\overset{\overset{\displaystyle O}{\|}}{C}CH_3} \xrightarrow[\Delta]{H_2/Ni} \mathrm{CH_3\overset{\overset{\displaystyle OH}{|}}{C}HCH_3}$$

Addition Reactions

Addition of Alcohols Compounds derived from aldehydes and ketones that contain an alkoxy and a hydroxy group on the same carbon atom are known as **hemiacetals** and **hemiketals**. In a like manner, compounds that have two alkoxy groups on the same carbon atom are known as **acetals** and **ketals**.

hemiacetal

hemiketal

acetal

ketal

R(H)C(OH)(OR′)	R(R)C(OH)(OR′)	R(H)C(OR′)(OR′)	R(R)C(OR′)(OR′)
Hemiacetal	Hemiketal	Acetal	Ketal

Most open-chain hemiacetals and hemiketals are so unstable that they cannot be isolated. On the other hand, acetals and ketals are stable in alkaline solutions but are unstable in acid solutions, in which they are hydrolyzed back to the original aldehyde or ketone.

In the reactions below we show only aldehydes in the equations, but keep in mind that ketones behave in a similar fashion, although they are not as reactive.

Aldehydes react with alcohols in the presence of a trace of acid to form hemiacetals:

$$\underset{\text{Propanal}}{\mathrm{CH_3CH_2\overset{\overset{\displaystyle O}{\|}}{C}{-}H}} + \underset{\text{Methanol}}{\mathrm{CH_3OH}} \overset{H^+}{\rightleftharpoons} \mathrm{CH_3CH_2CH(OH)(OCH_3)}$$

1-Methoxy-1-propanol
(Propionaldehyde methyl hemiacetal)

In the presence of excess alcohol and a strong acid such as dry HCl, aldehydes or hemiacetals react with a second molecule of the alcohol to give an acetal:

$$\mathrm{CH_3CH_2CH(OH)(OCH_3)} + \mathrm{CH_3OH} \overset{\text{Dry HCl}}{\rightleftharpoons} \mathrm{CH_3CH_2CH(OCH_3)(OCH_3)} + \mathrm{H_2O}$$

1,1-Dimethoxypropane
(Propionaldehyde dimethyl acetal)

A hemiacetal has both an alcohol and an ether group attached to the aldehyde carbon. An acetal has two ether groups attached to the aldehyde carbon.

If the alcohol and carbonyl groups are within the same molecule, the result is the formation of a cyclic hemiacetal (or hemiketal). This *intramolecular* cyclization is particularly significant in carbohydrate chemistry during the study of monosaccharides (Chapter 10).

$$\text{5-Hydroxypentanal (HOCH}_2\text{CH}_2\text{CH}_2\text{CH}_2\text{CHO)} \underset{}{\overset{H^+}{\rightleftarrows}} \text{Stable hemiacetal (cyclic: CH}_2\text{—O—C(OH)(H)—CH}_2\text{—CH}_2\text{—CH}_2\text{)}$$

5-Hydroxypentanal Stable hemiacetal

cyanohydrin

Addition of Hydrogen Cyanide The addition of hydrogen cyanide, HCN, to aldehydes and ketones forms a class of compounds known as cyanohydrins. **Cyanohydrins** have a cyano (—CN) group and a hydroxyl group on the same carbon atom. The reaction is catalyzed by a small amount of base:

$$CH_3\overset{O}{\overset{\|}{C}}-H + HCN \xrightarrow{OH^-} CH_3\overset{OH}{\overset{|}{C}}HCN$$

Acetaldehyde Acetaldehyde cyanohydrin

$$CH_3\underset{O}{\underset{\|}{C}}CH_3 + HCN \xrightarrow{OH^-} CH_3\overset{CH_3}{\overset{|}{\underset{OH}{\underset{|}{C}}}}-CN$$

Acetone Acetone cyanohydrin

In the cyanohydrin reaction, the more positive H atom of HCN adds to the oxygen of the carbonyl group, and the —CN group adds to the carbon atom of the carbonyl group. In the aldehyde addition, the length of the carbon chain is increased by one carbon. The ketone addition product also contains an additional carbon atom.

Cyanohydrins are useful intermediates for the synthesis of several important compounds. For example, the hydrolyses of cyanohydrins produce α-hydroxy acids:

$$CH_3\underset{OH}{\underset{|}{C}}H-CN + H_2O \xrightarrow{H^+} CH_3\underset{OH}{\underset{|}{C}}HCOOH + NH_4^+$$

Lactic acid

Acetaldehyde can also be converted into other important biochemical compounds such as the amino acid alanine:

$$CH_3-\overset{O}{\overset{\|}{C}}-H \xrightarrow{HCN} CH_3-\overset{OH}{\overset{|}{\underset{H}{\underset{|}{C}}}}-CN \xrightarrow{NH_3} CH_3-\overset{NH_2}{\overset{|}{\underset{H}{\underset{|}{C}}}}-CN \xrightarrow[H^+]{H_2O} CH_3-\overset{H_2N}{\overset{|}{\underset{H}{\underset{|}{C}}}}-\overset{O}{\overset{\|}{C}}-OH$$

Alanine

Some commercial reactions also involve the use of cyanohydrins. Acetone cyanohydrin can be converted to methyl methacrylate when refluxed with methanol and a strong acid. The methyl methacrylate can then be polymerized to Lucite or Plexiglas, both transparent plastics. See Chapter 8.

▲ **A sculpture formed from Lucite.**

Aldol Condensation (Self-addition) In a carbonyl compound the carbon atoms are labeled alpha (α), beta (β), gamma (γ), delta (δ), and so on, according to their positions with respect to the carbonyl group. The alpha carbon is adjacent to the carbonyl carbon, the beta carbon is next, the gamma carbon is third, and so forth. The hydrogens attached to the alpha-carbon atom are therefore called alpha hydrogens, and so on, as shown below:

$$\overset{\delta}{-C}-\overset{\gamma}{C}-\overset{\beta}{\underset{|}{C}}-\overset{\alpha}{\underset{|}{C}}-C{=}O$$

Beta H atom → H H ← Alpha H atom

The hydrogen atoms attached to the alpha carbon atom have the unique ability to be more easily released as protons than other hydrogens within the molecule.

An aldehyde or ketone that contains α-hydrogens may add to itself or to another α-hydrogen containing aldehyde or ketone. The product of this reaction contains both a carbonyl group and an alcohol group within the same molecule. The reaction is known as an **aldol condensation** and is catalyzed by dilute base. Remember that a *condensation* reaction is one in which two smaller molecules combine to form a larger molecule, usually with the loss of a small molecule in the process. The aldol condensation is very similar to the other carbonyl addition reactions. An α-hydrogen adds to the carbonyl oxygen, and the remainder of the molecule adds to the carbonyl carbon.

aldol condensation

$$CH_3-\overset{\overset{O}{\|}}{C}-H + H-\underset{H}{\overset{H}{C}}-\overset{\overset{O}{\|}}{C}-H \xrightarrow{\text{Dilute NaOH}} CH_3\overset{OH}{\overset{|}{C}}HCH_2\overset{O}{\overset{\|}{C}}-H$$

(α H)

Aldol

(3-Hydroxybutanal)

Acetone also undergoes the aldol condensation:

$$CH_3\overset{\overset{O}{\|}}{C}CH_3 + H-CH_2\overset{\overset{O}{\|}}{C}CH_3 \xrightarrow[\text{NaOH}]{\text{Dilute}} CH_3\underset{CH_3}{\overset{OH}{C}}-CH_2\overset{\overset{O}{\|}}{C}CH_3$$

Acetone | Acetone | Diacetone alcohol (4-Hydroxy-4-methyl-2-pentanone)

In the foregoing reaction an alpha hydrogen first transfers from one molecule to the oxygen of the other molecule. This breaks the C=O pi bond, leaving a carbon atom of each molecule with three bonds. The two carbon atoms then bond to each other, forming the product, diacetone alcohol.

EXAMPLE 5.3 Write the equation for the aldol condensation of propanal.

SOLUTION First write the structure for propanal and locate the alpha-hydrogen atoms:

$$CH_3CH(H)C(H){=}O \quad (\text{circled H} \longleftarrow \alpha\,H)$$

Now write two propanal molecules and transfer an alpha hydrogen from one molecule to the oxygen of the second molecule. After the pi bond breaks, the two carbon atoms that are bonded to only three other atoms are attached to each other to form the product.

$$CH_3CH_2C(=O){-}H + CH_3CH(H)C(=O){-}H \xrightarrow[\text{NaOH}]{\text{Dilute}} CH_3CH_2C^{+}(OH)H + CH_3C^{-}HC(=O){-}H \longrightarrow CH_3CH_2CH(OH)CH(CH_3)C(=O){-}H$$

3-Hydroxy-2-methylpentanal

PRACTICE Write the equation for the aldol condensation of butanal.

Answer:

$$2\,CH_3CH_2CH_2C(=O){-}H \xrightarrow{\text{dil } OH^-} CH_3CH_2CH_2C(OH)(H){-}CH(CH_2CH_3)C(=O){-}H$$

PRACTICE Write the equation for the aldol condensation of 3-pentanone.

Answer:

$$2\,CH_3CH_2C(=O)CH_2CH_3 \xrightarrow{\text{dil } OH^-} CH_3CH_2C(OH)(CH_2CH_3){-}CH(CH_3)C(=O)CH_2CH_3$$

The aldol condensation reaction is used often by living cells. By means of this reaction, smaller biochemicals can be combined to make larger molecules. For example, most cells can join two three-carbon carbohydrates to make one six-carbon sugar using the aldol condensation. Ultimately, this reaction sequence leads to the formation of glucose (see Chapter 17).

5.5 COMMON ALDEHYDES AND KETONES

Numerous methods have been devised for making aldehydes and ketones. The oxidation of alcohols is a very general method. Special methods are often used for the commercial production of individual aldehydes and ketones.

Formaldehyde (Methanal) This aldehyde is made from methanol by reaction with oxygen (air) in the presence of a silver or copper catalyst:

$$2\,CH_3OH + O_2 \xrightarrow[400^\circ C]{\text{Ag or Cu}} \underset{\substack{\text{Formaldehyde}\\\text{(methanal)}}}{2\,H_2C{=}O} + 2\,H_2O$$

Formaldehyde is a poisonous, irritating gas that is very soluble in water. It is marketed as a 40% aqueous solution called *formalin*. Because formaldehyde is a powerful germicide, it is used in embalming and to preserve biological specimens. Formaldehyde is also used for disinfecting dwellings, ships, and storage houses; for destroying flies; for tanning hides; and as a fungicide for plants and vegetables. But by far the largest use of this chemical is in the manufacture of polymers (Chapter 8). About 2.59×10^9 kg (5.7×10^9 lb) of formaldehyde is manufactured annually in the United States.

Formaldehyde vapors are intensely irritating to the mucous membranes. Ingestion may cause severe abdominal pains, leading to coma and death.

It is of interest that formaldehyde may have had a significant role in chemical evolution. Formaldehyde is believed to have been a component of the primitive atmosphere of the earth. It is theorized that the reactivity of this single-carbon aldehyde enabled it to form more complex organic molecules—molecules that were precursors of the still more complicated substances that today are essential components of every living organism.

Acetaldehyde (Ethanal) Acetaldehyde is a volatile liquid (bp 21°C) with a pungent, irritating odor. It has a general narcotic action and in large doses may cause respiratory paralysis. Its principal use is as an intermediate in the manufacture of other chemicals such as acetic acid, 1-butanol, and paraldehyde.

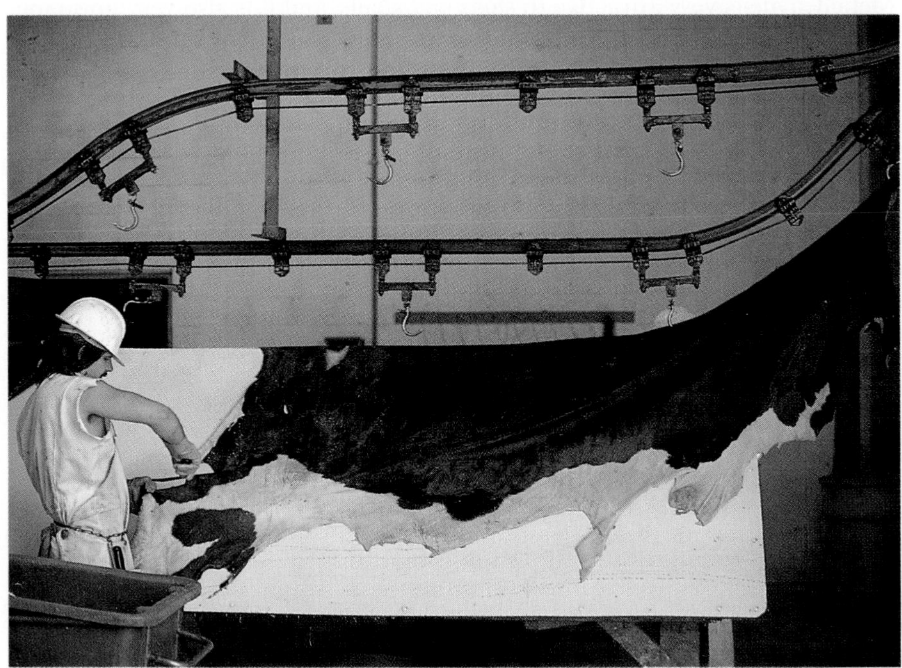

◀ **This Holstein hide is being scraped in preparation for tanning. Formalin can be used during the tanning process to soften and preserve the hide.**

Acetic acid, for example, is made by air oxidation of acetaldehyde:

$$2\,CH_3\overset{\overset{O}{\|}}{C}{-}H + O_2 \xrightarrow[\Delta]{Mn^{2+}} 2\,CH_3\overset{\overset{O}{\|}}{C}{-}OH$$

Acetaldehyde undergoes reactions in which three or four molecules condense or polymerize to form the cyclic compounds paraldehyde and metaldehyde:

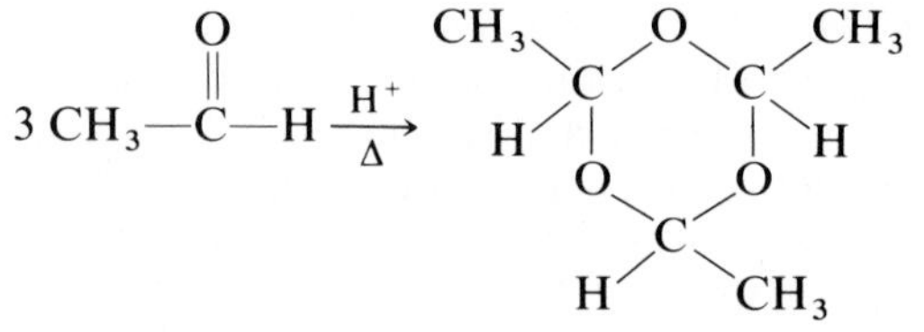

$$3\,CH_3{-}\overset{\overset{O}{\|}}{C}{-}H \xrightarrow[\Delta]{H^+} \text{(cyclic trimer: three } CH(CH_3) \text{ units joined through O)}$$

Paraldehyde
(bp 125°C)

Paraldehyde is used in medical practice as a hypnotic or sleep-inducing drug.

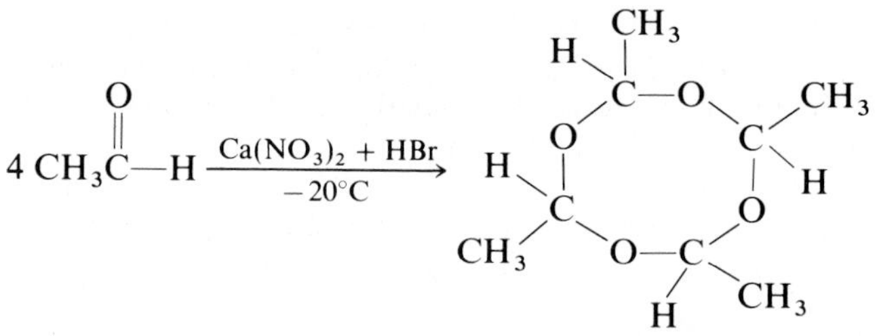

$$4\,CH_3\overset{\overset{O}{\|}}{C}{-}H \xrightarrow[-20^{\circ}C]{Ca(NO_3)_2 + HBr} \text{(cyclic tetramer: four } CH(CH_3) \text{ units joined through O)}$$

Metaldehyde
(mp 246°C)

Metaldehyde is very attractive to slugs and snails, and it is also very poisonous to them. For this reason it is an active ingredient in some pesticides that are sold for lawn and garden use. Metaldehyde is also used as a solid fuel.

Benzaldehyde Benzaldehyde (C_6H_5CHO) is known as *oil of bitter almonds.* It is found in almonds and in the seeds of stone fruits—for example, apricots and peaches. Benzaldehyde is made synthetically and used in the manufacture of artificial flavors. The synthesis begins with the free-radical chlorination of toluene, as shown in the following sequence of reactions:

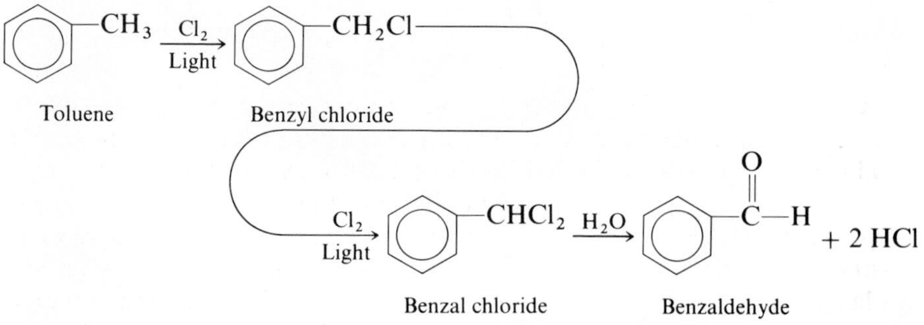

$$C_6H_5{-}CH_3 \xrightarrow[Light]{Cl_2} C_6H_5{-}CH_2Cl \xrightarrow[Light]{Cl_2} C_6H_5{-}CHCl_2 \xrightarrow{H_2O} C_6H_5{-}\overset{\overset{O}{\|}}{C}{-}H + 2\,HCl$$

Toluene — Benzyl chloride — Benzal chloride — Benzaldehyde

(*Note:* $C_6H_5CH_2—$ is called the benzyl group.)

Chemistry in Action

Familiar Aldehydes and Ketones

Aldehydes are most often used commercially in the production of plastics. The common polymers known as Formica, used on counters and in telephones, Melmac, used in plastic tableware, and Bakelite, found in handles on kitchen utensils, are all derived from formaldehyde.

Spices and flavorings are often complex mixtures of ingredients. The characteristic flavor and aroma of many common flavorings and spices result from the presence of aromatic aldehydes. Examples include vanillin, cinnamaldehyde, citral, and benzaldehyde (see Table 5.1).

Higher molar mass ketones are also useful because of their unique aromas. Camphor (Table 5.1) is a moth repellant. Muscone, extracted from the musk glands of the male musk deer, is frequently used to give the musky aroma to perfumes. A tiny amount of these chemicals can be used to produce long-lasting aromas. Perfume manufacturers closely guard the secret of their ingredients to keep their formulations unique and selling well.

In living organisms aldehydes and ketones are found in many different compounds. Sugars are often classified as containing an aldehyde group, as in glucose or ribose, or a ketone group, as in fructose. The compounds known as steroids, belonging to the lipid family, also often contain aldehyde or ketone groups. These lipids may function as hormones as in the case of cortisone.

▲ **Perfumes contain aromas attributable to aldehydes or ketones.**

Cinnamaldehyde, $C_6H_5CH{=}CHCHO$, is the principal substance contributing to the flavor of oil of cinnamon. Like benzaldehyde, it is made synthetically and used in the preparation of artificial flavoring agents.

$$C_6H_5{-}CH{=}CH{-}\overset{\overset{\large O}{\|}}{C}{-}H$$

Cinnamaldehyde

Acetone and Methyl Ethyl Ketone Ketones are widely used organic solvents. Acetone, in particular, is used in very large quantities for this purpose. U.S. production of acetone is about 8.2×10^8 kg (1.8×10^9 lb) annually. It is used as a solvent in the manufacture of drugs, chemicals, and explosives; for removal of paints, varnishes, and fingernail polish; and as a solvent in the plastics industry. Methyl ethyl ketone (MEK) is also widely used as a solvent, especially for lacquers. Both acetone and MEK are made by oxidation (dehydrogenation) of secondary alcohols. Acetone is also a coproduct in the manufacture of phenol (see Section 4.8).

$$\underset{\text{2-Propanol}}{\underset{\displaystyle \text{OH}}{\text{CH}_3\underset{|}{\text{C}}\text{HCH}_3}} \xrightarrow[250\text{–}300^\circ\text{C}]{\text{Cu}} \underset{\text{Acetone (Propanone)}}{\underset{\displaystyle \text{O}}{\text{CH}_3\underset{\|}{\text{C}}\text{CH}_3}} + \text{H}_2$$

$$\underset{\text{2-Butanol}}{\underset{\displaystyle \text{OH}}{\text{CH}_3\text{CH}_2\underset{|}{\text{C}}\text{HCH}_3}} \xrightarrow[250\text{–}300^\circ\text{C}]{\text{Cu}} \underset{\text{Methyl ethyl ketone (2-Butanone)}}{\underset{\displaystyle \text{O}}{\text{CH}_3\text{CH}_2\underset{\|}{\text{C}}\text{CH}_3}} + \text{H}_2$$

Acetone is also formed in the human body during lipid metabolism. Usually it is oxidized to carbon dioxide and water. Normal concentrations of acetone in the body are less than 1 mg/100 mL of blood volume. In patients with diabetes mellitus the concentration of acetone may rise, and it is then excreted in the urine where it can be easily detected. Sometimes the odor of acetone may also be detected on the breath of these patients.

Concepts in Review

1. Recognize aldehydes and ketones from their formulas.
2. Give IUPAC and common names of aldehydes and ketones.
3. Write formulas of aldehydes and ketones when given their names.
4. Understand why aldehydes and ketones have lower boiling points than alcohols.
5. Write equations showing the oxidation of alcohols to aldehydes and ketones.
6. Write the structure of the alcohol formed when an aldehyde or ketone is reduced.
7. Discuss the Tollens, Benedict, and Fehling tests, including the reagents used, evidence of a positive test, and the equations of the reactions that occur in positive tests.
8. Use the Tollens, Benedict, and Fehling tests to distinguish between aldehydes and ketones.
9. Recognize whether an aldehyde or ketone undergoes the aldol condensation.
10. Write equations showing the aldol condensation of aldehydes and ketones.
11. Write equations for the formation and hydrolysis of cyanohydrins.
12. Write equations for the formation and decomposition of hemiacetals, hemiketals, acetals, and ketals.

Equations in Review

Oxidation

$$R-\overset{O}{\overset{\|}{C}}-H \xrightarrow{[O]} R-\overset{O}{\overset{\|}{C}}-OH$$

$$R-\overset{O}{\overset{\|}{C}}-R \xrightarrow{[O]} \text{No reaction}$$

Reduction

$$R-\overset{O}{\overset{\|}{C}}-H \xrightarrow{[H]} R-CH_2-OH$$

$$R-\overset{O}{\overset{\|}{C}}-R \xrightarrow{[H]} R-\underset{OH}{\underset{|}{\overset{H}{\overset{|}{C}}}}-R$$

Addition reactions

Alcohol

$$R-\overset{O}{\overset{\|}{C}}-H + R-OH \longrightarrow R-\underset{OR}{\underset{|}{\overset{OH}{\overset{|}{C}}}}-H$$

$$R-\overset{O}{\overset{\|}{C}}-R + R-OH \longrightarrow R-\underset{OR}{\underset{|}{\overset{OH}{\overset{|}{C}}}}-R$$

Hydrogen cyanide

$$R-\overset{O}{\overset{\|}{C}}-H + HCN \xrightarrow{OH} R-\underset{H}{\underset{|}{\overset{OH}{\overset{|}{C}}}}-CN$$

$$R-\overset{O}{\overset{\|}{C}}-R + HCN \xrightarrow{OH} R-\underset{OH}{\underset{|}{\overset{R}{\overset{|}{C}}}}-CN$$

Aldol condensation

$$2\,R-CH_2-\overset{O}{\overset{\|}{C}}-H \xrightarrow{[\text{dil } OH^-]} R-CH_2-\overset{OH}{\overset{|}{C}H}-\underset{R}{\underset{|}{C}H}-\overset{O}{\overset{\|}{C}}-H$$

EXERCISES

1. Write generalized structures for
   (a) An aldehyde (e) A hemiketal
   (b) A ketone (f) An acetal
   (c) A dialdehyde (g) A ketal
   (d) A hemiacetal (h) A cyanohydrin
2. Name each of these aldehydes:
   (a) $H_2C{=}O$ (two names)
   (b) $CH_3CH_2CH_2C(=O){-}H$ (two names)
   (c) $CH_3CH(CH_3)CH_2C(=O){-}H$ (one name)
   (d) $C_6H_5{-}C(=O){-}H$ (one name)
   (e) $H{-}C(=O)CH_2CH_2C(=O){-}H$ (one name)
   (f) benzene ring bearing $-C(=O){-}H$, with Cl ortho to it and $CH(CH_3)_2$ para (one name)
   (g) $C_6H_5{-}CH{=}CH{-}C(=O){-}H$ (one name)
   (h) $CH_3CH(OH)CH_2C(=O){-}H$ (two names)
   (i) $CH_3(H)C{=}C(H){-}C(=O){-}H$ (one name)
3. Name each of these ketones:
   (a) CH_3COCH_3 (three names)
   (b) $CH_3CH_2COCH_3$ (two names)
   (c) $C_6H_5{-}C(=O){-}CH_2CH_3$ (two names)
   (d) $CH_3C(=O){-}C(CH_3)_2{-}CH_3$ (two names)
   (e) cyclopentanone, $C_5H_8{=}O$ (one name)
   (f) $CH_3C(=O)CH_2CH_2C(=O)CH_3$ (one name)
   (g) $CH_3C(CH_3)(OH){-}CH_2C(=O)CH_3$ (two names)
   (h) $C_6H_5{-}CH_2C(=O)CH_3$ (two names)
4. Write structural formulas for
   (a) 1,3-Dichloropropanone
   (b) Phenylacetaldehyde
   (c) 3-Butenal
   (d) 3-Hydroxypropanal
   (e) Diisopropyl ketone
   (f) 4-Methyl-3-hexanone
   (g) Hexanal
   (h) Cyclohexanone
5. Write structural formulas for propanal and propanone. Judging from these formulas, do you think that aldehydes and ketones are isomeric with each other? Show evidence and substantiate your answer by testing with a four-carbon aldehyde and a four-carbon ketone.
6. Explain, in terms of structure, why aldehydes and ketones have lower boiling points than alcohols of similar molar masses.
7. Which compound in each of the following pairs has the higher boiling point? (Try to answer without consulting tables.)
   (a) 1-Pentanol or pentanal
   (b) Pentane or pentanal
   (c) Benzaldehyde or benzyl alcohol
   (d) 2-Pentanone or 2-pentanol
   (e) Propanone or butanone
8. Write equations to show how each of the following is oxidized by (1) $K_2Cr_2O_7 + H_2SO_4$ and (2) air + Cu or Ag + heat:
   (a) 1-Propanol
   (b) 3-Pentanol
   (c) 2,3-Dimethyl-2-butanol

9. Ketones are prepared by oxidation of secondary alcohols. Which alcohol should be used to prepare:
   (a) Diethyl ketone
   (b) Diisopropyl ketone
   (c) 4-Phenyl-2-butanone
10. (a) What functional group is present in a compound that gives a positive Tollens test?
    (b) What is the visible evidence for a positive Tollens test?
    (c) Write an equation showing the reaction involved in a positive Tollens test.
11. (a) What functional group is present in a compound that gives a positive Fehling test?
    (b) What is the visible evidence for a positive Fehling test?
    (c) Write an equation showing the reaction involved in a positive Fehling test.
12. Give the products of the reaction of the following with Tollens' reagent:
    (a) Butanal
    (b) Benzaldehyde
    (c) Methyl ethyl ketone
13. Write equations showing the aldol condensation for the following compounds:
    (a) Acetaldehyde (c) Butanal
    (b) Propanal (d) 3-Pentanone
14. How many aldol condensation products are possible if a mixture of ethanal and propanal is reacted with dilute NaOH?
15. Complete the following equations:

$$\text{(a)}\ CH_3CH_2\overset{\overset{\displaystyle O}{\|}}{C}{-}H + CH_3CH_2CH_2OH \xrightleftharpoons{\text{Dry HCl}}$$

$$\text{(b)}\ CH_3\underset{\underset{\displaystyle O}{\|}}{C}CH_3 + \underset{\underset{\displaystyle OH}{|}}{C}H_2\underset{\underset{\displaystyle OH}{|}}{C}H_2 \xrightleftharpoons{\text{Dry HCl}}$$

$$\text{(c)}\ CH_3CH_2\overset{\overset{\displaystyle O}{\|}}{C}{-}H + CH_3CH_2OH \xrightleftharpoons{H^+}$$

$$\text{(d)}\ \text{(cyclohexanone)}{=}O + CH_3OH \xrightleftharpoons{H^+}$$

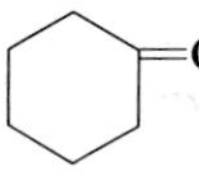

$$\text{(e)}\ CH_3CH_2CH_2CH(OCH_3)_2 \xrightarrow[H^+]{H_2O}$$

16. 3-Hydroxypropanal can form an intramolecular cyclic hemiacetal. What is the structure of the hemiacetal?
17. Write equations for the following sequence of reactions:
    (a) Benzaldehyde + HCN $\longrightarrow$
    (b) Product from part (a) + H_2O $\longrightarrow$
    (c) Product from part (b) + $K_2Cr_2O_7$ + H_2SO_4 $\longrightarrow$
18. Write equations to show how you could prepare lactic acid, $CH_3CH(OH)COOH$, from acetaldehyde through a cyanohydrin intermediate.
19. Give a simple visible chemical test that will distinguish between the compounds in each of the following pairs:

$$\text{(a)}\ CH_3CH_2\overset{\overset{\displaystyle O}{\|}}{C}{-}H \quad \text{and} \quad CH_3\overset{\overset{\displaystyle O}{\|}}{C}CH_3$$

$$\text{(b)}\ CH_3CH_2\overset{\overset{\displaystyle O}{\|}}{C}{-}H \quad \text{and} \quad CH_2{=}CH\overset{\overset{\displaystyle O}{\|}}{C}{-}H$$

$$\text{(c)}\ C_6H_5{-}CH_2CH_2OH \quad \text{and} \quad C_6H_5{-}\underset{\underset{\displaystyle OH}{|}}{C}HCH_3$$

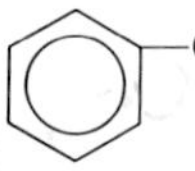

20. Which of the following statements are correct? Rewrite the incorrect statements to make them correct.
    (a) The functional group that characterizes aldehydes and ketones is called a carboxyl group.
    (b) The carbonyl group contains a sigma and a pi bond.
    (c) The carbonyl group is polar, with the oxygen atom being more electronegative than the carbon atom.
    (d) The higher-molar-mass aldehydes and ketones are very soluble in water.
    (e) Ketones, like aldehydes, are easily oxidized to carboxylic acids.
    (f) A compound of formula $C_6H_{12}O$ can be either an aliphatic aldehyde or ketone.
    (g) Diethyl ketone has the same molecular formula as butyraldehyde.
    (h) In aldehydes and ketones, the hydrogen atoms that are bonded to carbon atoms adjacent to the carbonyl group (alpha position) are more reactive than other hydrogen atoms in the molecule.
    (i) In order for an aldehyde or a ketone to undergo the aldol condensation, it must have at least one alpha-hydrogen atom.
    (j) A hemiacetal has an alcohol and an ether group bonded to the same carbon atom.
    (k) Acetals are stable in acid solution but not in alkaline solution.
    (l) Formaldehyde is a gas, but it is usually handled in a solution.
    (m) The major use for formaldehyde is for making plastics.

(n) Ethanal may be distinguished from propanal by use of Tollens' reagent.
(o) The general formula for the saturated homologous series of aldehydes and ketones is $C_nH_{2n}O$.
(p) The compound C_2H_4O can be an aldehyde or a ketone.
(q) The name for O=C(H)—C(H)=O is ethanedial.
(r) The oxidation product of 3-pentanol is diethylketone.
(s) $C_6H_5CH_2CH(OC_2H_5)_2$ is a ketal.
(t) When hydrolyzed, cyanohydrins form α-hydroxy acids.
(u) Of the three compounds ethanal, propanal, and butanal, ethanal has the lowest vapor pressure.
(v) Of the three compounds ethanal, propanal, and butanal, butanal has the highest boiling point.
(w) Reduction of aldehydes yields secondary alcohols.

6

Carboxylic Acids and Esters

◀ **Chapter Opening Photo: All citrus fruits contain carboxylic acids.**

Whenever we eat foods with a sour or tart taste, it is very likely that the taste results from the presence of at least one carboxylic acid. Lemons contain citric acid, vinegar contains acetic acid, and sour milk contains lactic acid. Carboxylic acids are also important compounds in biochemistry. Citric acid is found in the blood, and lactic acid is produced in the muscles during the breakdown of glucose. Most often in living systems these acids are found in the form of salts or acid derivatives. Carboxylic acid salts are commonly used in our lives as preservatives, especially in cheeses and breads. Some carboxylic acid salts are used to treat skin irritations like diaper rash and athlete's foot.

The sweet and pleasant odors and tastes of food are often the direct result of carboxylic acid derivatives known as esters. These compounds are frequently found as artificial flavors in foods in place of more expensive natural extracts. In biochemistry ester-like molecules act as the energy carriers in many cells. The properties of carboxylic acids are quite distinct from those of aldehydes and alcohols.

6.1 Carboxylic Acids

carboxyl group

The functional group of the carboxylic acids is called a **carboxyl group** and is represented in the following ways:

$$-\overset{\overset{\displaystyle O}{\|}}{C}-OH \quad \text{or} \quad -COOH \quad \text{or} \quad -CO_2H$$

Carboxylic acids can be either aliphatic or aromatic:

$$R\overset{\overset{\displaystyle O}{\|}}{C}-OH \qquad CH_3\overset{\overset{\displaystyle O}{\|}}{C}-OH \qquad\qquad Ar\overset{\overset{\displaystyle O}{\|}}{C}-OH \qquad C_6H_5-\overset{\overset{\displaystyle O}{\|}}{C}-OH$$

Aliphatic — Aromatic

Carboxylic acids react with many substances to produce derivatives. In these reactions the hydroxyl group is replaced by a halogen (—Cl), an acyloxy group (—OOCR), an alkoxy group (—OR), or an amino group (—NH_2). The general reactions are summarized below:

$$R{-}\overset{\overset{\displaystyle O}{\|}}{C}{-}OH \xrightarrow{-Cl} R{-}\overset{\overset{\displaystyle O}{\|}}{C}{-}Cl \quad \text{(acyl halide)}$$

$$R{-}\overset{\overset{\displaystyle O}{\|}}{C}{-}OH \xrightarrow{-OOCR} R{-}\overset{\overset{\displaystyle O}{\|}}{C}{-}O{-}\overset{\overset{\displaystyle O}{\|}}{C}{-}R \quad \text{(acid anhydride)}$$

$$R{-}\overset{\overset{\displaystyle O}{\|}}{C}{-}OH \xrightarrow{-OR} R{-}\overset{\overset{\displaystyle O}{\|}}{C}{-}OR \quad \text{(ester)}$$

$$R{-}\overset{\overset{\displaystyle O}{\|}}{C}{-}OH \xrightarrow{-NH_2} R{-}\overset{\overset{\displaystyle O}{\|}}{C}{-}NH_2 \quad \text{(amide)}$$

6.2 Nomenclature and Sources of Aliphatic Carboxylic Acids

Aliphatic carboxylic acids form a homologous series. The carboxyl group is always at the beginning of a carbon chain, and the C atom in this group is understood to be carbon number 1 in naming the compound.

To name a carboxylic acid by the IUPAC System, first identify the longest carbon chain including the carboxyl group. Then form the acid name by dropping the final *e* from the corresponding parent hydrocarbon name and adding *oic acid.* Thus, the names corresponding to the one-, two-, and three-carbon acids are methanoic acid, ethanoic acid, and propanoic acid. These names are derived from methane, ethane, and propane.

CH_4	Methane	$HCOOH$	Methanoic acid
CH_3CH_3	Ethane	CH_3COOH	Ethanoic acid
$CH_3CH_2CH_3$	Propane	CH_3CH_2COOH	Propanoic acid

Other groups bonded to the parent chain are numbered and named as we have done previously. For example,

$$\overset{5}{C}H_3\overset{4}{C}H_2\underset{\displaystyle CH_3}{\underset{|}{\overset{3}{C}H}}\overset{2}{C}H_2\overset{1}{C}OOH$$

3-Methylpentanoic acid

Unfortunately the IUPAC method is not the only, nor the most used, method of naming acids. Organic acids are usually known by common names. Methanoic, ethanoic, and propanoic acids are called formic, acetic, and propionic acids, respectively. These names usually refer to a natural source of the acid and are not systematic. Formic acid was named from the Latin word *formica,* meaning ant. This acid contributes to the stinging sensation of ant bites. Acetic acid is found in vinegar and is so named from the Latin word for vinegar. The name of butyric acid is derived from the Latin term for butter, since it is

▲ **The sting of an ant bite is caused by formic acid.**

TABLE 6.1 Names, Formulas, and Physical Properties of Saturated Carboxylic Acids

Common name (IUPAC name)	Formula	Melting point (°C)	Boiling point (°C)	Solubility in water[a]
Formic acid (Methanoic acid)	$HCOOH$	8.4	100.8	∞
Acetic acid (Ethanoic acid)	CH_3COOH	16.6	118	∞
Propionic acid (Propanoic acid)	CH_3CH_2COOH	−21.5	141.4	∞
Butyric acid (Butanoic acid)	$CH_3(CH_2)_2COOH$	−6	164	∞
Valeric acid (Pentanoic acid)	$CH_3(CH_2)_3COOH$	−34.5	186.4	3.3
Caproic acid (Hexanoic acid)	$CH_3(CH_2)_4COOH$	−3.4	205	1.1
Caprylic acid (Octanoic acid)	$CH_3(CH_2)_6COOH$	16.3	239	0.1
Capric acid (Decanoic acid)	$CH_3(CH_2)_8COOH$	31.4	269	Insoluble
Lauric acid (Dodecanoic acid)	$CH_3(CH_2)_{10}COOH$	44.1	225[b]	Insoluble
Myristic acid (Tetradecanoic acid)	$CH_3(CH_2)_{12}COOH$	54.2	251[b]	Insoluble
Palmitic acid (Hexadecanoic acid)	$CH_3(CH_2)_{14}COOH$	63	272[b]	Insoluble
Stearic acid (Octadecanoic acid)	$CH_3(CH_2)_{16}COOH$	69.6	287[b]	Insoluble
Arachidic acid (Eicosanoic acid)	$CH_3(CH_2)_{18}COOH$	77	298[b]	Insoluble

[a] Grams of acid per 100 g of water

[b] Boiling point is given at 100 mm Hg pressure instead of atmospheric pressure because thermal decomposition occurs before this acid reaches its boiling point at atmospheric pressure.

a constituent of butterfat. The 6-, 8-, and 10-carbon acids are found in goat fat and have names derived from the Latin word for goat. These three acids—caproic, caprylic, and capric—along with butyric acid have characteristic and disagreeable odors. In a similar way the names of the 12-, 14-, and 16-carbon acids—lauric, myristic, and palmitic—are from plants from which the corresponding acid has been isolated. The name stearic acid is derived from a Greek word meaning beef fat or tallow, which is a good source of this acid. Many of the carboxylic acids, principally those having even numbers of carbon atoms ranging from 4 to about 20, exist in combined form in plant and animal fats. These are called *fatty acids* (see Chapter 11). Table 6.1 lists the common and IUPAC names, together with some of the physical properties, of the more important saturated aliphatic acids.

Another common nomenclature method using letters of the Greek alphabet ($\alpha, \beta, \gamma, \delta, \ldots$) has traditionally been used in naming certain acid derivatives, especially hydroxy, amino, and halogen acids. When Greek letters are used, the carbon atoms, beginning with the one adjacent to the carboxyl group, are labeled α, β, γ, δ,.... When numbers are used, the numbers begin with the carbon in the —COOH group. Common and IUPAC nomenclature systems should not be intermixed.

$$\overset{\delta}{\underset{5}{C}}-\overset{\gamma}{\underset{4}{C}}-\overset{\beta}{\underset{3}{C}}-\overset{\alpha}{\underset{2}{C}}-\underset{1}{\overset{O}{\overset{\|}{C}}}-OH$$

	$CH_3CH_2CHCOOH$ (OH on C-2)	$CH_3CHCOOH$ (NH_2 on C-2)	CH_2ClCH_2COOH
Common name:	α-Hydroxybutyric acid	α-Aminopropionic acid	β-Chloropropionic acid
IUPAC name:	2-Hydroxybutanoic acid	2-Aminopropanoic acid	3-Chloropropanoic acid

EXAMPLE 6.1

Write formulas for the following:
(a) 3-Chloropentanoic acid (b) γ-Hydroxybutyric acid (c) Phenylacetic acid

SOLUTION

(a) *Pentanoic* indicates a five-carbon acid. Substituted on carbon 3 is a chlorine atom. Write five carbon atoms in a row. Make carbon 1 a carboxyl group, place a Cl on carbon 3, and add hydrogens to give each carbon four bonds. The formula is

$$CH_3CH_2CHClCH_2COOH$$

(b) *Butyric* indicates a four-carbon acid. The gamma (γ) position is three carbons removed from the carboxyl group. Therefore, the formula is

$$HO{-}CH_2CH_2CH_2COOH$$

(arrow: γ carbon → first CH_2)

(c) *Acetic acid* is the familiar two-carbon acid. There is only one place to substitute the phenyl group and still call the compound an acid–that is, at the CH_3 group. Substitute a phenyl group for one of the three H atoms to give the formula:

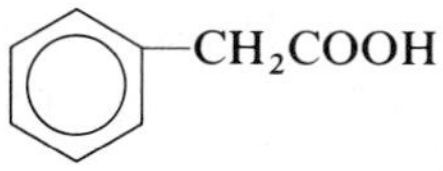

$$C_6H_5{-}CH_2COOH$$

PRACTICE Write formulas for (a) 2-methylpropanoic acid, (b) β-chlorocaproic acid, and (c) cyclohexanecarboxylic acid.

Answers:

(a) $CH_3CHCOOH$ (with CH_3 on C-2)

(b) $CH_3CH_2CH_2CHCH_2COOH$ (with Cl on C-3)

(c) cyclohexane ring —COOH

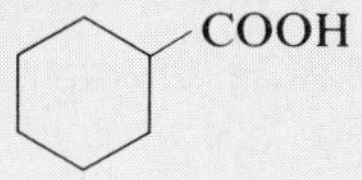

6.3 Physical Properties of Carboxylic Acids

Each aliphatic carboxylic acid molecule is polar and consists of a carboxyl group and a hydrocarbon radical. These two unlike parts have great bearing on the physical, as well as chemical, behavior of the molecule as a whole. The first four acids, formic through butyric, are completely soluble (miscible) in water (Table 6.1). Beginning with pentanoic acid (valeric acid), the water solubility falls sharply and is only about 0.1 g of acid per 100 g of water for octanoic acid (caprylic acid). Acids of this series with more than eight carbons are virtually insoluble in water. The water-solubility characteristics of the first four acids are evidently determined by the highly soluble polar carboxyl group. Thereafter the water solubility of the nonpolar hydrocarbon chain is dominant.

The polarity due to the carboxyl group is evident in the boiling-point data. Formic acid (HCOOH) boils at about 101°C. Carbon dioxide, a nonpolar substance of similar molar mass, remains in the gaseous state until it is cooled to −78°C. In like manner, the boiling point of acetic acid (molar mass 60) is 118°C, whereas nonpolar butane (molar mass 58) boils at −0.6°C. The comparatively high boiling points for carboxylic acids are due to intermolecular attractions resulting from hydrogen bonding. In fact, molar mass determinations on gaseous acetic acid (near its boiling point) show a value of about 120, indicating that two molecules are joined together to form a *dimer*, $(CH_3COOH)_2$.

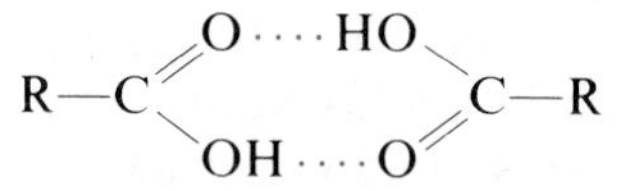

```
      O····HO                          O····HO
    //       \                       //       \
R—C           C—R          CH3—C               C—CH3
    \        //                      \        //
     OH····O                          OH····O
```

Hydrogen bonding in carboxylic acids

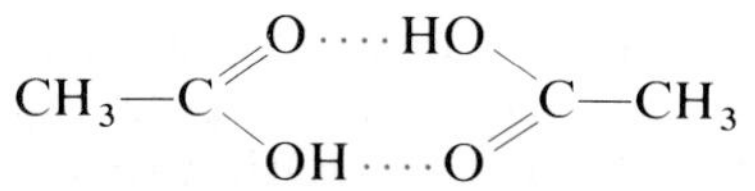

Acetic acid dimer

Saturated monocarboxylic acids that have fewer than ten carbon atoms are liquids at room temperature, whereas those with more than ten carbon atoms are waxlike solids.

Carboxylic acids and phenols, like mineral acids such as HCl, ionize in water to produce hydronium ions and anions. Carboxylic acids are generally weak; that is, they are only slightly ionized in water. Phenols are, in general, even weaker acids than carboxylic acids. For example, the ionization constant for acetic acid is 1.8×10^{-5} and that for phenol is 1.1×10^{-10}. Equations illustrating these ionizations are given below.

$$HCl + H_2O \longrightarrow H_3O^+ + Cl^-$$

Hydrogen chloride → Hydronium ion + Chloride ion

$$CH_3\overset{\overset{O}{\|}}{C}—OH + H_2O \rightleftharpoons H_3O^+ + CH_3\overset{\overset{O}{\|}}{C}—O^-$$

Acetic acid ⇌ Hydronium ion + Acetate ion

$$C_6H_5—OH + H_2O \rightleftharpoons H_3O^+ + C_6H_5—O^-$$

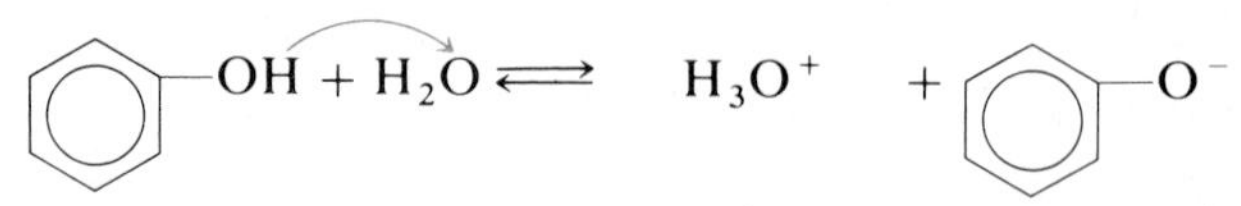

Phenol ⇌ Hydronium ion + Phenoxide ion

Carboxylic acids are very common in biological systems. Their tendency to ionize and form anions means that many biological molecules carry negative charges.

▲
Rhubarb is one of a number of vegetables containing carboxylic acids.

6.4 Classification of Carboxylic Acids

Thus far our discussion has dealt mainly with a single type of acid—that is, saturated monocarboxylic acids. But various other kinds of carboxylic acids are known. Some of the more important ones are discussed here.

Unsaturated Acids

An unsaturated acid contains one or more carbon–carbon double bonds. The first member of the homologous series of unsaturated carboxylic acids, containing one carbon–carbon double bond, is acrylic acid, $CH_2{=}CHCOOH$. The IUPAC name for $CH_2{=}CHCOOH$ is propenoic acid. Derivatives of acrylic acid are used to manufacture a class of synthetic polymers known as the acrylates (see Chapter 8). These polymers are widely used as textiles and in paints and lacquers. Unsaturated carboxylic acids undergo the reactions of both an unsaturated hydrocarbon and a carboxylic acid.

Even one carbon–carbon double bond in the molecule exerts a major influence on the physical and chemical properties of an acid. The effect of a double bond can be seen when comparing the two 18-carbon acids, stearic and oleic. Stearic acid, $CH_3(CH_2)_{16}COOH$, a solid that melts at 70°C, shows only the reactions of a carboxylic acid. On the other hand, oleic acid, $CH_3(CH_2)_7CH{=}CH(CH_2)_7COOH$ (mp 16°C), with one double bond, is a liquid at room temperature and shows the reactions of an unsaturated hydrocarbon as well as those of a carboxylic acid.

Aromatic Carboxylic Acids

In an aromatic carboxylic acid, the carbon of the carboxyl group (—COOH) is bonded directly to a carbon in an aromatic nucleus. The parent compound of this series is benzoic acid. Other common examples are the three isomeric toluic acids:

C_6H_5—COOH	CH_3 (ortho) —COOH	CH_3 (meta) —COOH	CH_3 (para) COOH
Benzoic acid	*o*-Toluic acid	*m*-Toluic acid	*p*-Toluic acid

Dicarboxylic Acids

Acids of both the aliphatic and aromatic series that contain two or more carboxyl groups are known. These are called dicarboxylic acids. The simplest member of the aliphatic series is oxalic acid. The next member in the homologous

TABLE 6.2 Names and Formulas of Selected Dicarboxylic Acids

Common name	IUPAC name	Formula
Oxalic acid	Ethanedioic acid	HOOCCOOH
Malonic acid	Propanedioic acid	$HOOCCH_2COOH$
Succinic acid	Butanedioic acid	$HOOC(CH_2)_2COOH$
Glutaric acid	Pentanedioic acid	$HOOC(CH_2)_3COOH$
Adipic acid	Hexanedioic acid	$HOOC(CH_2)_4COOH$
Fumaric acid	*trans*-2-Butenedioic acid	HOOCCH=CHCOOH
Maleic acid	*cis*-2-Butenedioic acid	HOOCCH=CHCOOH

series is malonic acid. Several dicarboxylic acids and their names are listed in Table 6.2.

The IUPAC names for dicarboxylic acids are formed by modifying the corresponding hydrocarbon names to end in *dioic acid*. Thus the two-carbon acid is ethanedioic acid (derived from ethane). However, the common names for dicarboxylic acids are frequently used.

Oxalic acid is found in various plants including spinach, cabbage, and rhubarb. Among its many uses are bleaching straw and leather and removing rust and ink stains. Although oxalic acid is poisonous, the amounts present in the above-mentioned vegetables are usually not harmful.

Malonic acid is made synthetically but was originally prepared from malic acid, which is commonly found in apples and many fruit juices. Malonic acid is one of the major compounds used in the manufacture of the class of drugs known as barbiturates. When heated above their melting points, malonic acid and substituted malonic acids lose carbon dioxide to give monocarboxylic acids. Thus, malonic acid yields acetic acid when strongly heated:

$$\begin{array}{l} \text{COOH} \\ | \\ \text{CH}_2 \\ | \\ \text{COOH} \end{array} \xrightarrow{150^\circ\text{C}} \text{CH}_3\text{COOH} + \text{CO}_2\uparrow$$

Malonic acid — Acetic acid

Malonic acid is used as the biological precursor for the synthesis of fatty acids. In living cells, when malonic acid loses carbon dioxide, the acetic acid units are linked together to begin formation of fatty acids.

Succinic acid has been known since the 16th century, when it was obtained as a distillation product of amber. Succinic, fumaric, and citric acids are among the important acids in the energy-producing metabolic pathway known as the citric acid cycle (see Chapter 17). Citric acid is a *tricarboxylic acid* that is widely distributed in plant and animal tissue, especially in citrus fruits (lemon juice contains 5–8%). The formula for citric acid is

$$\begin{array}{c} \text{CH}_2\text{COOH} \\ | \\ \text{HO}-\text{C}-\text{COOH} \\ | \\ \text{CH}_2\text{COOH} \end{array}$$

Citric acid

When succinic acid is heated, it loses water, forming succinic anhydride, an acid anhydride. Glutaric acid behaves similarly, forming glutaric anhydride.

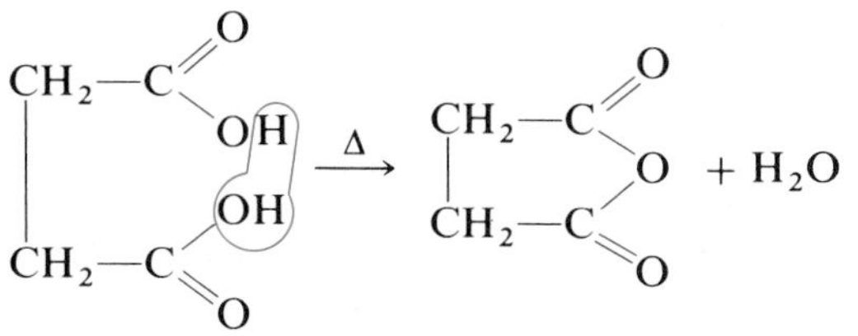

$$\begin{array}{l} CH_2-C(=O)-OH \\ | \\ CH_2-C(=O)-OH \end{array} \xrightarrow{\Delta} \begin{array}{l} CH_2-C(=O) \\ | \qquad\quad\; \backslash O \\ CH_2-C(=O) \end{array} + H_2O$$

Succinic acid　　Succinic anhydride

Adipic acid is the most important commercial dicarboxylic acid. It is made from benzene by converting it first to cyclohexene and then by oxidation to adipic acid. About 5.9×10^8 kg (1.3×10^9 lb) of adipic acid is produced annually in the United States. Most of the adipic acid is used to produce nylon (Chapter 8). It is also used in polyurethane foams, plasticizers, and lubricating-oil additives.

Aromatic dicarboxylic acids contain two carboxyl groups attached directly to an aromatic nucleus. Examples are the three isomeric phthalic acids, $C_6H_4(COOH)_2$:

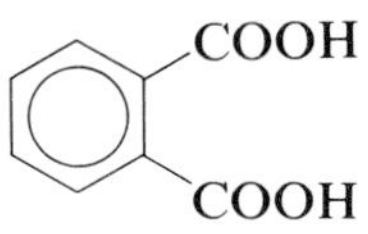

o-Phthalic acid (Phthalic acid) 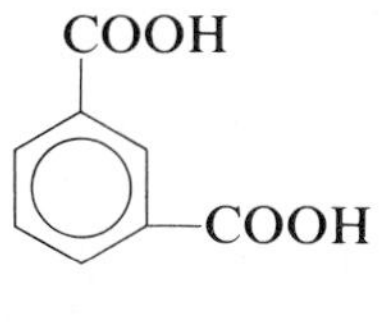　　*m*-Phthalic acid (Isophthalic acid) 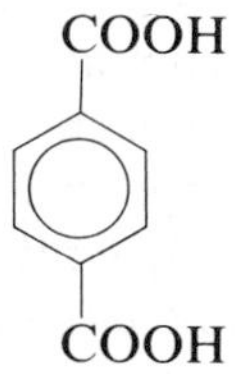　　*p*-Phthalic acid (Terephthalic acid)

Dicarboxylic acids are *bifunctional*; that is, they have two sites where reactions can occur. Therefore they are often used as monomers in the preparation of synthetic polymers such as Dacron polyester (Section 8.7).

Hydroxy Acids

Lactic acid, found in sour milk, sauerkraut, and dill pickles, has the functional groups of both a carboxylic acid and an alcohol. Lactic acid is the end product when our muscles use glucose for energy in the absence of oxygen, a process called *glycolysis* (see Chapter 17). Salicylic acid is both a carboxylic acid and a phenol. It is of special interest because a family of useful drugs—the salicylates—are derivatives of this acid. The salicylates include aspirin and function as *analgesics* (pain relievers) and as *antipyretics* (fever reducers). The structural formulas of several hydroxy acids follow:

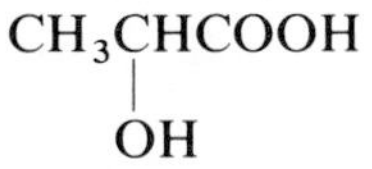

$$CH_3CH(OH)COOH$$

Lactic acid
(α-Hydroxypropionic acid)

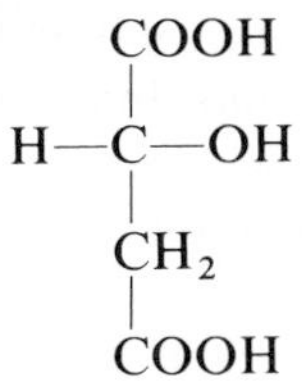

$$HOOC-CH(OH)-CH_2-COOH$$

Malic acid
(α-Hydroxysuccinic acid)

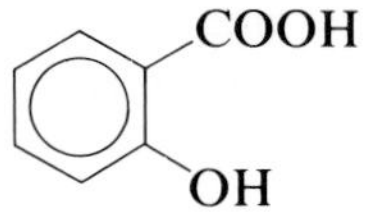

$$\text{C}_6\text{H}_4(\text{COOH})(\text{OH})$$

Salicylic acid
(o-Hydroxybenzoic acid)

$$\begin{array}{l} \text{HO—CHCOOH} \\ \quad\quad | \\ \text{HO—CHCOOH} \end{array}$$

Tartaric acid
(2,3-Dihydroxybutanedioic acid)

Amino Acids

Naturally occurring amino acids have this general formula; the amino group is in the alpha position:

$$\text{R—}\underset{\substack{|\\ \text{NH}_2}}{\text{CH}}\text{—}\overset{\substack{\text{O}\\ \|}}{\text{C}}\text{—OH}$$

Each amino acid molecule has a carboxyl group that acts as an acid and an amino group that acts as a base. About 20 biologically important amino acids, each with a different group represented by R, have been found in nature. (In amino acids, R does not always represent an alkyl group.) The immensely complicated protein molecules, found in every form of life, are built from amino acids. Some protein molecules contain more than 10,000 amino acid units. Amino acids and proteins are discussed in more detail in Chapter 12.

6.5 Preparation of Carboxylic Acids

Many different methods of preparing carboxylic acids are known. We will consider only a few examples.

Oxidation of an Aldehyde or a Primary Alcohol This is a general method that can be used to convert an aldehyde or primary alcohol to the corresponding carboxylic acid:

$$RCH_2OH \xrightarrow{[O]} RCOOH$$

$$R\overset{\substack{\text{O}\\ \|}}{\text{C}}\text{—H} \xrightarrow{[O]} RCOOH$$

Butyric acid (butanoic acid) can be obtained by oxidizing either 1-butanol or butanal with potassium dichromate in the presence of sulfuric acid. Aromatic acids may be prepared by the same general method. For example, benzoic acid is obtained by oxidizing benzyl alcohol.

$$\underset{\text{1-Butanol}}{CH_3CH_2CH_2CH_2OH} \xrightarrow[\substack{H_2SO_4\\ \Delta}]{Cr_2O_7^{2-}} \underset{\text{Butanoic acid}}{CH_3CH_2CH_2COOH}$$

$$\underset{\text{Butanal}}{CH_3CH_2CH_2\overset{\overset{\displaystyle O}{\|}}{C}{-}H} \xrightarrow[H_2SO_4,\ \Delta]{Cr_2O_7^{2-}} \underset{\text{Butanoic acid}}{CH_3CH_2CH_2COOH}$$

$$\underset{\text{Benzyl alcohol}}{C_6H_5{-}CH_2OH} \xrightarrow[H_2SO_4,\ \Delta]{Cr_2O_7^{2-}} \underset{\text{Benzoic acid}}{C_6H_5{-}COOH}$$

Carboxylic acids can also be obtained by the hydrolysis or saponification of esters (see Section 6.9).

Oxidation of Alkyl Groups Attached to Aromatic Rings When reacted with a strong oxidizing agent (alkaline permanganate solution or potassium dichromate and sulfuric acid), alkyl groups bonded to aromatic rings are oxidized to carboxyl groups. Regardless of the size or length of the alkyl group, the carbon atom adjacent to the ring remains bonded to the ring and is oxidized to a carboxyl group. The remainder of the alkyl group goes either to carbon dioxide or to a salt of a carboxylic acid. Thus sodium benzoate is obtained when toluene, ethylbenzene, or propylbenzene is heated with alkaline permanganate solution:

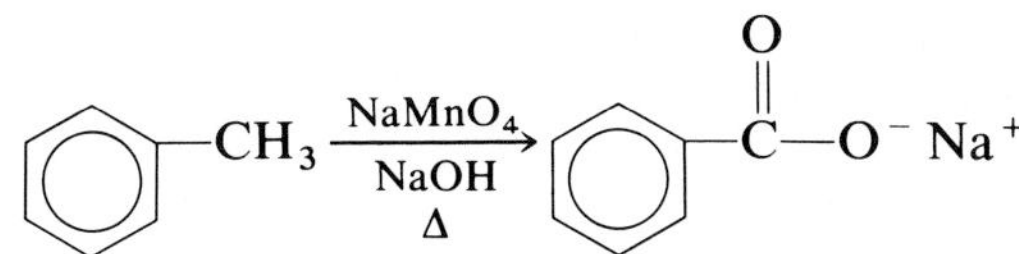

$$\underset{\text{Toluene}}{C_6H_5{-}CH_3} \xrightarrow[NaOH,\ \Delta]{NaMnO_4} \underset{\text{Sodium benzoate}}{C_6H_5{-}\overset{\overset{\displaystyle O}{\|}}{C}{-}O^-\,Na^+}$$

$$\underset{\text{Ethylbenzene}}{C_6H_5{-}CH_2CH_3} \xrightarrow[NaOH,\ \Delta]{NaMnO_4} \underset{\text{Sodium benzoate}}{C_6H_5{-}\overset{\overset{\displaystyle O}{\|}}{C}{-}O^-\,Na^+} + CO_2\uparrow$$

$$\underset{\text{Propylbenzene}}{C_6H_5{-}CH_2CH_2CH_3} \xrightarrow[NaOH,\ \Delta]{NaMnO_4} \underset{\text{Sodium benzoate}}{C_6H_5{-}\overset{\overset{\displaystyle O}{\|}}{C}{-}O^-\,Na^+} + \underset{\text{Sodium acetate}}{CH_3COO^-\,Na^+}$$

Since the reaction is conducted in an alkaline medium, a salt of the carboxylic acid (sodium benzoate) is formed instead of the free acid. To obtain the free carboxylic acid, the reaction mixture is acidified with a strong mineral acid (HCl or H_2SO_4) in a second step.

$$\underset{\text{Sodium benzoate}}{C_6H_5{-}COONa} + H^+ \longrightarrow \underset{\text{Benzoic acid}}{C_6H_5{-}COOH} + Na^+$$

Hydrolysis of Nitriles Nitriles, RCN, which can be prepared by adding HCN to aldehydes and ketones (Section 5.4) or by reacting alkyl halides with KCN, can be hydrolyzed to carboxylic acids:

$$\underset{\text{Alkyl halide}}{RX} + KCN \longrightarrow \underset{\text{A nitrile}}{RCN} + KX$$

$$RCN + 2\,H_2O \xrightarrow{H^+} RCOOH + NH_4^+$$

$$CH_3CN + 2\,H_2O \xrightarrow{H^+} CH_3COOH + NH_4^+$$

6.6 Chemical Properties of Carboxylic Acids

Acid–Base Reactions Because of their ability to form hydrogen ions in solution, acids in general have the following properties:

1. Sour taste
2. Change blue litmus to red and affect other suitable indicators
3. Form water solutions with pH values of less than 7
4. Undergo neutralization reactions with bases to form water and a salt

All of the foregoing general properties of an acid are readily seen in low molar mass carboxylic acids such as acetic acid. However, these general acid properties can be greatly influenced by the size of the hydrocarbon chain attached to the carboxyl group. In stearic acid, for example, taste, effect on indicators, and pH are not detectable because the large size of the hydrocarbon chain makes the acid insoluble in water. But stearic acid reacts with a base to form water and a salt. With sodium hydroxide, the equation for the reaction is

$$\underset{\text{Stearic acid}}{C_{17}H_{35}COOH} + NaOH \longrightarrow \underset{\text{Sodium stearate}}{C_{17}H_{35}COONa} + H_2O$$

The salts formed from this neutralization reaction have different properties than the acids. Salts are soluble in water and dissociate completely in solution. These properties assist in the separation of carboxylic acids from other nonpolar compounds. A base, like NaOH, is added to the mixture of compounds. The carboxylic acid reacts, forming its sodium salt and water. The salt dissolves in water while the remaining nonpolar molecules stay in the organic layer. Once the layers are separated, some mineral acid, HCl, can be added to the carboxylic acid salt to recover the acid.

Carboxylic acids generally react with sodium bicarbonate to release carbon dioxide. This reaction can be used to distinguish a carboxylic acid from a phenol (also a weak acid). Phenols do not react with bicarbonate, although they will be neutralized by a strong base.

Acid Chloride Formation Thionyl chloride ($SOCl_2$) reacts with carboxylic acids to form acid chlorides, which are very reactive and can be used to synthesize other substances such as amides and esters:

$$\underset{\text{Acid}}{\overset{\overset{\displaystyle O}{\|}}{RC}{-}OH} + \underset{\substack{\text{Thionyl}\\\text{chloride}}}{SOCl_2} \longrightarrow \underset{\text{Acid chloride}}{\overset{\overset{\displaystyle O}{\|}}{RC}{-}Cl} + SO_2 + HCl$$

$$CH_3\overset{\overset{\displaystyle O}{\|}}{C}{-}OH + SOCl_2 \longrightarrow \underset{\text{Acetyl chloride}}{CH_3\overset{\overset{\displaystyle O}{\|}}{C}{-}Cl} + SO_2 + HCl$$

Acid chlorides are extremely reactive substances. They must be kept away from moisture, or they will hydrolyze back to the acid:

$$\overset{\overset{\displaystyle O}{\|}}{RC}{-}Cl + H_2O \longrightarrow \overset{\overset{\displaystyle O}{\|}}{RC}{-}OH + HCl$$

Acid chlorides are more reactive than acids and can be used in place of acids to prepare esters and amides:

$$CH_3\overset{\overset{\displaystyle O}{\|}}{C}{-}Cl + CH_3OH \longrightarrow \underset{\text{Methyl acetate}}{CH_3\overset{\overset{\displaystyle O}{\|}}{C}{-}OCH_3} + HCl$$

$$CH_3\overset{\overset{\displaystyle O}{\|}}{C}{-}Cl + 2\,NH_3 \longrightarrow \underset{\text{Acetamide}}{CH_3\overset{\overset{\displaystyle O}{\|}}{C}{-}NH_2} + NH_4Cl$$

Acid Anhydride Formation Inorganic anhydrides are formed by the elimination of a molecule of water from an acid or a base:

$$H_2SO_3 \longrightarrow SO_2 + H_2O$$

$$Ba(OH)_2 \longrightarrow BaO + H_2O$$

An organic anhydride could be formed by the elimination of a molecule of water from two molecules of acid.

$$R{-}\overset{\overset{\displaystyle O}{\|}}{C}{-}OH + HO{-}\overset{\overset{\displaystyle O}{\|}}{C}{-}R' \longrightarrow R{-}\overset{\overset{\displaystyle O}{\|}}{C}{-}O{-}\overset{\overset{\displaystyle O}{\|}}{C}{-}R' + H_2O$$

The most commonly used organic anhydride is acetic anhydride. It can be prepared by the reaction of acetyl chloride with sodium acetate.

$$CH_3\overset{\overset{\displaystyle O}{\|}}{C}{-}Cl + Na^+\ {}^-O\overset{\overset{\displaystyle O}{\|}}{C}{-}CH_3 \longrightarrow \underset{\text{Acetic anhydride}}{CH_3\overset{\overset{\displaystyle O}{\|}}{C}{-}O{-}\overset{\overset{\displaystyle O}{\|}}{C}{-}CH_3} + NaCl$$

Acid anhydrides are very reactive and can be used to synthesize amides and esters. The anhydrides are not used as often as the acid chlorides in organic synthesis, however. In living cells acid anhydrides are commonly used to activate carboxylic acids for further reaction.

Ester Formation When an acid and an alcohol are heated in an acidic medium, a condensation reaction occurs. The products are an ester and water.

$$RC(=O)\!-\!\boxed{OH} + R'O\boxed{H} \underset{}{\overset{H^+}{\rightleftharpoons}} RC(=O)\!-\!OR' + H_2O$$

Carboxylic acid | Alcohol | Ester (R can be H, but R′ cannot be H)

$$H\!-\!C(=O)\!-\!OH + CH_3CH_2OH \overset{H^+}{\rightleftharpoons} H\!-\!C(=O)\!-\!OCH_2CH_3 + H_2O$$

Formic acid | Ethyl formate

At first glance this looks like the familiar acid–base neutralization reaction. But this is not the case, because the alcohol does not yield OH^- ions, and the ester, unlike a salt, is a molecular, not an ionic, substance. The forward reaction of an acid and an alcohol is called *esterification*; the reverse reaction of an ester with water is called *hydrolysis.* The work of a chemist may call for manipulating reaction conditions to favor the formation of either esters or their component parts, alcohols and acids.

Esterification is one of the most important reactions of carboxylic acids. Many biologically significant substances are esters.

6.7 Nomenclature of Esters

The general formula for an ester is RCOOR′, where R may be a hydrogen, alkyl group, or aryl group, and R′ may be an alkyl group, or aryl group, but *not* a hydrogen. Esters are found throughout nature. The ester linkage is particularly important in the study of fats and oils, both of which are esters. Esters of phosphoric acid are of vital importance to life as well.

Esters are alcohol derivatives of carboxylic acids. They are named in much the same way as salts. The alcohol part is named first, followed by the name of the acid modified to end in *ate.* The *ic* ending of the organic acid name is replaced by the ending *ate.* Thus in the IUPAC System, *ethanoic acid* becomes *ethanoate.* In the common names, *acetic acid* becomes *acetate.* To name an ester it is necessary to recognize the portion of the ester molecule that comes from the acid and the portion that comes from the alcohol. In the general formula for an ester, the RC=O comes from the acid, and the R′O comes from the alcohol:

$$R\!-\!C(=O)\!-\!O\!-\!R'$$

Acid | Alcohol

The R′ in R′O is named first, followed by the name of the acid modified by replacing *ic acid* with *ate.* The ester derived from ethyl alcohol and acetic acid

◀ **Bananas during the harvesting process. The odor of ripe bananas in the store or at home is caused by the ester isoamyl acetate.**

is called ethyl acetate or ethyl ethanoate. Consider the ester formed from CH_3CH_2COOH and CH_3OH:

$$\underset{\substack{\text{Propanoic acid}\\ \text{(Propionic acid)}}}{CH_3CH_2\overset{\overset{\displaystyle O}{\|}}{C}\text{—}\boxed{OH}} + \underset{\substack{\text{Methanol}\\ \text{(Methyl alcohol)}}}{\boxed{H}\text{—}OCH_3} \overset{H^+}{\rightleftharpoons} \underset{\substack{\text{Methyl propanoate}\\ \text{(Methyl propionate)}}}{CH_3CH_2\overset{\overset{\displaystyle O}{\|}}{C}\text{—}OCH_3} + H_2O$$

Esters of aromatic acids are named in the same general way as those of aliphatic acids. For example, the ester of benzoic acid and isopropyl alcohol is

$$C_6H_5\text{—}\overset{\overset{\displaystyle O}{\|}}{C}\text{—}O\text{—}CH(CH_3)_2$$

Isopropyl benzoate

Formulas and names for additional esters are given in Table 6.3.

6.8 Occurrence and Physical Properties of Esters

Since many acids and many alcohols are known, the number of esters theoretically possible is very large. In fact, both natural and man-made esters exist in almost endless variety. Simple esters derived from monocarboxylic acids and

TABLE 6.3 Formulas and Names of Selected Esters

Formula	IUPAC name	Common name	Odor or flavor
$CH_3C(=O)-OCH_2CH_2CH(CH_3)CH_3$	Isopentyl ethanoate	Isoamyl acetate	Banana, pear
$CH_3CH_2CH_2C(=O)-OCH_2CH_3$	Ethyl butanoate	Ethyl butyrate	Pineapple
$HC(=O)-OCH_2CH(CH_3)CH_3$	Isobutyl methanoate	Isobutyl formate	Raspberry
$CH_3C(=O)-OCH_2(CH_2)_6CH_3$	Octyl ethanoate	*n*-Octyl acetate	Orange
$C_6H_4(OH)-C(=O)-OCH_3$	Methyl-2-hydroxy-benzoate	Methyl salicylate	Wintergreen

monohydroxy alcohols are colorless, generally nonpolar liquids or solids. The low polarity of ester molecules is substantiated by the fact that both their water solubility and boiling points are lower than those of either acids or alcohols of similar molar masses.

Low- and intermediate-molar-mass esters (from both acids and alcohols up to about ten carbons) are liquids with characteristic, usually fragrant or fruity odors. The distinctive odor and flavor of many fruits are caused by one or more of these esters. The difference in properties between an acid and its esters is remarkable. For example, in contrast to the extremely unpleasant odor of butyric acid, ethyl butyrate has the pleasant odor of pineapple and methyl butyrate the odor of artificial rum. Esters are used in flavoring and scenting agents (see Table 6.3). They are generally good solvents for organic substances, and those having relatively low molar masses are volatile. Therefore esters such as ethyl acetate, butyl acetate, and isoamyl acetate are extensively used in paints, varnishes, and lacquers.

High-molar-mass esters (formed from acids and alcohols of 16 or more carbons) are waxes and are obtained from various plants. They are used in furniture wax and automobile wax preparations; for example, carnauba wax contains esters of 24- and 28-carbon fatty acids and 32- and 34-carbon alcohols. Polyesters with very high molar masses, such as Dacron, are widely used in the textile industries (see Chapter 8).

EXAMPLE 6.2

Name the following esters:

(a) $H-\overset{\overset{O}{\|}}{C}-OCH_2CH_2CH_3$

(b) $C_6H_5-\overset{\overset{O}{\|}}{C}-OCH_2CH_3$

(c) $O=C-OCH_2CH_3$ | CH_2 | $O=C-OCH_2CH_3$

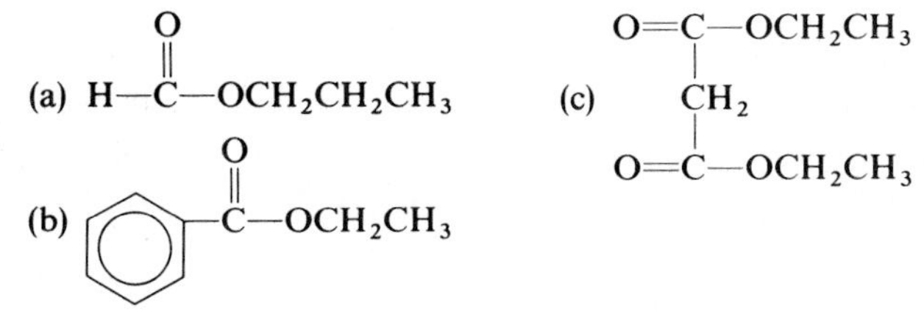

SOLUTION

(a) First identify the acid and alcohol components. The acid contains one carbon and is formic acid. The alcohol is propyl alcohol.

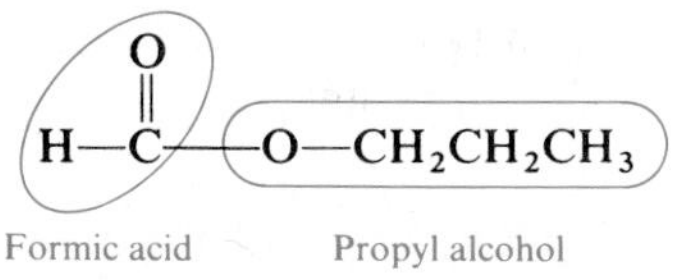

$H-\overset{\overset{O}{\|}}{C}-O-CH_2CH_2CH_3$

Formic acid Propyl alcohol

Change the *ic* ending of the acid to *ate*, making the name formate or methanoate. The name of the ester then is propyl formate or propyl methanoate.

(b) The acid is benzoic acid; the alcohol is ethyl alcohol. Using the same procedure as in part (a), the name of the ester is ethyl benzoate.

(c) The acid is the three-carbon dicarboxylic acid, malonic acid. The alcohol is ethyl alcohol. Both acid groups are in the ester form. The name, therefore, is diethyl malonate.

PRACTICE Name the following esters:

(a) $CH_3CH_2\underset{\underset{O}{\|}}{C}-O-CH_3$

(b) $CH_3-\underset{\underset{O}{\|}}{C}-O-C_6H_5$

(c) $CH_3-O-\overset{\overset{O}{\|}}{C}-CH_2CH_2-\overset{\overset{O}{\|}}{C}-O-CH_3$

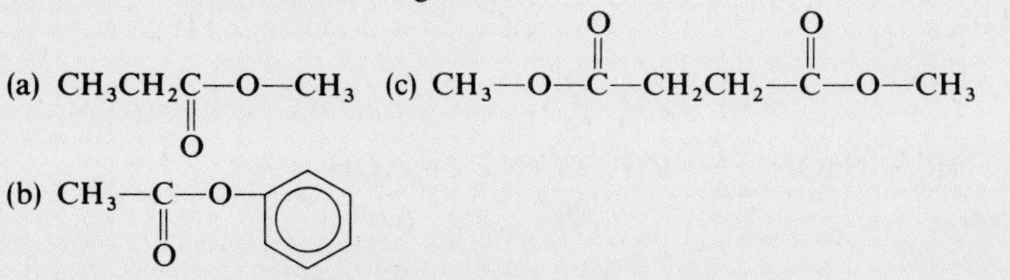

Answers: (a) Ethyl propanoate (b) Phenyl ethanoate (c) Dimethyl succinate

6.9 CHEMICAL PROPERTIES OF ESTERS

The most important reaction of esters is *hydrolysis*. Hydrolysis is the splitting of molecules through the addition of water. The majority of organic and biochemical substances react only very slowly, if at all, with water. In order to increase the rate of these reactions, a catalyst is required. In the laboratory the chemist often employs an acid or base as a catalyst for hydrolysis. In living systems the role of catalyst is filled by enzymes.

Acid Hydrolysis

Hydrolysis of an ester involves reaction with water to form an acid and an alcohol. The hydrolysis is catalyzed by strong acids (H_2SO_4 and HCl) or by certain enzymes.

$$\underset{\text{Ester}}{RC(=O)\text{—}OR'} + H_2O \xrightarrow[\text{or enzyme}]{H^+} \underset{\text{Acid}}{RC(=O)\text{—}OH} + \underset{\text{Alcohol}}{R'OH}$$

$$\underset{\text{Methyl propanoate}}{CH_3CH_2C(=O)\text{—}OCH_3} + H_2O \xrightarrow{H^+} \underset{\text{Propanoic acid}}{CH_3CH_2COOH} + \underset{\text{Methanol}}{CH_3OH}$$

$$\underset{\text{Methyl salicylate}}{C_6H_4(OH)\text{—}C(=O)\text{—}OCH_3} + H_2O \xrightarrow{H^+} \underset{\text{Salicylic acid}}{C_6H_4(OH)COOH} + \underset{\text{Methanol}}{CH_3OH}$$

Alkaline Hydrolysis (Saponification)

saponification

Saponification is the hydrolysis of an ester by a strong base (NaOH or KOH) to produce an alcohol and a salt (or soap if the salt formed is from a high molar mass acid):

$$\underset{\text{Ester}}{RC(=O)\text{—}OR'} + NaOH \xrightarrow[\Delta]{H_2O} \underset{\text{Salt}}{RC(=O)\text{—}O^- Na^+} + \underset{\text{Alcohol}}{R'OH}$$

$$\underset{\text{Ethyl stearate}}{CH_3(CH_2)_{16}C(=O)\text{—}OCH_2CH_3} + NaOH \xrightarrow[\Delta]{H_2O} \underset{\text{Sodium stearate}}{CH_3(CH_2)_{16}C(=O)ONa} + CH_3CH_2OH$$

The carboxylic acid may be obtained by reacting the salt with a strong acid such as HCl:

$$CH_3(CH_2)_{16}COONa + HCl \longrightarrow \underset{\text{Stearic acid}}{CH_3(CH_2)_{16}COOH} + NaCl$$

Notice that in saponification the base is a reactant and not a catalyst.

6.10 Glycerol Esters

Fats and **oils** are esters of glycerol and predominantly long-chain fatty acids. Fats and oils are also called **triacylglycerols** or triglycerides, since each molecule is derived from one molecule of glycerol and three molecules of fatty acid.

fats, oils

triacylglycerols

Glycerol portion →

$$\begin{array}{l} \qquad\qquad\quad CH_2{-}O{-}\overset{\displaystyle O}{\overset{\|}{C}}{-}R \\ \qquad\qquad\quad\;\; | \\ R'{-}\overset{\displaystyle O}{\overset{\|}{C}}{-}O{-}CH \\ \qquad\qquad\quad\;\; | \\ \qquad\qquad\quad CH_2{-}O{-}\overset{\displaystyle O}{\overset{\|}{C}}{-}R'' \end{array}$$

General formula for a triacylglycerol

$$\begin{array}{ll} \qquad\qquad\qquad\quad CH_2{-}O{-}\overset{\displaystyle O}{\overset{\|}{C}}{-}C_{17}H_{35} & \text{(Stearic)} \\ \qquad\qquad\qquad\quad\;\; | & \\ C_{15}H_{31}\overset{\displaystyle O}{\overset{\|}{C}}{-}O{-}CH & \text{(Palmitic)} \\ \qquad\qquad\qquad\quad\;\; | & \\ \qquad\qquad\qquad\quad CH_2{-}O{-}\overset{\displaystyle O}{\overset{\|}{C}}{-}C_{11}H_{23} & \text{(Lauric)} \end{array}$$

Typical triacylglycerol containing three different fatty acids

The structural formulas of triacylglycerol molecules vary because

1. The length of the fatty acid chain may vary from 4 to 20 carbons, but the number of carbon atoms in the chain is nearly always even.
2. Each fatty acid may be saturated or may be unsaturated and contain one, two, or three carbon–carbon double bonds.
3. A triacylglycerol may, and frequently does, contain three different fatty acids.

The most abundant saturated fatty acids in fats and oils are lauric, myristic, palmitic, and stearic acids (Table 6.1). The most abundant unsaturated acids in fats and oils contain 18 carbon atoms and have one, two, or three carbon–carbon double bonds. In all of these naturally occurring unsaturated acids, the configuration about the double bond is cis. Their formulas are:

$$CH_3(CH_2)_7CH{=}CH(CH_2)_7COOH$$

Oleic acid

$$CH_3(CH_2)_4CH{=}CHCH_2CH{=}CH(CH_2)_7COOH$$

Linoleic acid

$$CH_3CH_2CH{=}CHCH_2CH{=}CHCH_2CH{=}CH(CH_2)_7COOH$$

Linolenic acid

The major physical difference between fats and oils is that fats are solid and oils are liquid at room temperature (see Section 11.2). Since the glycerol part of the structure is the same for a fat and an oil, the difference must be due to the fatty acid end of the molecule. Fats contain a larger proportion of saturated fatty acids, whereas oils contain greater amounts of unsaturated fatty

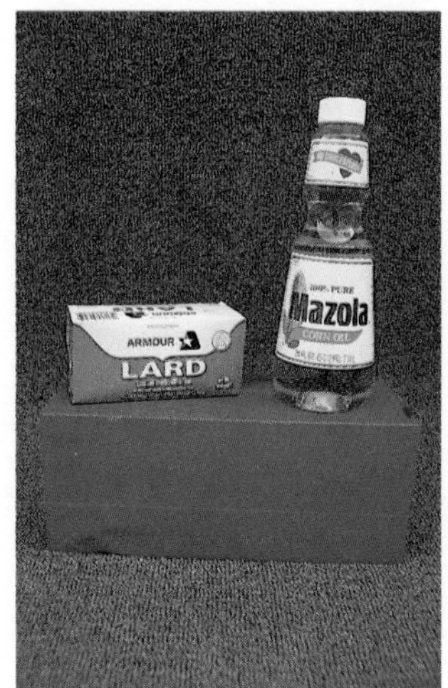

▲ **Solid fats such as lard contain saturated fatty acid portions. Vegetable oils contain unsaturated fatty acids.**

TABLE 6.4 Fatty Acid Composition of Selected Fats and Oils

	Fatty acid (%)				
Fat or oil	Myristic acid	Palmitic acid	Stearic acid	Oleic acid	Linoleic acid
Animal fat					
Butter[a]	7–10	23–26	10–13	30–40	4–5
Lard	1–2	28–30	12–18	41–48	6–7
Tallow	3–6	24–32	14–32	35–48	2–4
Vegetable oil					
Olive	0–1	5–15	1–4	49–84	4–12
Peanut	—	6–9	2–6	50–70	13–26
Corn	0–2	7–11	3–4	43–49	34–42
Cottonseed	0–2	19–24	1–2	23–33	40–48
Soybean	0–2	6–10	2–4	21–29	50–59
Linseed[b]	—	4–7	2–5	9–38	3–43

[a] Butyric acid, 3–4%
[b] Linolenic acid, 25–58%

acids. The term *polyunsaturated* has been popularized in recent years; it means that each molecule of fat in a particular product contains several double bonds.

Fats and oils are obtained from natural sources. In general, fats come from animal sources and oils from vegetable sources. Thus, lard is obtained from hogs and tallow from cattle and sheep. Olive, cottonseed, corn, peanut, soybean, linseed, and other oils are obtained from the fruit or seed of their respective vegetable sources. Table 6.4 shows the major constituents of several fats and oils.

Triacylglycerols are the principal form in which energy is stored in the body. The caloric value per unit of mass is over twice as great as that for carbohydrates and proteins. As a source of energy, triacylglycerols can be completely replaced by either carbohydrates or proteins. However, some minimum amount of fat is needed in the diet, because fat supplies the nutritionally essential unsaturated fatty acids (linoleic, linolenic, and arachidonic) required by the body (see Section 11.2).

Hydrogenation of Glycerides Addition of hydrogen is a characteristic reaction of the carbon–carbon pi bonds. Industrially, low-cost vegetable oils are partially hydrogenated to obtain solid fats that are useful as shortening in baking or in making margarine. In this process, hydrogen gas is bubbled through hot oil containing a finely dispersed nickel catalyst. The hydrogen adds to the carbon–carbon double bonds of the oil to saturate the double bonds and form fats:

$$H_2 + \underset{\text{In oil or fat}}{-CH{=}CH-} \xrightarrow{Ni} -CH_2-CH_2-$$

In actual practice, only some of the double bonds are allowed to become saturated. The degree of hydrogenation can be controlled to obtain a product of any desired degree of saturation. The products resulting from the partial hydrogenation of oils are marketed as solid shortening (Crisco, Spry, and so on) and are used for cooking and baking. Oils and fats are also partially hydrogenated to improve their keeping qualities. Rancidity in fats and oils results from air oxidation at points of unsaturation, producing low-molar-mass aldehydes and acids of disagreeable odor and flavor.

Hydrogenolysis Triacylglycerols can be split and reduced in a reaction called hydrogenolysis (splitting by hydrogen). Hydrogenolysis requires higher temperatures and pressures and a different catalyst (copper chromite) than does hydrogenation of double bonds. Each triacylglycerol molecule yields a molecule of glycerol and three primary alcohol molecules. The hydrogenolysis of glyceryl trilaurate is represented as follows:

$$\begin{array}{l} CH_2{-}O{-}\overset{O}{\overset{\|}{C}}{-}C_{11}H_{23} \\ | \\ C_{11}H_{23}{-}\overset{O}{\overset{\|}{C}}{-}O{-}CH \\ | \\ CH_2{-}O{-}\overset{O}{\overset{\|}{C}}{-}C_{11}H_{23} \end{array} + 6\,H_2 \xrightarrow[\Delta,\ \text{pressure}]{\text{Copper chromite}} 3\,CH_3(CH_2)_{10}CH_2OH + \begin{array}{c} CH_2OH \\ | \\ CHOH \\ | \\ CH_2OH \end{array}$$

Glyceryl trilaurate; Lauryl alcohol (1-Dodecanol); Glycerol

Long-chain primary alcohols obtained by this reaction are important, since they are used to manufacture other products, especially synthetic detergents (see Section 6.11).

Hydrolysis Triacylglycerols can be hydrolyzed, yielding fatty acids and glycerol. The hydrolysis is catalyzed by digestive enzymes at room temperatures and by mineral acids at high temperatures:

$$\begin{array}{l} CH_2{-}O{-}\overset{O}{\overset{\|}{C}}{-}R \\ | \\ R'{-}\overset{O}{\overset{\|}{C}}{-}O{-}CH \\ | \\ CH_2{-}O{-}\overset{O}{\overset{\|}{C}}{-}R'' \end{array} + 3\,H_2O \xrightarrow[\text{enzymes}]{H^+ \text{ or}} \begin{array}{l} RCOOH \\ R'COOH \\ R''COOH \end{array} + \begin{array}{c} CH_2OH \\ | \\ CHOH \\ | \\ CH_2OH \end{array}$$

Triacylglycerol; Fatty acids (3 molecules); Glycerol

The enzyme-catalyzed reaction occurs in digestive reactions and in biological degradation (or metabolic) processes. The acid-catalyzed reaction is employed in the commercial preparation of fatty acids and glycerol.

Saponification Saponification of a fat or oil involves the alkaline hydrolysis of a triester. The products formed are glycerol and the alkali metal salts of fatty acids, which are called soaps. As a specific example, glyceryl tripalmitate reacts with sodium hydroxide to produce sodium palmitate and glycerol:

$$\begin{array}{l} CH_2{-}O{-}\overset{\displaystyle O}{\overset{\|}{C}}{-}C_{15}H_{31} \\ | \\ C_{15}H_{31}{-}\overset{\displaystyle O}{\overset{\|}{C}}{-}O{-}CH \\ | \\ CH_2{-}O{-}\overset{\displaystyle O}{\overset{\|}{C}}{-}C_{15}H_{31} \end{array} + 3\,NaOH \xrightarrow{\Delta} 3\,C_{15}H_{31}COONa + \begin{array}{l} CH_2OH \\ | \\ CHOH \\ | \\ CH_2OH \end{array}$$

Glyceryl tripalmitate; Sodium palmitate (a soap); Glycerol

Glycerol, fatty acids, and soaps are valuable articles of commerce, and the processing of fats and oils to obtain these products is a major industry.

6.11 Soaps and Synthetic Detergents

In the broadest sense possible, a detergent is simply a cleansing agent. Soap has been used as a cleansing agent for at least 2000 years and thereby is classified as a detergent under this definition. Beginning about 1930 a number of new cleansing agents that were superior in many respects to ordinary soap began to appear on the market. Because they were both synthetic organic products and detergents, they were called **synthetic detergents**, or syndets. A soap is distinguished from a synthetic detergent on the basis of chemical composition and not on the basis of function or usage.

synthetic detergents

Soaps

In former times soap-making was a crude operation. Surplus fats were boiled with wood ashes or with some other alkaline material. Today, soap is made in large manufacturing plants under controlled conditions. Salts of long-chain fatty acids are called **soaps**. However, only the sodium and potassium salts of carboxylic acids containing 12 to 18 carbon atoms are of great value as soaps, because of their abundance in fats.

soaps

$$\text{Fat or oil} + NaOH \longrightarrow \text{Soap} + \text{Glycerol}$$

To understand how a soap works as a cleansing agent, let us consider sodium palmitate, $CH_3(CH_2)_{14}COONa$, as an example of a typical soap. In water this substance exists as sodium ions, Na^+, and palmitate ions, $CH_3(CH_2)_{14}COO^-$. The sodium ion is an ordinary hydrated metal ion. The cleansing property, then, must be centered in the palmitate ion. The palmitate ion contains both a **hydrophilic** (water-loving) and a **hydrophobic** (water-fearing) group. The hydrophilic end is the polar, negatively charged carboxylate group. The hydrophobic end is the long hydrocarbon group. The hydrocarbon group is soluble in oils and greases, but is not soluble in water. The hydrophilic carboxylate group is soluble in water.

hydrophilic

hydrophobic

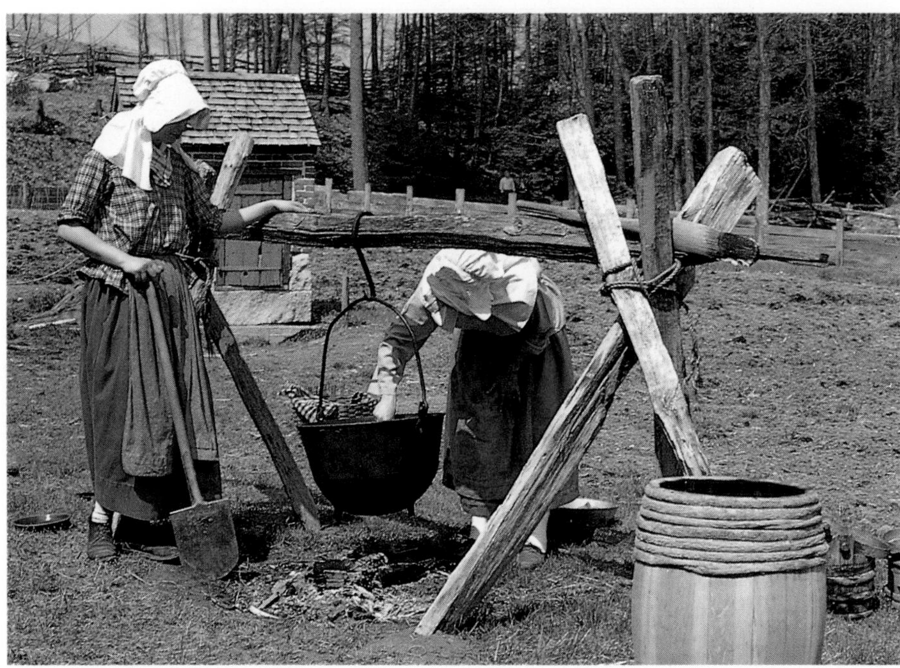

◀ **Old-fashioned soap making at Sturbridge Village. These women are making soap from lard boiled with wood ashes.**

The cleansing action of a soap is explained in this fashion: When the soap comes in contact with grease on a soiled surface, the hydrocarbon end of the soap dissolves in the grease, leaving the negatively charged carboxylate end exposed on the grease surface. Because the negatively charged carboxylate groups are strongly attracted by water, small droplets are formed, and the grease is literally lifted or floated away from the soiled object (see Figure 6.1).

The cleansing property of a soap is due to its ability to act as an emulsifying agent between water and water-insoluble greases and oils. The grease–soap emulsion is stable because the oil droplets repel each other due to the negatively charged carboxyl groups on their surfaces. Some insoluble particulate matter is carried away with the grease; the remainder is wetted and mechanically washed away in the water. Synthetic detergents function in a similar way.

Ordinary soap is a good cleansing agent in soft water, but it is not satisfactory in hard water because insoluble calcium, magnesium, and iron(III) salts are formed. Palmitate ions, for example, are precipitated by calcium ions:

$$Ca^{2+}(aq) + 2\,\underset{\text{Palmitate ion}}{CH_3(CH_2)_{14}COO^-}(aq) \longrightarrow \underset{\text{Calcium palmitate}}{[CH_3(CH_2)_{14}COO]_2Ca}(s)$$

These precipitates are sticky substances and are responsible for "bathtub ring" and the sticky feel of hair after being shampooed with soap in hard water.

Soaps are ineffective in acidic solutions because water-insoluble molecular fatty acids are formed:

$$CH_3(CH_2)_{14}COO^- + H^+ \longrightarrow \underset{\text{Palmitic acid molecule}}{CH_3(CH_2)_{14}COOH}$$

FIGURE 6.1 ► Cleansing action of soap: Dirt particles are embedded in a surface film of grease. The hydrocarbon ends of negative soap ions dissolve in the grease film, leaving exposed carboxylate groups. These carboxylate groups are attracted to water, and small droplets of grease-bearing dirt are formed and floated away from the surface.

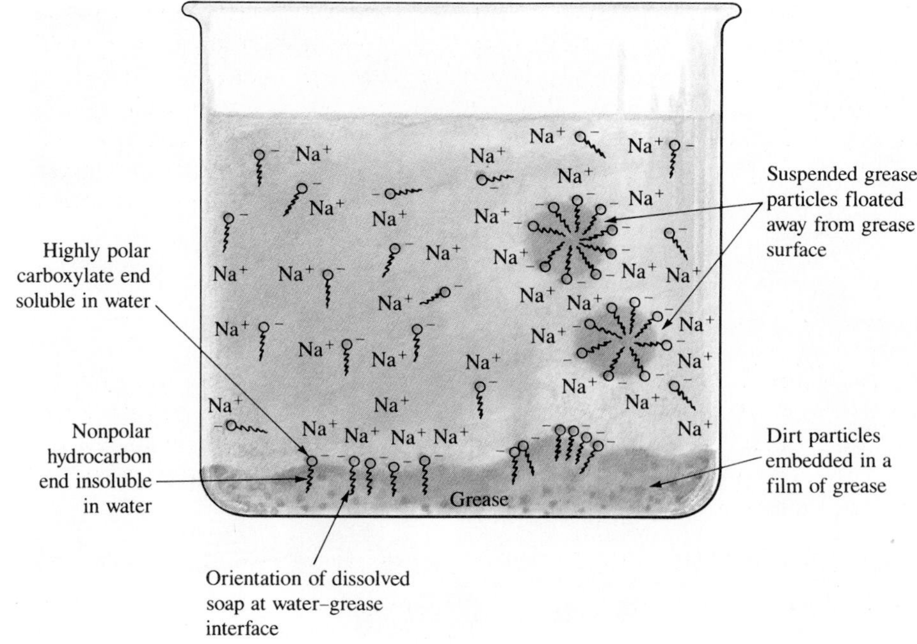

Synthetic Detergents

Once it was recognized that the insoluble hydrocarbon radical joined to a highly polar group was the key to the detergent action of soaps, chemists set out to make new substances that would have similar properties. About 1930, synthetic detergents (syndets) began to replace soaps, and at present about four pounds of syndets are sold for each pound of soap.

Although hundreds of substances having detergent properties are known, an idea of their general nature can be obtained from consideration of sodium lauryl sulfate and sodium *p*-dodecylbenzene sulfonate.

$$CH_3(CH_2)_{10}CH_2OSO_3^- \ Na^+$$

Sodium lauryl sulfate

$$CH_3(CH_2)_{10}CH_2-C_6H_4-SO_3^- \ Na^+$$

Sodium *p*-dodecylbenzene sulfonate

Sodium lauryl sulfate and sodium *p*-dodecylbenzene sulfonate act in water in much the same way as sodium palmitate. The negative ion of each substance is the detergent. For example, like the palmitate ion, the negative lauryl sulfate ion has a long hydrocarbon chain that is soluble in grease and a sulfate group that is attracted to water:

$$\underbrace{CH_3CH_2CH_2CH_2CH_2CH_2CH_2CH_2CH_2CH_2CH_2CH_2}_{\text{Nonpolar hydrophobic end, grease soluble}}-\underbrace{OSO_3^-}_{\text{Polar hydrophilic end, water soluble}}$$

The one great advantage these synthetic detergents have over soap is that their calcium, magnesium, and iron(III) salts, as well as their sodium salts, are soluble in water. Therefore, they are nearly as effective in hard water as in soft water.

The foregoing are anionic detergents, because the detergent activity is located in negative ions. Other detergents, both cationic and nonionic, have been developed for special purposes. The detergent activity of a cationic detergent is located in a cation that has a long hydrocarbon chain and a positive charge.

$$\underbrace{CH_3(CH_2)_{14}CH_2}_{\text{Grease soluble, hydrophobic}}-\underbrace{\overset{+}{N}(CH_3)_3}_{\text{Water soluble, hydrophilic}}$$

Nonionic detergents are molecular substances. The molecule of a nonionic detergent contains a grease-soluble component and a water-soluble component. Some of these substances are especially useful in automatic washing machines because they have good detergent but low sudsing properties. The structure of a representative nonionic detergent is

$$\underbrace{CH_3(CH_2)_{10}CH_2}_{\text{Grease soluble}}-O-\underbrace{(CH_2CH_2O)_7-CH_2CH_2OH}_{\text{Water soluble}}$$

Biodegradability

Organic substances that are readily decomposed by microorganisms in the environment are said to be **biodegradable**. All naturally occurring organic substances are eventually converted to simple inorganic molecules and ions such as CO_2, H_2O, N_2, Cl^-, and SO_4^{2-}. Most of these conversions are catalyzed by enzymes produced by microorganisms. These enzymes are capable of attacking only certain specific molecular configurations that are found in substances occurring in nature.

biodegradable

A number of years ago a serious environmental pollution problem arose in connection with synthetic detergents. Some of the early syndets containing highly branched-chain hydrocarbons had no counterparts in nature. Therefore, enzymes capable of degrading them did not exist, and the detergents were essentially nonbiodegradable and broke down very, very slowly. As a result these syndets accumulated in water supplies, where they caused severe pollution problems due to excessive foaming and other undesirable effects.

Detergent manufacturers, acting on the recommendations of chemists and biologists, changed from a branched-chain alkyl benzene to a straight-chain alkyl benzene raw material. Detergents containing the straight-chain alkyl groups are biodegradable.

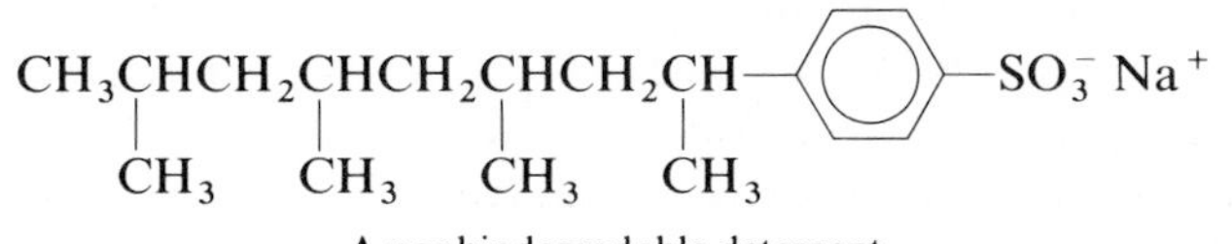

$$\underset{\substack{|\\CH_3}}{CH_3CH}\underset{\substack{|\\CH_3}}{CH_2CH}\underset{\substack{|\\CH_3}}{CH_2CH}\underset{\substack{|\\CH_3}}{CH_2CH}-C_6H_4-SO_3^-\ Na^+$$

A nonbiodegradable detergent

$$CH_3CH_2CH_2CH_2CH_2CH_2CH_2CH_2CH_2CH_2CH_2CH_2-C_6H_4-SO_3^-\ Na^+$$

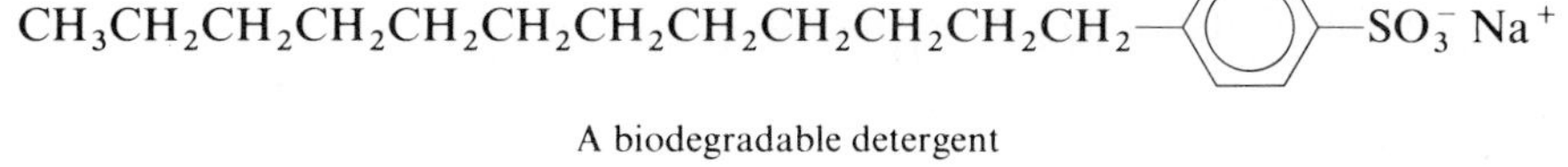

A biodegradable detergent

6.12 Esters and Anhydrides from Phosphoric Acid

Phosphoric acid has a Lewis structure similar to that of a carboxylic acid.

$$\underset{\text{Carboxylic acid}}{R-\overset{\overset{\displaystyle O}{\|}}{C}-OH} \qquad \underset{\text{Phosphoric acid}}{HO-\overset{\overset{\displaystyle O}{\|}}{\underset{\underset{\displaystyle OH}{|}}{P}}-OH}$$

In both molecules an —OH is attached to an element which is double bonded to an oxygen. In fact, phosphoric acid has three such —OH groups. This similarity in structure permits phosphoric acid to behave as a carboxylic acid in reaction with an alcohol. The product of the esterification reaction is called a phosphate ester.

$$\underset{\text{Phosphoric acid}}{HO-\overset{\overset{\displaystyle O}{\|}}{\underset{\underset{\displaystyle OH}{|}}{P}}-OH} + \underset{\text{Ethanol}}{HOCH_2CH_3} \xrightarrow{H^+} \underset{\text{Monoethyl phosphate}}{HO-\overset{\overset{\displaystyle O}{\|}}{\underset{\underset{\displaystyle OH}{|}}{P}}-OCH_2CH_3} + H_2O$$

Phosphate esters play a significant role in physiological processes. The esterification of an alcohol by phosphoric acid is one example of a process called **phosphorylation**.

phosphorylation

The phosphate ester still has other —OH groups, which allow further phosphorylation to occur. The result of a further condensation reaction is a molecule with two phosphate ester linkages. This is the structure commonly found in phospholipids, molecules that are key components of cell membranes and play significant roles in brain and nerve tissues (Chapter 11).

$$\begin{array}{l} CH_2-O-\overset{\overset{\displaystyle O}{\|}}{C}-R \\ | \\ CH-O-\overset{\overset{\displaystyle O}{\|}}{C}-R' \\ | \\ CH_2-O-\overset{\overset{\displaystyle O}{\|}}{\underset{\underset{\displaystyle OH}{|}}{P}}-O-CH_2CH_2\overset{+}{N}(CH_3)_3 \end{array}$$

Phosphate ester linkages

A phospholipid
(Lecithin)

Anhydrides of phosphoric acid can be formed by bringing two molecules together and eliminating a water molecule.

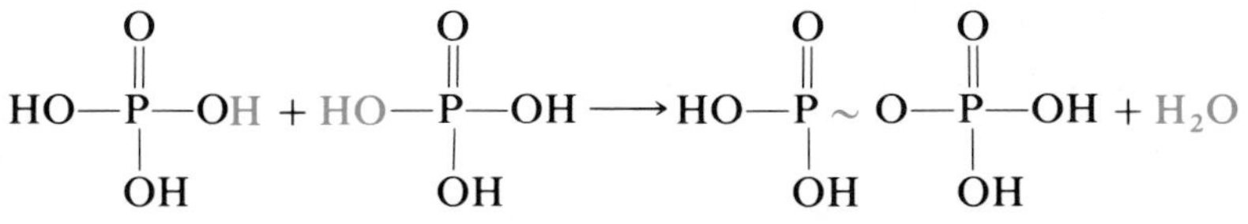

$$\underset{\text{Phosphoric acid}}{HO-\overset{\overset{O}{\|}}{\underset{\underset{OH}{|}}{P}}-OH} + \underset{\text{Phosphoric acid}}{HO-\overset{\overset{O}{\|}}{\underset{\underset{OH}{|}}{P}}-OH} \longrightarrow \underset{\text{Pyrophosphoric acid}}{HO-\overset{\overset{O}{\|}}{\underset{\underset{OH}{|}}{P}} \sim O-\overset{\overset{O}{\|}}{\underset{\underset{OH}{|}}{P}}-OH} + H_2O$$

This reaction is similar to a condensation reaction and results in a phosphoric anhydride linkage (shown as $\sim$). The pyrophosphoric acid can react with another phosphoric acid to produce triphosphoric acid.

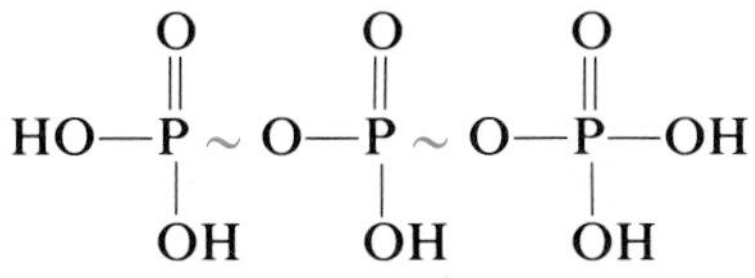

$$HO-\overset{\overset{O}{\|}}{\underset{\underset{OH}{|}}{P}} \sim O-\overset{\overset{O}{\|}}{\underset{\underset{OH}{|}}{P}} \sim O-\overset{\overset{O}{\|}}{\underset{\underset{OH}{|}}{P}}-OH$$

These anhydrides can then react with alcohols to form diphosphates or triphosphates. The most common triphosphate molecules in living systems are adenosine triphosphate (ATP).

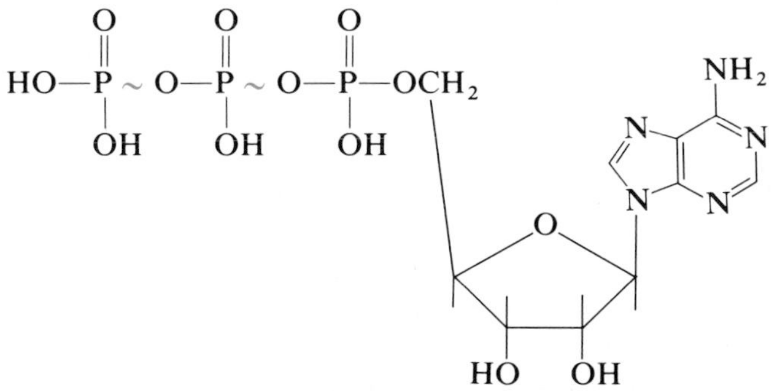

$$HO-\overset{\overset{O}{\|}}{\underset{\underset{OH}{|}}{P}} \sim O-\overset{\overset{O}{\|}}{\underset{\underset{OH}{|}}{P}} \sim O-\overset{\overset{O}{\|}}{\underset{\underset{OH}{|}}{P}}-OCH_2$$

NH₂ N N N N O HO OH

Adenosine triphosphate (ATP)

ATP was first isolated from skeletal tissue and is now known to occur in all kinds of plant and animal cells. Adenosine triphosphate is a carrier of energy in cells. The bonds between phosphates are high-energy bonds. These high energy bonds release large amounts of energy (>7000 cal/mol) when they are hydrolyzed, for instance when ATP is hydrolyzed to adenosine diphosphate (ADP):

$$\text{ATP} \overset{H_2O}{\rightleftarrows} \text{ADP} + H_2PO_4^- + \text{Energy}$$

An important feature of this reaction is its reversibility. Hydrolysis releases energy while synthesis requires energy. A typical ATP molecule can be recycled within a minute of forming. Although ATP is the principal energy carrier in the cell, there are other phosphate anhydrides that are also high energy compounds in living organisms.

Chemistry in Action

Aspirin

From the earliest days of medicine, people have obtained pain relief by chewing willow bark. In 1840 the active compound was isolated from the bark and identified as salicylic acid. Unfortunately, salicylic acid has several undesirable side effects, including a very sour taste and irritation of the stomach lining.

In 1883 an organic chemist reacted salicylic acid with acetic anhydride to form the ester acetylsalicylic acid.

$$\text{C}_6\text{H}_4(\text{COOH})\text{—O—}\overset{\text{O}}{\overset{\|}{\text{C}}}\text{—CH}_3$$

Acetylsalicylic acid

The chemist happened to work for the Bayer Company, and the name "aspirin" became popularized worldwide.

Aspirin is the most widely used drug in the world. It acts as a fever reducer (antipyretic), a pain reliever (analgesic), and an anti-inflammatory agent. In large doses (lethal is between 30 and 40 g) aspirin is also a poison. Tablets are manufactured by mixing 0.32 g of aspirin with an inert binder (often starch) to hold the tablet together. Approximately half of the aspirin manufactured in the United States (more than 45 million pounds) is made into aspirin tablets. The remainder is used in combination pain relievers and cold remedies.

Until relatively recently it was not understood how aspirin acted within the body. Chemists have now determined that aspirin inhibits an enzyme necessary for the synthesis of prostaglandins (Chapter 11). Functions of prostaglandins include elevation of the blood pressure, tissue inflammation, and activation of the pain receptors in tissues. A reduction in the synthesis of prostaglandins produces both analgesic and anti-inflammatory effects.

Aspirin usage poses undesirable side effects as well. It causes irritation of the stomach lining, can inhibit blood clotting, prolong labor, and is associated with the development of Reyes syndrome, a brain disease which occurs in children recovering from chicken pox or flu. Some people are allergic to aspirin.

Publicity over Reyes syndrome and allergic reactions have resulted in the development of alternatives to aspirin. The most common alternatives are acetaminophen and ibuprofen. Acetaminophen acts as an analgesic and antipyretic, but is not anti-inflammatory. Ibuprofen, a fairly recent addition to the nonprescriptive drug category, acts as a prostaglandin inhibitor in a manner similar to aspirin.

$$\text{HO—C}_6\text{H}_4\text{—NH—}\overset{\text{O}}{\overset{\|}{\text{C}}}\text{—CH}_3$$

Acetaminophen

$$\text{CH}_3\overset{\text{CH}_3}{\overset{|}{\text{CH}}}\text{CH}_2\text{—C}_6\text{H}_4\text{—}\underset{\underset{\text{CH}_3}{|}}{\text{CH}}\text{—COOH}$$

Ibuprofen

Other esters of salicylic acid also show medicinal effects. Methyl salicylate is an oil with the odor of wintergreen. It is commonly found as the active ingredient in pain-relieving liniments. It has the unusual property of penetrating the skin surface where it hydrolyzes, releasing salicylic acid and relieving the pain. Phenyl salicylate is an ester that is not hydrolyzed by acids. It is used to coat pills in order to permit them to pass through the stomach before disintegrating and releasing their contents.

Concepts in Review

1. Give the common and IUPAC names of carboxylic acids.
2. Write structural formulas for saturated carboxylic acids, unsaturated acids, hydroxy acids, aromatic carboxylic acids, and dicarboxylic acids.
3. Tell how water solubility of carboxylic acids varies with increasing molar mass.
4. Relate the boiling points of carboxylic acids to their structure.
5. Write equations for the preparation of carboxylic acids by (a) oxidation of alcohols and aldehydes, (b) hydrolysis or saponification of esters and fats, (c) oxidation of aromatic hydrocarbons, and (d) hydrolysis of nitriles.
6. Write equations showing the effect of heat on malonic, succinic, and glutaric acids.
7. Write equations for the reactions of carboxylic acids to form (a) salts, (b) esters, and (c) acid chlorides.
8. Write an equation to show the formation of an ester from an acid chloride.
9. Write common names, IUPAC names, and formulas of esters.
10. Identify the portion of an ester that is derived from a carboxylic acid and the portion derived from an alcohol.
11. Write the structure of a triacylglycerol (triglyceride) when given the fatty acid composition.
12. Explain the differences between a fat and an oil.
13. Write equations illustrating the (a) hydrogenation, (b) hydrogenolysis, (c) hydrolysis, and (d) saponification of a fat or oil.
14. Write the structural formulas for the three principal unsaturated carboxylic acids found in fats and oils.
15. Explain how a soap or synthetic detergent acts as a cleansing agent.
16. Explain why syndets are effective and soaps are not effective as cleansing agents in hard water.
17. Differentiate among cationic, anionic, and nonionic detergents.
18. Explain the similarities between a carboxylic acid and phosphoric acid.
19. Write an equation showing the formation of a phosphate ester.
20. Write an equation for the formation of a phosphoric anhydride.
21. Indicate the significant role of phosphate esters in living organisms.
22. Indicate the ways in which aspirin acts within the body.
23. Explain how aspirin and ibuprofen differ from acetaminophen in medicinal use within the body.

Equations in Review

Acid–Base Reactions

$$\text{RCOOH} + \text{M}^+\text{OH}^- \longrightarrow \text{RCOO}^-\,\text{M}^+ + \text{H}_2\text{O}$$

Formation of Acid Chlorides

$$\text{R—}\overset{\overset{\displaystyle\text{O}}{\|}}{\text{C}}\text{—OH} + \text{SOCl}_2 \longrightarrow \text{R—}\overset{\overset{\displaystyle\text{O}}{\|}}{\text{C}}\text{—Cl} + \text{SO}_2 + \text{HCl}$$

Esterification

$$\text{R—}\overset{\overset{\displaystyle\text{O}}{\|}}{\text{C}}\text{—OH} + \text{HOR}' \xrightarrow{\text{H}^+} \text{R—}\overset{\overset{\displaystyle\text{O}}{\|}}{\text{C}}\text{—OR}' + \text{H}_2\text{O}$$

Phosphorylation

$$\text{HO—}\underset{\underset{\displaystyle\text{OH}}{|}}{\overset{\overset{\displaystyle\text{O}}{\|}}{\text{P}}}\text{—OH} + \text{HOR}' \xrightarrow{\text{H}^+} \text{HO—}\underset{\underset{\displaystyle\text{OH}}{|}}{\overset{\overset{\displaystyle\text{O}}{\|}}{\text{P}}}\text{—OR}' + \text{H}_2\text{O}$$

Formation of Anhydrides

$$\text{R—}\overset{\overset{\displaystyle\text{O}}{\|}}{\text{C}}\text{—OH} + \text{HO—}\overset{\overset{\displaystyle\text{O}}{\|}}{\text{C}}\text{—R}' \longrightarrow \text{R—}\overset{\overset{\displaystyle\text{O}}{\|}}{\text{C}}\text{—O—}\overset{\overset{\displaystyle\text{O}}{\|}}{\text{C}}\text{—R}' + \text{H}_2\text{O}$$

$$\text{HO—}\underset{\underset{\displaystyle\text{OH}}{|}}{\overset{\overset{\displaystyle\text{O}}{\|}}{\text{P}}}\text{—OH} + \text{HO—}\underset{\underset{\displaystyle\text{OH}}{|}}{\overset{\overset{\displaystyle\text{O}}{\|}}{\text{P}}}\text{—OH} \longrightarrow \text{HO—}\underset{\underset{\displaystyle\text{OH}}{|}}{\overset{\overset{\displaystyle\text{O}}{\|}}{\text{P}}}\text{—O—}\underset{\underset{\displaystyle\text{OH}}{|}}{\overset{\overset{\displaystyle\text{O}}{\|}}{\text{P}}}\text{—OH} + \text{H}_2\text{O}$$

Acid Hydrolysis

$$\text{R—}\overset{\overset{\displaystyle\text{O}}{\|}}{\text{C}}\text{—OR}' + \text{H}_2\text{O} \xrightarrow{\text{H}^+} \text{R—}\overset{\overset{\displaystyle\text{O}}{\|}}{\text{C}}\text{—OH} + \text{HOR}'$$

Basic Hydrolysis (Saponification)

$$\text{R—}\overset{\overset{\displaystyle\text{O}}{\|}}{\text{C}}\text{—OR}' + \text{NaOH} \longrightarrow \text{R—}\overset{\overset{\displaystyle\text{O}}{\|}}{\text{C}}\text{—O}^-\,{}^+\text{Na} + \text{HOR}'$$

EXERCISES

1. Using a specific compound in each case, write structural formulas for the following:
   (a) An aliphatic carboxylic acid
   (b) An aromatic carboxylic acid
   (c) An α-hydroxy acid
   (d) An α-amino acid
   (e) A β-chloro acid
   (f) A dicarboxylic acid
   (g) An unsaturated acid
   (h) An ester
   (i) A nitrile
   (j) A sodium salt of a carboxylic acid
   (k) An acid halide
   (l) A triacylglycerol
2. Name the following compounds:
   (a) $CH_3(CH_2)_5COOH$
   (b) 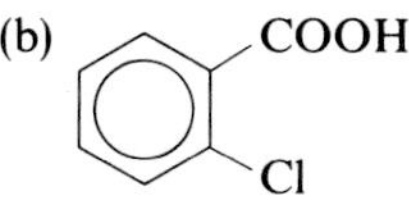

   (c) $CH_3CH{=}CHCOOH$
   (d) $CH_3(CH_2)_7CH{=}CH(CH_2)_7COOH$
   (e) COOH
   COOH
   (f) COOH
   CH_3
   (g) $CH_3(CH_2)_{16}COOH$
   (h) $CH_3CH_2\underset{\displaystyle OH}{\underset{|}{C}}HCOOH$
   (i) $CH_3CH_2COO^-\ Na^+$
   (j) $CH_3CH_2COO^-\ NH_4^+$
3. Write structures for the following compounds:
   (a) Caproic acid
   (b) Adipic acid
   (c) *o*-Toluic acid
   (d) Oxalic acid
   (e) β-Hydroxybutyric acid
   (f) *p*-Phthalic acid
   (g) Sodium benzoate
   (h) Linolenic acid
   (i) 2-Chloropropanoic acid
   (j) Ammonium benzoate
   (k) *p*-Aminobenzoic acid
   (l) *m*-Phthalic acid
4. Which of the following would have the more objectionable odor?
   (a) A 1% solution of butyric acid (C_3H_7COOH)
   (b) A 1% solution of sodium butyrate (C_3H_7COONa)
   Cite a satisfactory reason for your answer.
5. Suggest a logical scheme for obtaining reasonably pure stearic acid from a solution containing 2.0% sodium stearate, $CH_3(CH_2)_{16}COONa$, dissolved in water.
6. Assume that you have a 0.01 *M* solution of each of the following substances:
   (a) NH_3 (c) NaCl (e) CH_3COOH
   (b) HCl (d) NaOH (f) C_6H_5—OH
   Arrange them in order of increasing pH (list the most acidic solution first).
7. Give at least one name, more if you can, for each of the following:
   (a) $H\overset{O}{\overset{\|}{C}}{-}OCH_3$
   (b) $C_6H_5{-}\overset{O}{\overset{\|}{C}}{-}O{-}CH(CH_3)_2$
   (c) $C_6H_4(OH){-}\overset{O}{\overset{\|}{C}}{-}O{-}C_6H_5$ (OH ortho to the ester group)
   (d) $CH_3CH_2\overset{O}{\overset{\|}{C}}{-}OCH_2CH_3$
   (e) $CH_3CH_2O{-}\overset{O}{\overset{\|}{C}}{-}\overset{O}{\overset{\|}{C}}{-}OCH_2CH_3$
   (f) $CH_2{=}CH\overset{O}{\overset{\|}{C}}{-}OCH_3$
8. Write structural formulas for each:
   (a) Methyl formate (c) *n*-Propyl propanoate
   (b) *n*-Octyl acetate (d) Ethyl benzoate
9. Write the structural formula and name of the principal organic product for each of the following reactions:
   (a) $CH_3(CH_2)_7CH{=}CH(CH_2)_7\overset{O}{\overset{\|}{C}}OH + H_2 \xrightarrow{Ni}$

(b) $CH_3CH_2\overset{O}{\overset{\|}{C}}-OH + SOCl_2 \longrightarrow$

(c) 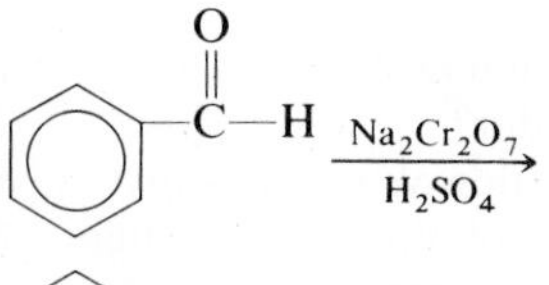 $C_6H_5-\overset{O}{\overset{\|}{C}}-H \xrightarrow[H_2SO_4]{Na_2Cr_2O_7}$

(d) 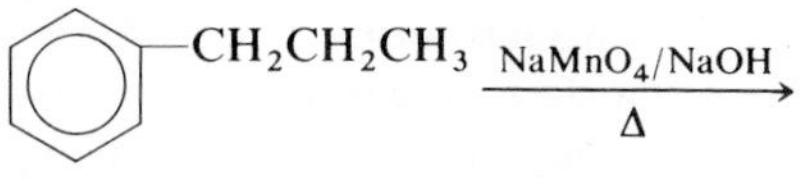 $C_6H_5-CH_2CH_2CH_3 \xrightarrow[\Delta]{NaMnO_4/NaOH}$

(e) 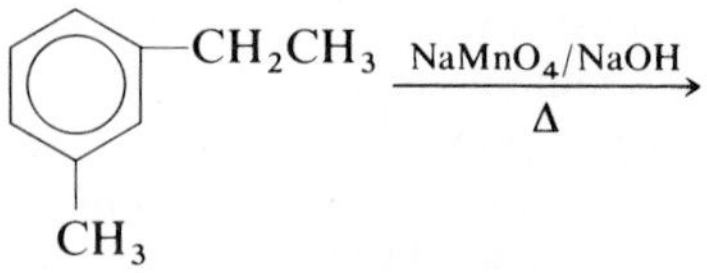 $CH_3-C_6H_4-CH_2CH_3 \xrightarrow[\Delta]{NaMnO_4/NaOH}$

(f) $CH_3CH_2COOH + NaOH \longrightarrow$

(g) $CH_3(CH_2)_3CH_2\overset{O}{\overset{\|}{C}}OCH_2CH_2CH_3 + NaOH \xrightarrow{\Delta}$

10. Write structural formulas for the organic products of the following reactions:

(a) 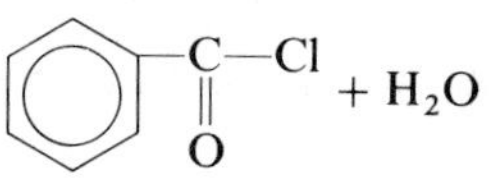 $C_6H_5-\underset{\underset{O}{\|}}{C}-Cl + H_2O$

(b) 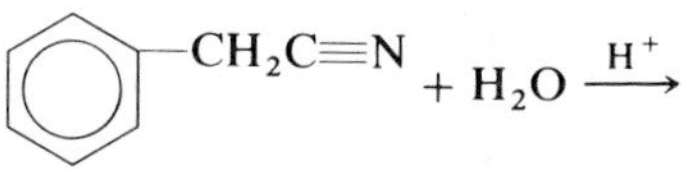 $C_6H_5-CH_2C{\equiv}N + H_2O \xrightarrow{H^+}$

11. Write structural formulas for the organic products of the following reactions:

(a) $CH_3-CH(COOH)-COOH \xrightarrow{150°C}$

(b) $HOOC-CH_2-CH_2-CH_2COOH \xrightarrow{\Delta}$

Glutaric acid

(c) 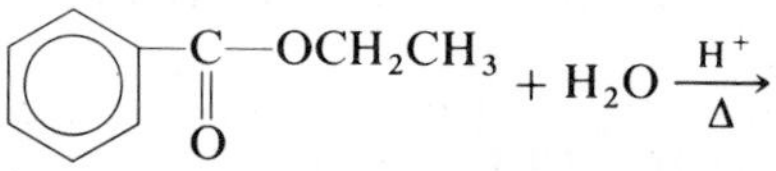 $C_6H_5-\underset{\underset{O}{\|}}{C}-OCH_2CH_3 + H_2O \xrightarrow[\Delta]{H^+}$

(d) 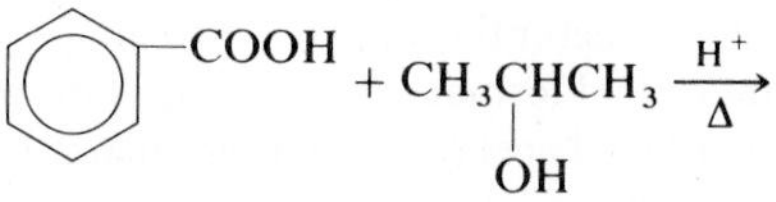 $C_6H_5-COOH + CH_3\underset{\underset{OH}{|}}{C}HCH_3 \xrightarrow[\Delta]{H^+}$

(e) 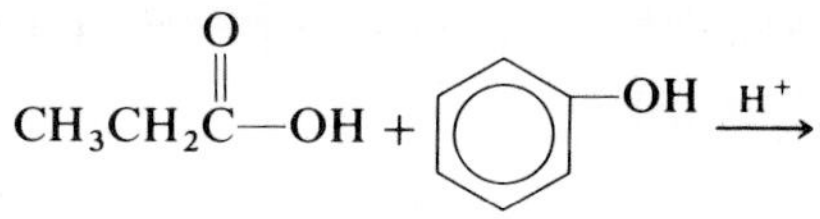 $CH_3CH_2\overset{O}{\overset{\|}{C}}-OH + C_6H_5-OH \xrightarrow{H^+}$

(f) $HOOC-CH_2-COOH + 2\,C_2H_5OH \xrightarrow{H^+}$ (2 mol)

12. Write the structural formulas for the organic products formed in the following reactions:

(a) 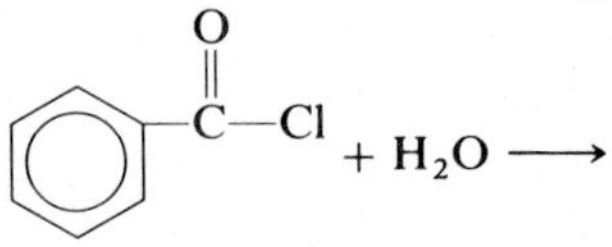 $C_6H_5-\overset{O}{\overset{\|}{C}}-Cl + H_2O \longrightarrow$

(b) $CH_2{=}CHCOOH + Br_2 \longrightarrow$

(c) $CH_3COOH + SOCl_2 \longrightarrow$

(d) $CH_3\overset{O}{\overset{\|}{C}}-Cl + NH_3 \longrightarrow$

(e) $CH_3\overset{O}{\overset{\|}{C}}-Cl + CH_3CH_2OH \longrightarrow$

13. Write the structural formula of the ester that when hydrolyzed would yield
(a) Methanol and acetic acid
(b) Ethanol and formic acid
(c) 1-Octanol and acetic acid
(d) 2-Propanol and benzoic acid
(e) Methanol and salicylic acid

14. Write structural formulas for the following compounds:
(a) Isopropyl formate
(b) Methyl palmitate
(c) Diethyl adipate
(d) Benzyl benzoate
(e) Phenyl propionate
(f) Methyl-2-chloropentanoate

15. What simple tests can be used to distinguish between the following pairs of compounds?
(a) Benzoic acid and sodium benzoate
(b) Maleic acid and malonic acid

16. The geometric configuration of naturally occurring unsaturated 18-carbon acids is all cis. Draw structural formulas for
(a) *cis*-Oleic acid (b) *cis,cis*-Linoleic acid

17. Write the structural formula of a triacylglycerol that contains one unit each of lauric acid, palmitic acid, and stearic acid. How many other triacylglycerols, each containing all three of these acids, are possible?

18. Triolein (glyceryl trioleate) has this structure:

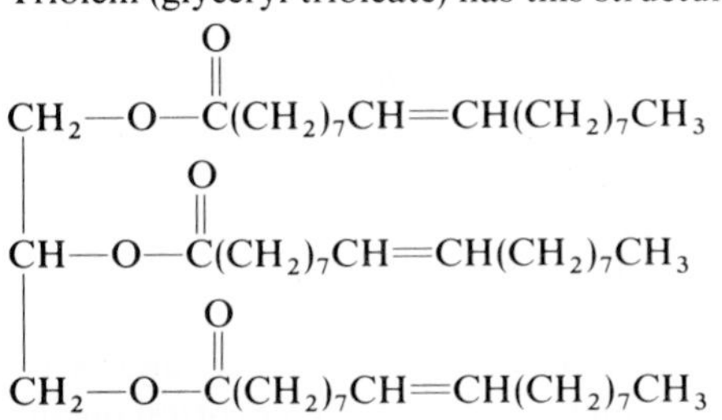

$$\begin{array}{l} CH_2-O-\overset{\overset{\large O}{\|}}{C}(CH_2)_7CH{=}CH(CH_2)_7CH_3 \\ | \\ CH-O-\overset{\overset{\large O}{\|}}{C}(CH_2)_7CH{=}CH(CH_2)_7CH_3 \\ | \\ CH_2-O-\overset{\overset{\large O}{\|}}{C}(CH_2)_7CH{=}CH(CH_2)_7CH_3 \end{array}$$

Write the names and formulas of all products expected when triolein is
(a) Reacted with hydrogen in the presence of Ni
(b) Reacted with water at high temperature and pressure in the presence of mineral acid
(c) Boiled with potassium hydroxide
(d) Reacted with hydrogen at relatively high pressure and temperature in the presence of a copper chromite catalyst

19. Which has the greater solubility in water?
(a) Methyl propanoate or propanoic acid
(b) Sodium palmitate or palmitic acid
(c) Sodium stearate or barium stearate
(d) Phenol or sodium phenoxide

20. Write the structural formulas for each pair of compounds mentioned in Question 19.

21. Explain the difference between
(a) A fat and an oil
(b) A soap and a syndet
(c) Hydrolysis and saponification

22. Cite the principal advantages synthetic detergents (syndets) have over soaps.

23. Would $CH_3(CH_2)_{12}COOH$ or $CH_3(CH_2)_{12}COONa$ be the more useful cleansing agent in soft water? Explain.

24. Would $CH_3(CH_2)_{11}OSO_3Na$ (sodium lauryl sulfate) or $CH_3CH_2CH_2OSO_3Na$ (sodium propyl sulfate) be the more effective detergent in hard water? Explain.

25. Explain the cleansing action of detergents.

26. Which one of the following substances is a good detergent in water? Is this substance a nonionic, anionic, or cationic detergent?
(a) $C_{16}H_{33}N(CH_3)_3^+ \, Cl^-$
Hexadecyltrimethyl ammonium chloride
(b) $C_{16}H_{34}$
Hexadecane
(c) $C_{15}H_{31}COOH$
Palmitic acid (Hexadecanoic acid)
(d) $C_{15}H_{31}\overset{\overset{\large O}{\|}}{C}-O-C_{16}H_{33}$
Cetyl palmitate (Hexadecyl hexadecanoate)

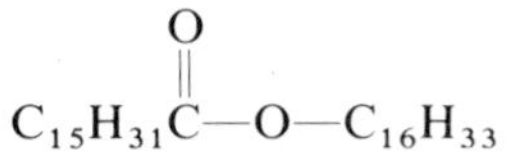

27. Margarine consists principally of a relatively small amount of water emulsified in vegetable or animal fats and oils. Monoacylglycerols (monoglycerides) such as glycerol monooleate,

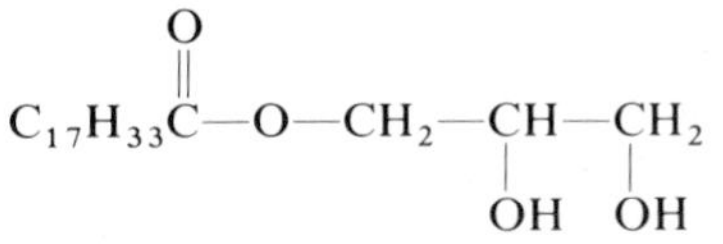

$$C_{17}H_{33}\overset{\overset{\large O}{\|}}{C}-O-CH_2-\underset{\underset{\large OH}{|}}{CH}-\underset{\underset{\large OH}{|}}{CH_2}$$

are often used in small quantities in making margarine.
(a) What is the function of the monoacylglycerols?
(b) Explain how this function is achieved.

28. If 1.00 kg of triolein (glyceryl trioleate) is converted to tristearin (glyceryl tristearate) by hydrogenation:
(a) How many liters of hydrogen (at STP) are required?
(b) What is the mass of the tristearin that is produced?

29. Which acid requires more base for neutralization, (a) 1 g of acetic acid or (b) 1 g of propanoic acid? Explain your answer.

30. Starting with ethyl alcohol as the only source of organic material and using any other reagents you desire, write equations to show the synthesis of
(a) Acetic acid
(b) Ethyl acetate
(c) β-Hydroxybutyric acid

31. Upon hydrolysis, an ester of formula $C_6H_{12}O_2$ yields an acid A and an alcohol B. When B is oxidized, it yields a product identical to A. What is the structure of the ester? Explain your answer.

32. Show the products of the reaction of 1 mole of phosphoric acid with
(a) 1 mole of ethanol
(b) 2 moles of ethanol
(c) 3 moles of ethanol

33. What type of chemical reaction is the conversion of ATP into ADP?

34. List the medicinal effects of aspirin within the body.

35. What are the risks associated with the use of aspirin?

36. What substances are commonly substituted for aspirin? Indicate their effects in contrast to those of aspirin.

37. Give two examples of other esters of salicylic acid that have medicinal uses.
38. Which of these statements are correct? Rewrite the incorrect statements to make them correct.
    (a) Carboxylic acids can be either aliphatic or aromatic.
    (b) The functional group —COOH is known as a carboxyl group.
    (c) The name for $CH_3CH_2CHBrCH_2COOH$ is γ-bromovaleric acid.
    (d) Acetic acid is a stronger acid than hydrochloric acid.
    (e) Benzoic acid is more soluble in water than sodium benzoate.
    (f) Carboxylic acids have relatively high boiling points because of hydrogen bonding between molecules.
    (g) The formula $C_{17}H_{33}COOH$ represents oleic acid.
    (h) Fumaric and maleic acids are cis–trans isomers.
    (i) If $CH_3CH_2CH_2COCl$ comes into contact with water, it is hydrolyzed to butyric acid.
    (j) Volatile esters generally have a pleasant odor.
    (k) Glycerol is a trihydroxy alcohol.
    (l) Fatty acids in fats usually have an even number of carbon atoms.
    (m) Fats and oils are esters of glycerol.
    (n) Oils are largely of vegetable origin.
    (o) The presence of unsaturation in the acid component of a fat tends to raise its melting point compared with the corresponding saturated compound.
    (p) Alkali metal salts of long-chain fatty acids are called soaps.
    (q) The chemical name for aspirin is acetylsalicylic acid.
    (r) ATP has one high energy phosphate bond.
    (s) The hydrophobic end of a detergent molecule is water soluble.
    (t) Saponification is the hydrolysis of a fat or an ester in an acid medium.
    (u) Methyl salicylate is a salt.

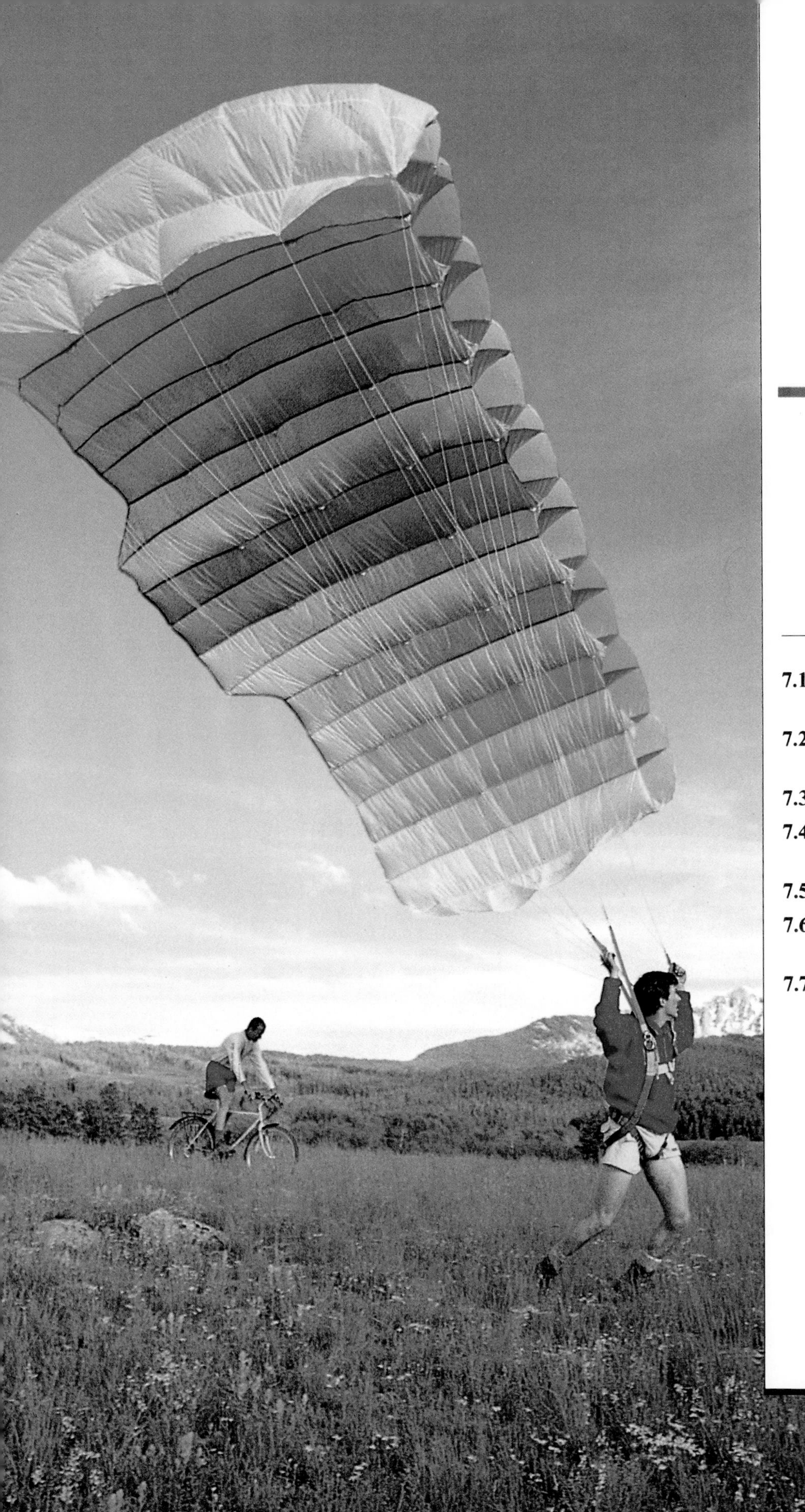

7

Amides and Amines: Organic Nitrogen Compounds

◄ CHAPTER OPENING PHOTO: **The nylon used in parachutes and in sports clothing is formed by linking amines and carboxylic acids into amides.**

Organic compounds can also contain nitrogen. Two major classes of nitrogen-containing compounds are amines and amides. Amines isolated from plants form a group of compounds called alkaloids. Thousands of alkaloids have been isolated. Many of these compounds exhibit physiological activity. Examples of common alkaloid compounds include quinine, used in the treatment of malaria; strychnine, a poison; morphine, a narcotic; and nicotine, a stimulant. Many other drugs are also nitrogen-containing compounds.

Amides are nitrogen derivatives of carboxylic acids. These compounds are found as polymers, both commercially as in nylon, and biologically as in proteins. An understanding of the chemistry of organic nitrogen compounds is the cornerstone of genetics, and is essential to unlocking the chemical secrets of living organisms.

7.1 AMIDES: NOMENCLATURE AND PHYSICAL PROPERTIES

Carboxylic acids react with ammonia to form ammonium salts:

$$\underset{\text{Carboxylic acid}}{\mathrm{R\overset{\overset{O}{\|}}{C}{-}OH}} + \underset{\text{Ammonia}}{\mathrm{NH_3}} \longrightarrow \underset{\text{Ammonium salt}}{\mathrm{R\overset{\overset{O}{\|}}{C}{-}O^-\ NH_4^+}}$$

$$\underset{\text{Acetic acid}}{\mathrm{CH_3\overset{\overset{O}{\|}}{C}{-}OH}} + \mathrm{NH_3} \longrightarrow \underset{\text{Ammonium acetate}}{\mathrm{CH_3\overset{\overset{O}{\|}}{C}{-}O^-\ NH_4^+}}$$

Ammonium salts of carboxylic acids are ionic substances. Ammonium acetate, for example, is ionized and exists as ammonium ions and acetate ions, both in the crystalline form and when dissolved in water.

When heated, ammonium salts of carboxylic acids are converted to *amides*:

$$\underset{\text{Ammonium salt}}{\mathrm{R\overset{\overset{O}{\|}}{C}{-}\bar{O}{-}NH_4^+}} \xrightarrow{\Delta} \underset{\text{Amide}}{\mathrm{R\overset{\overset{O}{\|}}{C}{-}NH_2}} + \mathrm{H_2O}$$

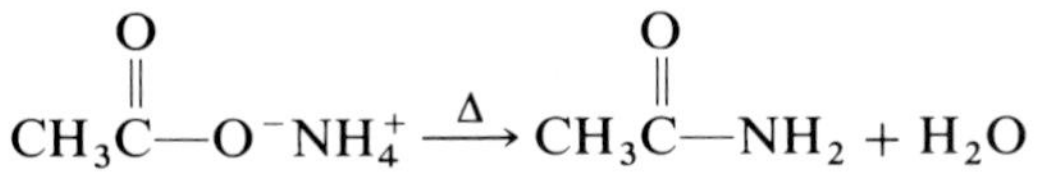

$$CH_3\overset{\overset{\displaystyle O}{\|}}{C}-O^-NH_4^+ \xrightarrow{\Delta} CH_3\overset{\overset{\displaystyle O}{\|}}{C}-NH_2 + H_2O$$

Ammonium acetate — Acetamide (Ethanamide)

Amides are molecular substances and exist as molecules (not ions) both in the crystalline form and when dissolved in water. An amide contains the following characteristic structure:

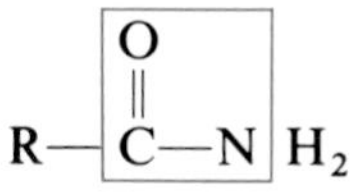

$$R-\boxed{\overset{\overset{\displaystyle O}{\|}}{C}-N}H_2$$

Amide structure

In amides the carbon atom of a carbonyl group is bonded directly to a nitrogen atom of an $-NH_2$, $-NHR$, or $-NR_2$ group. The amide structure occurs in numerous substances, including proteins and some synthetic polymers such as nylon.

Two systems are in use for naming amides. The IUPAC name is based on the longest carbon chain that includes the amide group. The amide name is formed by dropping the *oic acid* ending from the corresponding IUPAC acid name and adding the suffix *amide*. Thus,

Methanoic acid	becomes	Methanamide
$HCOOH$		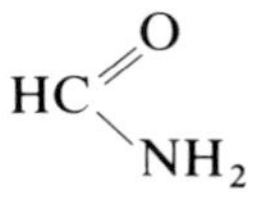 $HC(=O)NH_2$
Ethanoic acid	becomes	Ethanamide
CH_3COOH		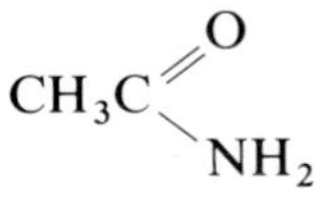 $CH_3C(=O)NH_2$

In a like manner, the common names for amides are formed from the common names of the corresponding carboxylic acids by dropping the *ic* or *oic acid* ending and adding the suffix *amide*. Thus,

Formic acid	becomes	Formamide
$HCOOH$		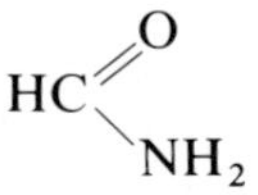 $HC(=O)NH_2$
Butyric acid	becomes	Butyramide
$CH_3CH_2CH_2COOH$		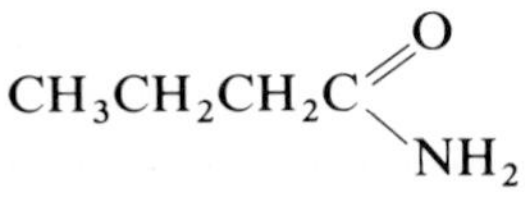 $CH_3CH_2CH_2C(=O)NH_2$

Benzoic acid becomes Benzamide

$$C_6H_5\text{—}COOH \qquad C_6H_5\text{—}\overset{\displaystyle O}{\overset{\|}{C}}\text{—}NH_2$$

When the nitrogen of an amide is connected to an alkyl or aryl group, the group is named as a prefix preceded by the letter *N*.

$$CH_3\text{—}\overset{\displaystyle O}{\overset{\|}{C}}\text{—}\underset{\displaystyle H}{\underset{|}{N}}\text{—}CH_3 \quad \text{is} \quad N\text{-methylacetamide}$$

$$CH_3CH_2\text{—}\overset{\displaystyle O}{\overset{\|}{C}}\text{—}\underset{\displaystyle CH_2CH_3}{\underset{|}{N}}\text{—}CH_2CH_3 \quad \text{is} \quad N,N\text{-diethylpropionamide}$$

Formulas and names of selected amides are shown in Table 7.1.

Except for formamide, a liquid, all other unsubstituted amides are solids at room temperature. Many are odorless and colorless. Low molar mass amides are soluble in water, but solubility decreases quickly as molar mass

TABLE 7.1 Formulas and Names of Selected Amides

Formula	IUPAC name	Common name
$H\overset{O}{\overset{\|}{C}}\text{—}NH_2$	Methanamide	Formamide
$CH_3\overset{O}{\overset{\|}{C}}\text{—}NH_2$	Ethanamide	Acetamide
$CH_3CH_2\overset{O}{\overset{\|}{C}}\text{—}NH_2$	Propanamide	Propionamide
$CH_3\underset{}{\overset{CH_3}{\overset{\mid}{C}}}H\text{—}\overset{O}{\overset{\|}{C}}\text{—}NH_2$	2-Methylpropanamide	Isobutyramide
$CH_3\text{—}\overset{O}{\overset{\|}{C}}\text{—}\overset{H}{\overset{\mid}{N}}\text{—}C_6H_5$	N-phenylethanamide	Acetanilide
$CH_3\text{—}\overset{O}{\overset{\|}{C}}\text{—}\underset{H}{\underset{\mid}{N}}\text{—}C_6H_4\text{—}OH$	N-*p*-hydroxyphenylethanamide	Acetaminophen

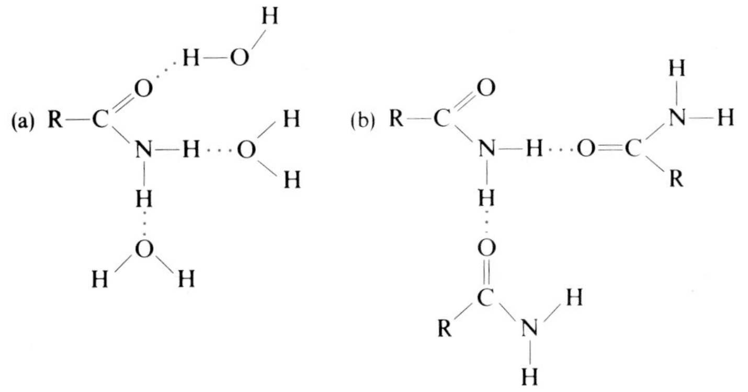

◄ FIGURE 7.1
Hydrogen bonding in amides. (a) Hydrogen bonding between amides and water molecules; (b) intermolecular hydrogen bonding.

increases. The amide functional group is polar, and nitrogen is capable of hydrogen bonding. The solubility of these molecules and their exceptionally high melting points and boiling points are the result of this polarity and hydrogen bonding between molecules, shown in Figure 7.1.

7.2 CHEMICAL PROPERTIES OF AMIDES

One of the more important reactions of amides is hydrolysis. This type of reaction is analogous to hydrolysis of carboxylic esters. The amide is cleaved into two parts, the carboxylic acid portion and the nitrogen-containing portion. As in ester hydrolysis, this reaction requires the presence of a strong acid or a strong base for it to occur in the laboratory. Amide hydrolysis is accomplished in living systems during the degradation of proteins by enzymatic reactions under much milder conditions (Chapter 12). Hydrolysis of an unsubstituted amide in an acid solution produces a carboxylic acid and an ammonium salt.

$$CH_3CH_2CH_2\overset{\overset{\displaystyle O}{\|}}{C}{-}NH_2 + H_2O + HCl \xrightarrow{\Delta} CH_3CH_2CH_2\overset{\overset{\displaystyle O}{\|}}{C}{-}OH + NH_4Cl$$

Basic hydrolysis results in the production of ammonia and the salt of a carboxylic acid.

$$CH_3{-}\overset{\overset{\displaystyle O}{\|}}{C}{-}NH_2 + OH^- \longrightarrow CH_3\overset{\overset{\displaystyle O}{\|}}{C}{-}O^- + NH_3$$

EXAMPLE 7.1

Show the products of acid and basic hydrolysis of

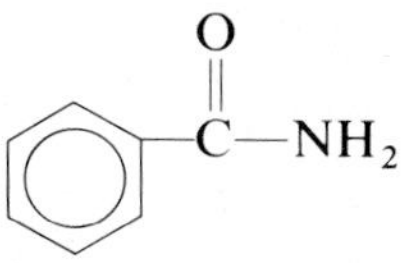

SOLUTION

(a) In acid hydrolysis the C—N bond is cleaved and the carboxylic acid is formed. The $-NH_2$ group is converted into an ammonium ion.

$$H^+ + C_6H_5\text{—}\overset{\overset{\large O}{\|}}{C}\text{—}NH_2 + HOH \longrightarrow C_6H_5\text{—}\overset{\overset{\large O}{\|}}{C}\text{—}OH + NH_4^+$$

(b) In basic solution the C—N bond is also cleaved, but since the solution is basic the salt of the carboxylic acid is formed along with ammonia.

$$C_6H_5\text{—}\overset{\overset{\large O}{\|}}{C}\text{—}NH_2 + OH^- \longrightarrow C_6H_5\text{—}\overset{\overset{\large O}{\|}}{C}\text{—}O^- + NH_3$$

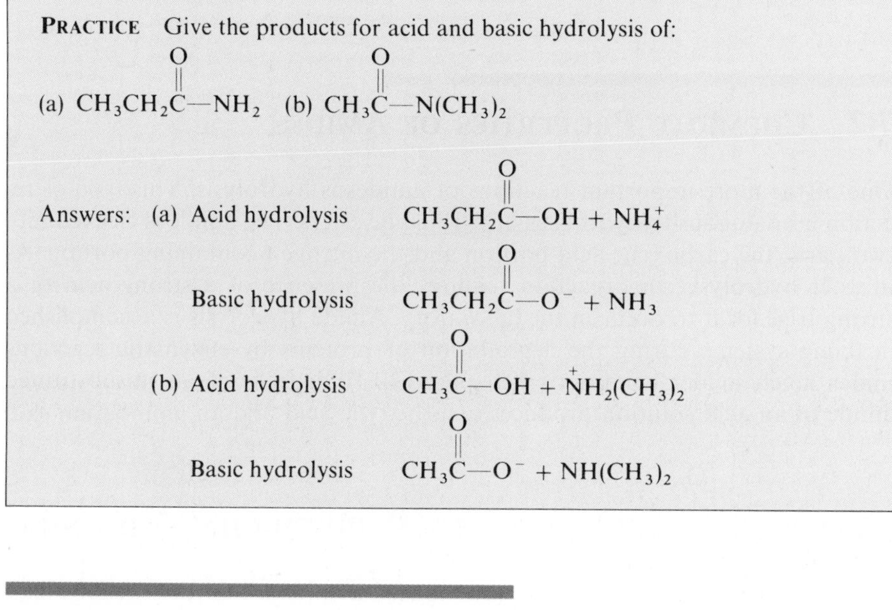

PRACTICE Give the products for acid and basic hydrolysis of:

(a) $CH_3CH_2\overset{\overset{\large O}{\|}}{C}\text{—}NH_2$ (b) $CH_3\overset{\overset{\large O}{\|}}{C}\text{—}N(CH_3)_2$

Answers: (a) Acid hydrolysis $CH_3CH_2\overset{\overset{\large O}{\|}}{C}\text{—}OH + NH_4^+$

Basic hydrolysis $CH_3CH_2\overset{\overset{\large O}{\|}}{C}\text{—}O^- + NH_3$

(b) Acid hydrolysis $CH_3\overset{\overset{\large O}{\|}}{C}\text{—}OH + \overset{+}{N}H_2(CH_3)_2$

Basic hydrolysis $CH_3\overset{\overset{\large O}{\|}}{C}\text{—}O^- + NH(CH_3)_2$

7.3 UREA

Hydrolysis of proteins in the digestion process involves cleavage of the amide linkage between adjacent amino acids (Chapter 12). The process begins in the acidic environment of the stomach, and hydrolysis continues in the small intestine.

The body disposes of nitrogen by the formation of a diamide known as urea.

$$H_2N\text{—}\overset{\overset{\large O}{\|}}{C}\text{—}NH_2$$

Urea

Urea is a white solid that melts at 133°C. It is soluble in water and therefore is excreted from the body as urine, an aqueous solution of urea. The normal adult excretes about 30 g of urea daily in urine.

Urea is a common commercial product as well. It is found most often as a fertilizer to add nitrogen to the soil, or as a starting material in the production of plastics and barbiturates.

7.4 Amines: Nomenclature and Physical Properties

amine

An **amine** is a substituted ammonia molecule and has the general formula RNH_2, R_2NH, or R_3N, where R is an alkyl or an aryl group. Amines are classified as primary (1°), secondary (2°), or tertiary (3°), depending on the number of hydrocarbon groups attached to the nitrogen atom. Examples are given below.

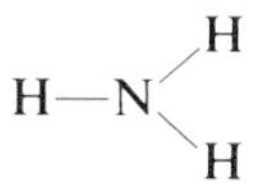

$H-NH_2$ — Ammonia

H_2N-CH_3 — Methylamine (1° amine)

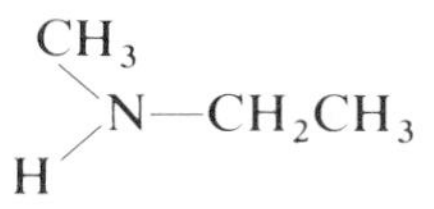

$(CH_3)(H)N-CH_2CH_3$ — Methylethylamine (2° amine)

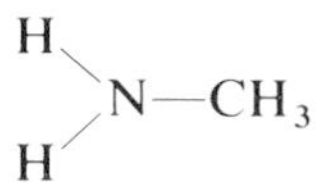

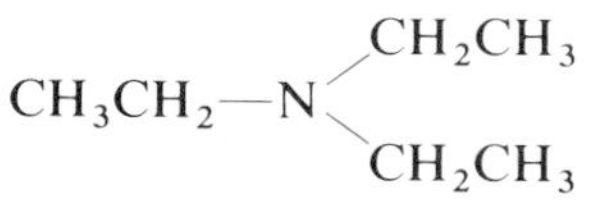

$CH_3CH_2-N(CH_2CH_3)_2$ — Triethylamine (3° amine)

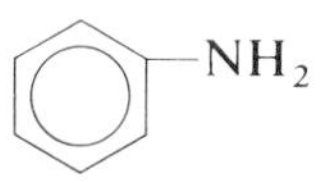

$C_6H_5-NH_2$ — Aniline (1° amine)

◄ **Mulching and fertilizing are ways of putting nitrogen into the soil.**

Common names for aliphatic amines are formed by naming the alkyl group or groups attached to the nitrogen atom followed by the ending *amine*. Thus, CH_3NH_2 is methylamine, $(CH_3)_2NH$ is dimethylamine, and $(CH_3)_3N$ is trimethylamine. A few more examples follow:

$CH_3CH_2NH_2$ Ethylamine

$CH_3CH_2CH_2NH_2$ Propylamine

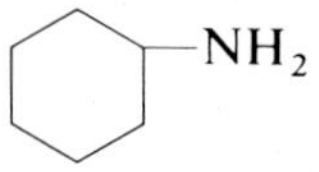

Cyclohexylamine ($C_6H_{11}NH_2$)

In the IUPAC System $-NH_2$ is called an amino group, and amines are named as amino-substituted hydrocarbons using the longest carbon chain as the parent compound (for example, $CH_3CH_2CH_2NH_2$ is called 1-aminopropane).

The most important aromatic amine is aniline ($C_6H_5NH_2$). Derivatives are named as substituted anilines. To identify a substituted aniline in which the substituent group is attached to the nitrogen atom, an *N*- is placed before the group name to indicate that the substituent is bonded to the nitrogen atom and not to a carbon atom in the ring. For example, the following compounds are called *N*-methylaniline and *N*,*N*-dimethylaniline:

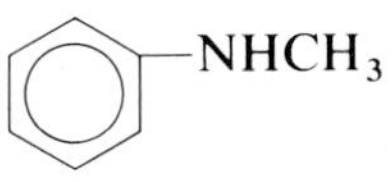

$C_6H_5-NHCH_3$ *N*-Methylaniline

$C_6H_5-N(CH_3)_2$ *N*,*N*-Dimethylaniline

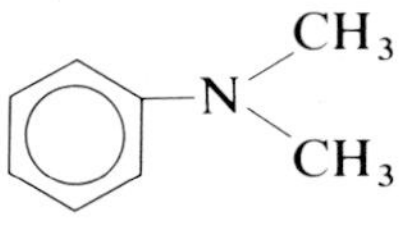

When a group is substituted for a hydrogen atom in the ring, the resulting ring-substituted aniline is named as we have previously done for naming aromatic compounds. The monomethyl ring-substituted anilines are known as toluidines. Study the names for the following substituted anilines:

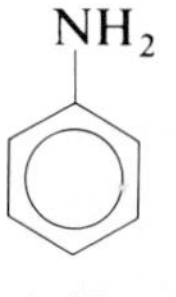

Aniline

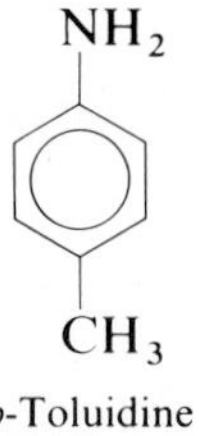

p-Toluidine (*p*-Methylaniline)

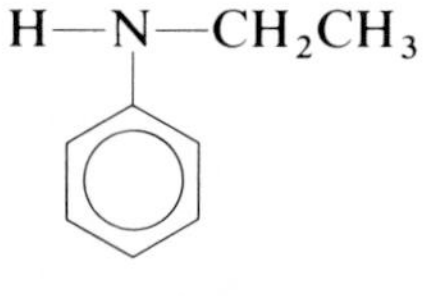

N-Ethylaniline ($H-N-CH_2CH_3$ on the ring)

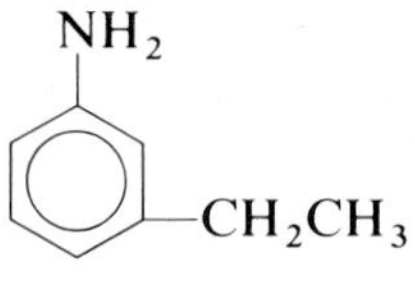

m-Ethylaniline

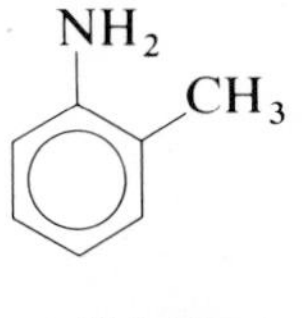

o-Toluidine (*o*-Methylaniline)

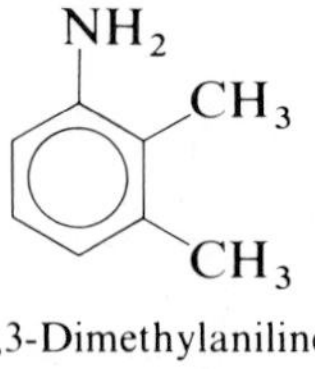

2,3-Dimethylaniline

p-Chloroaniline

Physiologically, aniline is a toxic substance. It is easily absorbed through the skin and affects both the blood and the nervous system. Aniline reduces the oxygen-carrying capacity of the blood by converting hemoglobin to methemoglobin. Methemoglobin is the oxidized form of hemoglobin in which the iron has gone from a +2 to a +3 oxidation state.

EXAMPLE 7.2

Name the two compounds given:

(a) $CH_3CH(CH_3)CH_2—NH_2$ (b) *p*-$H_2N—C_6H_4—COOH$ (COOH and NH_2 para on a benzene ring)

SOLUTION

(a) The alkyl group attached to NH_2 is an isobutyl group. Thus the common name is isobutylamine. The longest chain containing the NH_2 has three carbons. Therefore the parent carbon chain is propane, and the compound is called 1-amino-2-methylpropane.

(b) The parent compound on which the name is based is benzoic acid. With an amino group in the para position, the name is *p*-aminobenzoic acid. The acronym for *p*-aminobenzoic acid is PABA. In the human body PABA is a growth factor for certain bacteria. The main source of PABA for the human body is folic acid, an essential vitamin in the diet. Esters of PABA are some of the most effective ultraviolet screening agents and are used in suntanning lotions.

PRACTICE Name the following compounds.

(a) $CH_3CH_2CH_2NH_2$ (c) $CH_3CH(NH_2)CH_2CH_3$

(b) $NHCH_2CH_3$

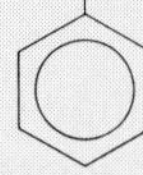

Answers: (a) propylamine (b) *N*-ethylaniline (c) 2-aminobutane

Ring compounds in which all the atoms in the ring are not alike are known as **heterocyclic compounds**. The most common heteroatoms are oxygen, nitrogen, and sulfur. A number of the nitrogen-containing heterocyclic compounds are present in naturally occurring biological substances such as DNA, which controls heredity. The structural formulas of several nitrogen-containing heterocyclics follow:

heterocyclic compounds

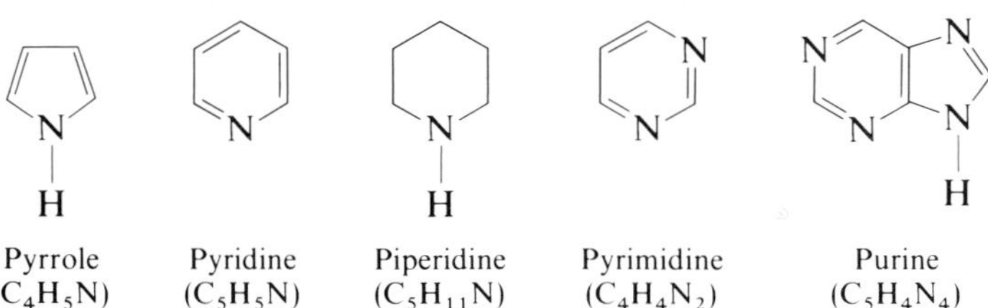

Pyrrole (C_4H_5N) Pyridine (C_5H_5N) Piperidine ($C_5H_{11}N$) Pyrimidine ($C_4H_4N_2$) Purine ($C_5H_4N_4$)

Amines are capable of hydrogen bonding with water. As a result the aliphatic amines with up to six carbons are quite soluble in water. The methylamines and ethylamine are flammable gases with a strong ammoniacal odor.

▲ The odor of dead fish is characteristic of the amines.

Trimethylamine has a "fishy" odor. Higher molar mass amines have obnoxious odors. The foul odors arising from dead fish and decaying flesh are due to amines released by bacterial decomposition. Two of these compounds are diamines, 1,4-butanediamine and 1,5-pentanediamine. Each compound contains two amino groups.

$$\underset{\text{(Putrescine)}}{\underset{\text{1,4-Butanediamine}}{H_2NCH_2CH_2CH_2CH_2NH_2}} \qquad \underset{\text{(Cadaverine)}}{\underset{\text{1,5-Pentanediamine}}{H_2NCH_2CH_2CH_2CH_2CH_2NH_2}}$$

Simple aromatic amines are all liquids or solids. They are colorless or almost colorless when freshly prepared but become dark brown or red when exposed to air and light.

7.5 Preparation of Amines

Alkylation of Ammonia and Amines The substitution of alkyl groups for hydrogen atoms of ammonia can be done by reacting ammonia with alkyl halides. Thus, in successive reactions, a primary, a secondary, and a tertiary amine can be formed.

$$NH_3 \xrightarrow{CH_3Br} \underset{\substack{\text{Methylamine}\\(1^\circ)}}{CH_3NH_2} \xrightarrow{CH_3Br} \underset{\substack{\text{Dimethylamine}\\(2^\circ)}}{(CH_3)_2NH} \xrightarrow{CH_3Br} \underset{\substack{\text{Trimethylamine}\\(3^\circ)}}{(CH_3)_3N}$$

quaternary ammonium salts

Tertiary amines can be further alkylated so that there are four organic groups bonded to the nitrogen atom. These types of compounds are called **quaternary ammonium salts**. For example,

$$CH_3-\underset{\underset{CH_3}{|}}{\ddot{N}}-CH_3 + CH_3Br \longrightarrow \underset{\text{Tetramethylammonium bromide}}{CH_3-\overset{\overset{CH_3}{|}}{\underset{\underset{CH_3}{|}}{N^+}}-CH_3Br^-}$$

Quaternary ammonium salts are well known in biologically active compounds and in many popular medicinals. For example, acetylcholine, an active neurotransmitter in the brain, is a quaternary salt. Choline is an important component of many biological membranes. Vitamin B_1 is marketed as the quaternary ammonium salt thiamine hydrochloride. Many well-known fabric softening agents used in laundering clothes are quaternary ammonium salts.

$$\underset{\text{Choline}}{CH_3-\overset{\overset{CH_3}{|}}{\underset{\underset{CH_3}{|}}{N^+}}-CH_2CH_2OH} \qquad \underset{\text{Acetylcholine}}{CH_3-\overset{\overset{CH_3}{|}}{\underset{\underset{CH_3}{|}}{N^+}}-CH_2CH_2O\underset{\underset{O}{\|}}{C}CH_3}$$

Reduction of Amides and Nitriles Amides can be reduced with lithium aluminum hydride to give amines. For example, acetamide can be reduced to ethylamine; and when *N*,*N*-diethylacetamide is reduced, triethylamine is formed:

$$CH_3\overset{\overset{O}{\|}}{C}-NH_2 \xrightarrow{LiAlH_4} \underset{\text{Ethylamine}}{CH_3CH_2NH_2}$$

$$CH_3\overset{\overset{O}{\|}}{C}-N\begin{matrix} CH_2CH_3 \\ CH_2CH_3 \end{matrix} \xrightarrow{LiAlH_4} \underset{\text{Triethylamine}}{(CH_3CH_2)_3N}$$

Nitriles, RCN, are also reducible to amines using hydrogen and a metal catalyst:

$$\underset{\text{Propionitrile}}{CH_3CH_2C{\equiv}N} \xrightarrow{H_2/Ni} \underset{n\text{-Propylamine}}{CH_3CH_2CH_2NH_2}$$

Reduction of Aromatic Nitro Compounds Aniline, the most widely used aromatic amine, is made by reducing nitrobenzene. The nitro group can be reduced by several reagents; Fe and HCl, or Sn and HCl, are commonly used.

$$C_6H_5-NO_2 \xrightarrow[HCl]{Sn} C_6H_5-NH_3^+Cl^- \xrightarrow{NaOH} C_6H_5-NH_2$$

7.6 Chemical Properties of Amines

Alkaline Properties of Amines

In many respects amines resemble ammonia in their reactions. Thus, amines are bases and, like ammonia, ionize in water to produce OH^- ions:

$$\underset{\text{Ammonia molecule}}{\ddot{N}H_3} + (H)OH \rightleftharpoons \underset{\text{Ammonium ion}}{NH_4^+} + \underset{\text{Hydroxide ion}}{OH^-}$$

Methylamine and aniline react in the same manner:

$$\underset{\text{Methylamine molecule}}{CH_3\ddot{N}H_2} + (H)OH \rightleftharpoons \underset{\text{Methylammonium ion}}{CH_3NH_3^+} + \underset{\text{Hydroxide ion}}{OH^-}$$

$$\underset{\text{Aniline molecule}}{C_6H_5-\ddot{N}H_2} + (H)OH \rightleftharpoons \underset{\text{Anilinium ion}}{C_6H_5-NH_3^+} + \underset{\text{Hydroxide ion}}{OH^-}$$

The ions formed are substituted ammonium ions. They are named by replacing the amine ending by ammonium and, for the aromatic amines, by replacing the aniline name by anilinium.

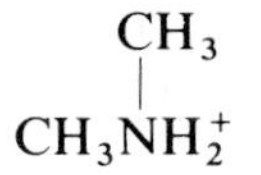

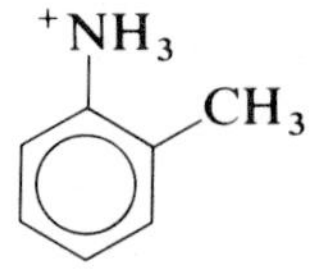

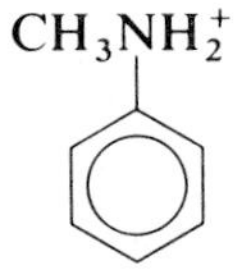

$$(CH_3)CH_3NH_2^+ \qquad o\text{-}CH_3C_6H_4NH_3^+ \qquad C_6H_5NH_2^+CH_3$$

Dimethylammonium ion — *o*-Methylanilinium ion — *N*-Methylanilinium ion

Like ammonia, amines are weak bases. Methylamine is a slightly stronger base than ammonia, and aniline is considerably weaker than ammonia. The pH values for 0.1 *M* solutions are: methylamine, 11.8; ammonia, 11.1; and aniline, 8.8.

Because amine groups form substituted ammonium ions under physiological conditions, they can provide the positive charge for biological molecules. For example, neurotransmitters are often positively charged. The structures of two such transmitter compounds, dopamine and serotonin, are shown here:

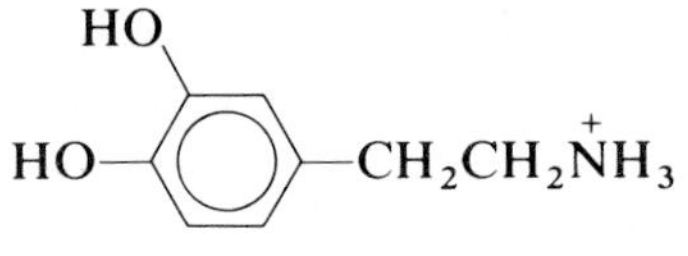

$$(HO)_2C_6H_3-CH_2CH_2\overset{+}{N}H_3$$

Dopamine

$$HO-C_8H_5N(H)-CH_2CH_2\overset{+}{N}H_3$$

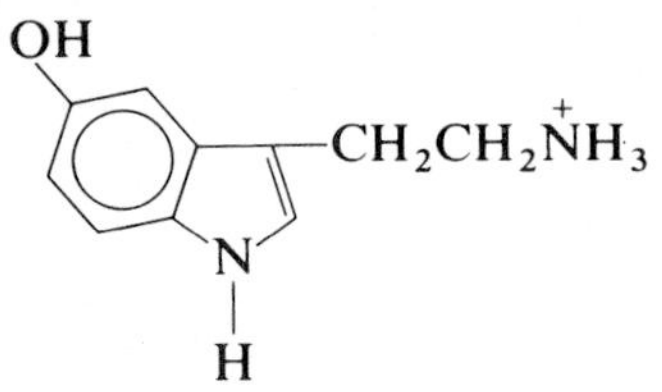

Serotonin

Salt Formation

An amine reacts with a strong acid to form a salt; for example, methylamine and hydrogen chloride react in this fashion:

$$CH_3NH_2(g) + HCl(g) \longrightarrow CH_3NH_3{}^+\,Cl^-$$

Methylamine molecule — Hydrogen chloride molecule — Methylammonium chloride (salt)

Methylammonium chloride is made up of methylammonium ions, $CH_3NH_3^+$, and chloride ions, Cl^-. It is a white crystalline salt that in physical appearance resembles ammonium chloride very closely.

Aniline reacts in a similar manner, forming anilinium chloride:

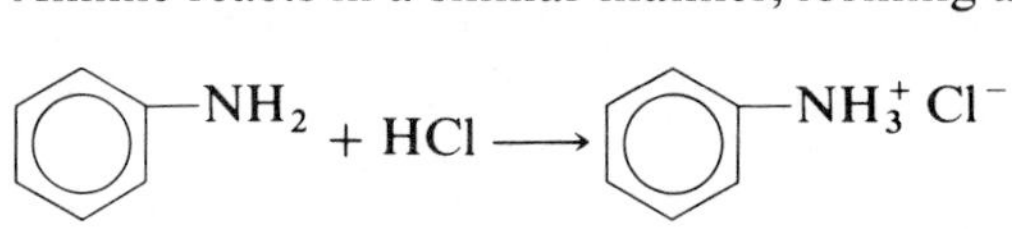

$$C_6H_5-NH_2 + HCl \longrightarrow C_6H_5-NH_3^+\,Cl^-$$

Anilinium chloride

Many amines or amino compounds are more stable in the form of the hydrochloride salt. When the free amine is wanted, the HCl is neutralized to liberate the free amine. Thus,

$$RNH_3^+\,Cl^-\ (\text{or } RNH_2\cdot HCl) + NaOH \longrightarrow RNH_2 + NaCl + H_2O$$

An amine hydrochloride salt — Free amine

(*continues on page 685*)

Chemistry in Action

Drugs for the Central Nervous System

Drugs that affect the central nervous system, including the brain and spinal cord, have become increasingly prevalent in modern society. Classification of these substances is often complex as a single drug may elicit different responses, depending upon dosage or activity of the individual user. A classification system based upon the major response and pattern of chemical action has been developed by the World Health Organization. Major categories include opiates, barbiturates, cocaine, cannabis, amphetamines, hallucinogens, tranquilizers, and designer drugs.

Basic compounds that are derived from plants and show physiological activity are known as **alkaloids**. These substances are usually amines. The opium alkaloids are often called the opiates and include both compounds derived from the opium poppy and synthetic compounds which have morphine-like activity (sleep-inducing and analgesic properties). These drugs are classified as *narcotics*, producing physical addiction, and are strictly regulated by federal law.

Barbiturates are synthetic drugs classified as sedatives. They are prepared from urea and substituted malonic acid and are usually prescribed as sodium salts to increase their solubility in water. The activity of these compounds depends on the nature of the substituents on the barbituric acid molecule. Seconal and Nembutal act over a period of three to four hours, and so are commonly found as sleeping pills. Pentothal acts within seconds and wears off quickly, explaining its use as a dental anesthetic. The formulas on this page show the structures of some common barbiturates.

CH_3CH_2, $CH_3CH_2CH_2CH(CH_3)$ — ring with two C=O, C=O and two N–H

Nembutal

$CH_2{=}CH{-}CH_2$, $CH_3CH_2CH_2CH(CH_3)$ — ring with two C=O, C=O and two N–H

Seconal

CH_3CH_2, $CH_3CH_2CH_2CH(CH_3)$ — ring with two C=O, C=S and two N–H

Pentothal

▲ **Some common barbiturates.**

The action of a barbiturate is to depress the activity of brain cells. For this reason they are often called "downers," and they are one of the more widely abused drugs. Barbiturate users require larger and larger doses of the drug to achieve the same effect as the body develops a tolerance to the drug. Dependency on barbiturates is becoming a more serious problem than narcotic addiction. This is because withdrawal from barbiturates is more dangerous and the margin of safety between a lethal dose and that dose necessary to achieve the desired effect decreases as an addict's tolerance increases. Barbiturate overdoses now account for over 20% of all reported poisonings.

Tranquilizers are drugs taken to modify psychotic behavior without inducing sleep, or to reduce anxiety or restlessness. Psychotic behavior is treated with strong tranquilizers such as Thorazine or reserpine. Thorazine (chlorpromazine) is extremely effective in treating schizophrenia and manic depression. Milder tranquilizers are often used to relieve the pressure and anxiety of daily life. These substances generally belong to a group known as benzodiazepines. The most popular tranquilizer is diazepam (Valium), followed closely by Librium, a drug used in treating neuroses and acute alcoholism. The structures of these common tranquilizers are shown on the next page.

▲ **The nicotine in cigarettes, the toxins in rat poison, the quinine in tonic water and the amphetamines in diet pills are all examples of alkaloids.**

(*continued*)

(continued)

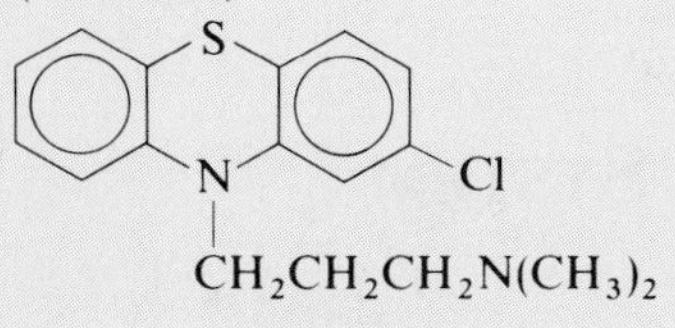

$CH_2CH_2CH_2N(CH_3)_2$

Chlorpromazine
(Thorazine)

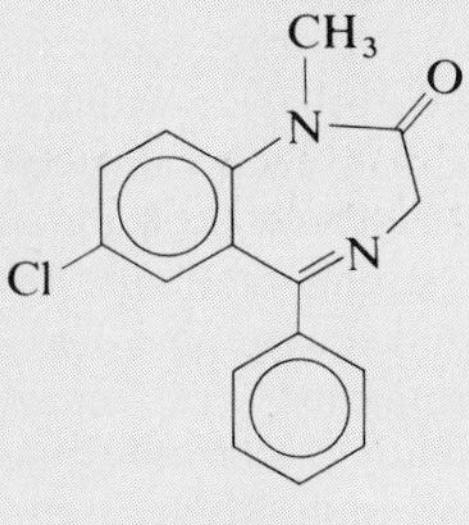

Diazepam
(Valium)

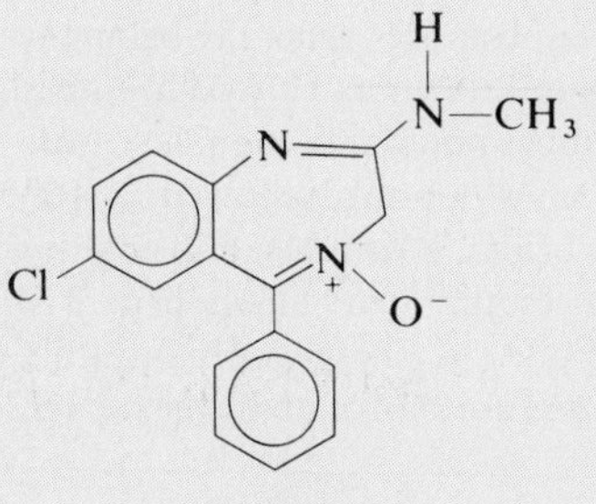

Chlordiazepoxide
(Librium)

▲
Several common tranquilizers.

In contrast, amphetamines are part of a group of drugs that stimulate the central nervous system. These drugs are referred to as *sympathomimetic amines* since they mimic the action of epinephrine and norepinephrine, both substances naturally produced in the body. In fact the parent drug, amphetamine, was first synthesized to simulate epinephrine. Several natural and synthetic amphetamines are shown above.

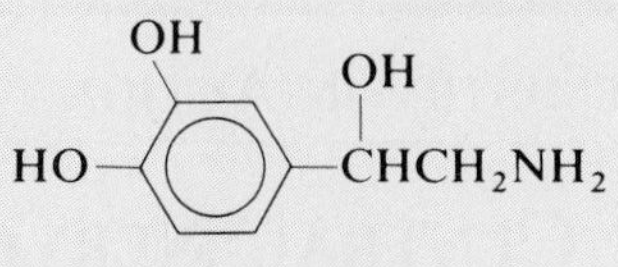

$HO-C_6H_3(OH)-CHOHCH_2NH_2$

Norepinephrine

$HO-C_6H_3(OH)-CHOHCH_2NHCH_3$

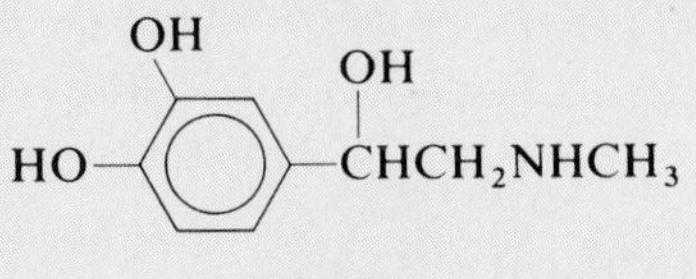

Epinephrine
(Adrenalin)

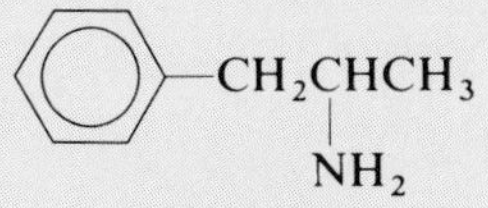

$C_6H_5-CH_2CH(NH_2)CH_3$

Amphetamine
(Benzedrine)

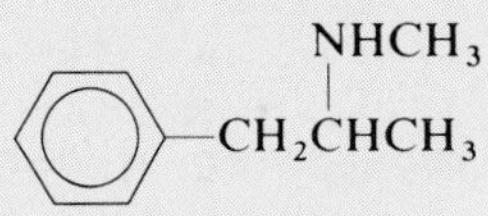

$C_6H_5-CH_2CH(NHCH_3)CH_3$

Methamphetamine
(Methedrine)

▲
Some natural and synthetic amphetamines.

These drugs are used medically to treat depression, narcolepsy, and obesity. Use of amphetamines produces a feeling of well-being, loss of fatigue, and increasing alertness. Overuse of amphetamines can result in severe health effects. These compounds tend to concentrate in the central nervous system and are not easily broken down. The most widely abused amphetamine is methamphetamine, commonly called "speed." This drug is used in progressively higher doses producing a state of constant wakefulness followed by exhaustion in an ongoing cycle.

In the 1980s analogs of pharmacological drugs have come to be known as designer drugs. These are manufactured in illegal laboratories and are sold on the street as other well-known drugs. By making slight modifications in the structure of a drug, these underground chemists try to produce more potent or longer lasting drugs. An example of this technology is an analog of Demerol (mepiridine) called MPPP, shown above. MPPP is 25 times as potent as Demerol and is also about 3 times as potent as heroin. Unfortunately, an impurity in the synthesis of MPPP resulted in several cases of irreversible Parkinson's disease. Designer drugs can often be lethal as a result of these impurities and a lack of testing under controlled conditions.

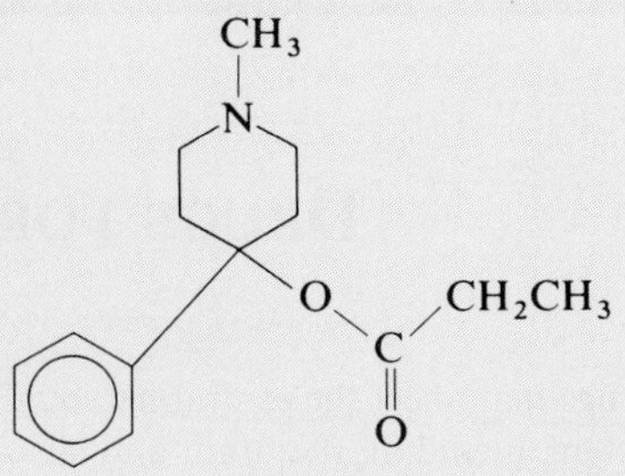

MPPP

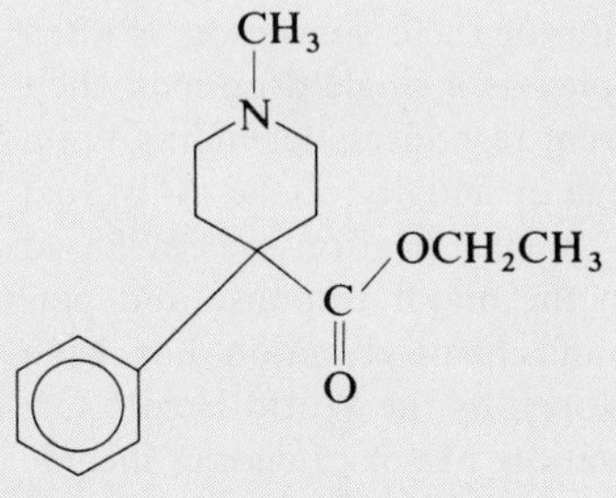

Demerol

▲
The designer drug MPPP is made by a slight change in the structure of a known drug, Demerol.

Formation of Amides

Primary and secondary amines react with acid chlorides to form substituted amides. For example,

$$CH_3\overset{\overset{\displaystyle O}{\|}}{C}—Cl + 2\,(CH_3CH_2)_2NH \longrightarrow CH_3\overset{\overset{\displaystyle O}{\|}}{C}—N\begin{matrix} CH_2CH_3 \\ CH_2CH_3 \end{matrix} + (CH_3CH_2)_2NH_2^+\,Cl^-$$

N,*N*-Diethylacetamide

7.7 Sources and Uses of Amines

Nitrogen compounds are found throughout the plant and animal kingdoms. Amines, substituted amines, and amides occur in every living cell. Colorful dyes, vitamins, and many medicinals including alkaloids, quinine and morphine, sulfa drugs, and amphetamines are but a few of the classes of substances in which organic nitrogen compounds are found. The formulas for several well-known nitrogen compounds are shown below:

NH_2 / SO_2NH_2

Sulfanilamide
(antibacterial agent)

$H_2N—C_6H_4—\overset{\overset{\displaystyle O}{\|}}{C}—OCH_2CH_3$

Benzocaine (Ethyl-*p*-aminobenzoate)
(topical anesthetic)

O, CH_3, $CH_3—N$, N, O, N, N, CH_3

Caffeine
(stimulant and diuretic)

$H_2N—C_6H_4—\overset{\overset{\displaystyle O}{\|}}{C}—OCH_2CH_2—\overset{+}{N}H(C_2H_5)_2\;Cl^-$

Procaine hydrochloride (novocaine)
(local anesthetic)

$C—NH_2$, O, N

Nicotinamide (niacin)
(antipellagra vitamin)

CH_3, N, N

Nicotine
(from tobacco leaves, used as an agricultural insecticide)

CH_2CH_3, $C{=}O$, $C—CH_2—CHCH_3$, N, $CH_3\;CH_3$

Methadone
(narcotic analgesic, substitute for heroin)

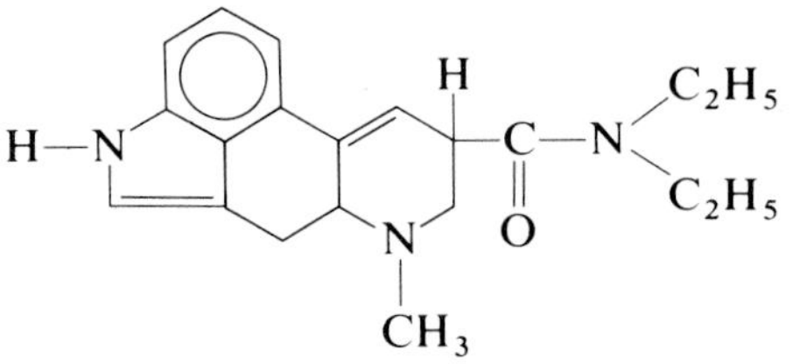

Lysergic acid diethylamide (LSD)
(hallucinogen)

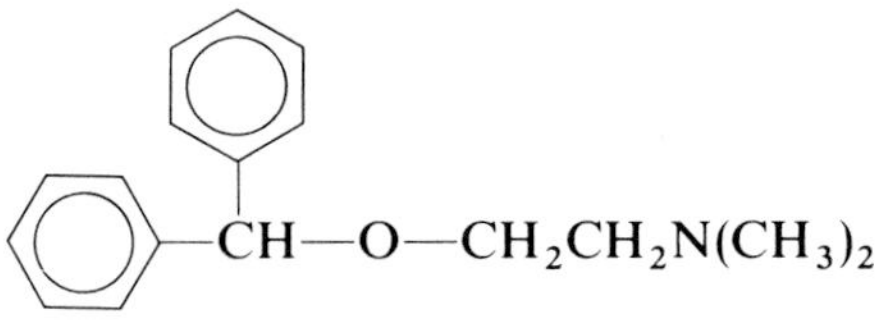

C_6H_5—CH—O—$CH_2CH_2N(CH_3)_2$ (with a second C_6H_5 on CH)

Benadryl
(antihistamine)

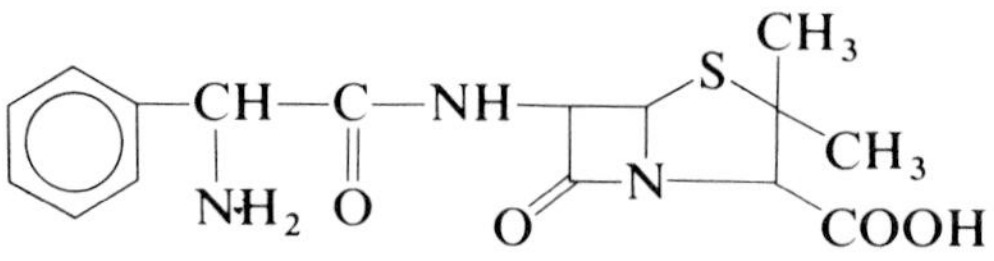

Ampicillin
(antibacterial agent)

Concepts in Review

1. Name and write structural formulas for amides.
2. Explain the high melting and boiling points of the amides, compared to alkanes of similar molar mass.
3. Write equations for both acidic and basic hydrolysis of amides.
4. Name and write structural formulas for amines.
5. Distinguish among primary, secondary, and tertiary amines.
6. Show that amines are bases in their reactions with water and with acids.
7. Write equations for reactions of amines to form substituted amides.
8. Write equations for the formation of amines from (a) alkyl halides plus ammonia, (b) reduction of amides with $LiAlH_4$, (c) reduction of nitriles with H_2 and Ni, and (d) reduction of aromatic nitro compounds.
9. Identify and write equations for the formation of quaternary ammonium salts.
10. Indicate the major physiological responses to barbiturates, tranquilizers, amphetamines, and alkaloids.
11. Explain the term "designer drug" and indicate the hazards associated with these substances.

Equations in Review

Formation of Amides

$$R{-}\overset{\displaystyle O}{\overset{\|}{C}}{-}Cl + NH_2R' \xrightarrow{\Delta} R{-}\overset{\displaystyle O}{\overset{\|}{C}}{-}NHR'$$

$$R-\overset{\overset{\large O}{\|}}{C}-Cl + NH_2R' \longrightarrow R-\overset{\overset{\large O}{\|}}{C}-NHR'$$

Hydrolysis of Amides

$$R-\overset{\overset{\large O}{\|}}{C}-NHR' + H_2O \longrightarrow R-\overset{\overset{\large O}{\|}}{C}-OH + H_2NR'$$

Amine Reaction as a Base

$$\underset{\text{Amine}}{R-NH_2} + \underset{\text{Acid}}{HX} \longrightarrow \underset{\text{Amine salt}}{R-\overset{+}{N}H_3X^-}$$

EXERCISES

1. Draw structural formulas for:

(a) Butylamine
(b) *p*-Methylaniline
(c) *N*-Methyl-*p*-bromobenzamide
(d) *N*,*N*-Diethylbenzamide

2. Name the following compounds.

(a) $CH_3-\overset{\overset{O}{\|}}{C}-NH_2$

(b) 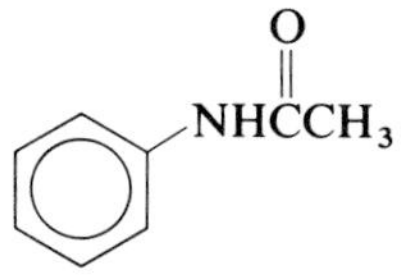 $C_6H_5-NH\overset{\overset{O}{\|}}{C}CH_3$

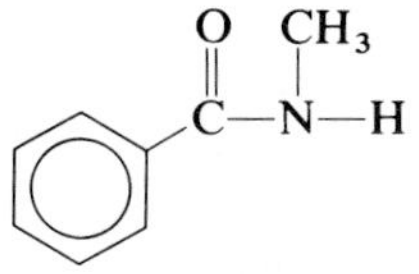

(c) $C_6H_5-\overset{\overset{O}{\|}}{C}-\underset{}{\overset{\overset{CH_3}{|}}{N}}-H$

3. Predict which of the four compounds will be the most soluble in water, ethylamine, $CH_3CH_2CH_2CH_2NH_2$, acetamide, or $CH_3CH_2CH_2\overset{\overset{O}{\|}}{C}-NH_2$. Explain your answer.

4. Predict the substituted amide products:
(a) Acetic acid and diethylamine and heat
(b) Acetic acid and propylamine and heat
(c) Butanoic acid and methylamine and heat

5. Predict whether each of the following compounds is an acid, a base, or neither.
(a) CH_3CH_2OH
(b) $CH_3CH_2NH_2$
(c) 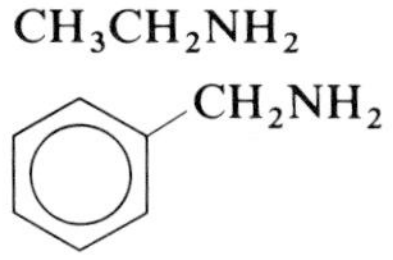 $C_6H_5-CH_2NH_2$
(d) 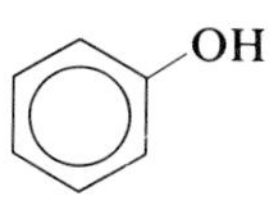 C_6H_5-OH
(e) $CH_3CH_2-\overset{\overset{O}{\|}}{C}-NH_2$
(f) $CH_3CH_2-\overset{\overset{O}{\|}}{C}-OH$

6. Show the hydrolysis products of these compounds.
(a) 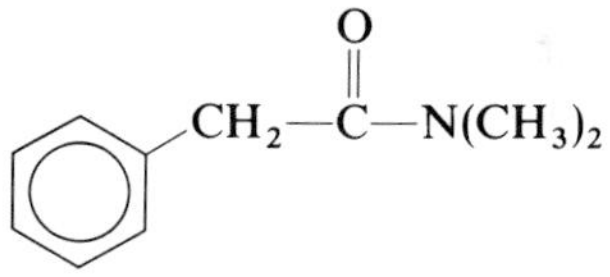 $C_6H_5-CH_2-\overset{\overset{O}{\|}}{C}-N(CH_3)_2$
(b) $CH_3-NH-\overset{\overset{O}{\|}}{C}-CH_3$
(c) 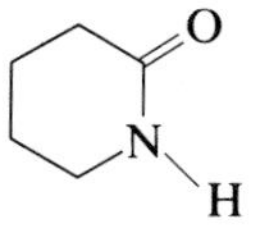 six-membered ring lactam: ring C=O adjacent to N—H

7. Contrast the physical properties of amides with those of amines.

8. Arrange each set of compounds in order of increasing solubility in water.

(a) $CH_3CH_2C(=O)—NHCH_3$

$CH_3CH_2C(=O)—N(CH_3)_2$

$CH_3CH_2C(=O)—NH_2$

(b) $CH_3(CH_2)_4C(=O)—NH_2$ $CH_3C(=O)—NH_2$

$C_6H_5—C(=O)—NH_2$

9. Urea is soluble in water. Show the possible hydrogen bonding that helps to explain this property.
10. Classify each of the following amines as primary, secondary, or tertiary.
    (a) $CH_3CH_2CH_2NH_2$
    (b) CH_3NHCH_3
    (c) $C_6H_5—NH_2$
    (d) $C_6H_{11}—N(H)—C_6H_5$
    (e) Piperidine ring with N—CH_3
11. Explain why amines have approximately the same solubility as alcohols of similar molar mass.
12. Propylamine, $CH_3CH_2CH_2NH_2$, ethylmethylamine, $CH_3CH_2NHCH_3$, and trimethylamine, $(CH_3)_3N$, are all isomers. Explain why the boiling point of trimethylamine is considerably lower than the boiling points of the other two.
13. After cleaning or packing fish, workers often use lemon juice to clean their hands. What is the purpose of the lemon juice?
14. Low molar mass aliphatic amines generally have odors suggestive of ammonia and/or stale fish. Which would have the more objectionable odor? Give a satisfactory reason for your answer.
    (a) A 1% trimethylamine solution in 1.0 *M* H_2SO_4 or
    (b) A 1% trimethylamine solution in 1.0 *M* NaOH
15. Draw structural formulas for
    (a) All the amines of formula C_3H_9N
    (b) All the amines of formula $C_4H_{11}N$
    (c) All the quaternary ammonium salts of formula $C_4H_{12}N^+Cl^-$
16. Name the following compounds.
    (a) Benzene ring with CH_2CH_3 and (ortho) NH_2
    (b) $CH_3CH_2NH_3^+ Br^+$

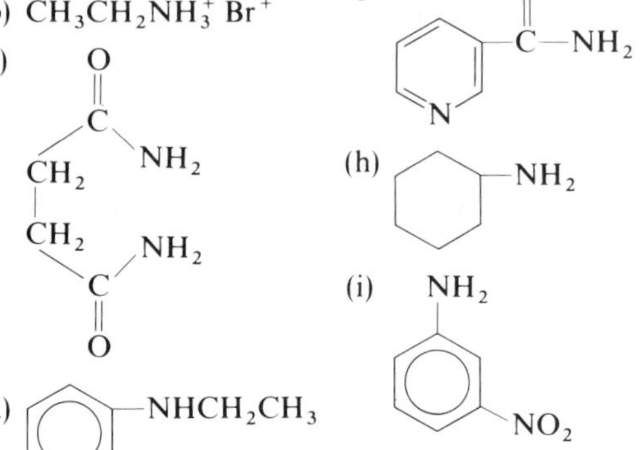

    (c) $H_2N—C(=O)—CH_2—CH_2—C(=O)—NH_2$
    (d) $C_6H_5—NHCH_2CH_3$
    (e) Pyridine ring (N)
    (f) $CH_3C(=O)—NHC_2H_5$
    (g) Pyridine ring (N) with $—C(=O)—NH_2$
    (h) Cyclohexane ring with $—NH_2$
    (i) Benzene ring with NH_2 and (meta) NO_2
    (j) $(C_2H_5)_4N^+ I^-$
    (k) $C_6H_5—NH—C_6H_5$
17. Draw structural formulas for the following compounds.
    (a) Methylethylamine
    (b) Tributylamine
    (c) Aniline
    (d) Ethylammonium chloride
    (e) *N*-methylanilinium chloride
    (f) 1,4-Butanediamine
    (g) *N*,*N*-dimethylaniline
    (h) Ethylisopropymethylamine
    (i) Pyridine
    (j) 2-Amino-1-pentanol
18. Write equations to show how each conversion may be accomplished. (Some conversions may require more than one step.)
    (a) $CH_3CH_2CH_2Br \longrightarrow CH_3CH_2CH_2NH_2$
    (b) $CH_3CH_2CH_2Br \longrightarrow CH_3CH_2CH_2CH_2NH_2$
    (c) $CH_3—C_6H_4—NO_2 \longrightarrow CH_3—C_6H_4—NH_2$

19. (a) What is a heterocyclic compound?
(b) How many heterocyclic rings are present in (1) LSD, (2) ampicillin, (3) methadone, and (4) nicotine?

20. Which of the following statements are correct? Rewrite the incorrect statements to make them correct.
(a) The common name for CH_3CONH_2 is methanamide.
(b) The general formula for a primary amine is $R\overset{O}{\overset{\|}{C}}NH_2$.
(c) Uric acid is the primary way that the body loses nitrogen.
(d) Heterocyclic compounds contain more than one ring.
(e) Alkaloids are used to settle upset stomachs.
(f) Barbiturates are stimulants.
(g) Amphetamines are also called sympathetic amines.
(h) Designer drugs are used in the manufacture of psychedelic clothing.
(i) The name for $[(CH_3)_2CH]_2NH$ is isopropyl amine.
(j) Aniline is soluble in dilute HCl because it forms a soluble salt.
(k) Most amines have pleasant odors.
(l) Lactic acid is an α-amino acid.
(m) Sulfanilamide is an aniline derivative.
(n) Isopropyl amine is a secondary amine.
(o) Butylamine and diethylamine are isomers.
(p) Aniline is made by the reduction of nitrobenzene.

21. List three classes of drugs and indicate the major effects of each.

22. Indicate the functional groups present in:
(a) Aspirin
(b) Acetaminophen
(c) Ibuprofen
(d) Adrenalin

23. Show the structure known as an amide linkage. Indicate the important classes of biochemicals that contain this linkage.

8

Polymers: Macromolecules

◀ CHAPTER OPENING PHOTO: **River rafting through the Grand Canyon is often done on rafts made from polymers.**

What is a "mer"? The terms *polymer* and *monomer* have entered our everyday speech, and we are familiar with the prefixes, *poly* meaning "many" and *mono* meaning "one." Although a "mer" sounds like something from a child's cartoon show, scientists have chosen this small three-letter root to convey an important concept. It is derived from the Greek *meros*, meaning "part." So, a monomer is a "one part" and a polymer is a "many part."

Look around you for a few minutes and see all the objects that could be described in these terms. A brick building could be described as a polymer, with each brick representing a monomer. A string of pearls is an elegant polymer, with each pearl a monomer. Starting with simple chemical monomers, chemists have learned to construct both utilitarian and elegant polymers. As you will see in this chapter, many of the polymers are of great commercial importance.

8.1 MACROMOLECULES

Up to now we have dealt mainly with rather small organic molecules that contain up to 50 atoms and some (fats) that contain up to about 150 atoms. But there exist in nature some very large molecules (macromolecules) containing tens of thousands of atoms. Some of these, such as starch, glycogen, cellulose, proteins, and DNA, have molar masses in the millions and are central to many of our life processes. Synthetic macromolecules touch every phase of modern living. It is hard today to imagine a world without polymers. Textiles for clothing, carpeting, and draperies, shoes, toys, automobile parts, construction materials, synthetic rubber, chemical equipment, medical supplies, cooking utensils, synthetic leather, recreational equipment—the list could go on and on. All these and a host of others that we consider to be essential in our daily lives are wholly or partly synthetic polymers. Most of these polymers were unknown 60 years ago. The vast majority of these polymeric materials are based on petroleum. Because petroleum is a nonreplaceable resource, our dependence on polymers is another good reason for not squandering the limited world supply of petroleum.

Polyethylene is an example of a synthetic polymer. Ethylene, derived from petroleum, is made to react with itself to form polyethylene (or polythene). Polyethylene is a long-chain hydrocarbon made from many ethylene units:

$$\underset{\text{Ethylene}}{n\,CH_2{=}CH_2} \longrightarrow \underset{\text{Polyethylene}}{-CH_2CH_2CH_2[CH_2CH_2]_nCH_2CH_2CH_2-}$$

A typical polyethylene molecule is made up of about 2,500–25,000 ethylene molecules joined in a continuous structure.

polymerization

polymer

monomer

The process of forming very large, high molar mass molecules from smaller units is called **polymerization**. The large molecule, or unit, is called the **polymer** and the small unit, the **monomer**. The term *polymer* is derived from the Greek word *polumerēs*, meaning "having many parts." Ethylene is a monomer, and polyethylene is a polymer. Because of their large size, polymers are often called *macromolecules*. Another commonly used term is *plastics*. The world *plastic* means "to be capable of being molded, or pliable." Although not all polymers are pliable and capable of being remolded, the word *plastics* has gained general use and has come to mean any of a variety of polymeric substances.

8.2 Synthetic Polymers

Some of the early commercial polymers were merely modifications of naturally occurring substances. One chemically modified natural polymer, nitrated cellulose, was made and sold as Celluloid late in the 19th century. But the first commercially successful fully synthetic polymer, Bakelite, was made from phenol and formaldehyde by Leo Baekeland in 1909. This was the beginning of the modern plastics industry. Chemists began to create many synthetic polymers in the late 1920s. Since then, ever-increasing numbers of synthetic macromolecular materials have become articles of commerce. Even greater numbers of polymers have been made and discarded for technical or economic reasons. Polymers are presently used extensively in nearly every industry. For example, the electronics industry uses "plastics" in applications ranging from microchip production to fabrication of heat and impact resistant cases for the assembled products. In the auto industry, huge amounts of polymers are used as body, engine, transmission, and electrical system components, as well as for tires. Vast quantities of polymers with varied and sometimes highly specialized characteristics are used for packaging; for example, packaging for frozen foods must withstand subfreezing temperatures as well as those met in either conventional or microwave ovens.

Although there is a great variety of synthetic polymers on the market, they can be classified into the following general groups based on properties and uses:

1. Rubberlike materials or elastomers
2. Flexible films
3. Synthetic textiles and fibers
4. Resins (or plastics) for casting, molding, and extruding
5. Coating resins for dip, spray, or solvent dispersed applications
6. Miscellaneous, including hydraulic fluids, foamed insulation, ion-exchange resins

8.3 Polymer Types

addition polymer

Two general types of polymers—addition and condensation—are known. An **addition polymer** is one that is produced by the successive addition of repeating

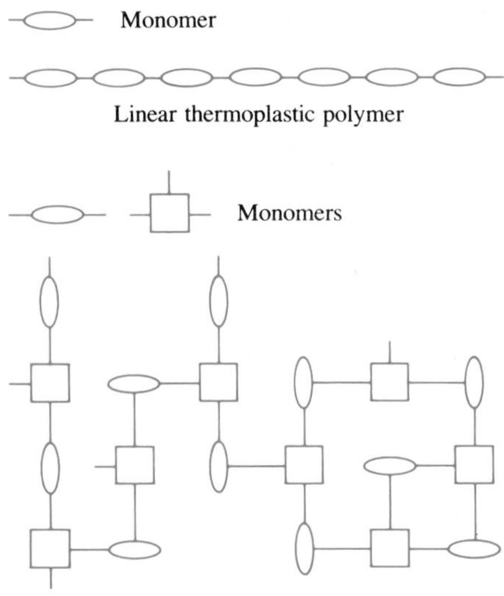

◄ **Figure 8.1**
Schematic diagrams of thermoplastic and thermosetting polymer structures.

monomer molecules. Polyethylene is an example of an addition polymer. A **condensation polymer** is one that is formed from monomers that react to split out water or some other simple substance.

condensation polymer

Polymers are also classified as being either thermoplastic or thermosetting. Those that soften on reheating are **thermoplastic polymers**; those that set to an infusible solid and do not soften on reheating are **thermosetting polymers**. Thermoplastic polymers are formed when monomer molecules join end to end in a linear chain with little or no cross-linking between the chains. Thermosetting polymers are macromolecules in which the polymeric chains are cross-linked to form a network structure. The structures of thermoplastic and thermosetting polymers are illustrated in the schematic diagram in Figure 8.1.

thermoplastic polymers

thermosetting polymers

8.4 Addition Polymerization

Ethylene polymerizes by addition to form polyethylene according to the reaction shown in Section 8.1. Polyethylene is the most important and widely used polymer on the market today. It is a tough, inert, but flexible thermoplastic material. Over 9.5×10^9 kg (2.1×10^{10} lb) of polyethylene is produced annually in the United States alone. Polyethylene is made into hundreds of different articles such as bread wrappers, toys, squeeze bottles, containers of all kinds, and electrical insulation.

The double bond is the key structural feature involved in the polymerization of ethylene. Ethylene derivatives, in which one or more hydrogen atoms have been replaced by other atoms or groups, can also be polymerized. This is often called *vinyl polymerization.* Many of our commercial synthetic polymers are made from such modified ethylene monomers. The names, structures, and uses of some of these polymers are given in Table 8.1.

Free radicals catalyze or initiate many addition polymerizations. Organic peroxides, ROOR, are frequently used for this purpose. The steps in the reaction

Table 8.1 Polymers Derived from Modified Ethylene Monomers

Monomer	Polymer	Uses
$CH_2{=}CH_2$ Ethylene	$\text{-(}CH_2{-}CH_2\text{)-}_n$ Polyethylene	Packing material, molded articles, containers, toys
$CH_2{=}CH{-}CH_3$ Propylene	$\text{-(}CH_2{-}CH(CH_3)\text{)-}_n$ Polypropylene	Textile fibers, molded articles, lightweight ropes, autoclavable biological equipment
$CH_2{=}C(CH_3)_2$ Isobutylene	$\text{-(}CH_2{-}C(CH_3)_2\text{)-}_n$ Polyisobutylene	Pressure-sensitive adhesives, butyl rubber (contains some isoprene as copolymer)
$CH_2{=}CH{-}Cl$ Vinyl chloride	$\text{-(}CH_2{-}CH(Cl)\text{)-}_n$ Polyvinyl chloride (PVC)	Phonograph records, garden hoses, pipes, molded articles, floor tile, electrical insulation, vinyl leather
$CH_2{=}CCl_2$ Vinylidene chloride	$\text{-(}CH_2{-}CCl_2\text{)-}_n$ Saran	Food packaging, textile fibers, pipes, tubing (contains some vinyl chloride as copolymer)
$CH_2{=}CH{-}CN$ Acrylonitrile	$\text{-(}CH_2{-}CH(CN)\text{)-}_n$ Orlon, Acrilan	Textile fibers
$CF_2{=}CF_2$ Tetrafluoroethylene	$\text{-(}CF_2{-}CF_2\text{)-}_n$ Teflon	Gaskets, valves, insulation, heat-resistant and chemical-resistant coatings, linings for pots and pans
$CH_2{=}CH{-}C_6H_5$ Styrene	$\text{-(}CH_2{-}CH(C_6H_5)\text{)-}_n$ Polystyrene	Molded articles, styrofoam, insulation, toys, disposable food containers
$CH_2{=}CH{-}OC({=}O){-}CH_3$ Vinyl acetate	$\text{-(}CH_2{-}CH(OC({=}O){-}CH_3)\text{)-}_n$ Polyvinyl acetate	Adhesives, paint, and varnish
$CH_2{=}C(CH_3){-}C({=}O){-}O{-}CH_3$ Methylmethacrylate	$\text{-(}CH_2{-}C(CH_3)(C({=}O){-}OCH_3)\text{)-}_n$ Lucite, Plexiglas (acrylic resins)	Contact lenses, clear sheets for windows and optical uses, molded articles, automobile finishes

are as follows.

Step 1 *Free radical formation.* The peroxide splits into free radicals:

$$RO{:}OR \longrightarrow 2\,RO\cdot$$

Step 2 *Propagation of polymeric chain.*

$$RO\cdot + CH_2{=}CH_2 \longrightarrow ROCH_2CH_2\cdot$$
$$ROCH_2CH_2\cdot + CH_2{=}CH_2 \longrightarrow ROCH_2CH_2CH_2CH_2\cdot \quad \text{(and so on)}$$

Step 3 *Termination.* Polymerization stops when the free radicals are used up:

$$RO(CH_2CH_2)_n\cdot + \cdot OR \longrightarrow RO(CH_2CH_2)_nOR$$
$$RO(CH_2CH_2)_n\cdot + \cdot(CH_2CH_2)_nOR \longrightarrow RO(CH_2CH_2)_n(CH_2CH_2)_nOR$$

Addition (or vinyl) polymerization of ethylene and its substituted derivatives yields saturated polymers—that is, polymer chains without carbon–carbon double bonds. The pi bond is eliminated when a free radical adds to an ethylene molecule. One of the electrons of the pi bond pairs with the unpaired electron of the free radical, thus bonding the radical to the ethylene unit. The other pi bond electron remains unpaired, generating a new and larger free radical. This new free radical then adds another ethylene molecule, continuing the building of the polymeric chain. This process is illustrated by the following electron-dot diagram:

```
      H  H                 H H
      |  |                 | |
   H—C::C—H  ——→  H—C:C—H      (ROCH2CH2·)
 RO·                       RÖ  ·
```

8.5 Butadiene Polymers

A diene is a compound that contains two carbon–carbon double bonds. Another type of addition polymer is based on the compound 1,3-butadiene or its derivatives.

$$\overset{1}{C}H_2{=}\overset{2}{C}H{-}\overset{3}{C}H{=}\overset{4}{C}H_2$$

1,3-Butadiene

Natural rubber is a polymer of isoprene (2-methyl-1,3-butadiene). Many synthetic elastomers or rubberlike materials are polymers of isoprene or of butadiene. Unlike the saturated ethylene polymers, these polymers are unsaturated; that is, they have double bonds in their polymeric structures.

The tires of these cars are ▶ made of rubber that has been vulcanized. This process improves the temperature range for use and resistance to abrasion.

$$n\,\mathrm{CH_2{=}\overset{\displaystyle CH_3}{\overset{|}{C}}{-}CH{=}CH_2} \longrightarrow \mathrm{\left(CH_2{-}\overset{\displaystyle CH_3}{\overset{|}{C}}{=}CH{-}CH_2\right)_{\!n}}$$

Isoprene — Rubber polymer chain (Polyisoprene)

$$n\,\mathrm{CH_2{=}CH{-}CH{=}CH_2} \longrightarrow \mathrm{\left(CH_2{-}CH{=}CH{-}CH_2\right)_{\!n}}$$

1,3-Butadiene — Butadiene polymer chain

$$n\,\mathrm{CH_2{=}\overset{\displaystyle Cl}{\overset{|}{C}}{-}CH{=}CH_2} \longrightarrow \mathrm{\left(CH_2{-}\overset{\displaystyle Cl}{\overset{|}{C}}{=}CH{-}CH_2\right)_{\!n}}$$

2-Chloro-1,3-butadiene (Chloroprene) — Neoprene polymer chain (Polychloroprene)

In this kind of polymerization, the free radical adds to the butadiene monomer at carbon 1 of the carbon–carbon double bond. At the same time, a double bond is formed between carbon 2 and carbon 3, and a new free radical is formed at carbon 4. This process is illustrated in the following diagram:

$$\begin{array}{c} \mathrm{H}\quad\mathrm{H}\;\mathrm{H}\quad\mathrm{H} \\ |_1\quad |_2\;|_3\quad |_4 \\ \mathrm{H{-}C{::}C{:}C{::}C{-}H} \\ \mathrm{RO\cdot} \end{array} \longrightarrow \begin{array}{c} \mathrm{H}\;\mathrm{H}\;\;\mathrm{H}\;\mathrm{H} \\ |\;\;|\;\;\;|\;\;| \\ \mathrm{RO{:}C{:}C{::}C{:}C\cdot} \\ |\qquad\quad| \\ \mathrm{H}\qquad\;\mathrm{H} \end{array}$$

Free radical — 1,3-Butadiene — Radical chain lengthened by four carbon atoms

One of the outstanding synthetic rubbers (styrene–butadiene rubber, SBR) is made from two monomers, styrene and 1,3-butadiene. These substances form a **copolymer**—that is, a polymer containing two different kinds of monomer

copolymer

units. Styrene and butadiene do not necessarily have to combine in a 1:1 ratio. In the actual manufacture of SBR polymers, about three moles of butadiene are used per mole of styrene. Thus, the butadiene and styrene units are intermixed, but in a ratio of about 3:1.

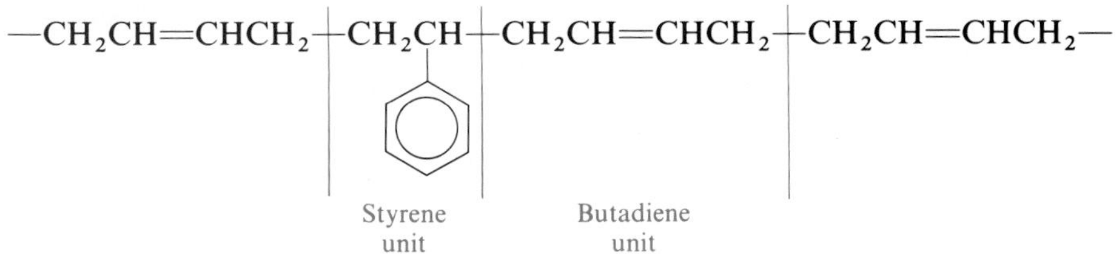

$$-CH_2CH{=}CHCH_2-CH_2CH(C_6H_5)-CH_2CH{=}CHCH_2-CH_2CH{=}CHCH_2-$$

Styrene unit   Butadiene unit

Segment of styrene–butadiene rubber (SBR)

The presence of double bonds at intervals along the chains of rubber and rubberlike synthetic polymers designed for use in tires is almost a necessity and, at the same time, a disadvantage. On the positive side, double bonds make vulcanization possible. On the negative side, double bonds afford sites where ozone, present especially in smoggy atmospheres, can attack the rubber, causing "age hardening" and cracking. Vulcanization extends the useful temperature range of rubber products and imparts greater abrasion resistance to them. The vulcanization process is usually accomplished by heating raw rubber with sulfur and other auxiliary agents. It consists of introducing sulfur atoms that connect or cross-link the long strands of polymeric chains. Vulcanization was devised through trial-and-error experimentation by the American inventor Charles Goodyear in 1839, long before any real understanding of the chemistry of the process was known. Goodyear's patent on "Improvement in India Rubber" was issued on June 15, 1844. In the segment of vulcanized rubber shown below, the chains of polymerized isoprene are cross-linked by sulfur–sulfur bonds giving the polymer more strength and elasticity.

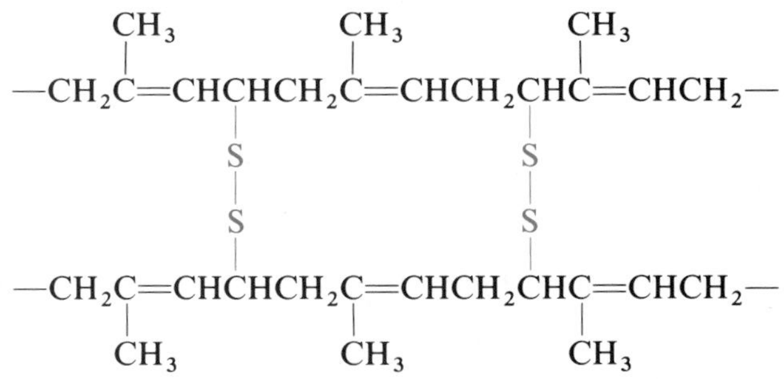

$$-CH_2C(CH_3){=}CHCH(S{-})CH_2C(CH_3){=}CHCH_2CH(S{-})C(CH_3){=}CHCH_2-$$

$$-CH_2C(CH_3){=}CHCH(S{-})CH_2C(CH_3){=}CHCH_2CH(S{-})C(CH_3){=}CHCH_2-$$

(the two chains joined by S–S bridges)

8.6 Geometric Isomerism in Polymers

The recurring double bonds in isoprene and butadiene polymers make it possible to have polymers with specific spatial orientation as a result of cis–trans isomerism. Recall from Section 3.4 that two carbon atoms joined by a double bond are not free to rotate and thus give rise to cis–trans isomerism. An isoprene polymer can have all-cis, all-trans, or a random distribution of cis and trans configurations about the double bonds.

Natural rubber is *cis*-polyisoprene with an all cis configuration about the carbon–carbon double bonds. Gutta-percha, also obtained from plants, is a *trans*-polyisoprene with an all trans configuration. Although these two polymers have the same composition, their properties are radically different. The cis natural rubber is a soft, elastic material, whereas the trans gutta-percha is a tough, nonelastic, hornlike substance. Natural rubber has many varied uses. Some uses of gutta-percha are for electrical insulation, dentistry, and golf balls.

```
—CH2         CH2—CH2         CH2—CH2         CH2—
     \      /       \       /       \       /
      C==C           C==C            C==C
     /      \       /       \       /       \
 CH3         H   CH3         H   CH3         H
```

All cis configuration of natural rubber

```
—CH2         H    CH3          CH2—CH2         H
     \      /        \        /       \       /
      C==C            C==C             C==C
     /      \        /        \       /       \
 CH3         CH2—CH2           H   CH3         CH2—
```

All trans configuration of gutta-percha

Chicle is another natural substance containing polyisoprenes. It is obtained by concentrating the latex from the sapodilla tree and contains about 5% *cis*-polyisoprene and 12% *trans*-polyisoprene. The chief use of chicle is in chewing gum.

Only random or nonstereospecific polymers are obtained by free radical polymerization. Synthetic polyisoprenes made by free radical polymerization are much inferior to natural rubber, since they contain both the cis and the trans isomers. But in the 1950s Karl Ziegler (1898–1973) of Germany and Giulio Natta (1903–1979) of Italy developed catalysts [for example, $(C_2H_5)_3Al/TiCl_4$] that allowed polymerization to proceed by an ionic mechanism, producing stereochemically controlled polymers. Ziegler–Natta catalysts made possible the synthesis of polyisoprene with an all cis configuration and with properties fully comparable to those of natural rubber. This material is known by the odd but logical name *synthetic natural rubber*. In 1963 Natta and Ziegler were jointly awarded the Nobel prize for their work on stereochemically controlled polymerization reactions.

8.7 Condensation Polymers

Condensation polymers are formed by reactions between functional groups on adjacent monomer molecules. As a rule a smaller molecule, usually water, is eliminated in the reaction. The monomers must be at least bifunctional, and if cross-linking is to occur, there must be more than two functional groups on some monomer molecules.

Most biochemical polymers are of the condensation type. Proteins are polyamides, whereas nucleic acids are polyesters. Just as with synthetic polymers, biological polymers can have varied physical properties and varied functions. The collagen protein is used to make durable structures such as feathers, hair, and hooves. The elastin protein can be used for structures that need to stretch, such as tendons. Other proteins provide the mucous coating that protects our nasal passages. These differences in physical properties are determined by (1) the functional groups that are incorporated in the polymer and (2) the structure into which the atoms have been bonded. This generalization applies to synthetic polymers as well.

Many different condensation polymers have been synthesized. Important classes include the polyesters, polyamides, phenol–formaldehyde polymers, and polyurethanes.

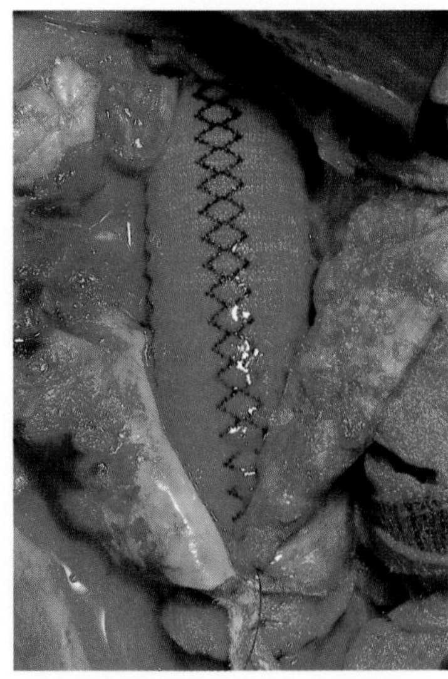

▲ **The synthetic fiber Dacron is used for patching in heart surgery.**

Polyesters

Polyesters are joined by ester linkages between carboxylic acid and alcohol groups; the macromolecule formed may be linear or cross-linked. From the bifunctional monomers terephthalic acid and ethylene glycol, a linear polyester is obtained. Esterification occurs between the alcohol and acid groups on both ends of both monomers, forming long-chain macromolecules:

$$HOOC-C_6H_4-COOH \qquad HOCH_2CH_2OH$$

Terephthalic acid   Ethylene glycol

$$-OCH_2CH_2O-\left[\overset{O}{\overset{\|}{C}}-C_6H_4-\overset{O}{\overset{\|}{C}}-OCH_2CH_2O-\right]_n\overset{O}{\overset{\|}{C}}-C_6H_4-\overset{O}{\overset{\|}{C}}-$$

This polymer may be drawn into fibers or formed into transparent films of great strength. Dacron and Terylene synthetic textiles and Mylar films are made from this polyester. In actual practice the dimethyl ester of terephthalic acid is used, and the molecule split out is methyl alcohol instead of water.

When trifunctional acids or alcohols are used as monomers, cross-linked thermosetting polyesters are obtained (see Figure 8.1). One common example is the reaction of glycerol and *o*-phthalic acid. The polymer formed is one of a group of polymers known as alkyd resins. Glycerol has three functional —OH groups, and phthalic acid has two functional —COOH groups:

$$HOCH_2\underset{}{\overset{OH}{\overset{|}{C}}}HCH_2OH \qquad C_6H_4(COOH)_2$$

Glycerol   *o*-Phthalic acid

A cross-linked macromolecular structure is formed that, with modifications, has proved to be one of the most outstanding materials used in the coatings industry. Alkyd resins have been used as "baked-on" finishes for automobiles and household appliances. Each year more than 3.6×10^8 kg (7.9×10^8 lb) of these resins are used in paints, varnishes, lacquers, electrical insulation, and so on.

Polyamides

Although there are several nylons, one of the best known and the first commercially successful polyamide is Nylon-66. This polymer was so named because it

Fibers made from polymers ▶ can be used to conduct light to a very specific location. This property is used extensively in the field of fiberoptics.

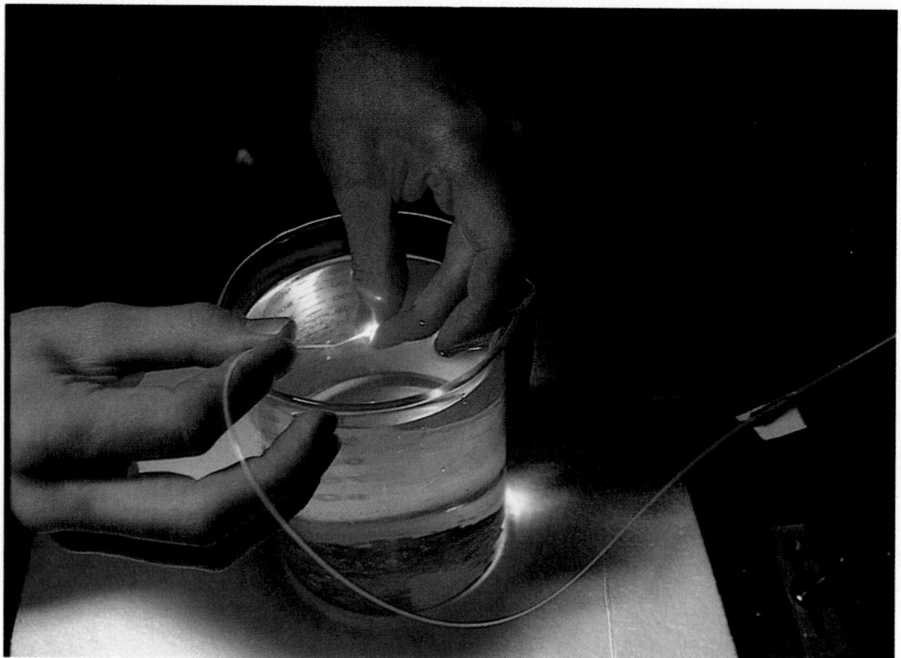

was made from two six-carbon monomers, adipic acid [$HOOC(CH_2)_4COOH$] and 1,6-diaminohexane [$H_2N(CH_2)_6NH_2$]. The polymer chains of polyamides contain recurring amide linkages. The amide linkage can be made by reacting a carboxylic acid group with an amine group:

$$\underset{\text{Carboxylic acid group}}{R{-}\overset{O}{\overset{\|}{C}}{-}OH} + \underset{\text{Amine group}}{H{-}\overset{H}{\overset{|}{N}}{-}CH_2{-}R'} \xrightarrow{\Delta} R{-}\underset{\text{Amide linkage}}{\overset{O}{\overset{\|}{C}}{-}NH}{-}CH_2{-}R' + H_2O$$

The repeating structural unit of the Nylon-66 chain consists of one adipic acid unit and one 1,6-diaminohexane unit:

$$\underset{\text{Adipic acid}}{HOOC{-}(CH_2)_4{-}COOH} \qquad \underset{\text{1,6-Diaminohexane (Hexamethylenediamine)}}{H_2N{-}(CH_2)_6{-}NH_2}$$

$$\underset{\text{Segment of Nylon-66 polyamide}}{{-}NH(CH_2)_6{-}NH{-}\left[\overset{O}{\overset{\|}{C}}(CH_2)_4{-}\overset{O}{\overset{\|}{C}}{-}NH(CH_2)_6{-}NH\right]_n\overset{O}{\overset{\|}{C}}{-}(CH_2)_4{-}\overset{O}{\overset{\|}{C}}{-}}$$

Nylon was developed as a synthetic fiber for the production of stockings and other wearing apparel. It was introduced to the public at the New York World's Fair in 1939. Nylon is used to make fibers for clothing and carpeting, filaments for fishing lines and ropes, bristles for brushes, and molded objects such as gears and bearings. For the latter application no lubrication is required, because nylon surfaces are inherently slippery.

Phenol–Formaldehyde Polymers

As noted earlier, a phenol–formaldehyde condensation polymer (Bakelite) was first marketed over 75 years ago. Polymers of this type are still widely used, especially in electrical equipment, because of their insulating and fire-resistant properties.

Each phenol molecule can react with formaldehyde to lose an H atom from the para position and from each of the ortho positions (indicated by arrows):

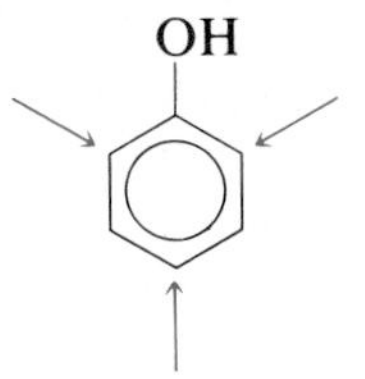

OH

Each formaldehyde molecule reacts with two phenol molecules to eliminate water:

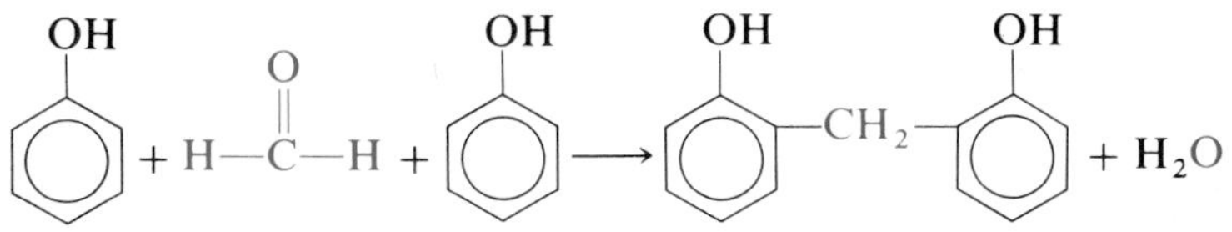

OH + H—C(=O)—H + OH → OH—CH$_2$—OH + H_2O

Similar reactions occur at the other two reactive sites on each phenol molecule, leading to the formation of the polymer. This polymer is thermosetting because it has an extensively cross-linked network structure. A typical section of this structure is illustrated as follows:

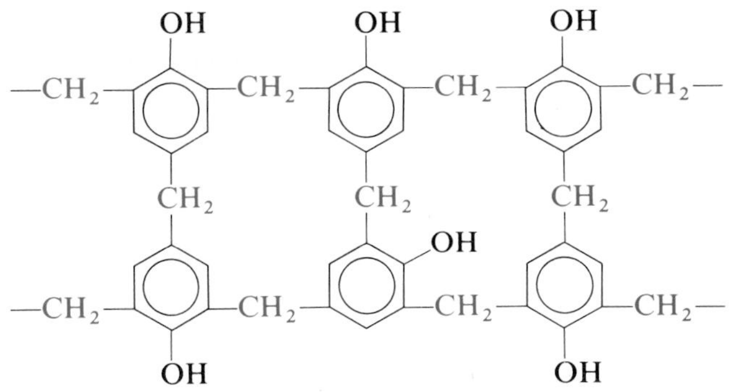

OH OH OH
—CH$_2$— —CH$_2$— —CH$_2$— —CH$_2$—
CH$_2$ CH$_2$ CH$_2$
OH
—CH$_2$— —CH$_2$— —CH$_2$— —CH$_2$—
OH OH

Phenol–formaldehyde polymer

Polyurethanes

The compound urethane has structural features of both an ester and an amide. Its formula is

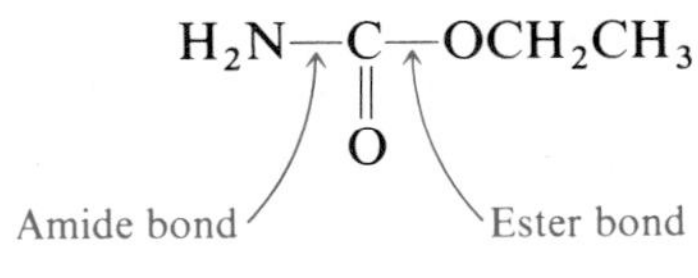

H_2N—C(=O)—OCH_2CH_3

Amide bond Ester bond

A substituted urethane can be made by reacting an isocyanate with an alcohol. For example,

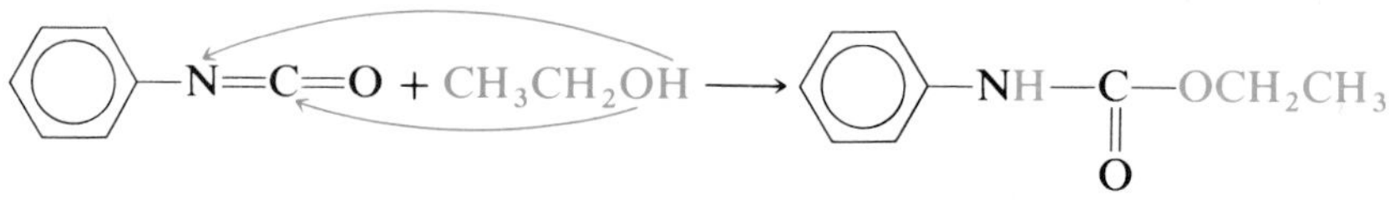

$$C_6H_5{-}N{=}C{=}O + CH_3CH_2OH \longrightarrow C_6H_5{-}NH{-}\underset{\underset{\displaystyle O}{\|}}{C}{-}OCH_2CH_3$$

Phenyl isocyanate N-Phenyl urethane

Diisocyanates and diols are both difunctional; therefore, they yield polymers called *polyurethanes*. The polyurethanes are classified as condensation polymers, although no water or other small molecule is split out when they are formed. From phenylene diisocyanate and ethylene glycol, we obtain a polyurethane that has a structure as shown:

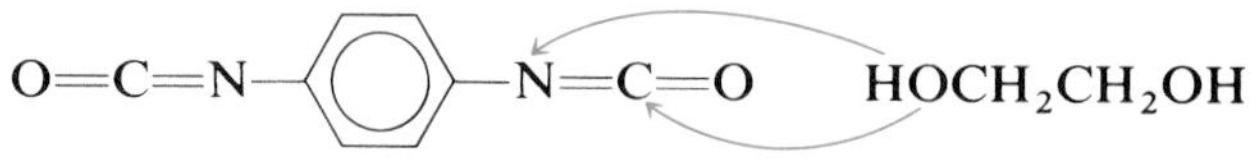

$$O{=}C{=}N{-}C_6H_4{-}N{=}C{=}O \qquad HOCH_2CH_2OH$$

p-Phenylene diisocyanate Ethylene glycol

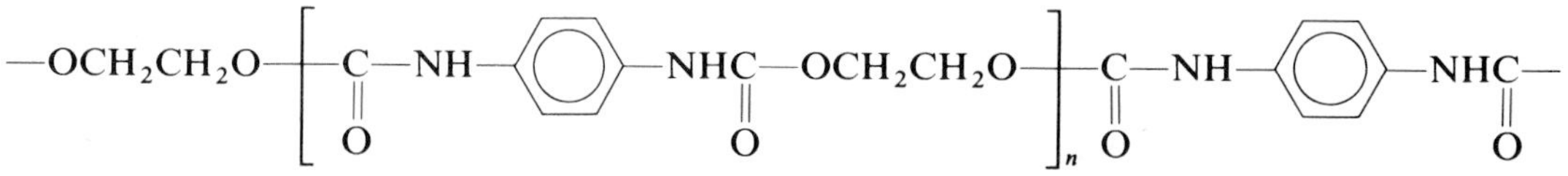

$$-OCH_2CH_2O{-}\left[\underset{\underset{\displaystyle O}{\|}}{C}{-}NH{-}C_6H_4{-}NH\underset{\underset{\displaystyle O}{\|}}{C}{-}OCH_2CH_2O\right]_n{-}\underset{\underset{\displaystyle O}{\|}}{C}{-}NH{-}C_6H_4{-}NH\underset{\underset{\displaystyle O}{\|}}{C}-$$

Segment of a polyurethane

Some polyurethanes are soft elastic materials that are widely used as *foam rubber* in upholstery and similar applications. There are many other applications, including automobile safety padding, insulation, life preservers, elastic fibers, and semirigid or rigid foams. Polyurethane can be made into a foam or spongy polymer by adding water during the polymerization or during the molding process. Water reacts with the isocyanate to produce carbon dioxide, which causes the polymer to foam. The effect is similar to that of baking powder releasing carbon dioxide in dough, causing it to rise and become light. The result is a polymer containing innumerable tiny gas filled cavities that give the product a spongelike quality.

8.8 Silicone Polymers

The silicones are an unusual group of polymers. They include oils and greases, molding resins, rubbers (elastomers), and Silly Putty, the latter being a remarkable material that bounces like a rubber ball when dropped but that can be shaped like putty! Silicones have properties common to both organic and inorganic compounds. The mineral quartz (found in igneous rocks and sand) has the empirical formula SiO_2 and is actually an inorganic high polymer. Each silicon atom is bonded to four oxygen atoms, and each oxygen to two silicon atoms to form a three-dimensional structure:

$$
\begin{array}{ccccccc}
 & & | & & | & & \\
 & & O & & O & & \\
| & & | & & | & & | \\
-Si- & O & -Si- & O & -Si- & O & -Si- \\
| & & | & & | & & | \\
 & & O & & O & & \\
 & & | & & | & & \\
 & & -Si- & & -Si- & & \\
 & & | & & | & &
\end{array}
$$

The silicon–oxygen bonds are very strong, and quartz is stable at very high temperatures. But it is also very hard and brittle and therefore difficult to form into useful shapes.

Linear silicone polymers, also called silicones or polysiloxanes, consist of silicon–oxygen chains with two alkyl groups attached to each silicon atom:

$$
-O-\overset{\overset{\displaystyle R}{|}}{\underset{\underset{\displaystyle R}{|}}{Si}}-O-\left[\overset{\overset{\displaystyle R}{|}}{\underset{\underset{\displaystyle R}{|}}{Si}}-O\right]_n-\overset{\overset{\displaystyle R}{|}}{\underset{\underset{\displaystyle R}{|}}{Si}}-O-
$$

The physical properties of silicones can be modified by (1) varying the length of the polymer chain, (2) varying the R groups, and (3) introducing cross-linking between the chains.

Because of their special properties, silicones have found a variety of uses despite their high cost. Some of their useful qualities are (1) good insulating properties (used in high temperature applications), (2) little viscosity change over a wide temperature range (therefore they are used as lubricating oils and greases at extreme temperatures), (3) excellent water repellency (used to waterproof many types of surfaces), and (4) good biological compatibility (hence their use in medical and plastic surgery applications). A few of the specific uses of silicone polymers are for coatings on printed electronic circuits, synthetic lubricants, hydraulic systems, brake fluids, electrical insulation, foam shields for nuclear power plants, solar energy, heat transfer systems, hair sprays, body and hand lotions, automobile and furniture polishes, and urethane foams. Because of their stability and tissue compatibility, silicones are frequently used for permanent surgical implants. For example, heart pacemakers are encased in protective casings made of silicone, and silicones are used to replace destroyed nose cartilage.

▲ **The safety of using silicone for breast implants has recently become an issue of controversy.**

Concepts in Review

1. Write formulas for addition polymers when given the monomer(s).
2. Write formulas for condensation polymers when given the monomers.

3. Describe the properties of a thermoplastic polymer and a thermosetting polymer.
4. Explain the free radical mechanism for polymer formation.
5. Identify polymers from their trade names (for example, Dacron, nylon, and Teflon).
6. Explain the effect of cross-linking in polymers.
7. Draw a segment of the structural formula of natural rubber to illustrate the all-cis configuration.
8. Explain how butadiene-type polymers are formed.
9. Explain vulcanization and its effect on rubber.
10. Identify polymers by type (such as vinyl, polyester, polyamide, or polyurethane).
11. Identify several useful qualities of silicones.

Equations in Review

Steps in Addition Polymerization

Free radical formation

$$RO{:}OR \longrightarrow 2\,RO\cdot$$

Propagation of polymeric chain

$$RO\cdot + CH_2{=}CH_2 \longrightarrow ROCH_2CH_2\cdot$$
$$ROCH_2CH_2\cdot + CH_2{=}CH_2 \longrightarrow ROCH_2CH_2CH_2CH_2\cdot$$

Termination

$$RO(CH_2CH_2)_n\cdot + \cdot OR \longrightarrow RO(CH_2CH_2)_nOR$$
$$RO(CH_2CH_2)_n\cdot + \cdot(CH_2CH_2)_nOR \longrightarrow RO(CH_2CH_2)_n(CH_2CH_2)_nOR$$

General Reactions Forming Condensation Polymers

Polyesters

$$HO{-}\overset{O}{\overset{\|}{C}}{-}(CH_2)_n{-}\overset{O}{\overset{\|}{C}}{-}OH + HO{+}CH_2)_n{-}OH \longrightarrow \left(\overset{O}{\overset{\|}{C}}{-}(CH_2)_n{-}\overset{O}{\overset{\|}{C}}{-}O{-}(CH_2)_n{-}O\right)_n$$

Polyamides

$$HO{-}\overset{O}{\overset{\|}{C}}{-}(CH_2)_n{-}\overset{O}{\overset{\|}{C}}{-}OH + H_2N{+}CH_2)_n{-}NH_2 \longrightarrow \left(\overset{O}{\overset{\|}{C}}{-}(CH_2)_n{-}\overset{O}{\overset{\|}{C}}{-}NH{-}(CH_2)_n{-}NH\right)_n$$

Urethanes

$$O{=}C{=}N{-}C_6H_4{-}N{=}C{=}O + HOCH_2CH_2OH \longrightarrow \left(\overset{O}{\overset{\|}{C}}{-}NH{-}C_6H_4{-}NH\overset{O}{\overset{\|}{C}}{-}OCH_2CH_2O \right)_n$$

Exercises

1. How does condensation polymerization differ from addition polymerization?
2. What property distinguishes a thermoplastic polymer from a thermosetting polymer?
3. Show the free radical mechanism for the polymerization of propylene to polypropylene.
4. How many ethylene units are in a polyethylene molecule that has a molar mass of approximately 25,000?
5. Write a structural formula showing the polymer that can be formed from
   (a) Ethylene (c) 1-Butene
   (b) Propylene (d) 2-Butene
6. Write structural formulas for the following polymers:
   (a) Saran (d) Polystyrene
   (b) Orlon (e) Lucite
   (c) Teflon
7. Write structures showing two possible ways in which vinyl chloride can polymerize to form polyvinyl chloride. Show four units in each structure.
8. (a) Write the structure for a polymer that can be formed from 2,3-dimethyl-1,3-butadiene.
   (b) Can 2,3-dimethyl-1,3-butadiene form cis and trans polymers? Explain.
9. Write the chemical structures for the monomers of
   (a) Natural rubber
   (b) Synthetic (SBR) rubber
   (c) Synthetic natural rubber
10. Why is the useful life of natural rubber and that of many synthetic rubbers shortened in smoggy atmospheres?
11. How are rubber molecules modified by vulcanization?
12. Natural rubber is the all cis polymer of isoprene, and gutta-percha is the all trans isomer. Write the structure for each polymer, showing at least three isoprene units.
13. Nitrile rubber (Buna N) is a copolymer of two parts of 1,3-butadiene to one part of acrylonitrile ($CH_2{=}CHCN$). Write a structure for this synthetic rubber, showing at least two units of the polymer.
14. Ziegler–Natta catalysts can orient the polymerization of propylene to form isotactic polypropylene—that is, polypropylene with all the methyl groups on the same side of the long carbon chain. Write the structure for (a) isotactic polypropylene and (b) another possible geometric form of polypropylene.
15. Write formulas showing the structure of
   (a) Dacron (c) Bakelite
   (b) Nylon-66 (d) Polyurethane
16. Using *p*-cresol (p-$CH_3{-}C_6H_4{-}OH$) in place of phenol to form a phenol–formaldehyde polymer results in a thermoplastic rather than a thermosetting polymer. Explain why this occurs.
17. Why must at least some monomer molecules be trifunctional to form a thermosetting polyester?
18. Glyptal polyesters are made from glycerol and phthalic acid. Would this kind of polymer more likely be thermoplastic or thermosetting? Explain.
19. How is "foam" introduced into foam or sponge rubber materials?
20. Silicone polymers are more resistant to high temperatures than the usual organic polymers. Suggest an explanation for this property of the silicones.
21. Which of these statements are correct? Rewrite each incorrect statement to make it correct.
   (a) The process of forming macromolecules from small units is called polymerization.
   (b) The monomers in condensation polymerization must be at least bifunctional.
   (c) The monomers of Nylon-66 are a dicarboxylic acid and a diol.
   (d) Dacron and Mylar are both made from the same monomers.

(e) Hexamethylene diamine is a secondary amine.
(f) Teflon is an addition polymer.
(g) Vulcanization was invented by Charles Goodrich.
(h) The monomer for polystyrene is

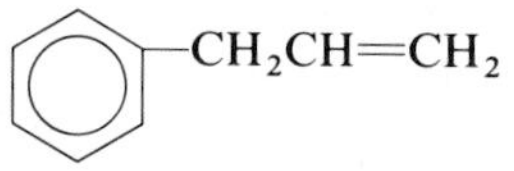

$C_6H_5-CH_2CH{=}CH_2$

(i) Polyurethanes have both ester and amide bonds in their structure.
(j) Bakelite is a copolymer of phenol and ethylene glycol.
(k) The monomer of natural rubber is 2-methyl-1,3-butadiene.

22. Write structures for the monomers of each of the polymers shown below, and classify each as polyvinyl, polyester, polyamide, or polyurethane.

(a) 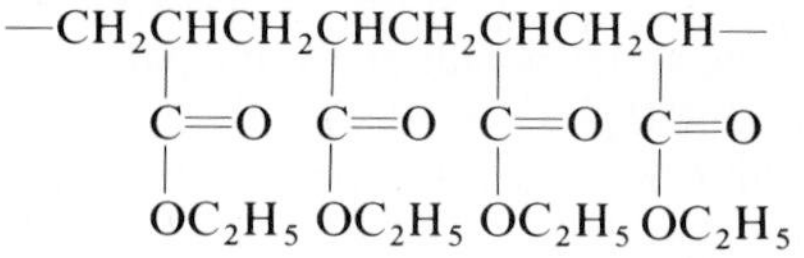 $-CH_2CH(C{=}O(OC_2H_5))CH_2CH(C{=}O(OC_2H_5))CH_2CH(C{=}O(OC_2H_5))CH_2CH(C{=}O(OC_2H_5))-$

(b) $-C(=O)-C_6H_4-C(=O)-OCH_2-C_6H_4-CH_2O-C(=O)-C_6H_4-C(=O)-OCH_2-C_6H_4-CH_2O-$

(c) $-C(=O)-NH-C_6H_3(CH_3)-NHC(=O)OCH_2CH_2-O-C(=O)-NH-C_6H_3(CH_3)-NH-C(=O)-OCH_2CH_2O-$

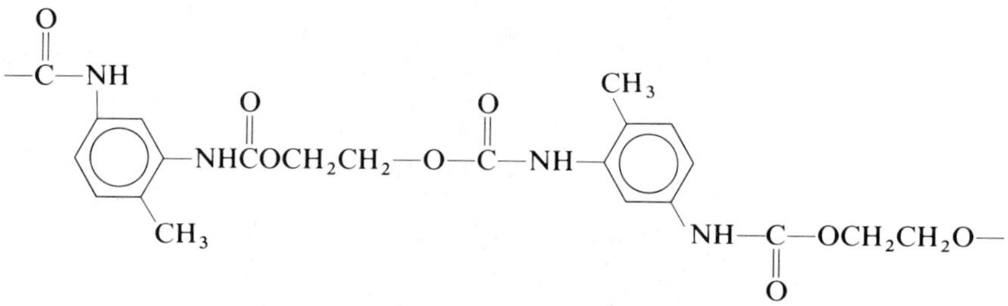

(d) 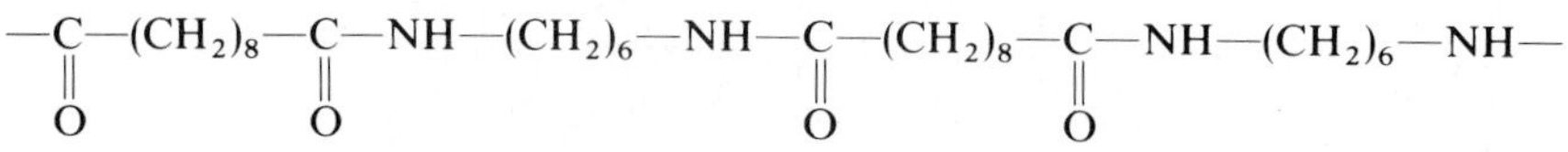 $-C(=O)-(CH_2)_8-C(=O)-NH-(CH_2)_6-NH-C(=O)-(CH_2)_8-C(=O)-NH-(CH_2)_6-NH-$

(e) 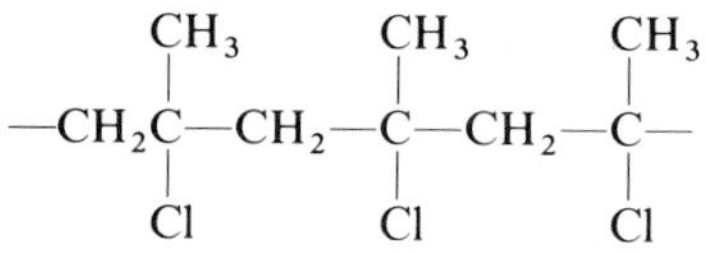 $-CH_2C(CH_3)(Cl)-CH_2-C(CH_3)(Cl)-CH_2-C(CH_3)(Cl)-$

(f) 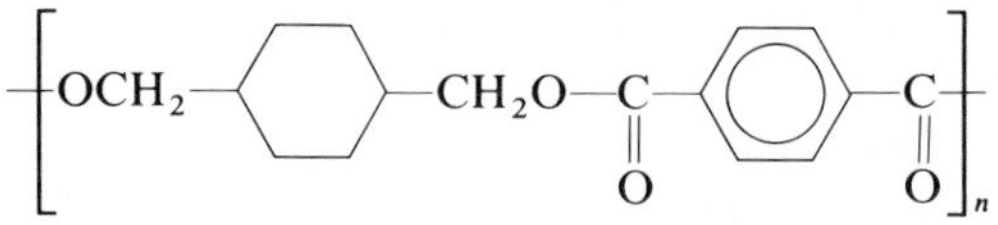 $\left[-OCH_2-C_6H_{10}-CH_2O-C(=O)-C_6H_4-C(=O)-\right]_n$

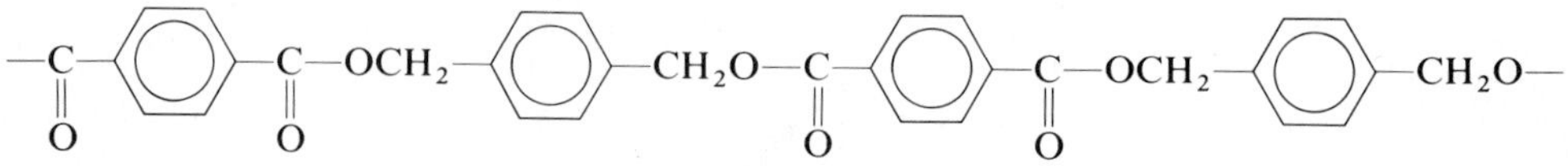

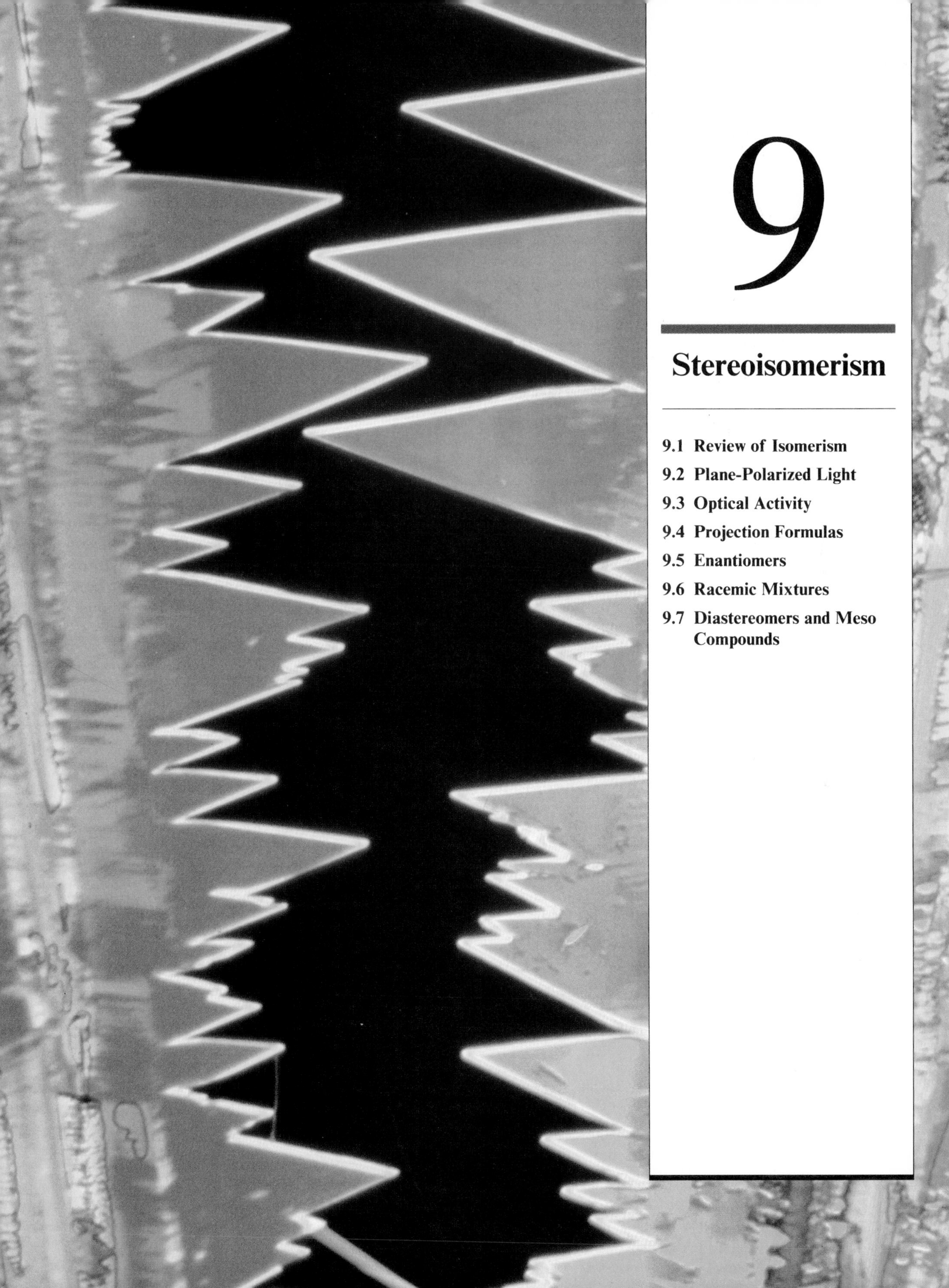

9

Stereoisomerism

◀ CHAPTER OPENING PHOTO: **These crystals of an ester of choline are seen through a polarizing light microscope.**

Many of us grew up hearing such comments as, "Can't you tell your left from your right?" Have you watched a small child try to differentiate between a right and left shoe? Not surprisingly, the distinction between right and left is difficult. After all, our bodies are reasonably symmetrical. For example, both hands are made up of the same components (four fingers, a thumb, and a palm) ordered in the same way (from thumb through little finger). Yet, there is a difference if we try to put a left-handed glove on our right hand or a right shoe on our left foot.

Molecules possess similar, subtle structural differences, which can have a major impact on chemical reactivity. For example, although there are two forms of blood sugar, related as closely as our left and right hands, only one of these structures can be used by our bodies for energy. Stereoisomerism is a subject that attempts to define these subtle differences in molecular structure.

9.1 REVIEW OF ISOMERISM

The phenomenon of two or more compounds having the same number and kinds of atoms is isomerism. Thus isomers are different compounds that have the same composition and the same molecular formula.

There are two types of isomerism. In the first type, known as structural isomerism, the difference between isomers is due to a different structural arrangement of the atoms to form different molecules. For example, butane and isobutane, ethanol and dimethyl ether, and 1-chloropropane and 2-chloropropane are structural isomers:

$CH_3CH_2CH_2CH_3$	CH_3CH_2OH	$CH_3CH_2CH_2Cl$
Butane	Ethanol	1-Chloropropane
$CH_3CH(CH_3)CH_3$	CH_3OCH_3	$CH_3CHClCH_3$
Isobutane	Dimethyl ether	2-Chloropropane

stereoisomerism

In the second type of isomerism, the isomers have the same structural formulas but differ in the arrangement of the atoms in space. This type of isomerism is known as **stereoisomerism**. Thus, compounds that have the same structural formulas but differ in their spatial arrangement are called **stereoisomers**. There are two types of stereoisomers: cis–trans or geometric isomers, which we have already considered, and optical isomers, the subject of this chapter. The outstanding feature of optical isomers is that they have the ability to rotate plane-polarized light.

stereoisomers

FIGURE 9.1 ►
(a) Diagram of ordinary light vibrating in all possible directions (planes) and (b) diagram of plane-polarized light vibrating in a single plane. The beam of light is coming toward the reader.

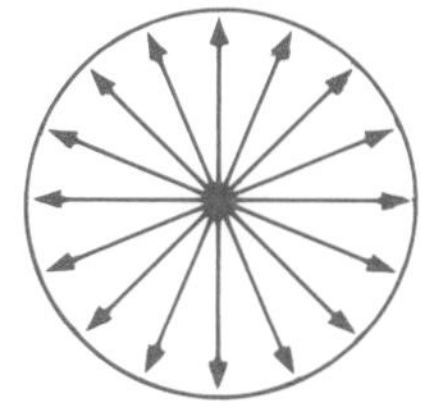

Ordinary (unpolarized) light
(a)

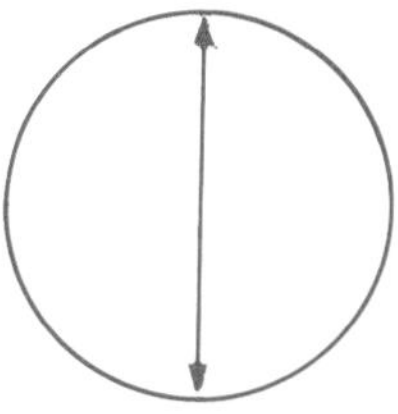

Plane-polarized light
(b)

9.2 Plane-Polarized Light

Plane-polarized light is light that is vibrating in only one plane. Ordinary (unpolarized) light consists of electromagnetic waves vibrating in all directions (planes) perpendicular to the direction in which it is traveling. When ordinary light passes through a polarizer, it emerges vibrating in only one plane and is called plane-polarized light (Figure 9.1).

plane-polarized light

Polarizers can be made from calcite or tourmaline crystals or from a Polaroid filter, which is a transparent plastic containing properly oriented embedded

(a)

(b)

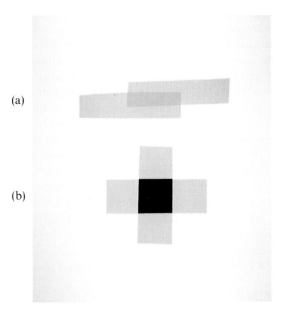

◄ FIGURE 9.2
Two Polaroid filters (a) with axes parallel and (b) with axes at right angles. In (a), light passes through both filters and emerges polarized. In (b), the polarized light that emerges from one filter is blocked and does not pass through the second filter, which is at right angles to the first. With no light emerging, the filters appear black.

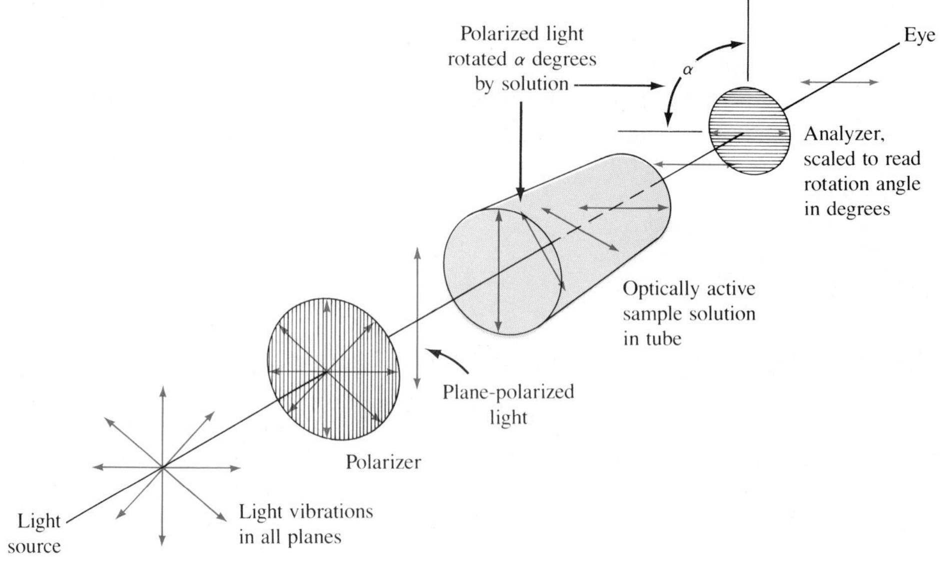

FIGURE 9.3 ▶ Schematic diagram of a polarimeter. This instrument is used to measure the angle α through which an optically active substance rotates the plane of polarized light.

crystals. Two Polaroid filters with their axes parallel allow the passage of plane-polarized light. But when one filter is placed so that its axis is at right angles to that of the other filter, the passage of light is blocked and the filters appear black (Figure 9.2).

Specific Rotation

The rotation of plane-polarized light is quantitatively measured with a polarimeter. The essential features of this instrument are (1) a light source (usually a sodium lamp), (2) a polarizer, (3) a sample tube, (4) an analyzer (which is another matched polarizer), and (5) a calibrated scale (360°) to measure the number of degrees the plane of polarized light is rotated. The calibrated scale is attached to the analyzer (see Figure 9.3). When the sample tube contains a solution of an optically inactive material, the axes of the polarizer and the analyzer are parallel and the scale is at zero degrees; the light passing through is at maximum intensity. When a solution of an optically active substance is placed in the sample tube, the plane in which the polarized light is vibrating is rotated through an angle (α). The analyzer is then rotated to the position where the emerging light is at maximum intensity. The number of degrees and the direction of rotation by the solution are then read from the scale as the observed rotation.

specific rotation

The **specific rotation**, [α], of a compound is the number of degrees that polarized light would be rotated by passage through 1 decimeter (dm) of a solution of the substance at a concentration of 1 gram per milliliter. The specific rotation of optically active substances is listed in chemical handbooks along with other physical properties. The following formula is used to calculate specific rotation from polarimeter data:

$$[\alpha] = \frac{\text{Observed rotation in degrees}}{\left(\begin{array}{c}\text{Length of}\\ \text{sample tube in decimeters}\end{array}\right)\left(\begin{array}{c}\text{Sample concentration in}\\ \text{grams per milliliter}\end{array}\right)}$$

9.3 Optical Activity

optical activity

dextrorotatory

levorotatory

Many naturally occurring substances are able to rotate the plane of polarized light. Because of this ability to rotate polarized light, such substances are said to be **optically active**. When plane-polarized light passes through an optically active substance, the plane of the polarized light is rotated. If the rotation is to the right (clockwise), the substance is said to be **dextrorotatory**; if the rotation is to the left (counterclockwise), the substance is said to be **levorotatory**.

Some minerals, notably quartz, rotate the plane of polarized light (in fact, optical activity was discovered in minerals). However, when such mineral crystals are melted, the optical activity disappears. This means that the optical activity of these crystals must be due to an ordered arrangement within the crystals.

In 1848 Louis Pasteur (1822–1895) observed that sodium ammonium tartrate, a salt of tartaric acid, exists as a mixture of two kinds of crystals. Pasteur carefully hand separated the two kinds of crystals. Investigating their properties, he found that solutions made from either kind of crystal would rotate the plane of polarized light, but in opposite directions. Since this optical activity was present in a solution, it could not be caused by a specific arrangement within a crystal.

asymmetric carbon atom

The tetrahedral arrangement of single bonds around a carbon atom makes asymmetry (lack of symmetry) possible in organic molecules. When four different atoms or functional groups are bonded to a carbon atom, the molecule formed is asymmetric, and the carbon atom is called an **asymmetric carbon atom** (see Figure 9.4). In 1874 J. H. van't Hoff (1852–1911) and J. A. Le Bel (1847–1930) concluded that the presence of at least one asymmetric carbon atom in a molecule of an optically active substance is a key factor for optical activity. The first Nobel prize in chemistry was awarded to van't Hoff in 1901.

D

A B

C

○ = Carbon atom

A, B, C, D = Four different atoms or groups of atoms

◄ **FIGURE 9.4 Three-dimensional representation of an asymmetric carbon atom with four different groups bonded to it. The carbon atom is a sphere. Bonds to A and B project from the sphere toward the observer. Bonds to C and D project from the sphere away from the observer.**

▲ **The mineral quartz can rotate a plane of polarized light.**

Molecules of optically active substances must have at least one center of dissymmetry. Although optically active compounds are known that do not contain asymmetric carbon atoms (their center of dissymmetry is due to some other structural feature), most optically active organic substances do contain one or more asymmetric carbon atoms.

9.4 Projection Formulas

Molecules of a compound that contain one asymmetric carbon atom occur in two optically active isomeric forms. This is because the four different groups bonded to the asymmetric carbon atom can be oriented in space in two different configurations. It is important to understand how we represent such isomers on paper.

Let us consider the spatial arrangement of a lactic acid molecule, $CH_3CH(OH)COOH$, that contains one asymmetric carbon atom:

$$\begin{array}{c} {}^{1}COOH \\ | \\ H-{}^{2}C^{*}-OH \\ | \\ {}^{3}CH_3 \end{array} \qquad C^{*} = \text{Asymmetric carbon atom}$$

Lactic acid

Three-dimensional models are the best means of representing such a molecule, but by adopting certain conventions and using imagination, we can formulate the images on paper. The geometrical arrangement of the four groups about the asymmetric carbon (carbon 2) is the key to the stereoisomerism of lactic acid. The four bonds attached to carbon 2 are separated by angles of about 109.5°. Diagram I in Figure 9.5 is a three-dimensional representation of lactic acid in which the asymmetric carbon atom is represented as a sphere, with its center in the plane of the paper. The —H and —OH groups are projected forward from the paper (toward the observer), and the —COOH and —CH_3 groups are projected back from the paper (away from the observer).

For convenience of expression, simpler diagrams such as II and III are used. These are much easier and faster to draw. In II, it is understood that the groups (—H and —OH) attached to the horizontal bonds are coming out of the plane of the paper toward the observer, and the groups attached to the vertical bonds are projected back from the paper. The molecule represented by formula III is made by drawing a cross and attaching the four groups in their respective positions, as in formula II. The asymmetric carbon atom is understood to be located where the lines cross. Formulas II and III are called **projection formulas**.

projection formula

$$\begin{array}{ccc} \begin{array}{c} COOH \\ H \;\; \bigcirc \;\; OH \\ CH_3 \end{array} & \begin{array}{c} COOH \\ | \\ H-C-OH \\ | \\ CH_3 \end{array} & \begin{array}{c} COOH \\ | \\ H-\!\!\!+\!\!\!-OH \\ | \\ CH_3 \end{array} \\ \text{I} & \text{II} & \text{III} \end{array}$$

Figure 9.5 ► **Methods of representing three-dimensional formulas of a compound that contains one asymmetric carbon atom. All three structures represent the same molecule.**

It is important to be careful when comparing projection formulas. Two rules apply: (1) projection formulas must not be turned 90°; (2) projection formulas must not be lifted or flipped out of the plane of the paper. Projection formulas may, however, be turned 180° in the plane of the paper without changing the spatial arrangement of the molecule. Consider the following projection formulas:

III: top COOH; left H; right OH; bottom CH_3

IV: top CH_3; left HO; right H; bottom COOH

V: top CH_3; left HO; right H; bottom COOH (three-dimensional)

Formulas I, III, IV, and V represent identical molecules. Formula IV was obtained by turning formula III 180°. Formula V is formula IV drawn in a three-dimensional representation. If formula III is turned 90°, the other stereoisomer of lactic acid is represented, as shown in formulas VI and VII.

VI: top H; left CH_3; right COOH; bottom OH

VII: top H; left CH_3; right COOH; bottom OH (three-dimensional)

EXAMPLE 9.1

(a) Redraw the three-dimensional formula (A) into a projection formula. (b) Draw the three-dimensional formula represented by the projection formula (B).

(A) top CH_3; left H; right CH_2NH_2; bottom Br (three-dimensional)

$CH_3CHBrCH_2NH_2$

(B) top CH_3; left H; right CH_2CH_3; bottom OH

$CH_3CH(OH)CH_2CH_3$

SOLUTION

(a) Draw a vertical and a horizontal line crossing each other. Place the CH_3 at the top and the Br at the bottom of the vertical line. Place the H at the left and the CH_2NH_2 at the right of the horizontal line to complete the projection formula:

top CH_3; left H; right CH_2NH_2; bottom Br

(b) Draw a small circle to represent the asymmetric carbon atom (C2) that is located where the two lines cross in the projection formula. Draw a short line extending from the top and from the bottom of the circle. Place the CH_3 on the top and the OH on the bottom at the end of these lines. Now draw two short lines from within the circle coming toward your left and right arms. Place the H at the end of the left line and the CH_2CH_3 at the end of the right line. The finished formula should look like this.

CH_3

H — (circle) — CH_2CH_3

OH

PRACTICE Redraw this projection formula as a three-dimensional formula.

Br

Cl —+— CH_3

F

Answer: Br

Cl — (circle) — CH_3

F

▲
FIGURE 9.6
The left hand is the same as the mirror image of the right hand. Right and left hands are not superimposable; hence they are chiral.

9.5 ENANTIOMERS

Your right and your left hands are mirror images of each other; that is, the left hand is a mirror reflection of the right hand and vice versa. Furthermore, the two hands are not superimposable on each other (see Figure 9.6). **Superimposable** means that, when we lay one object upon another, all parts of both objects coincide exactly.

superimposable

A molecule that is not superimposable on its mirror image is said to be **chiral**. The word *chiral* comes from the Greek word *cheir*, meaning hand. Chiral molecules have the property of "handedness"; that is, they are related to each other in the same manner as the right and left hands. An asymmetric carbon atom is often referred to as a chiral carbon or a chiral center. Molecules, or objects, that are superimposable are **achiral**. Some chiral and achiral objects are shown in Figure 9.7.

chiral

achiral

The formulas developed in Section 9.4 dealt primarily with a single kind of lactic acid molecule. But two stereoisomers of lactic acid are known, one that rotates the plane of polarized light to the right and one that rotates it to the left. These two forms of lactic acid are shown in Figure 9.8. If we examine these two structural formulas carefully, we can see that they are mirror images of each other. The reflection of either molecule in a mirror corresponds to the structure of the other molecule. Even though the two molecules have the same molecular formula and the same four groups attached to the central carbon atom, they are not superimposable. Therefore, the two molecules are not identical but are isomers. One molecule rotates the plane of polarized light to the left and is termed *levorotatory*; the other molecule rotates it to the right and is *dextrorotatory*. A plus (+) or a minus (−) sign written in parentheses and placed in front of a name or formula indicates the direction of rotation of polarized light and becomes part of the name of the compound. Plus (+) indicates rotation to the right and minus (−) to the left. Using projection formulas, we write the two lactic acids as follows:

```
    COOH             COOH
     |                |
  H—C—OH          HO—C—H
     |                |
    CH3              CH3
(−)-Lactic acid   (+)-Lactic acid
```

Originally it was not known which lactic acid structure was the (+) or the (−) compound. However, it is now known that they are as shown. Isomers that are

◄ **FIGURE 9.7**
(a) Chiral and (b) achiral objects.

Mirror Mirror

COOH — H, OH — CH_3 (−)-Lactic acid | COOH — HO, H — CH_3 (+)-Lactic acid

◄ **FIGURE 9.8**
Mirror-image isomers of lactic acid. Each isomer is the mirror reflection of the other. (−)-Lactic acid rotates plane-polarized light to the left, and (+)-lactic acid rotates plane-polarized light to the right.

enantiomer

mirror images of each other are called **enantiomers**. The word *enantiomer* comes from the Greek word *enantios*, which means opposite.

Many, but not all, molecules that contain an asymmetric carbon are chiral. Most of the molecules we shall study that have an asymmetric carbon atom are chiral. To decide whether a molecule is chiral and has an enantiomer, make models of the molecule and of its mirror image and see if they are superimposable. This is the ultimate test, but instead of making models every time, first examine the formula to see if it has an asymmetric carbon atom. If an asymmetric carbon atom is found, draw a cross and attach the four groups on the asymmetric carbon to the four ends of the cross. The asymmetric carbon is understood to be located where the lines cross. Remember that an asymmetric carbon atom has four different groups attached to it. Let us test the compounds 2-butanol and 2-chloropropane:

$CH_3CH_2CH(OH)CH_3$ — 2-Butanol

$CH_3CH(Cl)CH_3$ — 2-Chloropropane

In 2-butanol, carbon 2 is asymmetric. The four groups attached to carbon 2 are H, OH, CH_3, and CH_2CH_3. Draw the structure and its mirror image:

VIII	Mirror	IX	X (IX turned 180°)
top: CH_3; left: H; right: OH; bottom: CH_2–CH_3		top: CH_3; left: HO; right: H; bottom: CH_2–CH_3	top: CH_3–CH_2; left: H; right: OH; bottom: CH_3

Enantiomers

Turning structure IX 180° in the plane of the paper allows H and OH to coincide with their position in VIII, but CH_3 and CH_2CH_3 do not coincide. Therefore, we conclude that the mirror-image structures VIII and IX are enantiomers since they are not superimposable.

In 2-chloropropane, the four groups attached to carbon 2 are H, Cl, CH_3, and CH_3. Note that two groups are the same. Draw the structure and its mirror image:

XI	Mirror	XII	XIII (XII turned 180°)
top: CH_3; left: H; right: Cl; bottom: CH_3		top: CH_3; left: Cl; right: H; bottom: CH_3	top: CH_3; left: H; right: Cl; bottom: CH_3

When we turn structure XII 180° in the plane of the paper, the two structures XI and XIII are superimposable, proving that 2-chloropropane, which does not have an asymmetric carbon, does not exist in enantiomeric forms.

EXAMPLE 9.2

Draw mirror-image isomers for any of the following compounds that can exist as enantiomers:

(a) $CH_3CH_2CH_2OH$ (c) $CH_3CH_2CHClCH_2CH_2CH_3$
(b) $CH_3CH_2CHClCH_2CH_3$

SOLUTION

First check each formula for asymmetric carbon atoms:

(a) No asymmetric carbon atoms; each carbon has at least two groups that are the same.
(b) No asymmetric carbon atoms; carbon 3 has H, Cl, and two CH_2CH_3 groups.
(c) Carbon 3 is asymmetric; the four groups on carbon 3 are H, Cl, CH_3CH_2, and $CH_3CH_2CH_2$. Draw mirror images:

```
           H             |← Mirror        H
           |             |                |
CH3CH2—C—CH2CH2CH3       |   CH3CH2CH2—C—CH2CH3
           |             |                |
           Cl            |                Cl
```

PRACTICE Draw the mirror-image isomers for the following compounds that can exist as enantiomers:

(a) $NH_2CH_2CHBrCH_2OH$ (c) $NH_2CH_2CH_2CH_2OH$
(b) $NH_2CH_2CHBrCH_2NH_2$

Answers: (a)

```
           H          |← Mirror    H
           |          |            |
NH2CH2—C—CH2OH        |   HOCH2—C—CH2NH2
           |          |            |
           Br         |            Br
```

(b), (c) have no asymmetric carbons

The relationship between enantiomers is such that if we change the positions of any two groups on a compound containing only one asymmetric carbon atom, we obtain the structure of its enantiomer. If we make a second change, the structure of the original isomer is obtained again. In both cases shown below, (+)-lactic acid is formed by interchanging the positions of two groups on (−)-lactic acid:

```
    CH3                                   COOH                              COOH
     |                                     |                                  |
H————+————OH  ←Change position of——  H————+————OH  —Change position of→  HO————+————H
     |          CH3 and COOH               |          H and OH                 |
    COOH                                  CH3                                CH3
(+)-Lactic acid                      (−)-Lactic acid                    (+)-Lactic acid
```

To compare two projection formulas to test whether they are the same structure or are enantiomers, (1) turn one structure 180° in the plane of the paper and compare to see if they are superimposable, or (2) make successive group interchanges until the formulas are identical. If an odd number of interchanges are made, the two original formulas represent enantiomers; if an even number of interchanges are made, the two formulas represent the same compound. The following two examples illustrate this method. Are structures XIV and XV the same compound?

$$\begin{array}{c} CH_3 \\ Br-\!\!+\!\!-H \\ Cl \\ \text{XIV} \end{array} \qquad \begin{array}{c} H \\ Br-\!\!+\!\!-Cl \\ CH_3 \\ \text{XV} \end{array}$$

$$\begin{array}{c} H \\ Br-\!\!+\!\!-Cl \\ CH_3 \\ \text{XV} \end{array} \xrightarrow[\text{CH}_3\text{ and Cl}]{\text{Interchange}} \begin{array}{c} H \\ Br-\!\!+\!\!-CH_3 \\ Cl \end{array} \xrightarrow[\text{CH}_3\text{ and H}]{\text{Interchange}} \begin{array}{c} CH_3 \\ Br-\!\!+\!\!-H \\ Cl \\ \text{XIV} \end{array}$$

Two interchanges were needed to make structure XV identical to structure XIV. Therefore, structures XIV and XV represent the same compound.

Do structures XVI and XVII represent the same compound?

$$\begin{array}{c} CH_3 \\ HO-\!\!+\!\!-H \\ CH_2CH_3 \\ \text{XVI} \end{array} \qquad \begin{array}{c} OH \\ CH_3CH_2-\!\!+\!\!-CH_3 \\ H \\ \text{XVII} \end{array}$$

$$\begin{array}{c} OH \\ CH_3CH_2-\!\!+\!\!-CH_3 \\ H \\ \text{XVII} \end{array} \xrightarrow[\text{CH}_3\text{CH}_2\text{ and OH}]{\text{Interchange}} \begin{array}{c} CH_2CH_3 \\ HO-\!\!+\!\!-CH_3 \\ H \end{array} \xrightarrow[\text{CH}_3\text{ and H}]{\text{Interchange}}$$

$$\longrightarrow \begin{array}{c} CH_2CH_3 \\ HO-\!\!+\!\!-H \\ CH_3 \end{array} \xrightarrow[\text{CH}_3\text{ and CH}_3\text{CH}_2]{\text{Interchange}} \begin{array}{c} CH_3 \\ HO-\!\!+\!\!-H \\ CH_2CH_3 \\ \text{XVI} \end{array}$$

Three interchanges were needed to make structure XVII identical to structure XVI. Therefore, structures XVI and XVII do not represent the same compound; they are enantiomers.

Enantiomers ordinarily have the same chemical properties and the same physical properties other than optical rotation (see Table 9.1). They rotate plane-polarized light the same number of degrees but in opposite directions. Enantiomers differ in their physiological properties. Enzymes act on only one of a pair of enantiomers, since enzymes are stereoselective. For example, enzyme-catalyzed reduction of pyruvic acid in muscle tissue yields only (+)-lactic acid, but reduction of pyruvic acid catalyzed with H_2/Pt yields both (+)- and (−)-lactic acids (see Section 9.6).

A summary of the key factors of enantiomers and optical isomerism follows:

1. A carbon atom that has four different groups bonded to it is called an asymmetric or a chiral carbon atom.
2. A compound with one asymmetric carbon atom can exist in two isomeric forms called enantiomers.
3. Enantiomers are nonsuperimposable mirror-image isomers.
4. Enantiomers are optically active; that is, they are able to rotate plane-polarized light.
5. One isomer of an enantiomeric pair rotates polarized light to the left (counterclockwise). The other isomer rotates polarized light to the right (clockwise). The degree of rotation is the same but in opposite directions.
6. Rotation of polarized light to the right is indicated by (+), placed in front of the name of the compound. Rotation to the left is indicated by (−), for example, (+)-lactic acid and (−)-lactic acid.

9.6 Racemic Mixtures

A mixture containing equal amounts of a pair of enantiomers is known as a **racemic mixture**. Such a mixture is optically inactive and shows no rotation of polarized light when tested in a polarimeter. Each of the enantiomers rotates the plane of polarized light by the same amount but in opposite directions. Thus the rotation by each isomer is canceled. The (±) symbol is often used to designate racemic mixtures. For example, a racemic mixture of lactic acid is written as (±)-lactic acid because this mixture contains equal molar amounts of (+)-lactic acid and (−)-lactic acid.

racemic mixture

Racemic mixtures are usually obtained in laboratory syntheses of compounds in which an asymmetric carbon atom is formed. Thus, catalytic reduction of pyruvic acid (an achiral compound) to lactic acid produces a racemic mixture containing equal amounts of (+)- and (−)-lactic acid:

$$\underset{\text{Pyruvic acid}}{CH_3\underset{\underset{O}{\|}}{C}COOH} + H_2 \xrightarrow{Ni} \underset{(\pm)\text{-Lactic acid}}{CH_3\underset{\underset{OH}{|}}{C}HCOOH}$$

As a general rule, in the biological synthesis of potentially optically active compounds, only one of the isomers is produced. For example, (+)-lactic acid is produced by reactions occurring in muscle tissue, and (−)-lactic acid is produced by lactic acid bacteria in the souring of milk. These stereospecific reactions occur because biochemical syntheses are enzyme catalyzed. The preferential production of one isomer over another is apparently due to the configuration (shape) of the specific enzyme involved. Returning to the hand analogy, if the "right-handed" enantiomer is produced, then the enzyme responsible for the product can be likened to a right-handed glove.

The mirror-image isomers (enantiomers) of a racemic mixture are alike in all ordinary physical properties except in their action on polarized light. It is possible to separate or resolve racemic mixtures into their optically active components. In fact, Pasteur's original work with sodium ammonium tartrate involved such a separation. But a general consideration of the methods involved in such separations is beyond the scope of our present discussion.

Enantiomers usually differ in their biochemical properties. In fact, most living cells are able to use only one isomer of a mirror-image pair. For example, (+)-glucose ("blood sugar") can be used for metabolic energy, whereas (−)-glucose cannot. Enantiomers are truly different molecules and are treated as such by most organisms.

9.7 Diastereomers and Meso Compounds

The enantiomers discussed in the preceding sections are stereoisomers. That is, they differ only in the spatial arrangement of the atoms and groups within the molecule. The number of stereoisomers increases as the number of asymmetric carbon atoms increases. The maximum number of stereoisomers for a given compound is obtained by the formula 2^n, where n is the number of asymmetric carbon atoms in the compound.

2^n = Maximum number of stereoisomers for a given chiral compound
n = Number of asymmetric carbon atoms in a molecule

As we have seen, there are two ($2^1 = 2$) stereoisomers of lactic acid. But for a substance with two nonidentical asymmetric carbon atoms, such as 2-bromo-3-chlorobutane ($CH_3CHBrCHClCH_3$), four stereoisomers are possible ($2^2 = 4$). These four possible stereoisomers are written as projection formulas in this way (carbons 2 and 3 are asymmetric):

XVIII	XIX	XX	XXI
CH_3	CH_3	CH_3	CH_3
H—C—Br	Br—C—H	H—C—Br	Br—C—H
H—C—Cl	Cl—C—H	Cl—C—H	H—C—Cl
CH_3	CH_3	CH_3	CH_3

XVIII and XIX: Enantiomers; XX and XXI: Enantiomers

Remember that, for comparison, projection formulas may be turned 180° in the plane of the paper, but they cannot be lifted (flipped) out of the plane. Formulas XVIII and XIX, and formulas XX and XXI, represent two pairs of nonsuperimposable mirror-image isomers and are, therefore, two pairs of enantiomers. All four compounds are optically active. But the properties of XVIII and XIX differ from the properties of XX and XXI because they are not mirror-image isomers of each other. Stereoisomers that are not enantiomers (not mirror images of each other) are called **diastereomers**. There are four different pairs of diastereomers of 2-bromo-3-chlorobutane: They are XVIII and XX, XVIII and XXI, XIX and XX, and XIX and XXI.

diastereomer

The 2^n formula indicates that four stereoisomers of tartaric acid are possible. The projection formulas of these four possible stereoisomers are written in this way (carbons 2 and 3 are asymmetric):

```
        COOH                COOH
         |                   |
  HO ----+---- H       H ----+---- OH
         |                   |
   H ----+---- OH     HO ----+---- H
         |                   |
        COOH                COOH
        XXII                XXIII

        COOH                COOH
         |                   |
   H ----+---- OH     HO ----+---- H
         |                   |
   H ----+---- OH     HO ----+---- H
         |                   |
        COOH                COOH
        XXIV                XXV
```

Formulas XXII and XXIII represent nonsuperimposable mirror-image isomers and are, therefore, enantiomers. Formulas XXIV and XXV are also mirror images. But by turning XXV 180°, we see that it is exactly superimposable on XXIV. Therefore XXIV and XXV represent the same compound, and only *three* stereoisomers of tartaric acid actually exist. Compound XXIV is achiral and does not rotate polarized light. A plane of symmetry can be passed between carbons 2 and 3 so that the top and bottom halves of the molecule are mirror images:

```
      COOH
       |
   H — C — OH
  -----+-------- ← Plane of symmetry
   H — C — OH
       |
      COOH
```

Thus the molecule is internally compensated. The rotation of polarized light in one direction by half of the molecule is exactly compensated by an opposite rotation by the other half. Stereoisomers that contain asymmetric carbon atoms and are superimposable on their own mirror images are called **meso compounds**, or **meso structures**. All meso compounds are optically inactive.

meso compound

meso structure

The term *meso* comes from the Greek word *mesos*, meaning middle. It was first used by Pasteur to name a kind of tartaric acid that was optically inactive and could not be separated into different forms by any means. Pasteur called it *meso*-tartaric acid, because it seemed intermediate between the (+)- and (−)-tartaric acid. The three stereoisomers of tartaric acid are represented and designated in this fashion:

```
       COOH               COOH               COOH
        |                  |                  |
  HO — C — H         H — C — OH         H — C — OH
        |                  |                  |
   H — C — OH       HO — C — H          H — C — OH
        |                  |                  |
       COOH               COOH               COOH
 (−)-Tartaric acid  (+)-Tartaric acid  meso-Tartaric acid
```

TABLE 9.1 Properties of Tartaric Acid [HOOCCH(OH)CH(OH)COOH]

Name	Specific gravity	Melting point (°C)	Solubility ($g/100\ g\ H_2O$)	Specific rotation [α]
(+)-Tartaric acid	1.760	170	$147^{20\ C}$	+12°
(−)-Tartaric acid	1.760	170	$147^{20\ C}$	−12°
(±)-Tartaric acid (racemic mixture)	1.687	206	$20.6^{20\ C}$	0°
meso-Tartaric acid	1.666	140	$125^{15\ C}$	0°

The physical properties of tartaric acid stereoisomers are given in Table 9.1. Note that the properties of (+)-tartaric acid and (−)-tartaric acid are identical except for opposite rotation of polarized light. However, *meso*-tartaric acid has properties that are entirely different from those of the other isomers. But most surprising is the fact that the racemic mixture, though composed of equal parts of the (+) and (−) enantiomers, differs from them in specific gravity, melting point, and solubility. Why, for example, is the melting point of the racemic mixture higher than that of any of the other forms? The melting point of any substance is largely dependent on the attractive forces holding the ions or molecules together. The melting point of the racemic mixture is higher than that of either enantiomer. Therefore, we can conclude that the attraction between molecules of the (+) and (−) enantiomers in the racemic mixture is greater than the attraction between molecules of the (+) and (+) or the (−) and (−) enantiomers.

EXAMPLE 9.3

How many stereoisomers can exist for the following compounds? Write their structures and label any pairs of enantiomers and meso compounds. Point out any diastereomers.

(a) $CH_3CHBrCHBrCH_2CH_3$ (b) $CH_2BrCHClCHClCH_2Br$

SOLUTION

(a) Carbons 2 and 3 are asymmetric, so there can be a maximum of four stereoisomers ($2^2 = 4$). Write structures around the asymmetric carbons:

	I	II	III	IV
top	CH_3	CH_3	CH_3	CH_3
C-2	H—C—Br	Br—C—H	H—C—Br	Br—C—H
C-3	H—C—Br	Br—C—H	Br—C—H	H—C—Br
	CH_2	CH_2	CH_2	CH_2
bottom	CH_3	CH_3	CH_3	CH_3

I and II: Enantiomers; III and IV: Enantiomers

There are four stereoisomers: two pairs of enantiomers (I and II, and III and IV) and no meso compounds. Structures I and III, I and IV, II and III, and II and IV are diastereomers.

(b) Carbons 2 and 3 are asymmetric, so there can be a maximum of four stereoisomers. Write structures around the asymmetric carbons:

```
  CH2Br        CH2Br          CH2Br        CH2Br
    |            |              |            |
H—C—Cl      Cl—C—H         Cl—C—H       H—C—Cl
- - -|- - -  - - -|- - -        |            |
H—C—Cl      Cl—C—H         H—C—Cl       Cl—C—H
    |            |              |            |
  CH2Br        CH2Br          CH2Br        CH2Br
    V            VI             VII          VIII
      Meso compound                Enantiomers
```

There are three stereoisomers: one pair of enantiomers (VII and VIII) and one meso compound V. Structures V and VI represent the meso compound because there is a plane of symmetry between carbons 2 and 3, and turning VI 180° makes it superimposable on V. Structures V, VII, and VIII are diastereomers.

PRACTICE Write all stereoisomer structures and label any pairs of enantiomers and meso compounds for the following compound. Also, point out any diastereomers.

$HOOCCHClCH_2CH_2CHClCOOH$

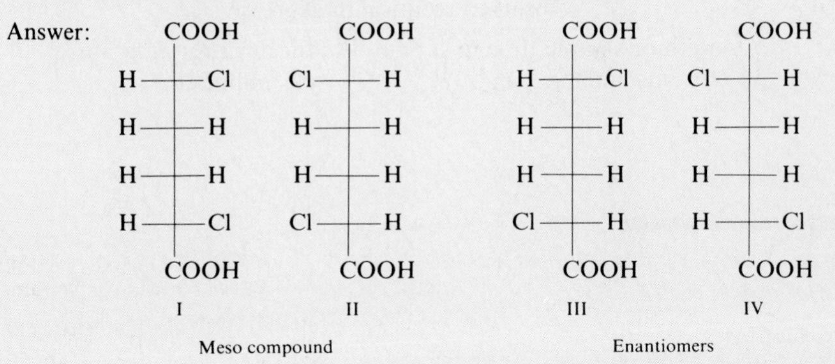

Structures I and III, I and IV, II and III, and II and IV are diasteromers.

Concepts in Review

1. Identify all asymmetric (chiral) carbon atoms in a given formula.
2. Explain the use of a polarimeter.
3. Explain how polarized light is obtained.
4. Calculate the specific rotation of a compound.
5. Explain the phenomenon of optical isomerism.

6. Determine whether a compound is chiral.
7. Draw projection formulas for all possible stereoisomers of a given compound. Label enantiomers, diastereomers, and meso compounds.
8. Calculate the maximum possible optical isomers given the formula of a compound.
9. Understand the meaning of (+) and (−) relative to the optical activity of a compound.
10. Draw the mirror image of a given structure.
11. Compare projection formulas to ascertain whether they represent identical compounds or enantiomers.
12. Compare the physical properties of enantiomers, diastereomers, and racemic mixtures.
13. Explain why meso compounds are optically inactive.
14. Determine whether optical isomers are formed in simple chemical reactions.

Equations in Review

Specific Rotation

$$[\alpha] = \frac{\text{Observed rotation in degrees}}{\left(\begin{array}{c}\text{Length of sample tube in} \\ \text{decimeters}\end{array}\right)\left(\begin{array}{c}\text{Sample concentration in grams} \\ \text{per milliliter}\end{array}\right)}$$

Exercises

1. Which of these objects are chiral?
   (a) A wood screw (d) The letter G
   (b) A pair of pliers (e) A coiled spring
   (c) The letter O (f) Your ear
2. What is an asymmetric carbon atom? Draw structural formulas of three different compounds that contain one asymmetric carbon atom, and mark the asymmetric carbon in each with an asterisk.
3. How can you tell when the axes of two Polaroid filters are parallel? When one filter has been rotated by 90°?
4. How many asymmetric carbon atoms are present in each of the following?

(a)
```
    H  Cl
    |  |
Cl—C—C—Br
    |  |
    H  H
```

(b)
```
   Br Cl
   |  |
H—C—C—H
   |  |
   H  H
```

(c) $CH_3CH_2CH_2CHClCH_3$

(d)
```
H—C=O
   |
H—C—OH
   |
H—C—OH
   |
H—C—OH
   |
   H
```

(e)
```
CH3CH2CHCH2CH3
       |
       OH
```

```
         H
         |
(f)  H—C—OH
         |
         C=O
         |
   HO—C—H
         |
     H—C—OH
         |
     H—C—OH
         |
     H—C—OH
         |
         H
```

```
           H   H   O
           |   |   ||
(g)  HO—C—C—C—OH
           |   |
           H   NH2
```

5. Write the formulas and decide which of the following compounds will show optical activity:
   (a) 1-Chloropentane
   (b) 2-Chloropentane
   (c) 3-Chloropentane
   (d) 1-Chloro-2-methylpentane
   (e) 2-Chloro-2-methylpentane
   (f) 3-Chloro-2-methylpentane
   (g) 4-Chloro-2-methylpentane
   (h) 3-Chloro-3-methylpentane
6. Suppose a carbon atom is located at the center of a square with four different groups attached to the corners in a planar arrangement. Would the compound rotate polarized light? Explain.
7. What is a necessary and sufficient condition for a compound to show enantiomerism?
8. Glucose ($C_6H_{12}O_6$) has four asymmetric carbon atoms. How many stereoisomers of glucose are theoretically possible?
9. Do structures A and B represent enantiomers or the same compound? Justify your answer.

```
           Cl                Br
           |                 |
(A)  Br—C—H        (B)  H—C—Cl
           |                 |
           F                 F
```

10. Which of these projection formulas represent (−)-lactic acid and which represent (+)-lactic acid?

```
(a)     CH3          (c)     COOH
         |                    |
   HO —+— H              H —+— CH3
         |                    |
        COOH                  OH

(b)     OH           (d)     CH3
         |                    |
    H —+— COOH           H —+— OH
         |                    |
        CH3                  COOH

(e)     COOH         (f)      H
         |                    |
  CH3 —+— H            CH3 —+— OH
         |                    |
         OH                  COOH
```

11. Draw projection formulas for all the possible stereoisomers of the following compounds. Label pairs of enantiomers and meso compounds.
    (a) 1,2-Dibromopropane
    (b) 2,3-Dichlorobutane
    (c) 2-Butanol
    (d) 2,4-Dibromopentane
    (e) 3-Chlorohexane
12. Draw projection formulas for all the stereoisomers of 1,2,3-trihydroxybutane. Point out enantiomers, meso compounds, and diastereomers, where present.
*13. Write structures for the four stereoisomers of 3-pentene-2-ol.
*14. Some substituted cycloalkanes are chiral. Draw the structures and enantiomers for any of the following that are chiral:

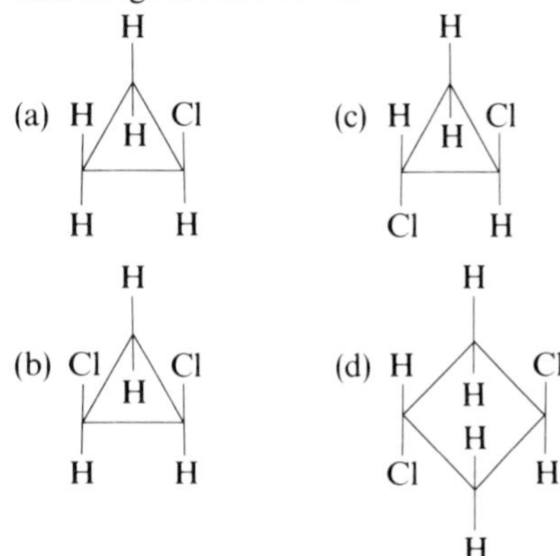

15. The physical properties for (+)-2-methyl-1-butanol are specific rotation, +5.76°; bp, 129°C; density, 0.819 g/mL. What are these same properties for (−)-2-methyl-1-butanol?
*16. Draw projection formulas for all the stereoisomers of 2,3,4-tribromopentane and point out enantiomers and meso compounds, where present.
17. (a) Draw the nine structural isomers of $C_4H_8Cl_2$.
    (b) Identify which structures represent chiral molecules, and draw all possible pairs of enantiomers and meso compounds, if any.
18. (+)-2-Chlorobutane is further chlorinated to give dichlorobutanes ($C_4H_8Cl_2$). Write structures for all the possible isomers formed and indicate which of these isomers will be optically active. [Remember that (+)-2-chlorobutane is optically active.]

19. In the chlorination of butane, 1-chlorobutane and 2-chlorobutane are obtained as products. After separation by distillation, neither product rotates the plane of polarized light. Explain these results.

20. (a) Explain why it is not possible to separate enantiomers by ordinary chemical and physical means.
(b) Explain why diastereomers can usually be separated by ordinary physical and chemical means.

21. The observed rotation of polarized light was 12.5° for a solution of compound X at a concentration of 10.0 g/100. mL. The measurement was made using a polarimeter sample tube 20.0 cm in length. Calculate the specific rotation, $[\alpha]$, for compound X.

22. Which, if any, of the following are meso compounds?

(a)
COOH
H—OH
HO—COOH
H

(c)
CH_3
H—Cl
Br—CH_3
H

(b)
CH_3
H—Cl
CH_3—Cl
H

(d)
CH_3
H—Cl
H—Br
H—Cl
CH_3

***23.** Substances of the type shown below are known to rotate the plane of polarized light. What inference can be drawn regarding the spatial character of the nitrogen bonds?

$$\left[R'''—\underset{R''}{\overset{R}{N}}—R' \right]^+ [X]^-$$

***24.** (a) A chiral substance was identified as a primary alcohol of formula $C_5H_{12}O$. What is its structure?
(b) The compound $C_6H_{14}O_3$ has three primary alcohol groups and is chiral. What is its structure?

***25.** What is the structure of a substance of formula $C_3H_8O_2$ that is (a) chiral and contains two —OH groups; (b) chiral and contains one —OH group; (c) achiral and contains two —OH groups? (Only one —OH group can be bonded to a carbon atom.)

26. Which of these statements are correct? Rewrite each incorrect statement to make it correct.
(a) The polarizer and the analyzer of a polarimeter are made of the same material.
(b) The specific rotation of a compound is dependent on the number of molecules in the path of the plane-polarized light.
(c) Very few natural products are optically active.
(d) Cis-trans isomers are not considered to be stereoisomers.
(e) J. A. Le Bel received the first Nobel prize in chemistry in 1901.
(f) A compound that rotates plane-polarized light +25° would be at the same position on the polarimeter as one that rotates the light −335°.
(g) Molecules that contain only one asymmetric carbon atom are chiral, but not all chiral molecules contain an asymmetric carbon atom.
(h) The compound $CH_3CHBrCHBrCH_2OH$ has eight optical isomers.
(i) The compounds shown in these projection formulas are enantiomers:

Cl
Br—H
CH_3

H
Br—Cl
CH_3

(j) Diastereomers have identical melting points.
(k) A molecule that contains two asymmetric carbon atoms may not be chiral.
(l) A racemic mixture contains equal amounts of dextrorotatory and levorotatory molecules of a compound.

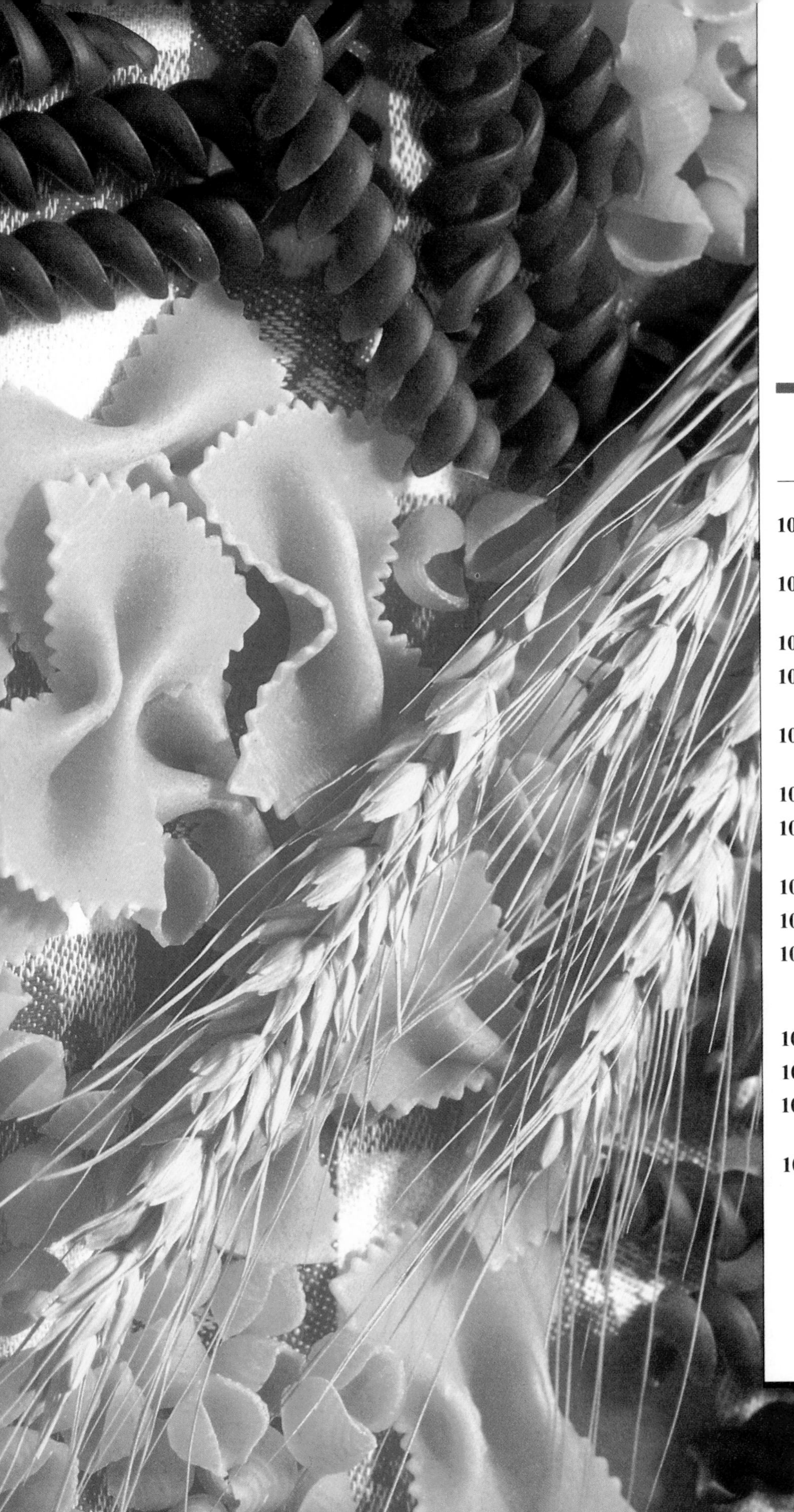

10

Carbohydrates

◀ **CHAPTER OPENING PHOTO: These varieties of pasta are examples of carbohydrates.**

What is the most abundant organic chemical in the world? The answer is not petroleum products, plastics, or drugs. Rather, it is cellulose. An amazing ten billion tons of this carbohydrate are formed daily in the biosphere. Aggregates of this substance allow the California redwoods to stretch hundreds of feet toward the sky and make a Brazil nut a "hard nut to crack." Products as diverse as the paper in this book and cotton in many articles of clothing also derive from cellulose. Perhaps it is not so surprising that this carbohydrate is the most widespread organic chemical in the world.

Carbohydrates are molecules of exceptional utility. These molecules provide a basic diet for many of us (starch and sugar), a roof over our heads, and clothes for our bodies (cellulose). But they also thicken our ice cream, stick our postage stamps to our letters, and provide biodegradable plastic trash sacks. Starting from relatively simple components (using carbon, hydrogen, and oxygen), nature has created one of the premier classes of biochemicals.

10.1 THE ROLE OF CARBOHYDRATES

Carbohydrates are among the most widespread and important biochemicals. Most of the matter in plants, except water, consists of these substances. Carbohydrates are one of the three principal classes of energy yielding nutrients; the other two are fats and proteins. Because of their widespread distribution and their role in many vital metabolic processes such as photosynthesis, carbohydrates have been subjected to a great deal of scientific study over the last 150 years.

The name *carbohydrates* was given to this class of compounds many years ago by French scientists who called them *hydrates de carbone*, because their empirical formulas approximated $(C \cdot H_2O)_n$. It was found later that not all substances classified as carbohydrates conform to this formula (for example, rhamnose, $C_6H_{12}O_5$, and deoxyribose, $C_5H_{10}O_4$). It seems clear that carbohydrates are not simply hydrated carbon; they are complex substances containing from three to many thousands of carbon atoms. The general definition is:

carbohydrates

Carbohydrates are polyhydroxy aldehydes or polyhydroxy ketones or substances that yield these compounds when hydrolyzed.

The simplest carbohydrates are glyceraldehyde and dihydroxyacetone:

$$\begin{array}{c} H-C=O \\ | \\ H-C-OH \\ | \\ H-C-OH \\ | \\ H \end{array}$$

Glyceraldehyde

$$\begin{array}{c} H \\ | \\ H-C-OH \\ | \\ C=O \\ | \\ H-C-OH \\ | \\ H \end{array}$$

Dihydroxyacetone

These substances are "polyhydroxy" because each molecule has more than one hydroxyl group. Glyceraldehyde contains a carbonyl carbon in a terminal position and, therefore, is an aldehyde. The internal carbonyl of dihydroxyacetone identifies it as a ketone. Much of the chemistry and biochemistry of carbohydrates can be understood from a basic knowledge of the chemistry of the hydroxyl and carbonyl functional groups (see Chapters 4 and 5 for review).

Carbohydrates provide an essential base for the world's food chain. Plants use light energy to convert carbon dioxide and water into carbohydrates. Herbivores eat these plants and are, in turn, eaten by carnivores. The energy originally present in the plant carbohydrate is transferred up the food chain. As we begin to study carbohydrates, it is worthwhile to consider this question: What are the essential characteristics that allow carbohydrates to act as foodstuffs and major sources of biological energy? In answer to this question, three relevant biochemical principles will be set forth.

First, a foodstuff must contain carbon. The preceding formulas show that carbohydrates provide much carbon. The average carbohydrate is about 40% carbon by mass.

Second, the carbon atoms in an energy providing molecule must be in a more reduced state than those in carbon dioxide. Reduced carbon atoms can react with atmospheric oxygen to produce carbon dioxide and energy (witness the heat of a wood fire or the energy of a gasoline engine). A useful estimate of a carbon's reduced state is the oxidation number (see Table 10.1). The lower the oxidation number, the more reduced the carbon is and the more energy it can supply. Carbohydrates are energy yielding nutrients partly because they contain carbons in an intermediate state of reduction, with oxidation numbers ranging from -1 to $+1$. As these carbons are oxidized to carbon dioxide during metabolism, much energy is released.

Third, an energy-providing foodstuff not only must contain reduced carbons, but it also must have a chemical reactivity and a physical structure appropriate for use in cells. Carbohydrate metabolism is aided by the presence of reactive hydroxyl and carbonyl functional groups.

10.2 Classification

A carbohydrate is classified as a monosaccharide, a disaccharide, an oligosaccharide, or a polysaccharide, depending on the number of monosaccharide units linked together to form a molecule. A **monosaccharide** is a carbohydrate that

monosaccharide

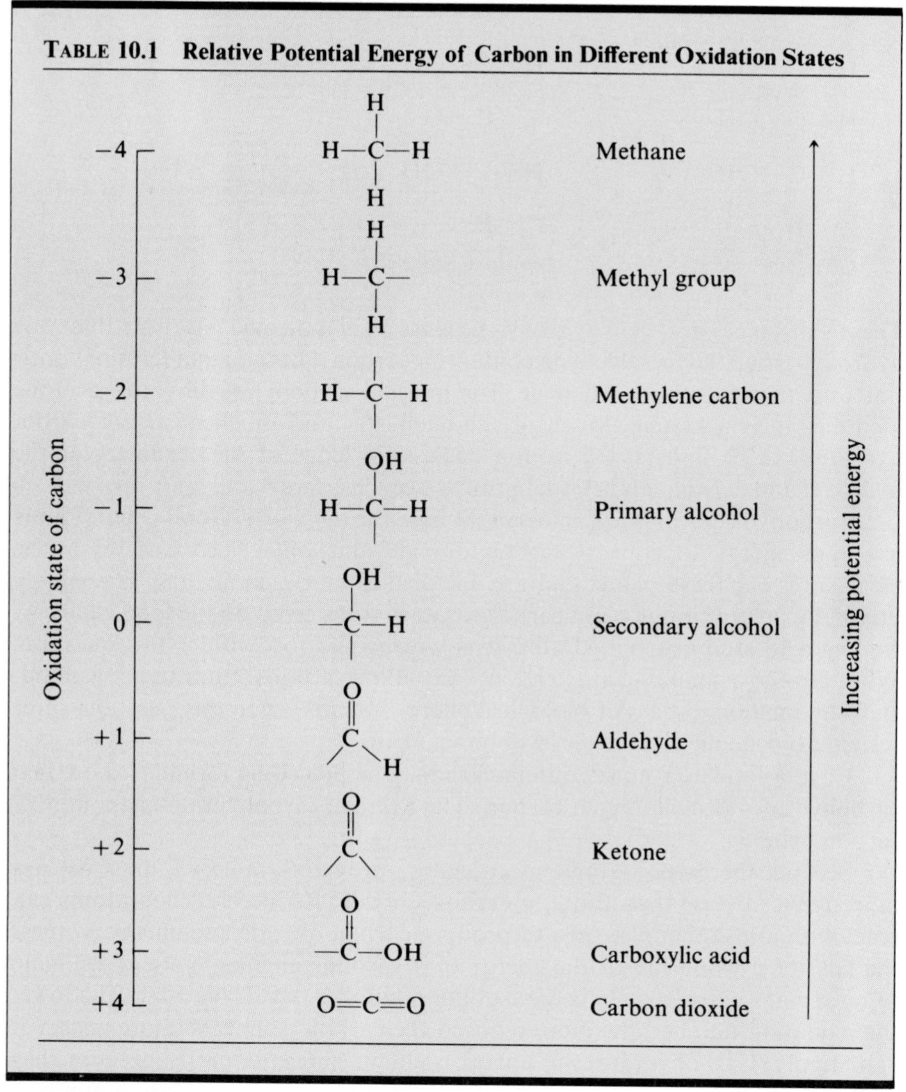

TABLE 10.1 Relative Potential Energy of Carbon in Different Oxidation States

Oxidation state of carbon		
−4	CH_4 (H—C—H with H above and below)	Methane
−3	$H_3C—$	Methyl group
−2	$—CH_2—$ (H—C—H)	Methylene carbon
−1	H—C(OH)—H	Primary alcohol
0	—C(OH)—H	Secondary alcohol
+1	—C(=O)—H	Aldehyde
+2	—C(=O)—	Ketone
+3	—C(=O)—OH	Carboxylic acid
+4	O=C=O	Carbon dioxide

cannot be hydrolyzed to simpler carbohydrate units. The monosaccharide is the basic carbohydrate unit of cellular metabolism. A **disaccharide** yields two monosaccharides—either alike or different—when hydrolyzed:

disaccharide

$$\text{Disaccharide} + \text{Water} \xrightarrow{H^+ \text{ or enzyme}} 2 \text{ Monosaccharides}$$

Disaccharides are often used by plants or animals to transport monosaccharides from one cell to another. The monosaccharides and disaccharides generally have names ending in *ose*—for example, glucose, sucrose, and lactose. These water-soluble carbohydrates, which have a characteristically sweet taste, are also called *sugars*.

oligosaccharide

An **oligosaccharide** has two to six monosaccharide units linked together. *Oligo* comes from the Greek word *oligos*, which means small or few. Free oligosaccharides containing more than two monosaccharide units are rarely found in nature.

A **polysaccharide** is a macromolecular substance that can be hydrolyzed to yield many monosaccharide units:

polysaccharide

$$\text{Polysaccharide} + \text{Water} \xrightarrow{H^+ \text{ or enzyme}} \text{Many monosaccharide units}$$

Polysaccharides are important as structural supports (particularly in plants) and also serve as a storage depot for monosaccharides (which cells use for energy).

Carbohydrates also can be classified in other ways. A monosaccharide might be described with respect to several of these categories:

1. As a *triose*, *tetrose*, *pentose*, *hexose*, or *heptose*. Theoretically, a monosaccharide can have any number of carbons greater than three, but only monosaccharides of three to seven carbons are commonly found in the biosphere.

Trioses	$C_3H_6O_3$
Tetroses	$C_4H_8O_4$
Pentoses	$C_5H_{10}O_5$
Hexoses	$C_6H_{12}O_6$
Heptoses	$C_7H_{14}O_7$

2. As an *aldose* or *ketose*, depending on whether an aldehyde group (—CHO) or keto group ($>$C=O) is present.
3. As a D or L isomer, depending on the spatial orientation of the —H and —OH groups attached to the carbon atom that is adjacent to the terminal primary alcohol group. When the —OH is written to the right of this carbon in the *projection formula*, the D isomer is represented. When the —OH is written to the left, the L isomer is represented. The reference compounds for this classification are the trioses D-glyceraldehyde and L-glyceraldehyde, whose formulas follow. Also shown are two aldohexoses (D- and L-glucose) and a ketohexose (D-fructose).

```
                        H—C=O                 H—C=O
                          |                     |
D-configuration ——→ H—C—OH              HO—C—H ←—— L-configuration
                          |                     |
Terminal 1° ROH ———→ CH2OH                CH2OH ←—— Terminal 1° ROH

                  D-Glyceraldehyde     L-Glyceraldehyde
```

```
                     H—C=O            H—C=O                   CH2OH
                       |                |                       |
                    HO—C—H            H—C—OH                   C=O
                       |                |                       |
                     H—C—OH          HO—C—H                 HO—C—H
                       |                |                       |
                    HO—C—H            H—C—OH                  H—C—OH
                       |                |                       |
L-configuration ——→ HO—C—H            H—C—OH ←— D-configuration —→ H—C—OH
                       |                |                       |
Terminal 1° ROH ——→  CH2OH            CH2OH ←— Terminal 1° ROH —→ CH2OH

                  L-Glucose          D-Glucose                D-Fructose
```

The letters D and L do not in any way refer to the direction of optical rotation of a carbohydrate. The D and L forms of any specific compound are *enantiomers* (for example, D- and L-glucose).

4. As a (+) or (−) isomer, depending on whether the monosaccharide rotates the plane of polarized light to the right (+) or to the left (−). (See Section 9.5.)
5. As a *furanose* or a *pyranose*, depending on whether the cyclic structure of the carbohydrate is related to that of the five-membered or six-membered heterocyclic ring compound furan or pyran (a heterocyclic ring contains more than one kind of atom in the ring):

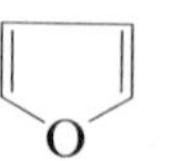

Furan, C_4H_4O
(five-membered ring containing oxygen in the ring)

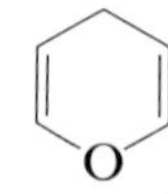

Pyran, C_5H_6O
(six-membered ring containing oxygen in the ring)

6. As having an alpha (α) or beta (β) configuration, based on the orientation of the —H and —OH groups about a specific asymmetric carbon in the cyclic form of the monosaccharide (Section 10.5).

EXAMPLE 10.1

Write projection formulas for (a) an L-aldotriose, (b) a D-ketotetrose, and (c) a D-aldopentose. Determine which carbons can provide the most energy for a cell.

SOLUTION

(a) *Triose* indicates a three-carbon carbohydrate; *aldo* indicates that the compound is an aldehyde; L- indicates that the —OH on carbon 2 (adjacent to the terminal CH_2OH) is on the left. The aldehyde group is carbon 1.

```
  H—C=O
     |
HO—C—H
     |
    CH₂OH
```

An L-aldotriose

The aldehyde carbon has an oxidation number of +1; the secondary alcohol, 0; the primary alcohol, −1. The primary alcohol carbon is most reduced and should provide the most energy.

(b) *Tetrose* indicates a four-carbon carbohydrate; *keto* indicates a ketone group (on carbon 2); D- indicates that the —OH on carbon 3 (adjacent to the terminal CH_2OH) is on the right. Carbons 1 and 4 are primary alcohols.

```
   CH₂OH
   |
   C=O
   |
H—C—OH
   |
   CH₂OH
```

A D-ketotetrose

The ketone carbon has an oxidation number of +2; the secondary alcohol carbon, 0; each primary alcohol carbon, −1. The primary alcohol carbons are the most reduced and have the most potential energy.

(c) *Pentose* indicates a five-carbon carbohydrate; *aldo* indicates an aldehyde group (on carbon 1); D- indicates that the —OH on carbon 4 (adjacent to the terminal CH_2OH) is on the right. The orientation of the —OH groups on carbons 2 and 3 is not specified here and therefore can be written in either direction for this problem.

```
H—C=O
   |
H—C—OH
   |
H—C—OH
   |
H—C—OH
   |
   CH2OH
```

A D-aldopentose

The aldehyde carbon has an oxidation number of +1; each secondary alcohol carbon, 0; the primary alcohol carbon, −1. The primary alcohol carbon is the most reduced and has the most potential energy.

PRACTICE Identify the most reduced carbons in a ketoheptose.

Answer: The primary alcohol carbons

PRACTICE In a projection formula for a D-aldotriose, is the —OH of the secondary alcohol carbon written on the right or the left side?

Answer: The right side

10.3 MONOSACCHARIDES

Although a great many monosaccharides have been synthesized, only a very few appear to be of much biological significance. One pentose monosaccharide (ribose) and its deoxy derivative are essential components of ribonucleic acid (RNA) and of deoxyribonucleic acid (DNA) (see Chapter 14). However, the hexose monosaccharides are the most important carbohydrate sources of cellular energy. Three hexoses—glucose, galactose, and fructose—are of major significance in nutrition. All three have the same molecular formula, $C_6H_{12}O_6$, and thus contain an equal number of reduced carbons. They differ in structure but are biologically interconvertible. Glucose plays a central role in carbohydrate energy utilization. Other carbohydrates are usually converted to glucose before cellular utilization. The structure of glucose is considered in detail in Section 10.4.

Glucose

Glucose is the most important of the monosaccharides. It is an aldohexose and is found in the free state in plant and animal tissue. Glucose is commonly known as *dextrose* or *grape sugar*. It is a component of the disaccharides sucrose, maltose, and lactose, and is also the monomer of the polysaccharides starch, cellulose,

▲
Sucrose is converted into monosaccharides, fructose and glucose by an enzyme found in bees.

and glycogen. Among the common sugars, glucose is of intermediate sweetness (see Section 10.11).

Glucose is the key sugar of the body and is carried by the bloodstream to all body parts. The concentration of glucose in the blood is normally 80–100 mg per 100 mL of blood. Because glucose is the most abundant carbohydrate in the blood, it is also sometimes known as *blood sugar*. Glucose requires no digestion and therefore may be given intravenously to patients who cannot take food by mouth. Glucose is found in the urine of those who have diabetes mellitus (sugar diabetes). The condition in which glucose is excreted in the urine is called glycosuria.

Galactose

Galactose is also an aldohexose and occurs, along with glucose, in lactose and in many oligo- and polysaccharides such as pectin, gums, and mucilages. Galactose is an isomer of glucose, differing only in the spatial arrangement of the —H and —OH groups around carbon 4 (see Section 10.4). Galactose is synthesized in the mammary glands to make the lactose of milk. It is also a constituent of glycolipids and glycoproteins in many cell membranes such as those in nervous tissue. Galactose is less than half as sweet as glucose.

A severe inherited disease, called galactosemia, is the inability of infants to metabolize galactose. The galactose concentration increases markedly in the blood, and also appears in the urine. Galactosemia causes vomiting, diarrhea, enlargement of the liver, and often mental retardation. If not recognized within a few days after birth, it can lead to death. If diagnosis is made early and lactose is excluded from the diet, the symptoms disappear and normal growth may be resumed.

Fructose

Fructose, also known as *levulose*, is a ketohexose that occurs in fruit juices, honey, and (along with glucose) as a constituent of sucrose. Fructose is the major constituent of the polysaccharide inulin, a starchlike substance present in many plants such as dahlia tubers, chicory roots, and Jerusalem artichokes. Fructose is the sweetest of all the sugars, being about twice as sweet as glucose. This accounts for the sweetness of honey. The enzyme invertase, present in bees, splits sucrose into glucose and fructose. Fructose is metabolized directly but is also readily converted to glucose in the liver.

10.4 Structure of Glucose and Other Aldoses

In one of the classic feats of research in organic chemistry, Emil Fischer (1852–1919), working in Germany, established the structural configuration of glucose along with that of many other sugars. He received the Nobel prize in chemistry in 1902. Fischer devised projection formulas that relate the structure of a sugar to one or the other of the two enantiomeric forms of glyceraldehyde. These projection formulas represent three-dimensional stereoisomers (see Chapter 9) in a two-dimensional plane. (Remember that stereoisomers cannot be interconverted without breaking and reforming covalent bonds. Each carbohydrate isomer has a different shape and thus reacts differently in biological systems.)

In Fischer projection formulas, the molecule is represented with the aldehyde (or ketone) group at the top. The —H and —OH groups attached to interior carbons are written to the right or to the left as they would appear when projected toward the observer. The two glyceraldehydes are represented thus:

H—C=O
H ◄ ► OH
CH_2OH

D-Glyceraldehyde (three-dimensional representation)

H—^{1}C=O
H—^{2}C—OH
$^{3}CH_2OH$

D-Glyceraldehyde (projection formula)

H—C=O
HO ◄ ► H
CH_2OH

L-Glyceraldehyde (three-dimensional representation)

H—^{1}C=O
HO—^{2}C—H
$^{3}CH_2OH$

L-Glyceraldehyde (projection formula)

In the three-dimensional molecules represented by these formulas, the number-2 carbon atoms are in the plane of the paper. The —H and —OH groups project forward (toward the observer); the —CHO and —CH_2OH groups project backward (away from the observer). Any two monosaccharides that differ only in the configuration around a single carbon atom are called **epimers**. Thus D- and L-glyceraldehyde are epimers. epimer

Fischer recognized that there were two enantiomeric forms of glucose. To these forms he assigned the following structures and names:

H—^{1}C=O
H—^{2}C—OH
HO—^{3}C—H
H—^{4}C—OH
H—^{5}C—OH
$^{6}CH_2OH$

D-Glucose

H—^{1}C=O
HO—^{2}C—H
H—^{3}C—OH
HO—^{4}C—H
HO—^{5}C—H
$^{6}CH_2OH$

L-Glucose

The structure called D-glucose is so named because the —H and —OH on carbon 5 are in the same configuration as the —H and —OH on carbon 2 in D-glyceraldehyde. The configuration of the —H and —OH on carbon 5 in L-glucose corresponds to the —H and —OH on carbon 2 in L-glyceraldehyde.

Fischer recognized that 16 different aldohexoses, 8 with the D configuration and 8 with the L configuration, were possible. This follows our formula 2^n for optical isomers (see Section 9.7). Glucose has four asymmetric carbon atoms and should have 16 stereoisomers (2^4). The configurations of the D-aldose family are shown in Figure 10.1. In this family, new asymmetric carbon atoms are formed as we go from triose to tetrose to pentose to hexose. Each time a new asymmetric carbon is added, a pair of epimers is formed that differ only in the structure around carbon 2. This sequence continues until eight D-aldohexoses are created. A similar series starting with L-glyceraldehyde is known, making a total of 16 aldohexoses.

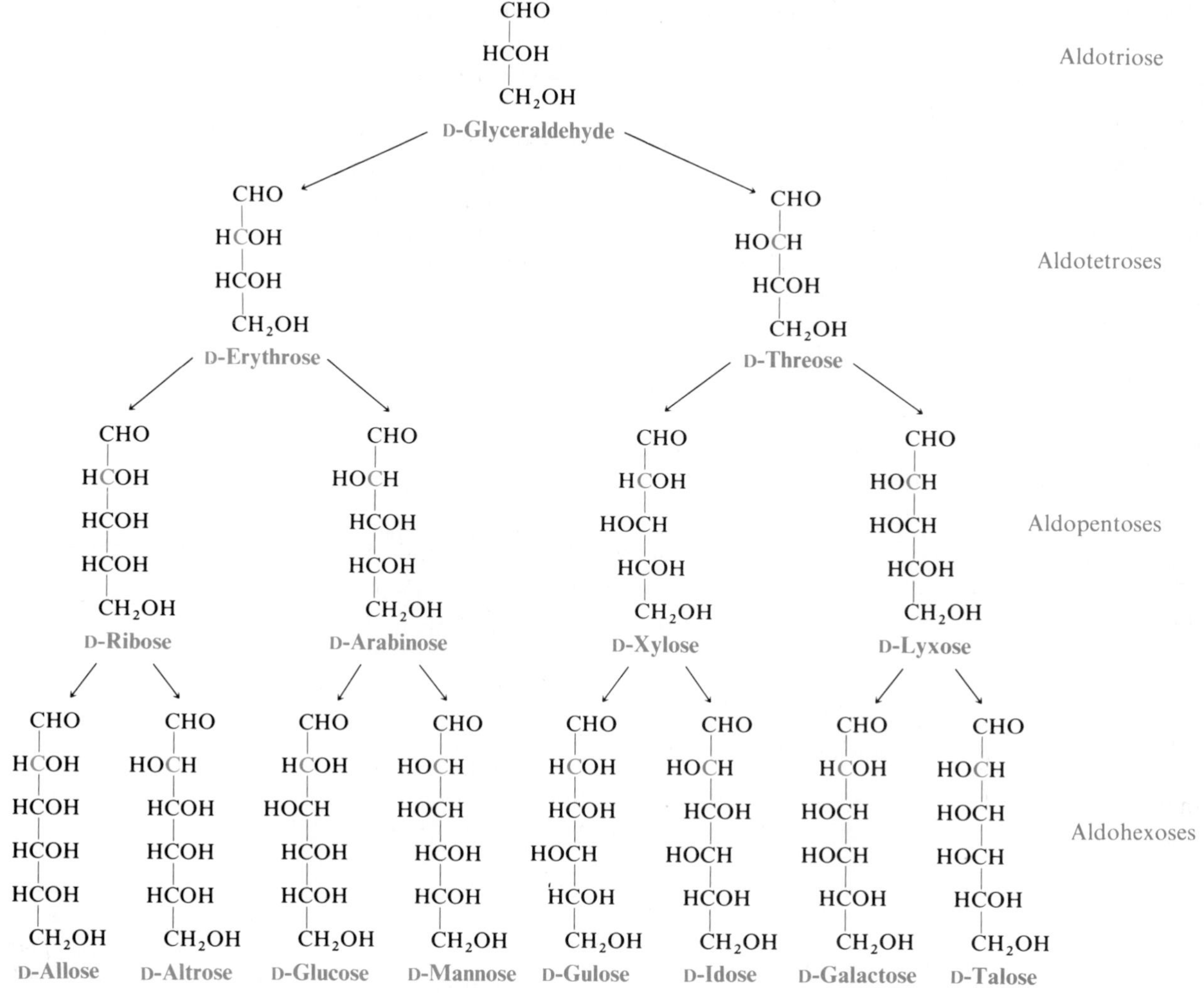

▲
FIGURE 10.1
Configurations of the D family of aldoses. The new asymmetric carbon atom added in going from triose to tetrose to pentose to hexose is marked in color.

FIGURE 10.2 ►
An example of the Kiliani–Fischer synthesis in which two aldotetrose molecules are formed from an aldotriose molecule.

H—C=O | H—C—OH | CH_2OH (D-Glyceraldehyde) —HCN→

CN | H—C—OH | H—C—OH | CH_2OH —H_2O, H^+→ COOH | H—C—OH | H—C—OH | CH_2OH —Na(Hg)→ H—C=O | H—C—OH | H—C—OH | CH_2OH (D-Erythrose)

CN | HO—C—H | H—C—OH | CH_2OH —H_2O, H^+→ COOH | HO—C—H | H—C—OH | CH_2OH —Na(Hg)→ H—C=O | HO—C—H | H—C—OH | CH_2OH (D-Threose)

All of the 16 aldohexoses have been synthesized, but only D-glucose and D-galactose appear to be of considerable biological importance. Since the metabolism of most living organisms revolves about D-glucose, our discussion will be centered on this substance.

The laboratory conversion of one aldose into another aldose containing one more carbon atom is known as the Kiliani–Fischer synthesis. This synthesis makes use of the aldehyde's ability to bond to an additional group (see Section 5.4). The synthesis involves (1) the addition of HCN to form a cyanohydrin, (2) hydrolysis of the —CN group to —COOH, and (3) reduction with sodium amalgam, Na(Hg), to form the aldehyde. As an example, the formation of two aldotetroses from an aldotriose is shown in Figure 10.2.

10.5 Cyclic Structure of Glucose; Mutarotation

Straight open chain D-glucose is so reactive that almost all molecules quickly rearrange their bonds to form two new structures. These two forms are diastereomers and differ with respect to their rotation of polarized light. One form, labeled α-D-glucopyranose, has a specific rotation, $[\alpha]$, of $+112°$; the other, labeled β-D-glucopyranose, has a specific rotation of $+18.7°$. An interesting phenomenon occurs when these two forms of glucose are put into separate solutions and allowed to stand for several hours. The specific rotation of each solution changes to $+52.7°$. This phenomenon is known as mutarotation. An explanation of mutarotation is that D-glucose exists in solution as an equilibrium mixture of two cyclic forms and the open-chain form (see Figure 10.3). The two

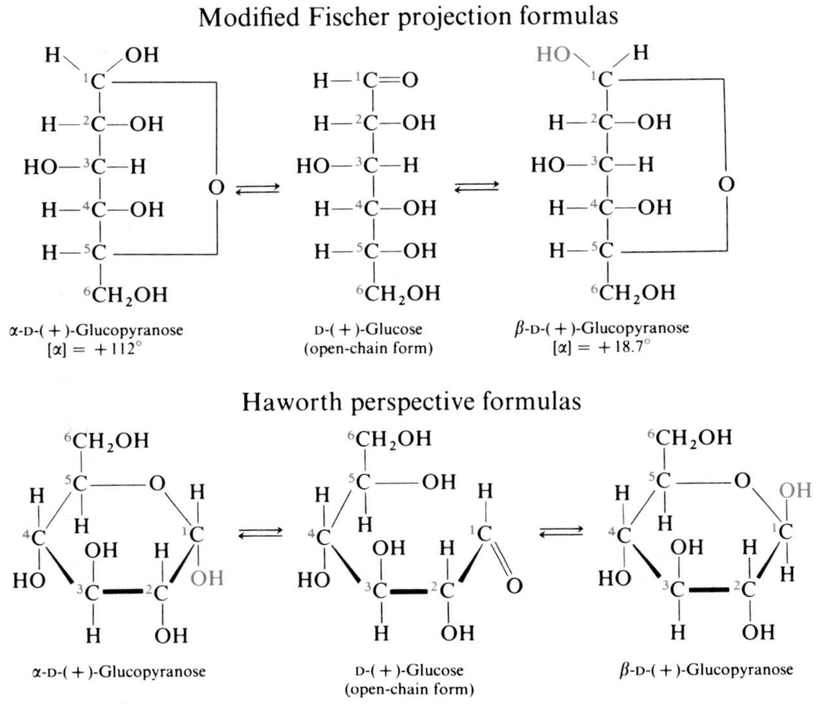

Modified Fischer projection formulas

α-D-(+)-Glucopyranose $[\alpha] = +112°$ ⇌ D-(+)-Glucose (open-chain form) ⇌ β-D-(+)-Glucopyranose $[\alpha] = +18.7°$

Haworth perspective formulas

α-D-(+)-Glucopyranose ⇌ D-(+)-Glucose (open-chain form) ⇌ β-D-(+)-Glucopyranose

FIGURE 10.3 Mutarotation of D-glucose, shown in both the modified Fischer projection formulas and the Haworth perspective formulas.

cyclic molecules are optical isomers, differing only in the orientation of the —H and —OH groups about carbon 1. When dissolved, some α-D-glucopyranose molecules are transformed into β-D-glucopyranose, and vice versa, until an equilibrium is reached between the α and β forms. (Note that no other chiral centers in D-glucose are altered when this sugar is dissolved.) The equilibrium solution contains about 36% α molecules and 64% β molecules, with a trace of open-chain molecules. When two cyclic isomers differ only in their stereo arrangement about the carbon involved in mutarotation, they are called **anomers**. For example, α- and β-D-glucopyranose and anomers (see Figure 10.3). **Mutarotation** is the process by which anomers are interconverted.

anomer

mutarotation

The cyclic forms of D-glucose may be represented by either Fischer projection formulas or by Haworth perspective formulas. These structures are shown in Figure 10.3. In the cyclic Fischer projection formulas of the D-aldoses, the α form has the —OH on carbon 1 written to the right; in the β form the —OH on carbon 1 is on the left. The Haworth structure represents the molecule as a flat hexagon with the —H and —OH groups above and below the plane of the hexagon. In the α form the —OH on carbon 1 is written below the plane; in the β form the —OH on carbon 1 is above the plane. In converting the projection formula of a D-aldohexose to the Haworth formula, the —OH groups on carbons 2, 3, and 4 are written below the plane if they project to the right and above the plane if they project to the left. Carbon 6 is written above the plane.

Haworth formulas are sometimes shown in abbreviated schematic form. For example, α-D-(+)-glucopyranose is shown in this diagram:

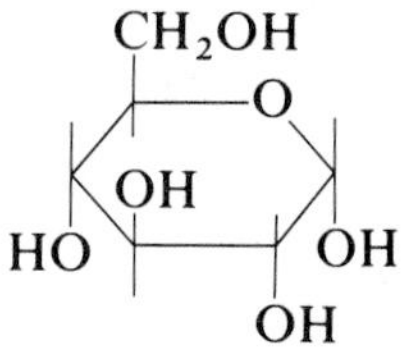

CH_2OH
O
OH
HO
OH
OH

α-D-(+)-Glucopyranose

Although both the Fischer projection formula and the Haworth formula provide useful representations of carbohydrate molecules, it is important to understand that these structures only approximate the true molecular shapes. We know, for example, that the pyranose ring is not flat but, rather, can assume either a chair or boat conformation like the cycloalkanes (see Section 2.13). Most naturally occurring monosaccharides are found in the chair form as shown in Figure 10.4 for α-D-glucopyranose. Even this three-dimensional structure does not truly capture how a sugar molecule must appear. For, unlike this representation, we know that atoms move as close together as possible when they form molecules. Perhaps the most accurate representation of a sugar molecule is the space-filling model. A space-filling model of α-D-glucopyranose is shown in Figure 10.4. At best, any two-dimensional representation is a compromise in portraying the three-dimensional configuration of such molecules. Structural models are much more effective, especially if constructed by the student.

The two cyclic forms of D-glucose differ only in the relative positions of the —H and —OH groups attached to carbon 1. Yet, this seemingly minor structural difference has important biochemical consequences because the phys-

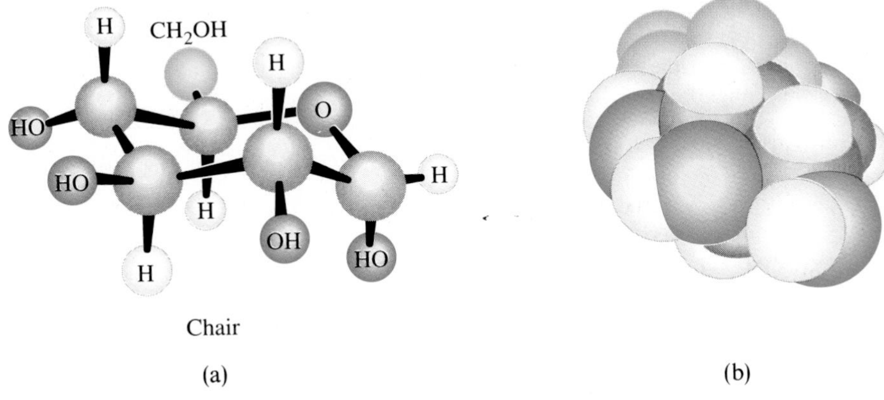

◄ **FIGURE 10.4 Three-dimensional representations of α-D-glycopyranose: (a) ball-and-stick model; (b) space-filling model.**

ical shape of a molecule often determines its biological use. For example, the fundamental structural difference between starch and cellulose is that starch is a polymer of α-D-glucopyranose, whereas cellulose is a polymer of β-D-glucopyranose. As a consequence, starch is a major and easily digested human food, but we are totally unable to digest cellulose.

EXAMPLE 10.2

Write the pyranose Haworth perspective formulas for the two anomers of D-mannose and name these isomers.

SOLUTION

First, write the open-chain Fischer projection formula for D-mannose (you must memorize this structure or know where to find it in the text) and number the carbons from top (the aldehyde group) to bottom (the primary alcohol group).

H—^{1}C=O
HO—^{2}C—H
HO—^{3}C—H
H—^{4}C—OH
H—^{5}C—OH
$^6CH_2OH$

Next, draw the structure of the Haworth pyranose ring. Number the carbons from the right-hand point of the hexagon clockwise around the cyclic form, placing the CH_2OH(C6) group in the up position on the ring.

$^6CH_2OH$
5 O
4 1
3 2

Then, refer to the open-chain Fischer projection formula. All the hydroxyl groups on the right of the open chain should be written down in the Haworth formula, and all the hydroxyl groups on the left should be written up. Since this rule only applies to chiral centers, we can ignore the hydroxyl on carbon 6.

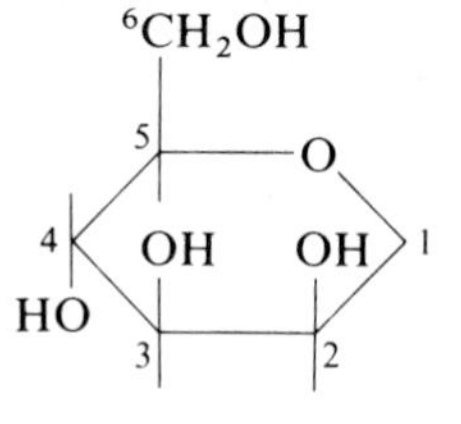

$^6CH_2OH$
5 O
4 OH OH 1
HO
3 2

The carbon involved in mutarotation, carbon 1, can have either of two configurations, the α-anomer when the hydroxyl is pointed down or the β-anomer when the hydroxyl is pointed up. The last step in this exercise is to add the hydroxyl group at carbon 1 and name the two anomers.

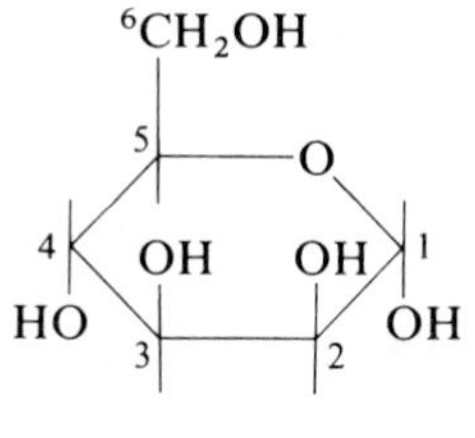

$^6CH_2OH$
5 O
4 OH OH 1
HO OH
3 2

α-D-Mannopyranose

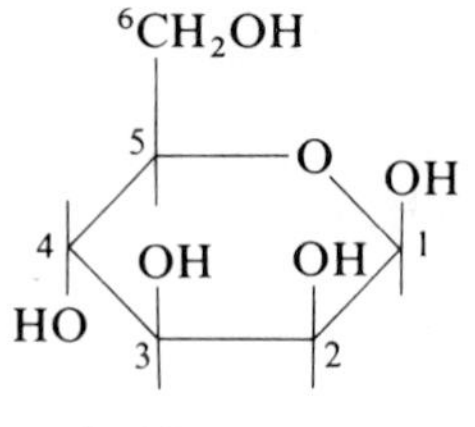

$^6CH_2OH$
5 O OH
4 OH OH 1
HO
3 2

β-D-Mannopyranose

PRACTICE Draw the Haworth formula for α-D-galactopyranose.

Answer: $^6CH_2OH$
HO 5 O
4 OH 1
OH
3 2
OH

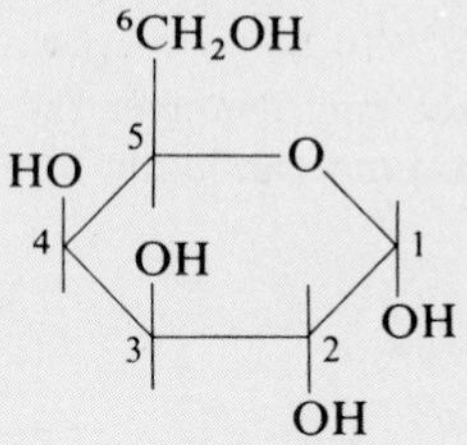

10.6 Hemiacetals and Acetals

In Chapter 5 we studied the reactions of aldehydes (and ketones) to form hemiacetals and acetals. The hemiacetal structure consists of an ether linkage and an alcohol linkage on the same carbon atom (shown in red), whereas the acetal structure has two ether linkages to the same carbon atom:

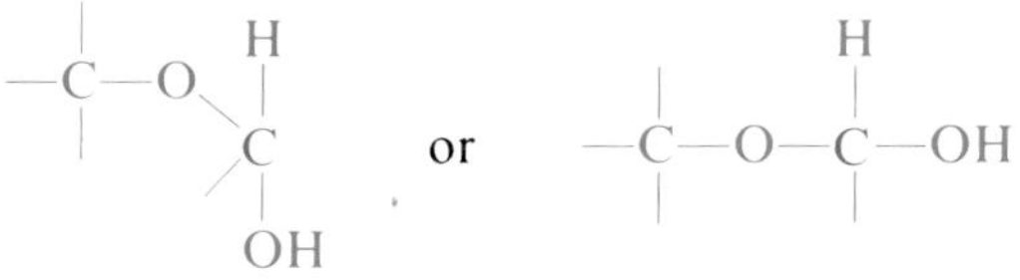

Hemiacetal

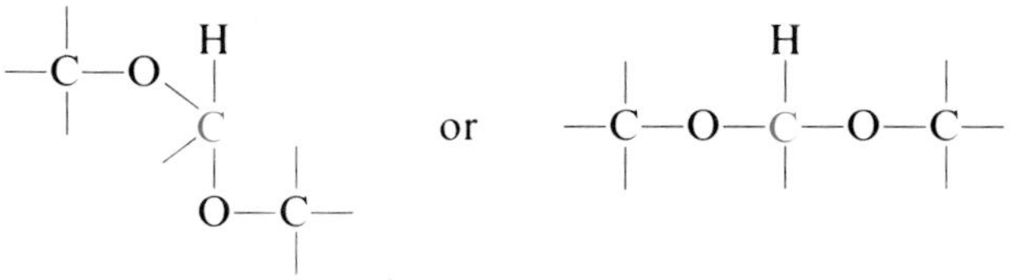

Acetal

Cyclic structures of monosaccharides are intramolecular hemiacetals. Five- or six-membered rings are especially stable.

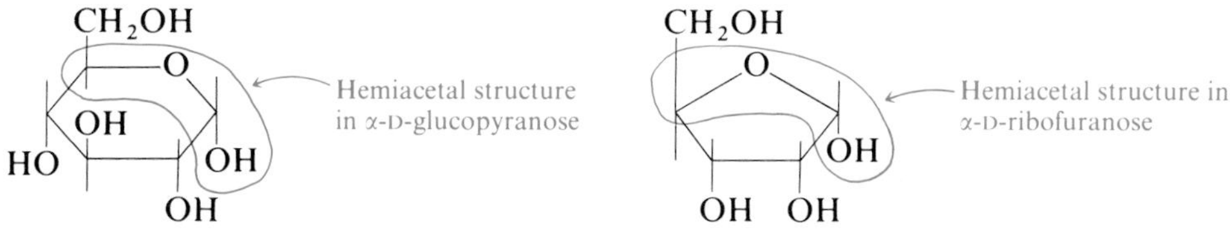

Hemiacetal structure in α-D-glucopyranose

Hemiacetal structure in α-D-ribofuranose

However, in an aqueous solution, the ring often opens and the hemiacetal momentarily reverts to the open-chain aldehyde. When the open chain closes, it forms either the α or the β anomer. Mutarotation results from this opening and closing of the hemiacetal ring (see Figure 10.3).

When an alcohol, ROH, reacts with another alcohol, R′OH to split out H_2O, the product formed can be an ether, ROR′. Carbohydrates are alcohols and behave in a similar manner. When a monosaccharide hemiacetal reacts with an alcohol, the product is an acetal. In carbohydrate terminology this acetal structure is called a **glycoside** (derived from the Greek word *glykys*, meaning sweet). In the case of glucose, it would be a glucoside; if galactose, a galactoside; and so on.

glycoside

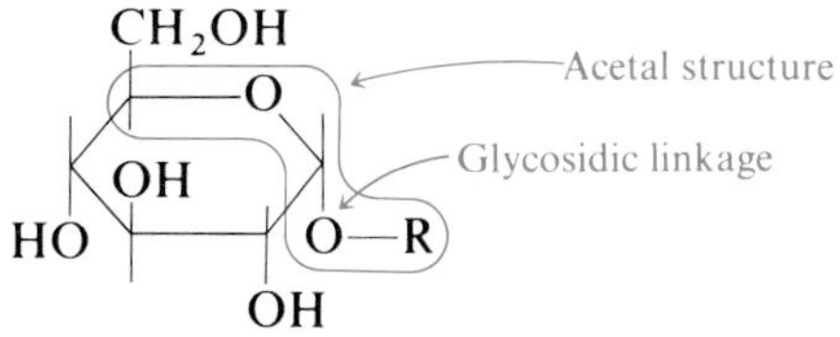

Acetal structure

Glycosidic linkage

An α-glycoside
(R = a variety of groups)

A glycoside differs significantly from a monosaccharide with respect to chemical reactivity.

When α-D-glucopyranose is heated with methyl alcohol and a small quantity of hydrogen chloride is added, two optically active isomers are formed—methyl α-D-glucopyranoside and methyl β-D-glucopyranoside:

$$\alpha\text{-D-Glucopyranose} \underset{HCl}{\overset{CH_3OH}{\rightleftharpoons}} \text{Methyl }\alpha\text{-D-glucopyranoside} + \text{Methyl }\beta\text{-D-glucopyranoside}$$

α-D-Glucopyranose

Methyl α-D-glucopyranoside (mp 165°C, [α] = +158°)

Methyl β-D-glucopyranoside (mp 107°C, [α] = −33°)

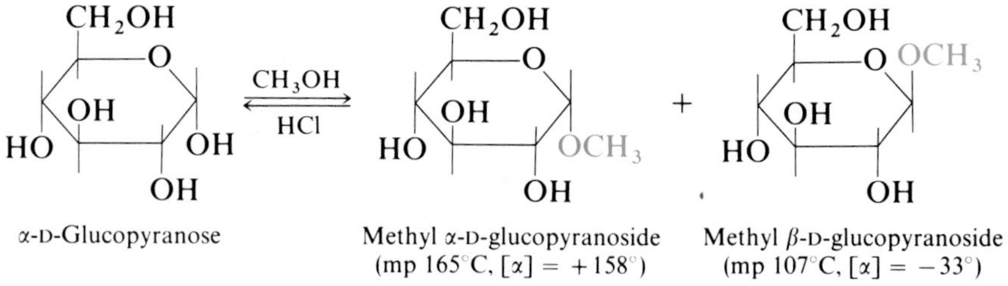

Unlike D-glucose, the two glycoside products no longer undergo mutarotation. They do not form open-chain compounds in aqueous solution. Acetals tend to be more stable and less reactive than hemiacetals.

The glycosidic linkage occurs in a wide variety of natural substances. All carbohydrates other than monosaccharides are glycosides. Heart stimulants such as digitalis and ouabain are known as heart glycosides. Several antibiotics such as streptomycin and erythromycin are also glycosides.

10.7 Structures of Galactose and Fructose

Galactose, like glucose, is an aldohexose and differs structurally from glucose only in the configuration of the —H and —OH group on the fourth carbon:

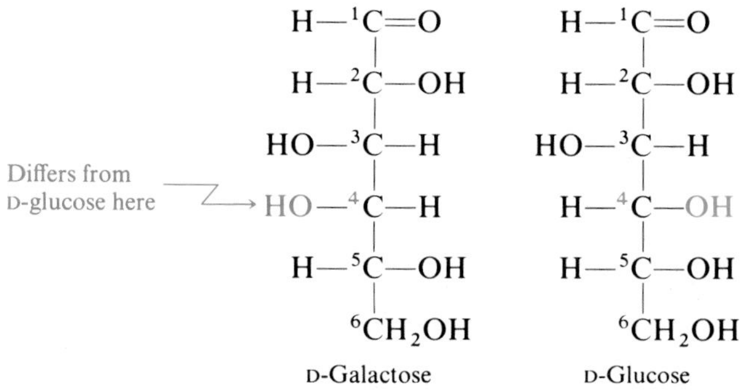

D-Galactose	D-Glucose
$H-{}^1C=O$	$H-{}^1C=O$
$H-{}^2C-OH$	$H-{}^2C-OH$
$HO-{}^3C-H$	$HO-{}^3C-H$
$HO-{}^4C-H$ (Differs from D-glucose here)	$H-{}^4C-OH$
$H-{}^5C-OH$	$H-{}^5C-OH$
${}^6CH_2OH$	${}^6CH_2OH$

Galactose, like glucose, also exists primarily in two cyclic pyranose forms that have hemiacetal structures and undergo mutarotation:

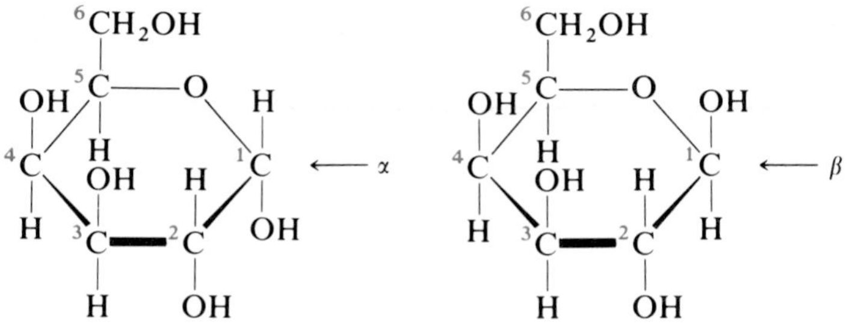

α-D-Galactopyranose

β-D-Galactopyranose

Fructose is a ketohexose. The open-chain form may be represented in a Fischer projection formula:

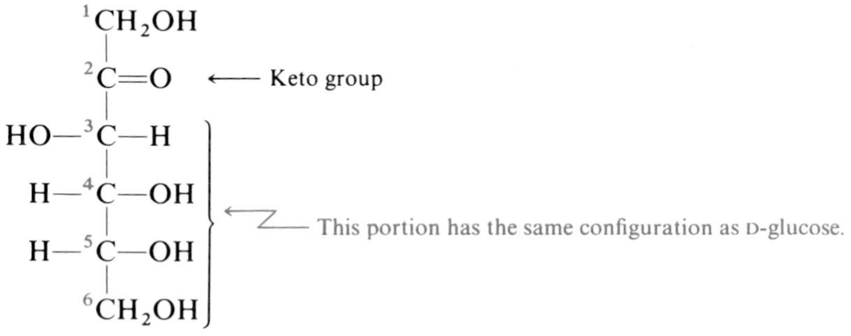

$$
\begin{array}{c}
{}^{1}CH_2OH \\
| \\
{}^{2}C{=}O \quad \leftarrow \text{Keto group} \\
| \\
HO-{}^{3}C-H \\
| \\
H-{}^{4}C-OH \\
| \\
H-{}^{5}C-OH \\
| \\
{}^{6}CH_2OH
\end{array}
$$

← This portion has the same configuration as D-glucose.

D-Fructose

Like glucose and galactose, fructose exists in both cyclic and open-chain forms. One common cyclic structure is a five-membered furanose ring in the β configuration:

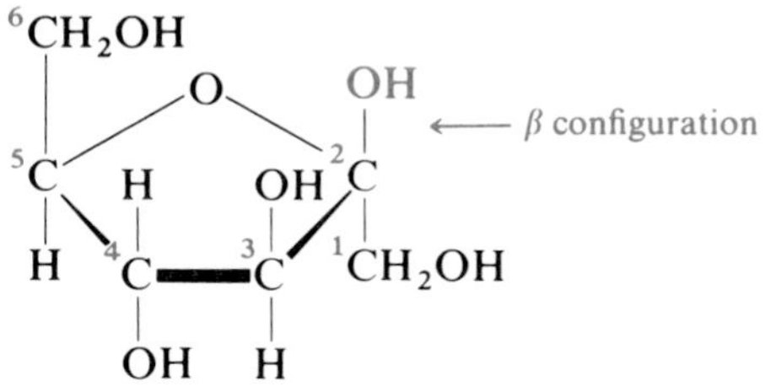

← β configuration

β-D-Fructofuranose

10.8 Pentoses

An open chain aldopentose has three asymmetric carbon atoms. Therefore eight (2^3) isomeric aldopentoses are possible. The four possible D-pentoses are shown on page 736 (Figure 10.7). Arabinose and xylose occur in some plants as polysaccharides called pentosans. D-ribose and its derivative D-2-deoxyribose are the most interesting pentoses because of their relationship to nucleic acids and the genetic code (Chapter 14). Note the difference between the two names D-ribose and D-2-deoxyribose. In the latter name, the 2-deoxy means that oxygen is missing from the D-ribose molecule at carbon 2. Check the formulas that follow to verify this difference.

H—[1]C=O
H—[2]C—OH
H—[3]C—OH
H—[4]C—OH
[5]CH_2OH

D-Ribose

[5]CH_2OH, O, OH, 4, 1, H, H, H, 3, H, 2, OH OH

or

CH_2OH, O, OH, OH OH

β-D-Ribofuranose

H—[1]C=O
H—[2]C—H
H—[3]C—OH
H—[4]C—OH
[5]CH_2OH

D-2-Deoxyribose

[5]CH_2OH, O, OH, 4, 1, H, H, H, 3, H, 2, OH H

or

CH_2OH, O, OH, OH

β-D-2-Deoxyribofuranose

The ketose that is closely related to D-ribose is named D-ribulose. (Ketose names are often derived from the corresponding aldose name by modifying the suffix *-ose* to *-ulose*.) This ketose is an intermediate that allows cells to make many other monosaccharides. In photosynthetic organisms, D-ribulose is used to capture carbon dioxide and thus make new carbohydrates.

CH_2OH
C=O
H—C—OH
H—C—OH
CH_2OH

D-Ribulose

▲ Sugar cane is a major source for sucrose, or table sugar.

10.9 DISACCHARIDES

Disaccharides are carbohydrates composed of two monosaccharide residues united by a glycosidic linkage. The two important disaccharides that are found in the free state in nature are sucrose and lactose. Sucrose, commonly known as *table sugar*, exists throughout the plant kingdom. Sugar cane contains 15–20%

sucrose, and sugar beets 10–17%. Maple syrup and sorghum are also good sources of sucrose. Lactose, also known as *milk sugar*, is found free in nature mainly in the milk of mammals. Human milk contains about 6.7% lactose and cow milk about 4.5% of this sugar.

Unlike sucrose and lactose, several other important disaccharides are derived directly from polysaccharides by hydrolysis (see Section 10.14). For example, maltose, isomaltose, and cellobiose are formed when specific polysaccharides are hydrolyzed. Of this group, maltose is the most common and is found as a constituent of sprouting grain.

Upon hydrolysis, disaccharides yield two monosaccharide molecules. The hydrolysis is catalyzed by hydrogen ions (acids), usually at elevated temperatures, or by certain enzymes that act effectively at room or body temperatures. A different enzyme is required for the hydrolysis of each of the three disaccharides:

$$\text{Sucrose} + \text{Water} \xrightarrow{\text{H}^+ \text{ or sucrase}} \text{Glucose} + \text{Fructose}$$

$$\text{Lactose} + \text{Water} \xrightarrow{\text{H}^+ \text{ or lactase}} \text{Galactose} + \text{Glucose}$$

$$\text{Maltose} + \text{Water} \xrightarrow{\text{H}^+ \text{ or maltase}} \text{Glucose} + \text{Glucose}$$

The enzyme lactase is present in the small intestine of infants and allows them to easily digest lactose from their milk diet. Unfortunately, as people mature their intestines often stop producing the lactase enzyme, and they lose the ability to digest lactose. Instead, this sugar is metabolized by common bacteria that live in the large intestine. The gas and intestinal discomfort that results is termed milk or lactose intolerance and is a condition that afflicts many adults. Carefully note the small structural differences between lactose and the other common disaccharides in the next section. Small differences in molecular shape often determine what our bodies do with specific molecules.

10.10 Structures and Properties of Disaccharides

Disaccharides contain an acetal structure (glycosidic linkage), and some also contain a hemiacetal structure. The acetal structure in maltose may be considered as being derived from two glucose molecules by the elimination of a molecule of water between the —OH group on carbon 1 of one glucose unit and the —OH group of carbon 4 on the other glucose unit. This is an α-1,4-glycosidic linkage, since the glucose units have the α configuration and are joined at carbons 1 and 4. In a more systematic nomenclature, this form of maltose is known as α-D-glucopyranosyl-(1-4)-α-D-glucopyranose. If the structure of glucose is known, this name provides a complete description for drawing the maltose formula.

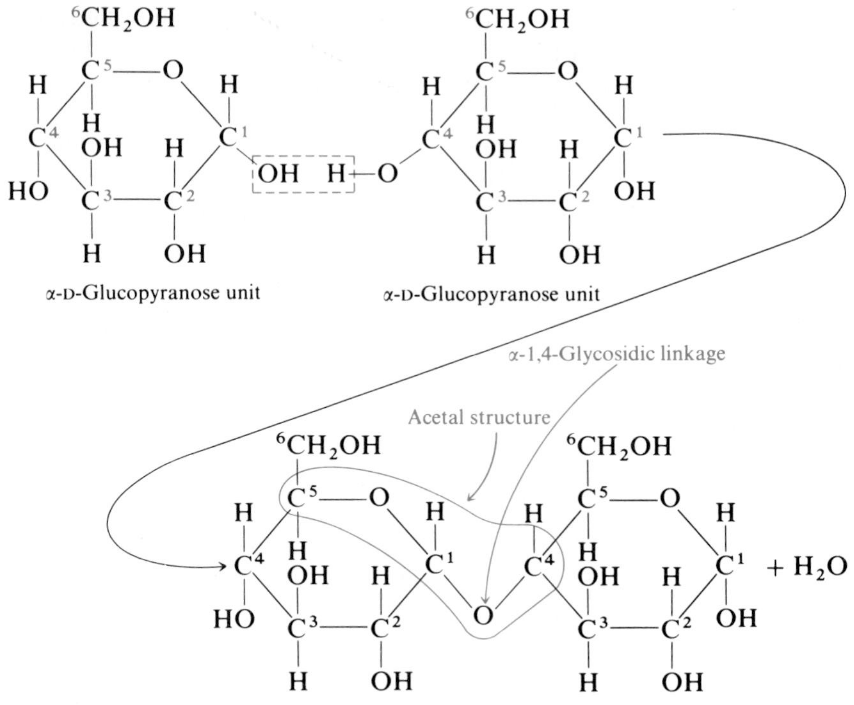

α-D-Glucopyranose unit α-D-Glucopyranose unit

α-1,4-Glycosidic linkage

Acetal structure

$+ H_2O$

Maltose
[α-D-Glucopyranosyl-(1-4)-α-D-glucopyranose]

Common lactose consists of a β-D-galactopyranose unit linked to an α-D-glucopyranose unit. These are joined by a β-1,4-glycosidic linkage from carbon 1 on galactose to carbon 4 on glucose. The more systematic name for lactose is β-D-galactopyranosyl-(1-4)-α-D-glucopyranose. Note that, although glycosidic bonds are straight carbon–oxygen linkages, the structural formula represents them in a bent fashion to provide stereochemical information. Carbon 1 of the galactose is in a β configuration, so its bent bond initially points up. The oxygen on carbon 4 of the glucose is below the carbon in the Haworth formula, and thus the bent bond initially points down.

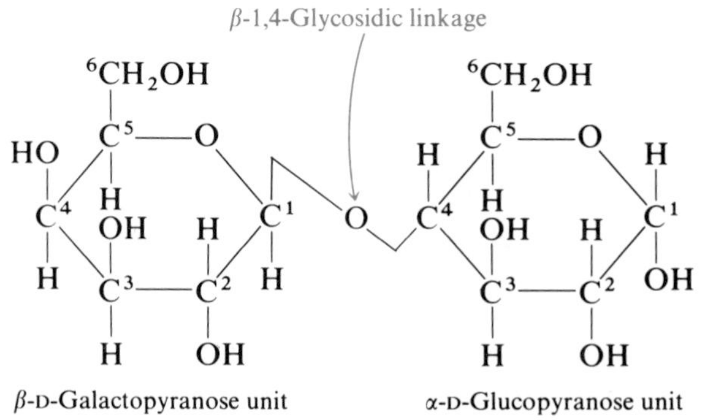

β-1,4-Glycosidic linkage

β-D-Galactopyranose unit α-D-Glucopyranose unit

Lactose
[β-D-Galactopyranosyl-(1-4)-α-D-glucopyranose]

Sucrose consists of an α-D-glucopyranose unit and a β-D-fructofuranose unit. These monosaccharides are joined by an oxygen bridge from carbon 1 on glucose to carbon 2 on fructose—that is, by an α-1,2-glycosidic linkage.

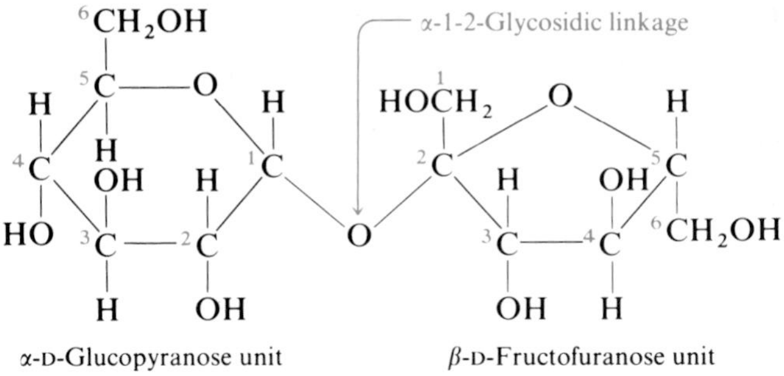

α-D-Glucopyranose unit β-D-Fructofuranose unit

Sucrose
[α-D-Glucopyranosyl-(1-2)-β-D-fructofuranose]

In this perspective formula, the fructose unit has been flipped to bring its number 2 carbon close to the number 1 carbon on the glucose unit. The groups on the fructose unit are therefore shown reversed from the perspective representation in Section 10.7.

EXAMPLE 10.3

Write the Haworth formula for isomaltose, α-D-glucopyranosyl-(1-6)-α-D-glucopyranose.

SOLUTION

Recognize that this disaccharide is composed of two α-D-glucopyranose units linked between carbon 6 of one sugar and carbon 1 of the other. First, write the Haworth formula for the monosaccharides and number their carbons.

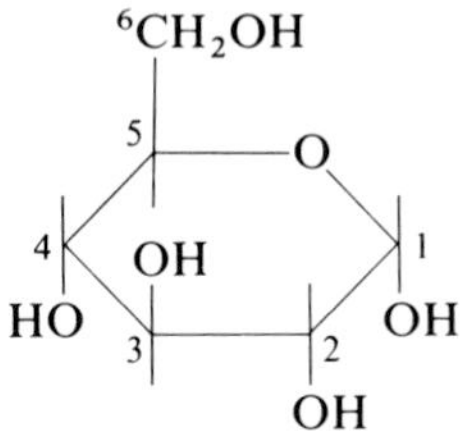

The two α-D-glucopyranose units must be linked in such a way that the stereochemistry at carbon 1 is preserved (carbon 6 is not an asymmetric center). One correct way to write the isomaltose structure is as follows:

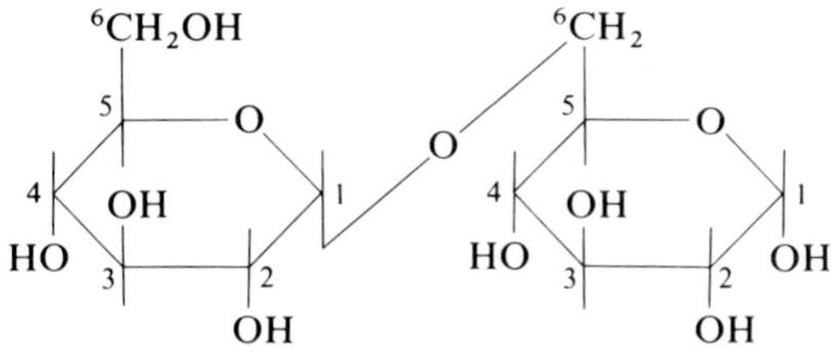

PRACTICE Write the structure for cellobiose (a disaccharide that can be derived from plants), β-D-glucopyranosyl-(1-4)-β-D-glucopyranose.

Answer:

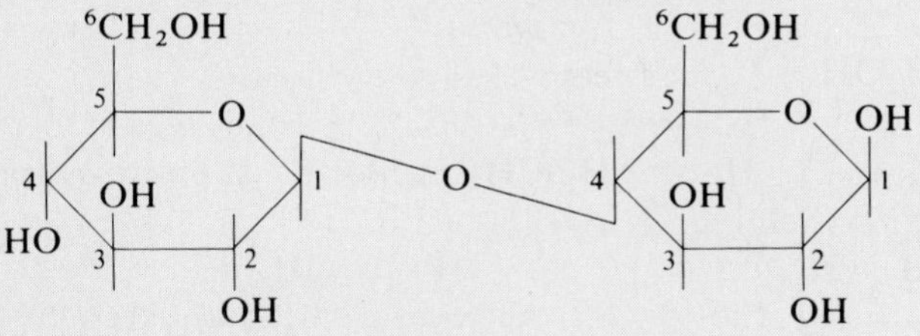

$^6CH_2OH$ $^6CH_2OH$

5 O 5 O OH

4 OH 1 O 4 OH 1

HO 3 2 3 2

OH OH

Lactose and maltose both show mutarotation, which indicates that one of the monosaccharide units has a hemiacetal ring that can open and close to interchange anomers. Sucrose has no hemiacetal structure and hence does not mutarotate.

The three disaccharides sucrose, lactose, and maltose have physical properties associated with large polar molecules. All three are crystalline solids and are quite soluble in water; the solubility of sucrose amounts to 179 g per 100 g of water at 0°C. Hydrogen bonding between the polar —OH groups on the sugar molecules and the water molecules is a major factor in this high solubility. These sugars are not easily melted. In fact, lactose is the only one with a clearly defined melting point (201.6°C). Sucrose and maltose begin to decompose when heated to 186°C and 102.5°C, respectively. When sucrose is heated to melting, it darkens and undergoes partial decomposition. The resulting mixture is known as caramel, or burnt sugar, and is used as coloring and as a flavoring agent in foods.

10.11 Sweeteners and Diet

Carbohydrates have long been valued for their ability to sweeten foods. Fructose is the sweetest of the common sugars (a scale of relative sweetness is given in Table 10.2), although sucrose (table sugar) is the most commonly used sweetener.

TABLE 10.2 Relative Sweetness of Sugars

Fructose	100	Galactose	19
Sucrose	58	Lactose	9.2
Glucose	43	Invert sugar	75
Maltose	19		

Astonishingly large amounts of sucrose are produced from sugar beets and cane: World production is on the order of 90 million tons annually. There are no essential chemical differences between cane and beet sugar. In the United States, approximately 20–30% of the average caloric intake is sucrose (about 150 g/day per person). Low price and sweet taste are the major reasons for high sucrose consumption. Note that sucrose is only 58% as sweet as fructose (Table 10.2). However, because sucrose is inexpensive to produce and is amenable to a variety of food processing techniques, approximately 60–80% of all sweeteners is sucrose.

Sucrose has a tendency to crystallize from concentrated solutions or syrups. Therefore, in commercial food preparations (for example, candies, jellies, and canned fruits) the sucrose is often hydrolyzed:

$$\text{Sucrose} + H_2O \xrightarrow{H^+} \text{Glucose} + \text{Fructose}$$

invert sugar

The resulting mixture of glucose and fructose, usually in solution, is called **invert sugar**. Invert sugar has less tendency to crystallize than sucrose, and it has greater sweetening power than an equivalent amount of sucrose. The nutritive value of the sucrose is not affected in any way by the conversion to invert sugar because the same hydrolysis reaction occurs in normal digestion.

High fructose corn syrups provide an alternate means of sweetening liquids such as soft drinks. These syrups are produced from corn starch and derive their sweet taste from fructose. Of course, starch is not sweet; as discussed in Section 10.14, it is a glucose polymer and contains no fructose. So, to produce this sweetener, the starch polymer must be broken down to yield some glucose monosaccharides, and in turn, glucose must be converted to fructose. Biotechnology has provided the means to accomplish this conversion. The starch polymers are hydrolyzed and some of the glucose is converted into fructose by a relatively new manufacturing process using enzymes. High-fructose corn syrups are economical because corn starch is much cheaper than cane or beet sugar.

Unfortunately, high sugar consumption has presented problems. Sucrose and other common sugars are ready sources of metabolic energy. Thus, for many people, sucrose is a source of too many calories. Oral bacteria also find sucrose easy to metabolize, increasing the incidence of dental caries. Finally, because the monosaccharides, fructose and glucose, are quickly absorbed from the small intestine, sugar consumption leads to a rapid increase in blood sugar. Such a sharp rise can be dangerous for people with impaired carbohydrate metabolism—for example, diabetes mellitus.

Scientists have searched for sugar substitutes. The ideal substitute might be sweeter than sucrose but lack the structural features and chemical reactivity that allow sugar to be absorbed and metabolized. Purely artificial, noncarbohydrate sweeteners have been developed starting with saccharin in 1879. This molecule is about 300 times sweeter than sucrose, cannot be metabolized, and so is nonnutritive. However, the search for other artificial sweeteners has continued because of saccharin's aftertaste and because of its potential health risks. Sodium cyclamate (20 times sweeter than fructose) was introduced in the early 1960s, but this molecule has been shown to cause cancer in laboratory animals. More recently, aspartame has become the artificial sweetener of choice. This molecule is about 200 times sweeter than fructose and poses no known health risks for most individuals, with the notable exception of people who suffer from phenylketonuria (PKU). Aspartame is composed of two amino acids (see Chapter 12) and can be metabolized to yield energy. However, foods sweetened with aspartame have much fewer calories than those containing sucrose because the same sweet taste is achieved with about 200 times less aspartame.

$HN{-}SO_3^-\ Na^+$ (on cyclohexane ring)

Sodium cyclamate

Saccharin

$H_2NCH(CH_2COOH)C(=O)NHCH(CH_2C_6H_5)C(=O){-}OCH_3$

Aspartame

10.12 Reducing Sugars

reducing sugar

Some sugars are capable of reducing silver ions to free silver, and copper(II) ions to copper(I) ions, under prescribed conditions. Such sugars are called **reducing sugars**. This reducing ability, which is useful in classifying sugars and in certain clinical tests, is dependent on the presence of (1) aldehydes, (2) α-hydroxyketone groups ($-CH_2COCH_2OH$) such as in fructose, or (3) hemiacetal structures in cyclic molecules such as maltose. These groups are easily oxidized to carboxylic acid (or carboxylate ion) groups; the metal ions are thereby reduced ($Ag^+ \longrightarrow Ag^0$; $Cu^{2+} \longrightarrow Cu^+$). Several different reagents, including Tollens', Fehling's, Benedict's, and Barfoed's reagents, are used to detect reducing sugars (see Section 5.4). The Benedict, Fehling, and Barfoed tests depend on the formation of copper(I) oxide precipitate to indicate a positive reaction.

$$\underset{\text{Aldehyde group}}{RC(H){=}O} + \underset{\text{(blue)}}{2\,Cu^{2+}} + 5\,OH^- \longrightarrow \underset{\text{Carboxylate ion group}}{RC(=O){-}O^-} + \underset{\text{Copper(I) oxide (brick red)}}{Cu_2O(s)} + 3\,H_2O$$

Barfoed's reagent contains Cu^{2+} ions in the presence of acetic acid. It is used to distinguish reducing monosaccharides from reducing disaccharides. Under the same reaction conditions, the reagent is reduced more rapidly by monosaccharides.

Glucose and galactose contain aldehyde groups; fructose contains an α-hydroxyketone group. Therefore, all three of these monosaccharides are reducing sugars.

A carbohydrate molecule need not have a free aldehyde or α-hydroxyketone group to be a reducing sugar. A hemiacetal structure (see below) is a potential aldehyde group. Maltose and the cyclic form of glucose are examples of molecules with the hemiacetal structure.

Hemiacetal structure that opens to form an aldehyde group

Glucose

Maltose

Under mildly alkaline conditions, the rings open at the points indicated by the arrows to form aldehyde groups:

Ring opens here

$\xrightarrow[H_2O]{OH^-}$

Glucose (ring structure)

Glucose (open-chain structure)

Any sugar that has the hemiacetal structure is classified as a reducing sugar. Among the disaccharides, lactose and maltose have hemiacetal structures and are therefore reducing sugars. Sucrose is not a reducing sugar because it does not have the hemiacetal structure.

Many clinical tests monitor glucose as a reducing sugar. For example, Benedict's and Fehling's reagents are used to detect the presence of glucose in urine. Initially the reagents are deep blue in color. A positive test is indicated by a color change to greenish-yellow, yellowish-orange, or brick-red, corresponding to an increasing glucose (reducing sugar) concentration. These tests are used for estimating the amount of glucose in the urine of diabetics in order to adjust the amount of insulin needed for proper glucose utilization.

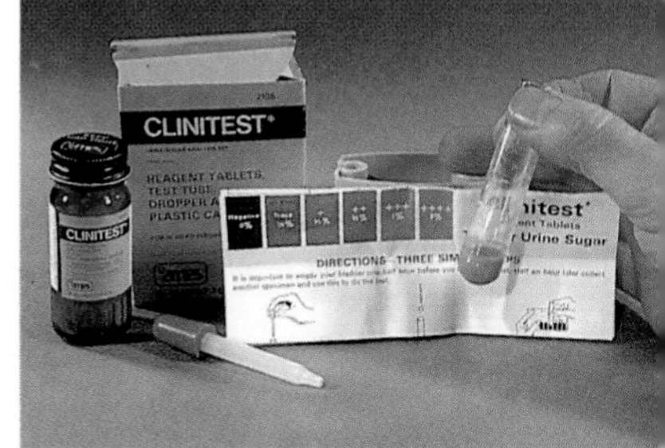

Alternatively, a clinical test (glucose oxidase test) makes use of an enzyme catalyzed oxidation of glucose to test for urine sugar. The inclusion of an enzyme ensures a reaction that is specific for the glucose structure, allowing a more selective test for glucose in the urine.

10.13 Reactions of Monosaccharides

Oxidation

The oxidation of monosaccharides by copper ions is described in Section 10.12. The aldehyde groups in monosaccharides are also oxidized to monocarboxylic acids by other mild oxidizing agents such as bromine water. The carboxylic acid group is formed at carbon 1. The name of the resulting acid is formed by changing the *ose* ending to *onic acid.* Glucose yields gluconic acid; galactose, galactonic acid; and so on.

$$
\begin{array}{c}
\text{H—C=O} \\
| \\
\text{H—C—OH} \\
| \\
\text{HO—C—H} \\
| \\
\text{H—C—OH} \\
| \\
\text{H—C—OH} \\
| \\
CH_2OH \\
\text{D-Glucose}
\end{array}
+ Br_2 + H_2O \longrightarrow
\begin{array}{c}
\text{COOH} \\
| \\
\text{H—C—OH} \\
| \\
\text{HO—C—H} \\
| \\
\text{H—C—OH} \\
| \\
\text{H—C—OH} \\
| \\
CH_2OH \\
\text{D-Gluconic acid}
\end{array}
+ 2\,HBr
$$

Dilute nitric acid, a vigorous oxidizing agent, oxidizes both carbon 1 and carbon 6 of aldohexoses to form dicarboxylic acids. The resulting acid is named by changing the *ose* sugar suffix to *aric acid.* Glucose yields glucaric acid (saccharic acid); galactose, galactaric acid (mucic acid).

$$
\begin{array}{c}
\text{H—C=O} \\
| \\
\text{H—C—OH} \\
| \\
\text{HO—C—H} \\
| \\
\text{H—C—OH} \\
| \\
\text{H—C—OH} \\
| \\
CH_2OH \\
\text{D-Glucose}
\end{array}
\xrightarrow{\text{Warm } HNO_3}
\begin{array}{c}
\text{COOH} \\
| \\
\text{H—C—OH} \\
| \\
\text{HO—C—H} \\
| \\
\text{H—C—OH} \\
| \\
\text{H—C—OH} \\
| \\
\text{COOH} \\
\text{Glucaric acid}
\end{array}
\qquad
\begin{array}{c}
\text{COOH} \\
| \\
\text{H—C—OH} \\
| \\
\text{HO—C—H} \\
| \\
\text{HO—C—H} \\
| \\
\text{H—C—OH} \\
| \\
\text{COOH} \\
\text{Galactaric acid}
\end{array}
$$

This reaction serves as the basis of the *galactaric* (*mucic*) *acid test*, which is sometimes used to distinguish glucose from galactose. Galactaric acid is only slightly soluble in dilute nitric acid, whereas glucaric acid is quite soluble. Hence, when oxidized with nitric acid, galactose (and lactose, which hydrolyzes to form glucose and galactose) yields a precipitate of galactaric acid crystals. When glucose is oxidized under the same conditions, the glucaric acid does not precipitate. Note also that galactaric acid is an optically inactive meso compound, whereas glucaric acid is an optically active compound (see Section 9.3).

Osazone Formation

Phenylhydrazine ($C_6H_5NHNH_2$) reacts with carbons 1 and 2 of reducing sugars to form derivatives called osazones. The formation of these distinctive crystalline derivatives is useful for comparing the structures of sugars. Glucose and fructose react as shown in Figure 10.5.

Identical osazones are obtained from D-glucose and D-fructose. This demonstrates that carbons 3 through 6 of D-glucose and D-fructose molecules are identical. The same osazone is also obtained from D-mannose. This indicates that

H—C=O
H—C—OH
HO—C—H
H—C—OH
H—C—OH
CH_2OH
D-Glucose

$\xrightarrow{C_6H_5NHNH_2}$

H—C=$NNHC_6H_5$
H—C—OH
HO—C—H
H—C—OH
H—C—OH
CH_2OH

$\xrightarrow{C_6H_5NHNH_2}$

H—C=$NNHC_6H_5$
C=O
HO—C—H
H—C—OH
H—C—OH
CH_2OH

$\xrightarrow{C_6H_5NHNH_2}$

H—C=$NNHC_6H_5$
C=$NNHC_6H_5$
HO—C—H
H—C—OH
H—C—OH
CH_2OH
Osazone
(from either glucose or fructose)

CH_2OH
C=O
HO—C—H
H—C—OH
H—C—OH
CH_2OH
D-Fructose

$\xrightarrow{C_6H_5NHNH_2}$

CH_2OH
C=$NNHC_6H_5$
HO—C—H
H—C—OH
H—C—OH
CH_2OH

$\xrightarrow{C_6H_5NHNH_2}$

H—C=O
C=$NNHC_6H_5$
HO—C—H
H—C—OH
H—C—OH
CH_2OH

$\xrightarrow{C_6H_5NHNH_2}$ Osazone

▲
FIGURE 10.5
Reaction of glucose and fructose to form osazones. Common sugars form the same structure at carbons 1 and 2. Since D-glucose and D-fructose are identical at all other positions, these sugars yield the same osazone.

carbons 3 through 6 of the D-mannose molecule are the same as those of D-glucose and D-fructose molecules. In fact, D-mannose differs from D-glucose only in the configuration of the —H and —OH groups on carbon 2.

Reduction

Monosaccharides may be reduced to their corresponding polyhydroxy alcohols by reducing agents such as H_2/Pt or sodium amalgam, Na(Hg). For example, glucose yields sorbitol (glucitol), galactose yields galactitol (dulcitol), and mannose yields mannitol; all of these are hexahydric alcohols (containing six —OH groups).

H—C=O
H—C—OH
HO—C—H
H—C—OH
H—C—OH
CH_2OH
D-Glucose

$\xrightarrow{H_2/Pt}$

CH_2OH
H—C—OH
HO—C—H
H—C—OH
H—C—OH
CH_2OH
D-Glucitol
(Sorbitol)

Hexahydric alcohols have properties resembling those of glycerol (Section 4.6). Because of their affinity for water, they are used as moisturizing agents in food and cosmetics. Sorbitol, galactitol, and mannitol occur naturally in a variety of plants.

EXAMPLE 10.4

Two samples labeled A and B are known to be D-threose and D-erythrose. Water solutions of each sample are optically active. However, when each solution was warmed with nitric acid, the solution from sample A became optically inactive while that from sample B was still optically active. Determine which sample (A or B) contains D-threose and which sample contains D-erythrose.

SOLUTION

In this problem we need to examine the structures of D-threose and D-erythrose, write equations for the reaction with nitric acid, and examine the products to see why one is optically active and the other optically inactive. Start by writing the formulas for D-threose and D-erythrose:

```
    H—C=O          H—C=O
      |              |
   HO—C—H          H—C—OH
      |              |
    H—C—OH         H—C—OH
      |              |
     CH₂OH          CH₂OH
  D-Threose      D-Erythrose
```

The oxidation of these tetroses would yield dicarboxylic acids:

```
    H—C=O                 COOH          H—C=O                 COOH
      |                    |              |                    |
   HO—C—H    Warm     HO—C—H            H—C—OH    Warm       H—C—OH
      |      ---->         |              |       ---->        |
    H—C—OH   HNO₃      H—C—OH           H—C—OH    HNO₃       H—C—OH
      |                    |              |                    |
     CH₂OH                COOH           CH₂OH                COOH
                            I                                   II
```

Product I is a chiral molecule and is optically active. Product II is a meso compound and is optically inactive. Therefore, sample A is D-erythrose, since oxidation yields the meso acid. Sample B then must be D-threose.

PRACTICE A disaccharide yields no copper(I) oxide when treated in Benedict's test. This carbohydrate is composed of two α-D-galactopyranose units. Identify the carbon from each monosaccharide involved in the acetal linkage.

Answer: Carbon 1 from each α-D-galactopyranose?

PRACTICE Write the structure of the product formed when D-galactose is reduced with H_2/Pt. Is this compound optically active?

Answer:

```
     CH₂OH
       |
     H—C—OH
       |
    HO—C—H
       |
    HO—C—H
       |
     H—C—OH
       |
     CH₂OH
```

No, it is a meso compound.

10.14 Polysaccharides Derived from Glucose

Although many naturally occurring polysaccharides are known, three—starch, cellulose, and glycogen—are of outstanding importance. All three, when hydrolyzed, yield D-glucose as the only product, according to this approximate general equation:

$$\underset{\substack{\text{Polysaccharide molecule}\\\text{(approximate}\\\text{formula)}}}{(C_6H_{10}O_5)_n} + n\,H_2O \longrightarrow \underset{\text{D-Glucose}}{n\,C_6H_{12}O_6}$$

This hydrolysis reaction establishes that all three polysaccharides are polymers made up of glucose monosaccharide units. It also means that the differences in properties among the three polysaccharides must be due to differences in the structures and/or sizes of these molecules.

Many years of research were required to determine the detailed structures for polysaccharide molecules. Consideration of all this work is beyond the scope of our discussion, but an abbreviated summary of the results is given in the following paragraphs.

Starch

Starch is found in plants, mainly in the seeds, roots, or tubers (see Figure 10.6). Corn, wheat, potatoes, rice, and cassava are the chief sources of dietary starch. The two main components of starch are amylose and amylopectin. Amylose molecules are unbranched chains composed of about 25 to 1300 α-D-glucose

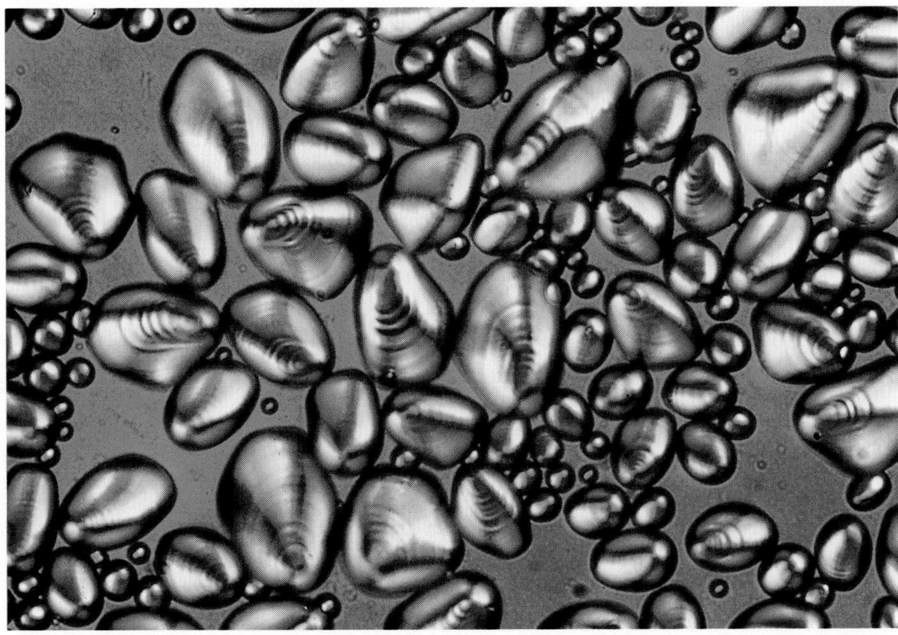

◀ **Figure 10.6**
Scanning electron micrograph of starch granules in potato tuber cells.

units joined by α-1,4-glycosidic linkages, as shown in Figure 10.7. The stereochemistry of the α-anomer causes amylose to coil into a helical conformation. Partial hydrolysis of this linear polymer yields the disaccharide maltose.

Amylopectin is a branched-chain polysaccharide with much larger molecules than those of amylose. Amylopectin molecules consist on the average of several thousand α-D-glucose units with molar masses ranging up to 1 million or more. The main chain contains glucose units connected by α-1,4-glycosidic linkages. Branch chains are linked to the main chain through α-1,6-glycosidic linkages about every 25 glucose units, as shown in Figure 10.7. This molecule has a characteristic treelike structure because of its many branch chains. Partial hydrolysis of amylopectin yields both maltose and the related disaccharide isomaltose, α-D-glucopyranosyl-(1-6)-α-D-glucopyranose.

Despite the presence of many polar —OH groups, starch molecules are insoluble in cold water, apparently because of their very large size. Starch readily forms colloidal dispersions in hot water. Such starch "solutions" form an intense blue-black color in the presence of free iodine. Hence, a starch solution can be used to detect free iodine, or a dilute iodine solution can be used to detect starch.

Starch is readily converted to glucose by heating with water and a little acid (for example, hydrochloric or sulfuric acid). It is also readily hydrolyzed at room temperature by certain digestive enzymes. The hydrolysis of starch to maltose and glucose is shown in the following equation:

$$\text{Starch} \xrightarrow[\text{or salivary and pancreatic amylase}]{\text{Acid} + \Delta} \text{Dextrins and Maltose} \xrightarrow[\text{or maltase and other intestinal enzymes}]{\text{Acid} + \Delta} \text{D-Glucose}$$

The hydrolysis of starch can be followed qualitatively by periodically testing samples from a mixture of starch and saliva with a very dilute iodine solution. The change of color sequence is blue-black ⟶ blue ⟶ purple ⟶ pink ⟶ colorless as the starch molecules are broken down into smaller and smaller fragments.

Hydrolysis is a key chemical reaction in the digestion of starchy foods. If these foods are well-chewed, salivary amylase normally decreases the starch polymer chain length from on the order of a thousand glucose units to about eight per chain. In the small intestine, pancreatic amylase continues digestion to form maltose. Enzymes in the small intestine membranes complete the conversion of starch to glucose, which is then absorbed into the bloodstream.

Starch is the most important energy storage carbohydrate of the plant kingdom. In turn, humans and other animals consume huge quantities of starch. This polymer is such an important food source because it has the appropriate structure to be readily broken down to D-glucose. The reduced carbons from starch provide much of our daily energy needs as they are oxidized to carbon dioxide.

Glycogen

Glycogen is the energy storage carbohydrate of the animal kingdom. It is formed in the body by polymerization of glucose and stored in the liver and in muscle tissues. Structurally, it is very similar to the amylopectin fraction of starch except that it is more highly branched. The α-1,6-glycosidic linkages occur on one of every 12 to 18 glucose units.

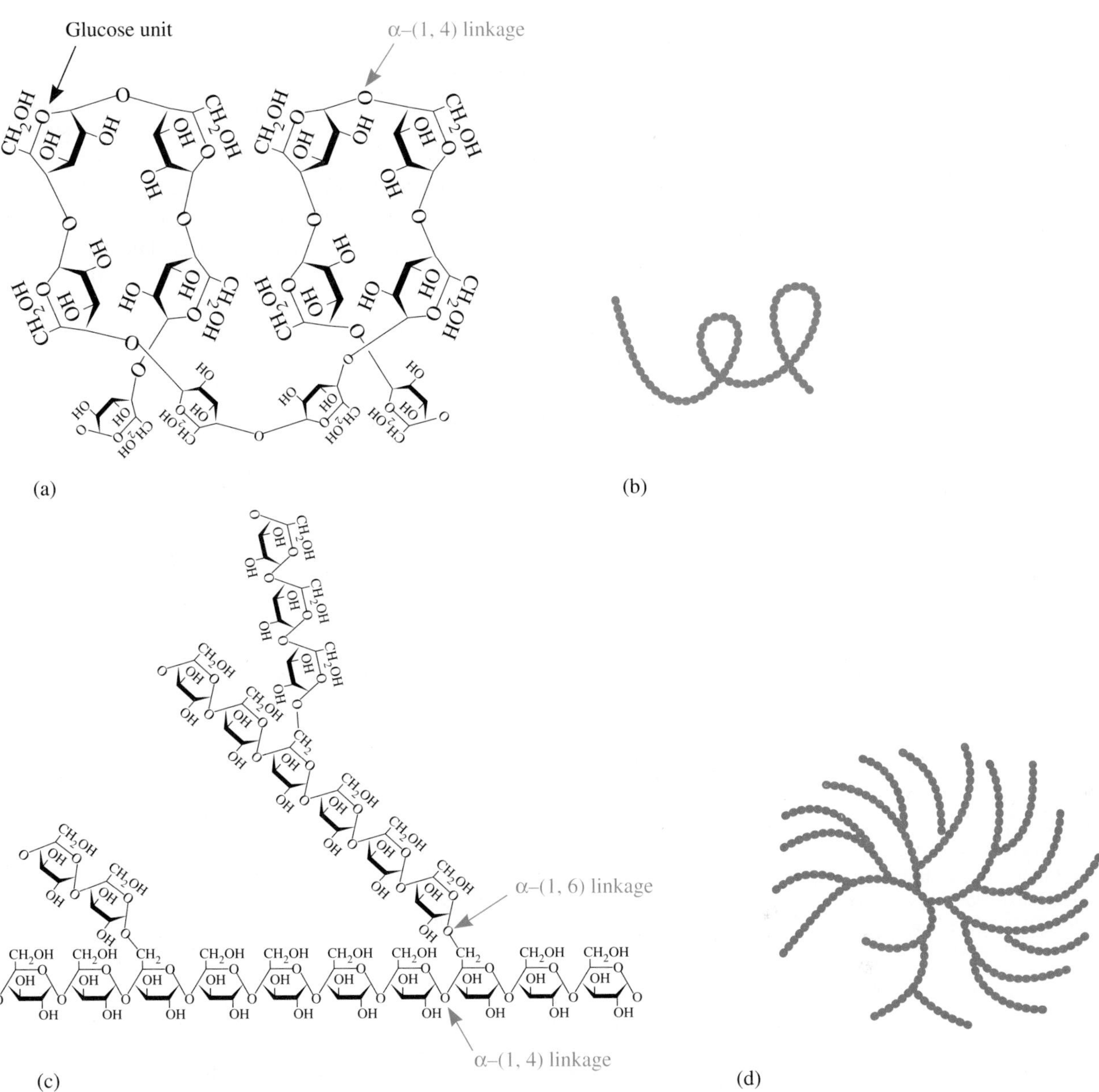

▲
FIGURE 10.7
(a) Molecular structure of amylose chain; (b) array of glucose units (dots) in amylose; (c) molecular structure of amylopectin; (d) branched array of glucose units (dots) in amylopectin.

Cellulose

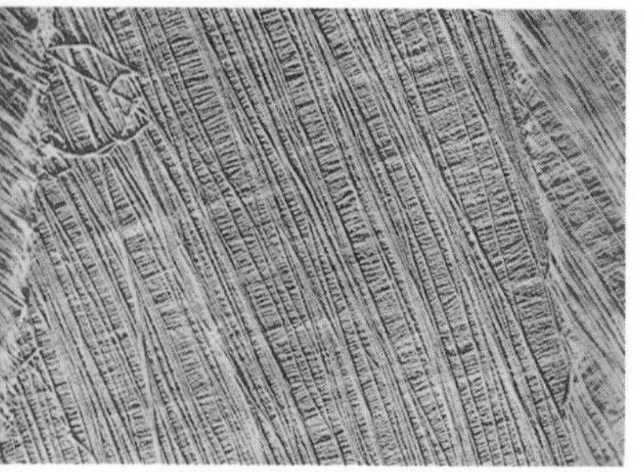

▲ **FIGURE 10.8**
Scanning electron micrograph of cellulose fibers in a plant cell wall.

Cellulose is the most abundant organic substance found in nature. It is the chief structural component of plants and wood (Figure 10.8). Cotton fibers are almost pure cellulose; wood, after removal of moisture, consists of about 50% cellulose. Cellulose is an important substance in the textile and paper industries.

Cellulose, like starch and glycogen, is a polymer of glucose. But cellulose differs from starch and glycogen because the glucose units are joined by β-1,4-glycosidic linkages instead of α-1,4-glycosidic linkages. The stereochemistry of the β-anomer allows this polymer to form an extended chain that can hydrogen-bond to adjacent cellulose molecules. The large number of hydrogen bonds so formed partially accounts for the strength of the resulting plant cell walls. The cellulose structure is illustrated in Figure 10.9.

A partial hydrolysis of cellulose produces the disaccharide cellobiose, β-D-glucopyranosyl-(1-4)-β-D-glucopyranose. However, cellulose has greater resistance to hydrolysis than either starch or glycogen. It is not appreciably hydrolyzed when boiled in a 1% sulfuric acid solution. It does not show a color reaction with iodine. Humans cannot digest cellulose, because they have no enzymes capable of catalyzing its hydrolysis. Fortunately, some microorganisms found in soil and in the digestive tracts of certain animals produce enzymes that do catalyze the breakdown of cellulose. The presence of these microorganisms explains why cows and other herbivorous animals thrive on grass—and also why termites thrive on wood.

The —OH groups of starch and cellulose can be reacted without destruction of the macromolecular structures. For example, nitric acid converts an —OH

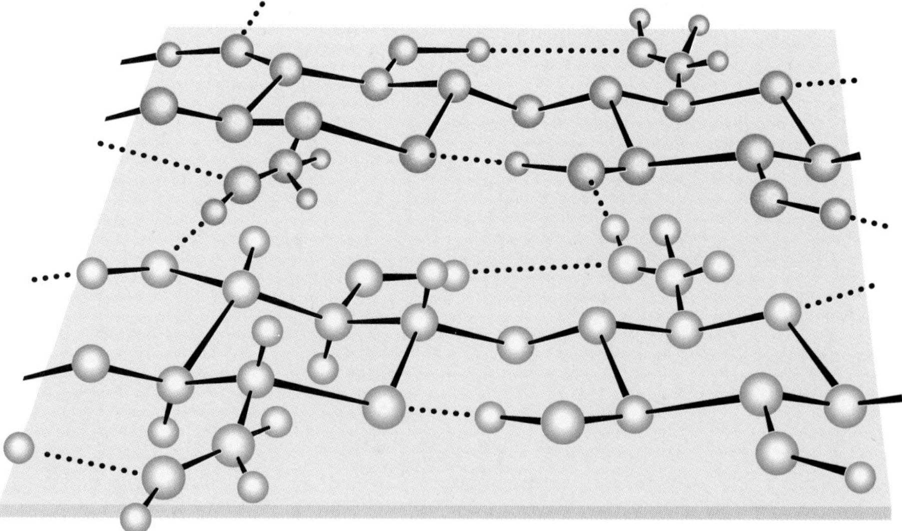

FIGURE 10.9 ▶
Haworth and three-dimensional representations of cellulose. In the three-dimensional drawing, note the hydrogen bonding that links the extended cellulose polymers to form cellulose fibers.

Chemistry in Action

Polysaccharides

Many carbohydrate polymers are composed of monosaccharides other than glucose and serve a variety of purposes for both plants and animals. Some polysaccharides are made up of only one type of monosaccharide. For example, D-mannose-containing polymers are found in many plants including pine trees and orchid tubers. Polysaccharides composed of the pentose D-xylose are also found widely distributed in wood and vegetable products.

More complex polysaccharides are often found in animals. These carbohydrates are linked together by glycosidic bonds at various positions on the monosaccharides. Thus, a sugar may be bonded to its neighbor from carbon 1 to carbon 3, or carbon 1 to carbon 4, or carbon 1 to carbon 6, and so on. Because of these numerous linkages, the polysaccharides often have a complex, branching structure. Also, it is not uncommon for these molecules to contain many different kinds of monosaccharides. These complex carbohydrates serve a variety of functions in animals.

Mucopolysaccharides (or glycosaminoglycans) make up part of the connective tissue, and are found in the joints and the skin. The slimy, mucuslike consistency of these molecules derives from their special chemical properties. About half of the sugar units are acidic in these carbohydrates. These acid groups become negatively charged under physiological conditions, causing the polymer chains to repel each other.

Water fills the space between the polymer chains and gives the mucopolysaccharide a spongelike consistency. One gram of some mucopolysaccharides can absorb up to 20 liters of water. This natural shock absorber and lubricant is necessary for animal locomotion.

Even more complicated polysaccharides are found on the surfaces of almost all cells. These carbohydrates serve as "labels" or antigens allowing organisms to distinguish their own cells from invading bacteria, for example. Antigen recognition illustrates a very important biochemical principle: *molecular shape carries information which guides the reactions of life.*

In humans, the polysaccharides on the surface of the red blood cells give rise to a number of blood types, often classified by the ABO system. Cells of different blood types have surface polysaccharides with different structures. Cells carrying one carbohydrate structure are commonly not tolerated by an individual of another blood type. Thus, for example, if type AB blood is transfused into someone with type O red blood cells, the new cells will be attacked by the immunosystem. Red cell destruction can lead to serious injury or death.

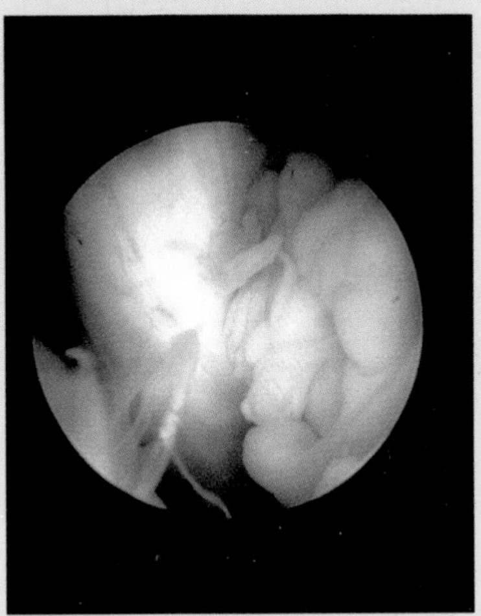

▲ **The connective tissue inside the knee contains mucopolysaccharides.**

group to a nitrate group in this fashion:

$$\text{Cellulose}—\boxed{\text{OH} + \text{H}}\,\text{ONO}_2 \longrightarrow \text{Cellulose}—\text{ONO}_2 + \text{H}_2\text{O}$$

Hydroxyl group on cellulose molecule; Nitric acid; Nitrate group on cellulose molecule; Water

If only a portion of the —OH groups on the cellulose molecule are nitrated, a plastic nitrocellulose material known as celluloid or pyroxylin is obtained. This material has been used to make such diverse articles as billiard balls, celluloid shirt collars, and photographic film. By nitration of nearly all —OH groups, a powerful high explosive is obtained. This highly nitrated cellulose, or "guncotton," is the basic ingredient in modern "smokeless" gunpowder.

Another modified cellulose, cellulose acetate, is made by esterification of —OH groups with acetic acid (acetic anhydride). About two-thirds of the —OH groups are esterified:

$$\text{Cellulose—O}\boxed{\text{H} + \text{CH}_3\text{—}\overset{\text{O}}{\overset{\|}{\text{C}}}\text{—O}}\text{—}\overset{\text{O}}{\overset{\|}{\text{C}}}\text{—CH}_3 \longrightarrow \text{Cellulose—O—}\overset{\text{O}}{\overset{\|}{\text{C}}}\text{—CH}_3 + \text{CH}_3\text{COOH}$$

Hydroxyl group on cellulose molecule; Acetic anhydride; Acetate group on cellulose molecule

Cellulose acetate, unlike the dangerously flammable cellulose nitrate, can be made to burn only with difficulty. For this reason, cellulose acetate has displaced cellulose nitrate in almost all kinds of photographic films. The textile known as acetate rayon is made from cellulose acetate. Cellulose acetate is also used as a clear, transparent packaging film. In another process, cellulose reacts with carbon disulfide in the presence of sodium hydroxide to form a soluble cellulose derivative called cellulose xanthate, from which cellulose can be regenerated. Viscose rayon textiles and cellophane packaging materials are made of regenerated cellulose prepared by this process.

Concepts in Review

1. List three important characteristics of an energy-providing food.
2. Compare the oxidation state of carbon in carbohydrates with that of carbon in carbon dioxide.
3. Classify carbohydrates as mono-, di-, oligo-, or polysaccharides.
4. Explain the use of D, L, (+), and (−) in naming carbohydrates.
5. Identify and write pyranose and furanose ring structures of carbohydrates.
6. Identify and write Fischer projection and Haworth formulas for carbohydrates.
7. Identify the structural feature of a carbohydrate that makes it a reducing sugar.
8. Explain the phenomenon of mutarotation.
9. Distinguish between hemiacetal and acetal structures in a carbohydrate.
10. Understand what a glycoside linkage is.
11. Understand disaccharide composition and the manner in which monosaccharides are linked together in sucrose, lactose, and maltose.

12. Identify monosaccharides that are epimers.
13. List the major sources of glucose, galactose, fructose, sucrose, lactose, and maltose.
14. Describe some disadvantage of a diet high in sucrose and some alternatives to this sweetener.
15. Identify three disaccharides that are derived from polysaccharides.
16. Describe the Benedict test and tell what evidence must be seen to indicate a positive test.
17. Write chemical equations for the oxidation of monosaccharides by bromine and by nitric acid.
18. Write chemical equations for the reduction of monosaccharides.
19. Write chemical equations for the formation of osazones.
20. Identify monosaccharides that give identical osazones.
21. Identify monosaccharides that give optically inactive (meso) products when reduced to polyhydroxy alcohols or when oxidized to dicarboxylic acids.
22. Discuss the structural differences between amylose, amylopectin, and cellulose.
23. Compare the common polymers of glucose with more complex polysaccharides.

EQUATIONS IN REVIEW

Formation of Sugar Ring Structures from Open-Chain Forms—Hemiacetal/Hemiketal Formation (example)

α-D-(+)-Glucopyranose ⇌ D-(+)-Glucose (open-chain form) ⇌ β-D-(+)-Glucopyranose

Reaction of Monosaccharides with Alcohols—Acetal/Ketal Formation (example)

$$\text{Glucopyranose} \underset{\text{HCl}}{\overset{\text{ROH}}{\rightleftharpoons}} \alpha\text{-glycoside (OR)} + \beta\text{-glycoside (OR)}$$

Kiliani–Fischer Synthesis for Increasing the Number of Carbons in an Aldose

$$\underset{\substack{| \\ R}}{H—C=O} \xrightarrow{HCN} \underset{\substack{| \\ CHOH \\ | \\ R}}{CN} \xrightarrow[H^+]{H_2O} \underset{\substack{| \\ CHOH \\ | \\ R}}{COOH} \xrightarrow{Na(Hg)} \underset{\substack{| \\ CHOH \\ | \\ R}}{H—C=O}$$

Oxidation of Carbohydrates

$$\underset{\substack{| \\ (CHOH)_n \\ | \\ CH_2OH}}{H—C=O} + Br_2 + H_2O \longrightarrow \underset{\substack{| \\ (CHOH)_n \\ | \\ CH_2OH}}{COOH} + 2\,HBr$$

$$\underset{\substack{| \\ (CHOH)_n \\ | \\ CH_2OH}}{H—C=O} + 2\,Cu^{2+} + 5\,OH^- \longrightarrow \underset{\substack{| \\ (CHOH)_n \\ | \\ CH_2OH}}{COOH} + Cu_2O + 3\,H_2O$$

$$\underset{\substack{| \\ (CHOH)_n \\ | \\ CH_2OH}}{H—C=O} \xrightarrow{\text{Warm } HNO_3} \underset{\substack{| \\ (CHOH)_n \\ | \\ COOH}}{COOH}$$

Reduction of Carbohydrates

$$\underset{\substack{| \\ R}}{H—C=O} \xrightarrow{H_2/Pt} \underset{\substack{| \\ R}}{CH_2OH}$$

Formation of Osazones from Carbohydrates

$$\underset{\substack{| \\ CHOH \\ | \\ R}}{H—C=O} \quad \text{or} \quad \underset{\substack{| \\ C=O \\ | \\ R}}{CH_2OH} \xrightarrow{2\,C_6H_5NHNH_2} \underset{\substack{| \\ C=NNHC_6H_5 \\ | \\ R}}{H—C=NNHC_6H_5}$$

Exercises

1. Why is the oxidation state of a carbohydrate carbon important in metabolism?
2. What is the significance of the notations D and L in the name of a carbohydrate?
3. What is the significance of the notations (+) and (−) in the name of a carbohydrate?
4. Explain how a carbohydrate with a pyranose structure differs from one with a furanose structure.
5. What is galactosemia and what are its effects on humans?
6. Which of the D-aldohexoses in Figure 10.1 are epimers?
7. Write the cyclic structures for α-D-glucopyranose, β-D-galactopyranose, and α-D-mannopyranose.
8. Explain how α-D-glycopyranose differs from β-D-glucopyranose.
9. Write the structure of L-glyceraldehyde and show, using oxidation numbers, which carbon is most reduced.
10. Would D-mannose provide more metabolic energy than D-galactose? Explain.

11. Starting with the proper D-tetrose, show the steps for the synthesis of D-glucose by the Kiliani–Fischer synthesis.
12. Are the cyclic forms of monosaccharides hemiacetals or glycosides?
13. Explain the phenomenon of mutarotation.
14. Is D-2-deoxyarabinose the same as D-2-deoxyribose? Explain.
15. What is (are) the major source(s) of each?
(a) Sucrose (b) Lactose (c) Maltose
16. What is the monosaccharide composition of each of the following?
(a) Sucrose (c) Lactose (e) Amylose
(b) Maltose (d) Glycogen
17. How does the structure of cellobiose differ from that of isomaltose?
18. Cite two advantages of aspartame, as a sweetener, over sucrose.
19. Explain why invert sugar is sweeter than sucrose.
20. Which of the disaccharides sucrose, maltose, and lactose show mutarotation? Explain why.
21. Draw structural formulas for maltose and sucrose. Point out the portion of the structure that is responsible for one of these disaccharides being classified as a reducing sugar.
22. Give the systematic names for isomaltose and lactose.
23. What visual difference would you expect between a dilute glucose solution and a concentrated glucose solution in the Benedict test?
24. Which of the D-aldopentoses (Figure 10.1) is optically inactive when reduced with H_2/Pt? Write structures for the reduced products and explain why they are optically inactive.
25. Glyceraldehyde, $CH_2(OH)CH(OH)CHO$, is the simplest aldose.
(a) Write projection formulas for and identify the D and L forms of glyceraldehyde.
(b) Write the structural formula of the product obtained by reacting glyceraldehyde with hydrogen in the presence of a platinum catalyst.
26. Consider the eight aldohexoses given in Figure 10.1 and answer the following:
(a) Which of these aldohexoses give the same osazone?
(b) The eight aldohexoses are oxidized by nitric acid to dicarboxylic acids. Which of these give meso (optically inactive) dicarboxylic acids?
(c) Write the structures and names for the enantiomers of D-(+)-mannose and D-(−)-idose.
27. Describe the principal structural differences and similarities between the members of each of the following pairs:
(a) D-Glucose and D-fructose
(b) D-Ribose and D-2-deoxyribose
(c) Maltose and sucrose
(d) Amylose and amylopectin
(e) Cellulose and glycogen
(f) D-(−)-Ribose and D-(+)-glucose
28. When glucose is oxidized with nitric acid, glucaric acid is formed. Write the structural formula and the name of the dicarboxylic acid that is formed when galactose is oxidized with nitric acid.
29. Write the formulas for the four L-aldopentoses. Indicate which pair (or pairs) of the L-aldopentoses give identical osazones with phenylhydrazine.
30. Write the structure of a disaccharide that hydrolyzes to give only D-glucose and (a) is a reducing sugar, shows mutarotation, and forms an osazone; (b) is a nonreducing sugar, does not mutarotate, and does not form an osazone.
31. What are the structural differences between starch and cellulose?
32. What are the two main components of starch? How are they alike and how do they differ?
33. Write the structure for cellobiose, a disaccharide obtained by the hydrolysis of cellulose.
34. Draw the Haworth formulas for
(a) β-D-glucopyranosyl-(1-4)-α-D-galactopyranose
(b) β-D-galactopyranosyl-(1-6)-β-D-mannopyranose
35. A molar mass value of about 325,000 was calculated for a sample of amylopectin. Approximately how many glucose units are present in an average molecule of this amylopectin? (*Hint:* As each glucose is added to a growing amylopectin chain, a molecule of water is removed.)
36. Draw enough of the structural formula of cellulose acetate to show the repeating units and how they are linked.
37. Write three units of the polymeric structure of amylose.
38. How is the acidic nature of the mucopolysaccharides related to their biological function?
39. What changes must take place to convert cornstarch into the sweetener high fructose corn syrup?
40. Glucose units in cellulose are connected by β-1,4-glycosidic linkages. How is the β stereochemistry important in allowing the cellulose polymers to bond together to form cellulose fibers?
41. We sometimes hear the comment, “It is important that you chew your food carefully.” How

does this statement apply to the digestion of starchy foods?

42. Which of these statements are correct? Rewrite each incorrect statement to make it correct.

(a) α-D-Glucopyranose and β-D-glucopyranose are enantiomers.

(b) The carbon of a secondary alcohol is more reduced than the carbon of a primary alcohol.

(c) D-Glyceraldehyde and L-glyceraldehyde are epimers.

(d) D-Threose and L-threose are epimers.

(e) There are eight stereoisomers of the aldopentoses.

(f) D-Glucose and L-glucose form identical osazones.

(g) Raffinose, which consists of one unit each of galactose, glucose, and fructose, is an oligosaccharide.

(h) Two aldohexoses that react with phenylhydrazine to yield identical osazones are epimers.

(i) Dextrose is another name for glucose.

(j) D-Mannitol is obtained from D-mannose by oxidation.

(k) Methyl glucosides are capable of reducing Fehling's and Barfoed's reagents.

(l) Humans are incapable of using cellulose directly as a food.

(m) Fructose can be classified as a hexose, a monosaccharide, and an aldose.

(n) The change in the specific rotation of a carbohydrate solution to an equilibrium value is called mutarotation.

(o) The disaccharide found in mammalian milk is galactose.

(p) The reserve carbohydrate of animals is glycogen.

(q) Starch consists of two polysaccharides known as amylose and amylopectin.

(r) Carbohydrates that are capable of reducing copper ions in Benedict's reagent are called reducing sugars.

(s) The polysaccharides cellulose, starch, and glycogen are all composed of glucose units.

(t) Invert sugar is sweeter than fructose.

(u) Sucrose, glucose, galactose, and fructose are reducing sugars.

(v) Methyl glycosides do not undergo mutarotation.

(w) Oxidation of D-erythrose with dilute HNO_3 yields *meso*-tartaric acid.

(x) The amylose polysaccharide coils into a helical shape.

(y) Aspartame is a non-nutritive sweetener.

(z) Mucopolysaccharides have many sugar units that act as bases.

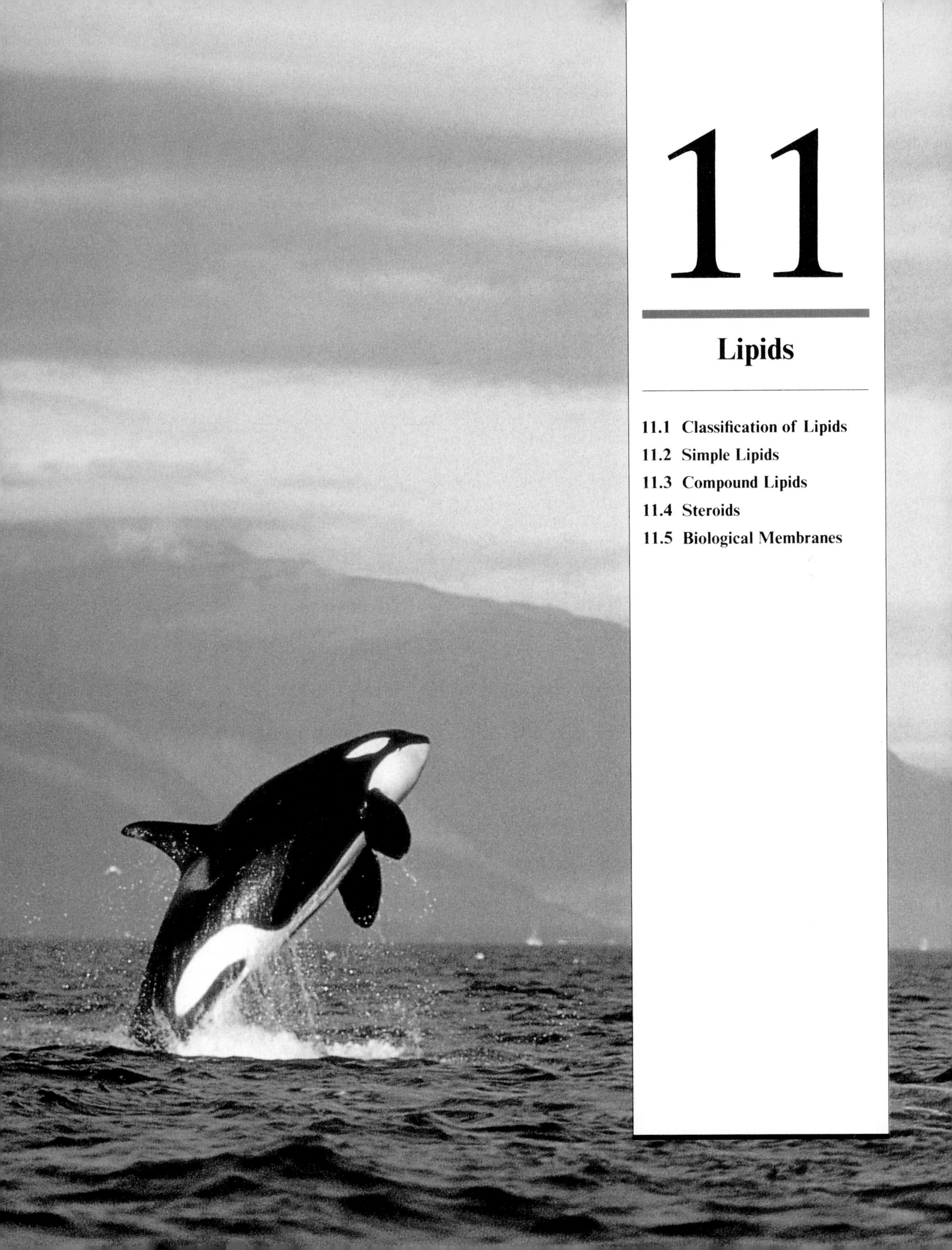

11

Lipids

◀ CHAPTER OPENING PHOTO: **The killer whale has a huge reserve of lipids.**

Lipids provide the bad, the good, and the ugly of the cleaning industry. For example, it can be bad luck to splatter a drop of oil (a lipid) on a new shirt—this spot just won't wash out with water. But, thank goodness for soap, another form of lipid. Even the ugliest stack of greasy dishes is no match for a sudsy basin of hot water and soap.

The way lipids interact with water is a key to their importance in nature. They are insoluble. An oil slick can spread for many square miles on the surface of the ocean partly because oil and water don't mix. Based on this same principle, cells surround themselves with a thin film of lipid, the cell membrane. We protect a fine wood floor with wax, another lipid, because we can depend on this material to adhere to the floor and not dissolve in water. A lipid's stickiness and lack of water solubility also can create diseases such as atherosclerosis, where arteries become partially clogged by lipids. Lipid characteristics bring both benefits and problems—these molecules are truly a mixed blessing.

11.1 CLASSIFICATION OF LIPIDS

lipids

Lipids are water insoluble, oily or greasy biochemical compounds that can be extracted from cells by nonpolar solvents such as ether, chloroform, or benzene. Unlike carbohydrates, lipids share no common chemical structure but are a catch all class. Still, these molecules must possess some structural similarities because of their shared water insolubility.

What makes a molecule, such as a lipid, insoluble in water? To answer this question, we must establish two important principles about water solutions: A compound may dissolve in water (1) if the water molecules bond well to the potential solute and (2) if the water molecules can still move relatively freely around the dissolved compound. For example, salt (sodium chloride) dissolves because it forms ions to which water molecules can bond *and* because these ions are small and do not significantly impede the movement of the water molecules. Sugar (sucrose) dissolves because it can form hydrogen bonds with water and because it is still a relatively small molecule. On the other hand, starch, a collection of glucose polymers, is too large to truly dissolve (although it can hydrogen-bond to water).

Lipid structures and solubilities differ from both salts and carbohydrates. Even though lipid molecules are not as big as a starch polymer, they are big enough to substantially affect the free movement of water molecules. In addition, lipids cannot hydrogen-bond to the extent of carbohydrates, nor do they form the large number of positive and negative charges found in a salt solution. Lipids are large and relatively nonpolar molecules and, thus, are water insoluble.

Compounds such as most carbohydrates and salts are said to be *hydrophilic* ("water loving"). In contrast, lipids are said to be *hydrophobic* ("water fearing").

Consider fatty acids, which are common components of lipids. As shown in Table 11.1, when the number of atoms in a fatty acid molecule increases, the water solubility of the fatty acid decreases dramatically. Water molecules can easily maneuver around smaller compounds like butyric acid, which is infinitely soluble in water. However, these same water molecules run into a huge barrier when they encounter the 18-carbon chain of stearic acid, and so only a little of this fatty acid dissolves in water (0.0003 g/100 g of water).

The hydrophobic nature of lipids contributes significantly to the biological functions of these molecules. Their water insolubility allows lipids to serve as barriers to aqueous solutions. This property, as we shall see later, is of great importance when lipids form cellular membranes. Lipids are classified as follows:

1. **Simple lipids**
   (**a**) *Fats and oils:* esters of fatty acids and glycerol
   (**b**) *Waxes:* esters of high-molar-mass fatty acids and high molar mass alcohols
2. **Compound lipids**
   (**a**) *Phospholipids:* substances that yield glycerol, phosphoric acid, fatty acids, and nitrogen-containing bases upon hydrolysis
   (**b**) *Sphingolipids:* substances that yield an unsaturated amino alcohol (sphingosine), a long-chain fatty acid, and either a carbohydrate or phosphate and a nitrogen base upon hydrolysis
   (**c**) *Glycolipids:* substances that yield sphingosine, fatty acids, a nitrogen-containing base, and a carbohydrate upon hydrolysis
3. **Steroids**
   Substances possessing the steroid nucleus, which is a 17-carbon structure consisting of four fused carbocyclic rings. Cholesterol and several hormones are in this class.
4. **Miscellaneous lipids**
   Substances that do not fit into the preceding classifications; these include the fat-soluble vitamins A, D, E, and K.

The most abundant lipids are the fats and oils. These substances constitute one of the three important classes of foods. The discussion that follows is centered on fats and oils. A more complete consideration of the properties and composition of various fats and oils is given in Section 6.10.

11.2 Simple Lipids

Fatty Acids

Fatty acids, which form a part of most lipids, are carboxylic acids with long, hydrophobic side chains. The formulas for some of the most common fatty acids are shown in Table 11.1. All these acids are straight chain compounds with an even number of carbon atoms. Five of the fatty acids in this table—palmitoleic,

TABLE 11.1 Some Naturally Occurring Fatty Acids

Fatty acid	Number of C atoms	Formula	Solubility (g/100 g water)	Melting point (°C)
Saturated acids				
Butyric acid	4	$CH_3CH_2CH_2COOH$	∞	−4.7
Caproic acid	6	$CH_3(CH_2)_4COOH$	1.08	−1.5
Caprylic acid	8	$CH_3(CH_2)_6COOH$	0.07	16
Capric acid	10	$CH_3(CH_2)_8COOH$	0.015	32
Lauric acid	12	$CH_3(CH_2)_{10}COOH$	0.006	48
Myristic acid	14	$CH_3(CH_2)_{12}COOH$	0.002	57
Palmitic acid	16	$CH_3(CH_2)_{14}COOH$	0.0007	63
Stearic acid	18	$CH_3(CH_2)_{16}COOH$	0.0003	70
Arachidic acid	20	$CH_3(CH_2)_{18}COOH$	—	77
Unsaturated acids				
Palmitoleic acid	16	$CH_3(CH_2)_5CH{=}CH(CH_2)_7COOH$	—	0.5
Oleic acid	18	$CH_3(CH_2)_7CH{=}CH(CH_2)_7COOH$	—	13
Linoleic acid	18	$CH_3(CH_2)_4CH{=}CHCH_2CH{=}CH(CH_2)_7COOH$	—	−5
Linolenic acid	18	$CH_3CH_2CH{=}CHCH_2CH{=}CHCH_2CH{=}CH(CH_2)_7COOH$	—	−11
Arachidonic acid	20	$CH_3(CH_2)_4(CH{=}CHCH_2)_4CH_2CH_2COOH$	—	−50

oleic, linoleic, linolenic, and arachidonic—are unsaturated, having carbon–carbon double bonds in their structures. Animal and higher plant cells produce lipids in which palmitic, oleic, linoleic, and stearic acids predominate. Over one-half of plant and animal fatty acids are unsaturated, plant lipids tending to be more unsaturated than their animal counterparts.

Double bonds impart some special characteristics to the unsaturated fatty acids. Remember that the presence of double bonds raises the possibility of geometric isomerism (Section 3.3). Unsaturated fatty acids may be either cis or trans isomers. To illustrate the effect of these double bonds on fatty acid structure, the following two fatty acids are portrayed in a simplified manner with each of the many $—CH_2—$groups as an apex at the intersection between two single bonds.

Cis isomer

Trans isomer

Note that the trans isomer is almost a linear molecule while the double bond in the cis isomer introduces a kink in the fatty acid structure. Unsaturated fatty acids found in nature are almost always cis isomers. These kinked fatty acids cannot stack closely together and, hence, they do not solidify easily. As shown in Table 11.1, unsaturated fatty acids have lower melting points than saturated fatty acids of a similar size. Cooking oils purchased from your market are liquids at room temperature because a high percentage of their fatty acids are unsaturated. In like manner, biological membranes are very fluid because of the presence of double bonds in their component fatty acids (see Section 11.5).

Three unsaturated fatty acids—linoleic, linolenic, and arachidonic—are essential for animal nutrition and must be present in the diet. Diets lacking these fatty acids lead to impaired growth and reproduction, and skin disorders such as eczema and dermatitis. A dermatitis disorder can be attributed to an unsaturated fatty acid deficiency if the symptoms clear up when that fatty acid is supplied in the diet.

Selected fatty acids, as well as other lipids, are biochemical precursors of several classes of hormones. The well-known steroid hormones are synthesized from cholesterol and will be discussed later in this chapter. Arachidonic acid and, to a lesser extent, linolenic acid are also used by the body to make hormonelike substances. The biochemicals derived from arachidonic acid are collectively termed eicosanoids using a derivative of the Greek word for twenty, *eikosi*, to indicate that these compounds have 20 carbon atoms. Prostaglandins are perhaps the best known of the eicosanoid class, which also includes the leukotrienes, prostacyclins, and thromboxanes. Cell membranes release arachidonic acid in response to a variety of circumstances, including infection and allergic reactions. In turn, enzymes in the surrounding fluid convert this fatty acid to specific eicosanoids by catalyzing the addition of oxygen to the arachidonic double bonds. Some examples of eicosanoids are shown in Figure 11.1.

Unlike true hormones, eicosanoids are not transported via the bloodstream to their site of action but rather take effect where they are synthesized. Prostaglandins are a primary cause of the swelling, redness, and pain associated with tissue inflammation. Platelets in the bloodstream form the thromboxanes, which act as vasoconstrictors and stimulate platelet aggregation, as an initial step in blood clotting. Leukotrienes are formed by a variety of white blood cells as well as other tissues and cause many of the symptoms associated with an allergy attack. For example, asthma is thought to be mediated by the leukotrienes.

Some relatively common medications affect the formation of the eicosanoids. Aspirin, by blocking the reaction between arachidonic acid and oxygen, stops inflammation caused by the prostaglandins. Recent research indicates that low levels of aspirin may prevent heart attacks and strokes, possibly by blocking synthesis of the thromboxanes that participate in blood clotting. Cortisone acts as an anti-inflammatory drug by decreasing release of arachidonic acid from the cell membranes. It also seems that diet may have a significant effect on eicosanoid formation. Fish oils contain fatty acids that inhibit formation of the thromboxanes and lead to formation of the less potent leukotrienes. It has been suggested that cultures for which fish is a dietary staple (such as the Greenland Eskimos) have a low level of heart disease, possibly because of a decrease in thromboxane formation.

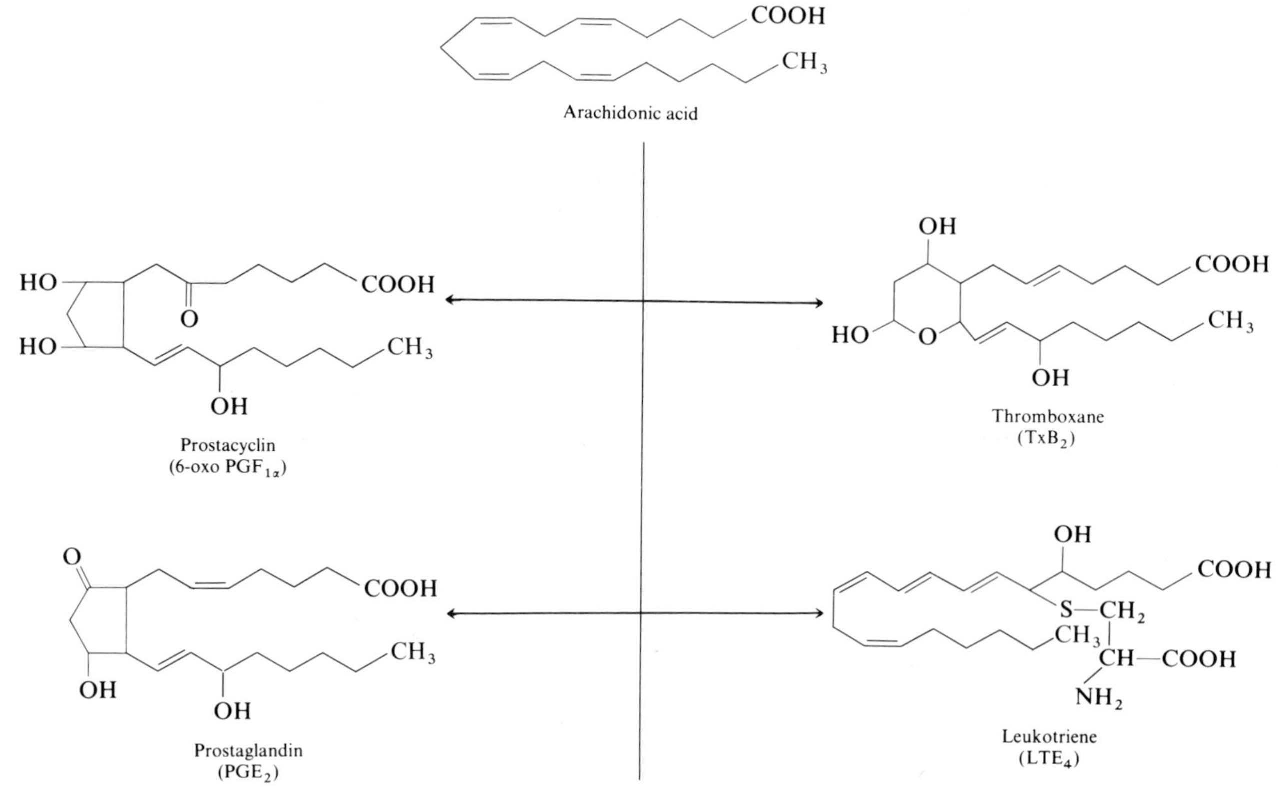

Arachidonic acid

Prostacyclin (6-oxo $PGF_{1\alpha}$)

Thromboxane (TxB_2)

Prostaglandin (PGE_2)

Leukotriene (LTE_4)

▲
FIGURE 11.1
Several examples of eicosanoids. Each of these molecules is derived from arachidonic acid.

Fats and Oils

Chemically, fats and oils are esters of glycerol and the higher molar mass fatty acids. They have the general formula

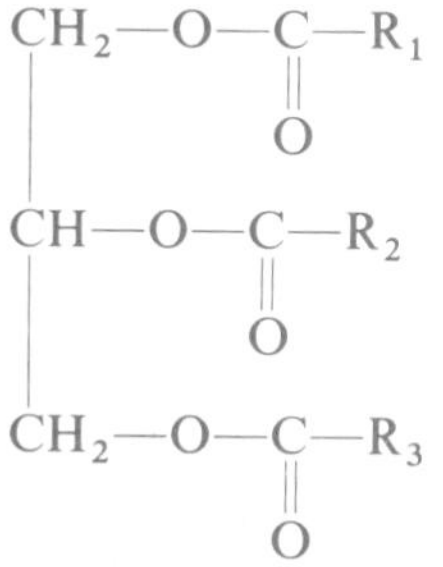

$$\begin{array}{l} CH_2-O-\overset{\displaystyle O}{\underset{}{\overset{\|}{C}}}-R_1 \\ CH-O-\overset{\|}{C}(=O)-R_2 \\ CH_2-O-\overset{\|}{C}(=O)-R_3 \end{array}$$

where the R's can be either long-chain saturated or unsaturated hydrocarbon groups. Figure 11.2 shows a three-dimensional representation of a typical fat.

Fats may be considered to be triesters formed from the trihydroxy alcohol glycerol and three molecules of fatty acids. Most of the fatty acids in these esters have 14 to 18 carbons. Because there are three ester groups per glycerol, these molecules are called triacylglycerols, or triglycerides (an older name that is still commonly used). The three R groups are usually different.

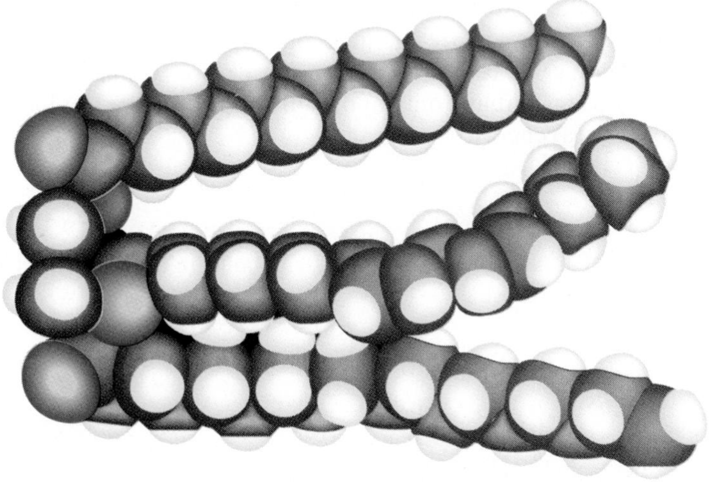

◀ FIGURE 11.2
Space-filling model of a triacylglycerol formed by reacting glycerol with one palmitic acid, one oleic acid, and one stearic acid. Note the kink introduced into oleic acid by the cis double bond.

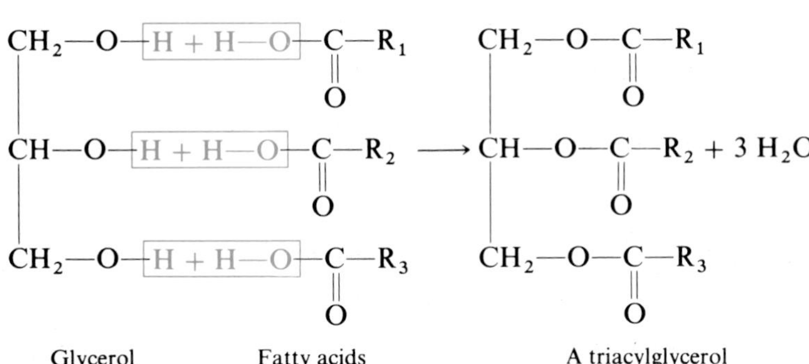

Fats and oils fit the general description of a lipid. They are large molecules, averaging more than 50 carbon atoms per molecule, with many nonpolar, uncharged groups. Because they contain large numbers of saturated carbons, the triacylglycerols are hydrophobic and water insoluble.

Fats are an important food source for humans and normally account for about 25–50% of their caloric intake. When oxidized to carbon dioxide and water, fats supply about 40 kJ of energy per gram (9.5 kcal/g), which is more than twice the amount obtained from carbohydrates or proteins.

The energy from a fat is released when the reduced carbons are oxidized. In general, the more reduced a carbon, the more energy it contains (see Section 10.1). Triacylglycerol carbons are more reduced than those of most other foods. The typical carbon from a fat has an oxidation number of -2, whereas the typical carbon from a carbohydrate has an oxidation number of 0:

OH — 0 (Oxidation number)
C—C—C (central C bearing OH and H)

In a carbohydrate

H — -2 (Oxidation number)
C—C—C (central C bearing H and H)

In a fat

This difference in oxidation numbers makes it clear that almost every carbon in a fat contains and can release more energy than a typical carbohydrate carbon. In addition, the average fat contains about 75% carbon by mass, whereas the average carbohydrate contains only about 40% carbon. Fats are indeed a rich source of biochemical energy.

Waxes

waxes

Waxes are esters of high molar mass fatty acids and high molar mass alcohols. They have the general formula

$$R'-\overset{\overset{\displaystyle O}{\|}}{C}-O-R$$

in which the alcohol (ROH) contributes up to about 30 carbons, and the fatty acid (R′COOH) provides an equivalent number of carbons. Waxes are very large molecules with almost no polar groups. They represent one of the most hydrophobic lipid classes.

Their extreme water insolubility allows waxes to serve a protective function. Leaves, feathers, fruit, and fur are often naturally coated with a wax. Hardwood floors, cars, and leather goods are just a few of the man-made products that can be protected by a wax. Waxes tend to be the hardest of the lipids because their carbon chains are long and have very few double bonds. As with fats and oils, the size of the wax molecule and the number of double bonds contained in its carbon chains determine how solid or liquid the wax will be.

11.3 Compound Lipids

Phospholipids

phospholipids

The **phospholipids** are a group of compounds that yield one or more fatty acid molecules, a phosphate group, and usually a nitrogenous base upon hydrolysis. The phosphate group and the nitrogenous base, which are found at one end of the phospholipid molecule, often have negative and positive charges. Consequently, in contrast to the triacylglycerols, phospholipids have hydrophobic ends that repel water and hydrophilic ends that interact with water.

$$\left.\begin{array}{l} CH_2-O-\boxed{\text{Fatty acid}} \\ \ \ | \\ CH-O-\boxed{\text{Fatty acid}} \\ \ \ | \\ CH_2-O-\boxed{\text{Fatty acid}} \end{array}\right\}\ \text{All hydrophobic}$$

A triacylglycerol

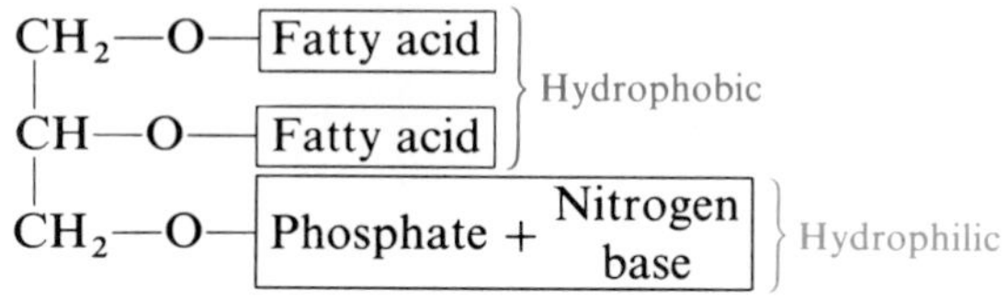

$$\begin{array}{l} CH_2{-}O{-}\boxed{\text{Fatty acid}} \\ | \\ CH{-}O{-}\boxed{\text{Fatty acid}} \\ | \\ CH_2{-}O{-}\boxed{\text{Phosphate + Nitrogen base}} \end{array} \begin{array}{l} \left.\right\} \text{Hydrophobic} \\ \\ \left.\right\} \text{Hydrophilic} \end{array}$$

A phospholipid

As will be seen later in this chapter, a lipid with both hydrophobic and hydrophilic character is needed to make membranes. It is not surprising that phospholipids are one of the most important membrane components.

Phospholipids are also involved in the metabolism of other lipids and nonlipids. Although they are produced to some extent by almost all cells, most of the phospholipids that enter the bloodstream are formed in the liver. Representative phospholipids are described below.

Phosphatidic Acids Phosphatidic acids are glyceryl esters of fatty acids and phosphoric acid. The phosphatidic acids are important intermediates in the synthesis of triacylglycerols and other phospholipids.

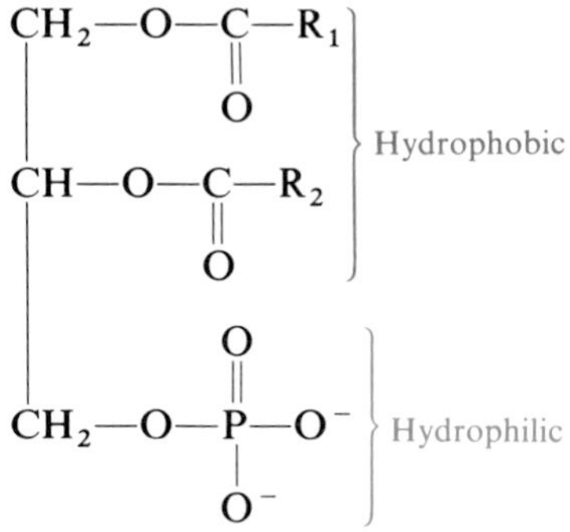

$$\begin{array}{l} CH_2{-}O{-}C(=O){-}R_1 \\ | \\ CH{-}O{-}C(=O){-}R_2 \\ | \\ CH_2{-}O{-}P(=O)(O^-){-}O^- \end{array} \begin{array}{l} \left.\right\} \text{Hydrophobic} \\ \\ \left.\right\} \text{Hydrophilic} \end{array}$$

A phosphatidic acid

A three-dimensional representation of a typical phosphatidic acid is given in Figure 11.3. As with all common phospholipids, the fatty acid chains are large relative to the rest of this molecule. Other phospholipids are formed from a given phosphatidic acid when specific nitrogen-containing compounds are linked to the phosphate group by an ester bond. Three commonly used nitrogen compounds are choline, ethanolamine, and L-serine:

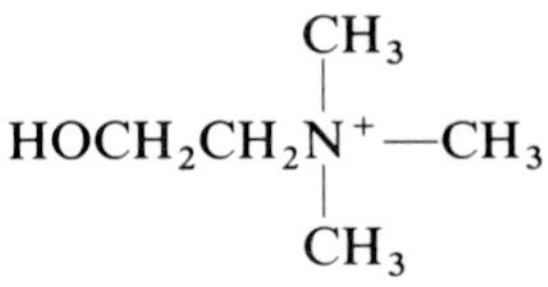

$$HOCH_2CH_2N^+(CH_3)_2{-}CH_3 \qquad HOCH_2CH_2NH_3^+ \qquad HOCH_2CH(COO^-)(NH_3^+)$$

Choline 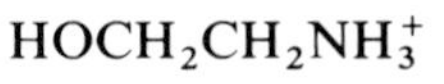 Ethanolamine 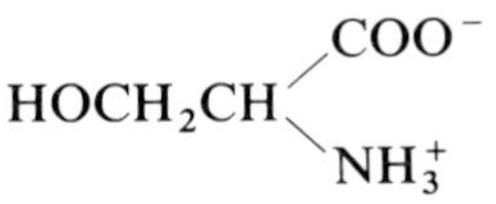 L-Serine

Because other phospholipids are structurally related to phosphatidic acids, their names are also closely related.

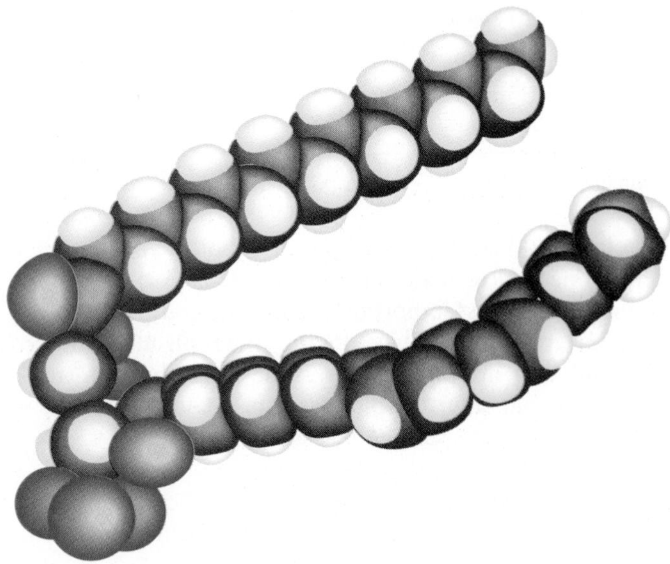

FIGURE 11.3 ► **Space-filling model of a phosphatidic acid which is esterified to palmitic acid at the top glycerol carbon and to oleic acid at the middle carbon. Note the kink introduced into the linoleic acid by the two cis double bonds.**

▲ **Chocolate is emulsified with phosphatidyl choline.**

Phosphatidyl Cholines (Lecithins) Phosphatidyl cholines (lecithins) are glyceryl esters of fatty acids, phosphoric acid, and choline. The synonym *lecithin* is an older term that is still used, particularly in commercial products that contain phosphatidyl choline. Phosphatidyl cholines are synthesized in the liver and are present in considerable amounts in nerve tissue and brain substance. Most commercial phosphatidyl choline is obtained from soybean oil and contains palmitic, stearic, palmitoleic, oleic, linoleic, linolenic, and arachidonic acids. Phosphatidyl choline is an edible and digestible emulsifying agent that is used extensively in the food industry. For example, chocolate and margarine are generally emulsified with phosphatidyl choline. Phosphatidyl choline is also used as an emulsifier in many pharmaceutical preparations.

The single most important biological function for phosphatidyl choline is as a membrane component. This phospholipid makes up between 10 and 20 percent of many membranes.

$$
\begin{array}{l}
CH_2{-}O{-}\underset{\underset{O}{\|}}{C}{-}R_1 \\
| \\
CH{-}O{-}\underset{\underset{O}{\|}}{C}{-}R_2 \\
| \\
CH_2{-}O{-}\underset{\underset{O^-}{|}}{\overset{\overset{O}{\|}}{P}}{-}\overbrace{O{-}CH_2CH_2\underset{\underset{CH_3}{|}}{\overset{\overset{CH_3}{|}}{N^+}}{-}CH_3}^{\text{Choline}}
\end{array}
\quad
\begin{array}{l}
\left.\right\}\text{Hydrophobic (R}_1\text{, R}_2\text{ ester portion)} \\
\left.\right\}\text{Hydrophilic (phosphate–choline portion)}
\end{array}
$$

A phosphatidyl choline (lecithin) molecule

Phosphatidyl Ethanolamines (Cephalins) Another important constituent of biological membranes is the phosphatidyl ethanolamines (cephalins). These lipids are glyceryl esters of fatty acids, phosphoric acid, and ethanolamine ($HOCH_2CH_2NH_2$). They are found in essentially all living organisms.

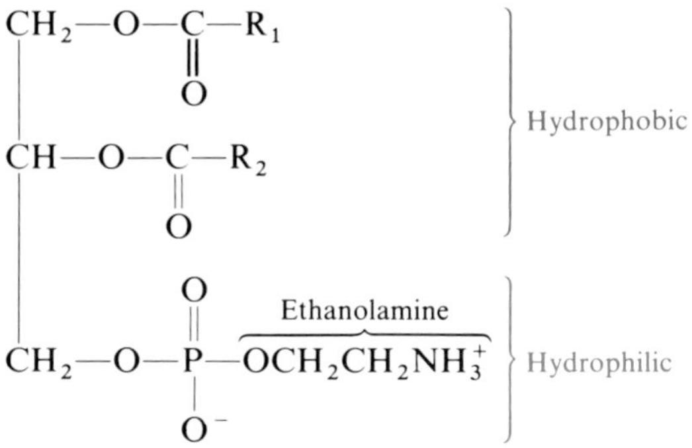

$$
\left.\begin{array}{l}
CH_2-O-\overset{\displaystyle O}{\overset{\|}{C}}-R_1 \\
CH-O-\overset{\displaystyle O}{\overset{\|}{C}}-R_2
\end{array}\right\} \text{Hydrophobic}
$$

$$
\left. CH_2-O-\underset{\displaystyle O^-}{\underset{|}{\overset{\displaystyle O}{\overset{\|}{P}}}}-\overbrace{OCH_2CH_2NH_3^+}^{\text{Ethanolamine}} \right\} \text{Hydrophilic}
$$

A phosphatidyl ethanolamine (cephalin) molecule

Sphingolipids

sphingolipids

Sphingolipids are compounds that, when hydrolyzed, yield a long chain fatty acid (18 to 26 carbons), a hydrophilic group (either phosphate and choline or a carbohydrate), and sphingosine (an unsaturated amino alcohol). Sphingosine substitutes for glycerol in these lipids. When drawn as follows, sphingosine can be seen as similar to glycerol esterified to one fatty acid:

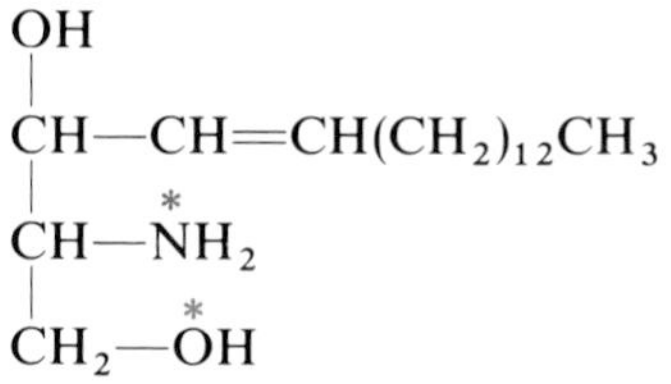

$$
\begin{array}{l}
\underset{|}{OH} \\
CH-CH{=}CH(CH_2)_{12}CH_3 \\
| \quad * \\
CH-NH_2 \\
| \quad * \\
CH_2-OH
\end{array}
\qquad\qquad
\begin{array}{l}
CH_2-O-\overset{\displaystyle O}{\overset{\|}{C}}(CH_2)_nCH_3 \\
| \quad * \\
CH-OH \\
| \quad * \\
CH_2-OH
\end{array}
$$

Sphingosine 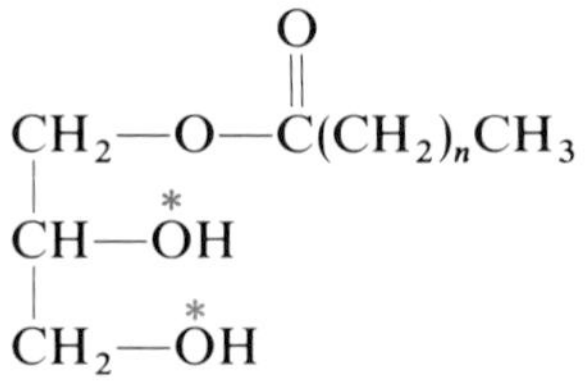 — Glycerol esterified with one fatty acid

The starred atoms on sphingosine react further to make sphingolipids, just as the starred atoms on the glycerol compound react further to give triacylglycerols or phospholipids.

Sphingolipids are common membrane components because they have both hydrophobic and hydrophilic character. For example, sphingomyelins are found in the myelin sheath membranes that surround nerves:

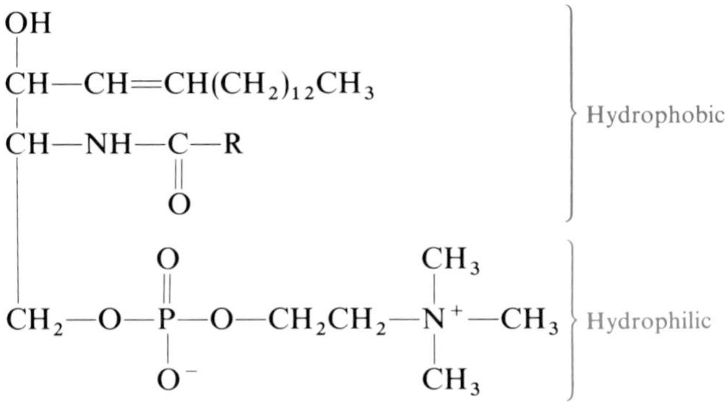

$$
\left.\begin{array}{l}
\underset{|}{OH} \\
CH-CH{=}CH(CH_2)_{12}CH_3 \\
| \\
CH-NH-\overset{\displaystyle O}{\overset{\|}{C}}-R
\end{array}\right\} \text{Hydrophobic}
$$

$$
\left. CH_2-O-\underset{\displaystyle O^-}{\underset{|}{\overset{\displaystyle O}{\overset{\|}{P}}}}-O-CH_2CH_2-\underset{\displaystyle CH_3}{\underset{|}{\overset{\displaystyle CH_3}{\overset{|}{N^+}}}}-CH_3 \right\} \text{Hydrophilic}
$$

A sphingomyelin

Notice the hydrophobic and hydrophilic parts of this molecule. Sphingomyelins can also be classified as phospholipids.

Glycolipids

glycolipids

Sphingolipids that contain carbohydrate groups are also known as **glycolipids**. The two most important classes of glycolipids are cerebrosides and gangliosides. These substances are found mainly in cell membranes of nerve and brain tissue. A cerebroside may contain either D-galactose or D-glucose. The following formula of a galactocerebroside shows the typical structure of cerebrosides:

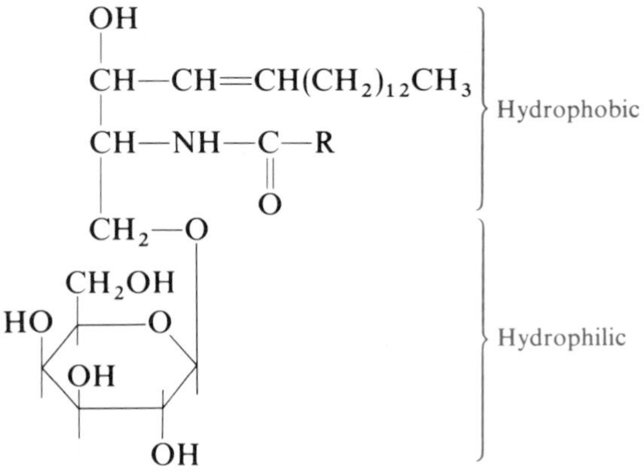

```
        OH
        |
        CH—CH=CH(CH2)12CH3      }
        |                       } Hydrophobic
        CH—NH—C—R               }
        |     ||
        |     O
        CH2—O
     CH2OH   |                  }
  HO  |——O   |                  }
     / OH  \ |                  } Hydrophilic
     \_____/                    }
        |
        OH
```

A β-galactocerebroside

Gangliosides are similar to cerebrosides in structure but contain complex oligosaccharides instead of simple monosaccharides.

EXAMPLE 11.1

Write the formula for a phosphatidyl ethanolamine that contains two palmitic acid groups.

SOLUTION

Phosphatidyl ethanolamine is a phospholipid and so contains glycerol, phosphate, fatty acids, and a nitrogen base. First, write the structure for glycerol.

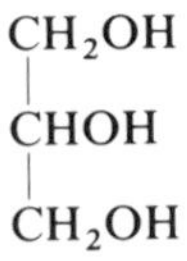

```
CH2OH
|
CHOH
|
CH2OH
```

The two palmitic acids are linked by ester bonds to the top two carbons of glycerol.

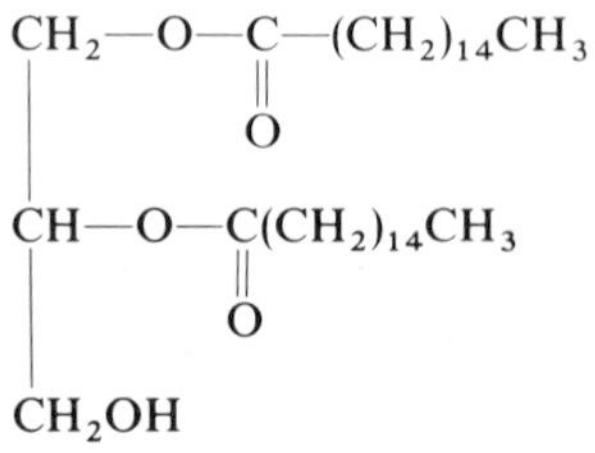

```
CH2—O—C—(CH2)14CH3
|     ||
|     O
|
CH—O—C(CH2)14CH3
|    ||
|    O
|
CH2OH
```

The phosphate group is connected via an ester bond to the bottom glycerol carbon to form a phosphatidic acid.

```
CH2—O—C—(CH2)14CH3
|     ||
|     O
|
CH—O—C(CH2)14CH3
|    ||
|    O
|
|     O
|     ||
CH2—O—P—O⁻
      |
      O⁻
```

Finally, the ethanolamine is linked to the phosphate group to yield phosphatidyl choline.

```
CH2—O—C—(CH2)14CH3
|     ||
|     O
|
CH—O—C(CH2)14CH3
|    ||
|    O
|
|     O
|     ||
CH2—O—P—OCH2CH2NH3⁺
      |
      O⁻
```

PRACTICE Give the structure of a sphingomyelin that contains stearic acid.

Answer:

```
OH
|
CH—CH=CH(CH2)12CH3
|
CH—NH—C(CH2)16CH3
|     ||
|     O
|
|     O            CH3
|     ||           |
CH2—O—P—OCH2CH2—N⁺—CH3
      |            |
      O⁻           CH3
```

11.4 STEROIDS

steroids

Steroids are compounds that have the steroid nucleus, which consists of four fused carbocyclic rings. This nucleus contains 17 carbon atoms in one five-membered and three six-membered rings. Modifications of this nucleus in the

▲ **Muscle mass can be increased through the use of steriods.**

various steroid compounds include added side chains, hydroxyl groups, carbonyl groups, ring double bonds, and so on.

Steroid ring nucleus

Steroids are closely related in structure but are highly diverse in function. Examples of steroids and steroid containing materials are (1) cholesterol, the most abundant steroid in the body, which is widely distributed in all cells and serves as a major membrane component; (2) bile salts, which aid in the digestion of fats; (3) ergosterol, a yeast steroid, which is converted to vitamin D by ultraviolet radiation; (4) digitalis and related substances called cardiac glycosides, which are potent heart drugs; (5) the adrenal cortex hormones, which are involved in metabolism; and (6) the sex hormones, which control sexual characteristics and reproduction. The formulas for several steroids are given in Figure 11.4.

Cholesterol is the parent compound from which the steroid hormones are synthesized. As we will see, only small changes in steroid structure can lead to large changes in hormonal action. Cholesterol is first converted to progesterone, a compound which helps control the menstrual cycle and pregnancy. This hormone is, in turn, the parent compound from which testosterone and the adrenal corticosteroids are produced. Notice that the long side chain on carbon 17 in cholesterol (Figure 11.4) is smaller in progesterone and is eliminated when testosterone is formed. Interestingly, testosterone is the precursor for the female sex hormones such as estradiol. These sex hormones are produced by the gonads, either the male testes or the female ovaries. The small structural differences between testosterone and estradiol trigger vastly different physiological responses. If the embryonic male gonads are surgically removed and testosterone is no longer available, the embryo develops as a female. In contrast, the female hormones seem to be important in sexual maturation and function but not in embryonic development. It appears that embryonic mammals are programmed to develop as females unless this program is overridden by the action of testosterone.

Cholesterol is also used to build cell membranes, many of which contain about 25% by mass of this steroid. In fact, often there is as much cholesterol as there is phospholipid, sphingolipid, or glycolipid. These latter three lipid classes cause the membrane to be more oily; cholesterol solidifies the membrane. This different behavior arises from an important structural difference. Cholesterol's four fused rings make it a rigid molecule while other membrane lipids are more flexible because of their fatty acid chains. When biological membranes are synthesized, their cholesterol level is adjusted to achieve an appropriate balance between a solid and liquid consistency.

Cholesterol is a steroid of special interest not only because it is the precursor of many other steroids and an important membrane component, but because of its association with atherosclerosis. This metabolic disease leads to the deposition

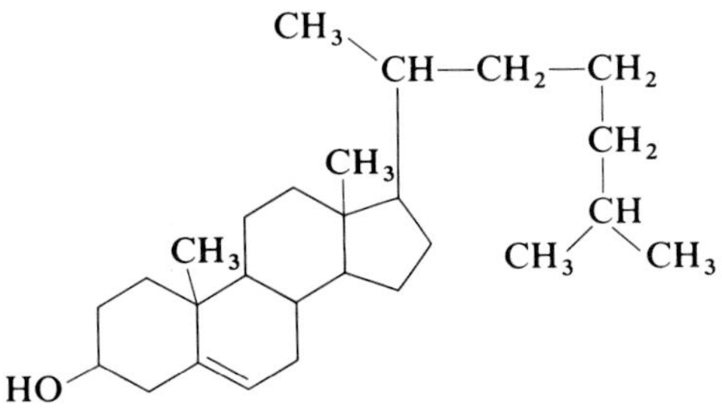

Cholesterol
(parent steroid compound—precursor for steroid hormones and bile acids)

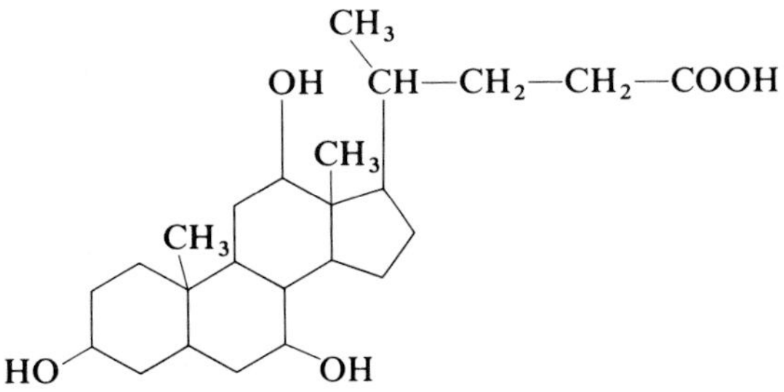

Cholic acid
(a bile acid)

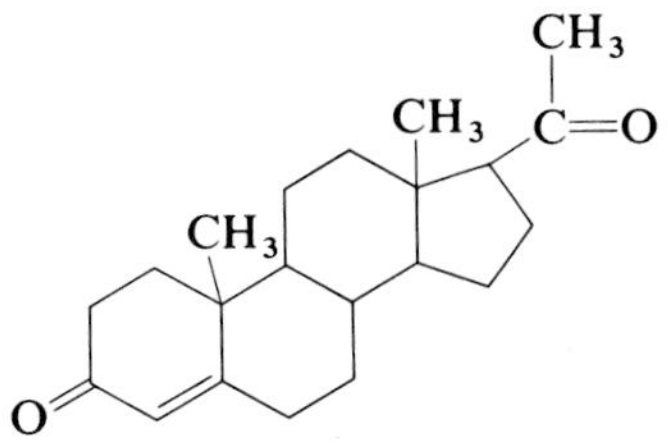

Progesterone
(progestational hormone)

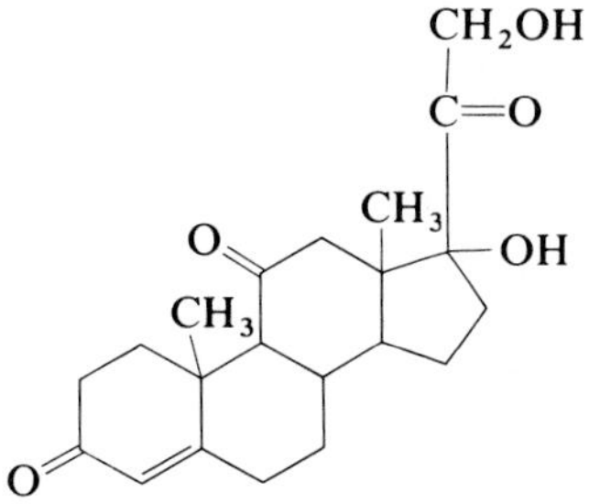

Cortisone
(adrenal corticosteroid hormone)

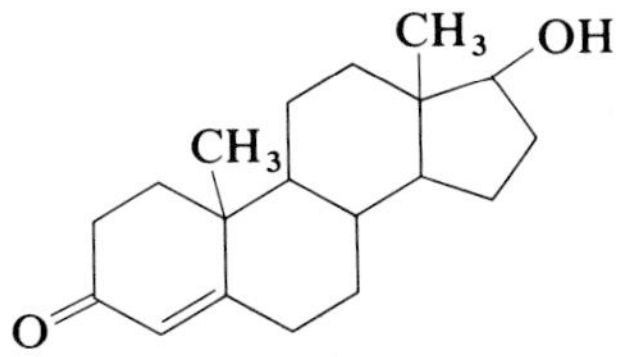

Testosterone
(male sex hormone)

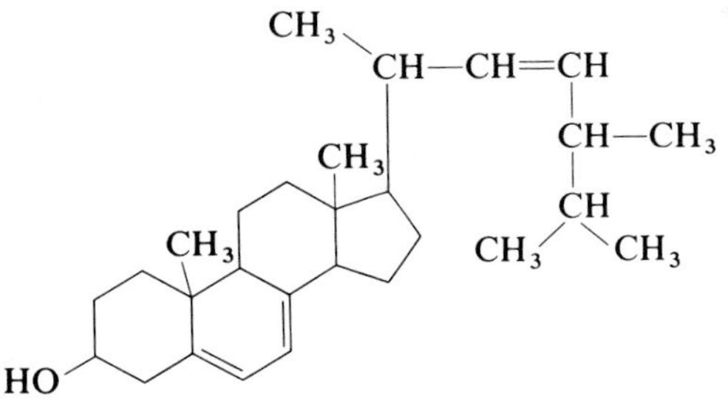

Ergosterol
(precursor of vitamin D_2)

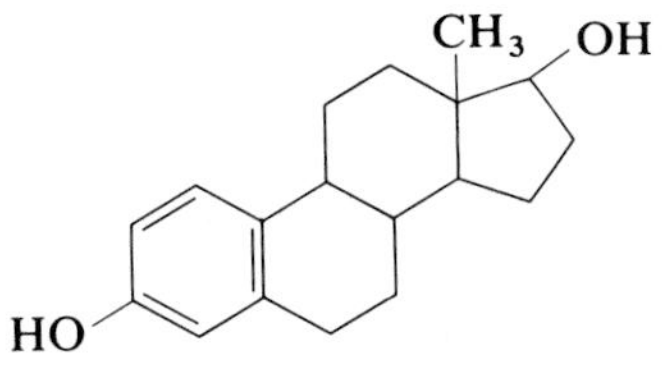

Estradiol
(female sex hormone)

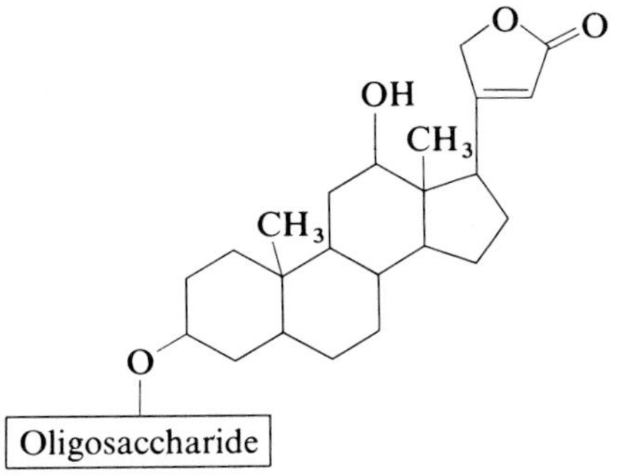

Oligosaccharide

Digoxin
(a cardiac glycoside)

▲
FIGURE 11.4
Structures of selected steroids. Arrows show the biosynthetic relationship between steroids derived from cholesterol.

of cholesterol and other lipids on the inner walls of the large arteries. Since cholesterol is relatively water insoluble, high serum cholesterol levels often lead to these deposits, called *plaque*. The accumulation of plaque causes the arterial passages to become progressively narrower. The walls of the arteries also lose their elasticity and their ability to expand to accommodate the volume of blood pumped by the heart. Blood pressure increases as the heart works to pump sufficient blood through the narrowed passages; this may eventually lead to a heart attack. The build-up of plaque also causes the inner walls to have a rough rather than a normal smooth surface. This condition is favorable to coronary thrombosis (heart attack due to blood clots).

Physicians are concerned about serum cholesterol levels and often advise us to watch our dietary intake. We ingest about 300 mg of cholesterol per day on the average while our bodies synthesize another 1 g. Note that only a small part of the daily supply of cholesterol comes from the diet. However, the dietary amount is critical because the quantity of cholesterol which is excreted (about 500 mg per day) is also very small. It appears that once cholesterol has been absorbed from the intestines, this steroid is only very gradually eliminated from the body. Thus, an important means for lowering serum cholesterol levels is to severely restrict major dietary sources such as red meat, liver, and eggs.

Because of the variety of both beneficial and dangerous effects of cholesterol, the body has developed a careful distribution system for this steroid (see Figure 11.5). Dietary cholesterol is transferred to the liver, which is the clearinghouse for cholesterol transport to the rest of the body. Cholesterol leaves the liver in association with other lipids and certain proteins in the form of an aggregate known as the *very low density lipoprotein* (VLDL). As the other lipids and proteins are removed from this aggregate, it is converted first to an *intermediate density lipoprotein* (IDL) and then to a *low density lipoprotein* (LDL). Cells needing cholesterol are able to absorb the low density lipoprotein. Proper

FIGURE 11.5 ► Schematic representation of the lipoprotein distribution system.

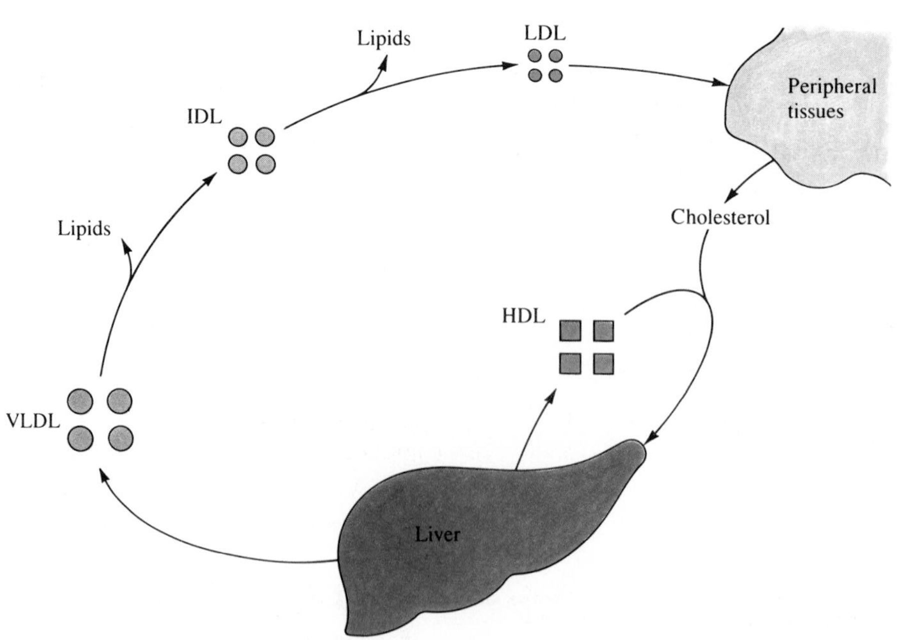

transfer of cholesterol also depends on a fourth lipoprotein, the *high density lipoprotein* (HDL). HDL acts as a cholesterol scavenger by collecting this steroid and returning it to the liver, essentially opposing the action of LDL, which delivers cholesterol to body tissues. A normal cholesterol metabolism must involve a proper balance of these lipoprotein factors.

Atherosclerosis can result from an imbalance in the cholesterol distribution system as well as an increase in serum cholesterol. High cholesterol diets correlate with plaque formation and also lead to an increase in amounts of LDL. However, any defect in the steroid distribution system can also cause plaque formation. People with high plasma LDL concentrations are prone to atherosclerosis, even though they may be on low cholesterol diets. In contrast, large amounts of HDL seem to prevent plaque formation. HDL levels can be increased by strenous exercise, weight loss, and the female sex hormones. However, the most common drug treatments to prevent atherosclerosis still involve the reduction of serum cholesterol, either by preventing absorption of cholesterol from the intestine or by inhibiting cellular synthesis of this steroid. Treatments such as these can decrease serum cholesterol levels by about 50%.

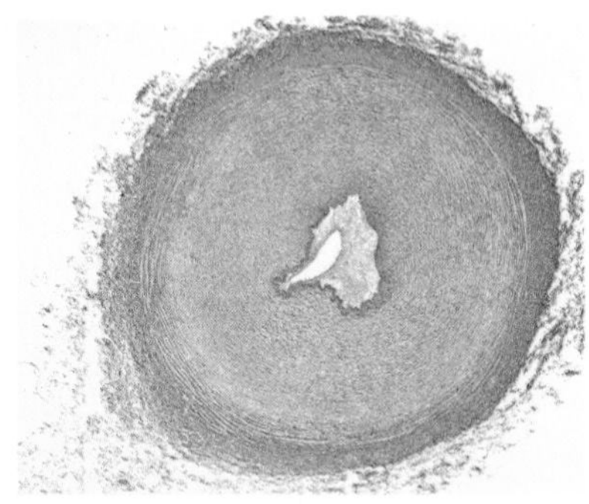

▲ **This clogged artery shows plaque formation on the artery wall.**

11.5 Biological Membranes

Biological membranes are thin, semipermeable cellular barriers. The general function of these barriers is to exclude dangerous chemicals from the cell while allowing nutrients to enter. Membranes also confine special molecules to specific sections of the cell. Because almost all the dangerous chemicals, nutrients, and special molecules are water soluble, the membranes can act as effective barriers only if they impede the movement of hydrophilic (water soluble) molecules.

To act as such a barrier, a membrane must have some special properties. To exclude water and water solutes, the bulk of a membrane must be hydrophobic. But a membrane necessarily touches water both inside and outside the cell. Therefore, the surface of a membrane must be hydrophilic. Thus a membrane can be visualized as being layered much like a piece of laminated plywood.

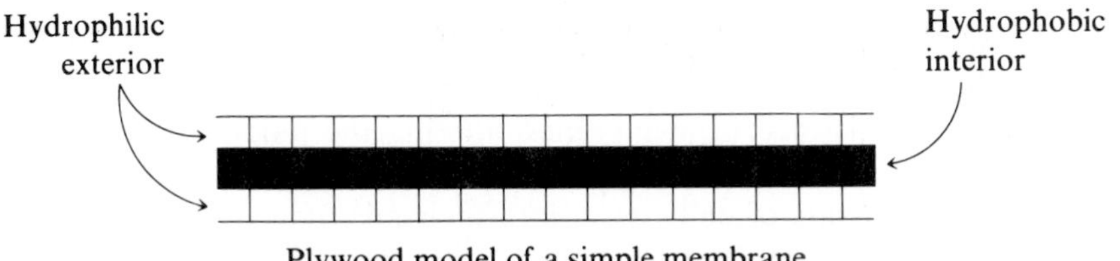

Plywood model of a simple membrane

The interior provides the barrier while the exterior interacts with the aqueous environment.

The cell uses lipids to give the membrane its hydrophobic nature. In fact, by selecting the right lipids, both the hydrophobic and hydrophilic portions of a membrane can be assembled. There are several classes of membrane lipids. The most important of these are the phospholipids and sphingolipids. Remember that these lipids have both a hydrophobic and a hydrophilic section.

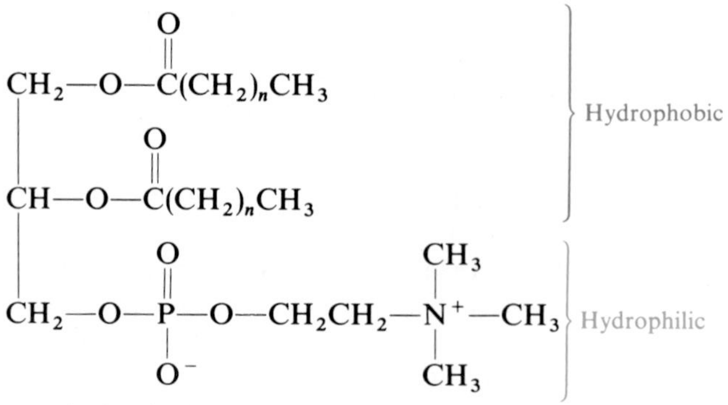

$$
\begin{array}{l}
\text{CH}_2\text{—O—}\overset{\overset{\text{O}}{\|}}{\text{C}}\text{(CH}_2)_n\text{CH}_3 \\
| \\
\text{CH—O—}\overset{\overset{\text{O}}{\|}}{\text{C}}\text{(CH}_2)_n\text{CH}_3 \\
| \\
\text{CH}_2\text{—O—}\underset{\underset{\text{O}^-}{|}}{\overset{\overset{\text{O}}{\|}}{\text{P}}}\text{—O—CH}_2\text{CH}_2\text{—}\underset{\underset{\text{CH}_3}{|}}{\overset{\overset{\text{CH}_3}{|}}{\text{N}^+}}\text{—CH}_3
\end{array}
\quad
\begin{array}{l}
\left.\right\}\ \text{Hydrophobic} \\
\left.\right\}\ \text{Hydrophilic}
\end{array}
$$

A phosphatidyl choline (lecithin) molecule

A membrane lipid can be pictured as having two long, hydrophobic tails (the fatty acids in the example given) and a small, hydrophilic end (the phosphate and choline in the example). Often a membrane lipid is drawn schematically as follows:

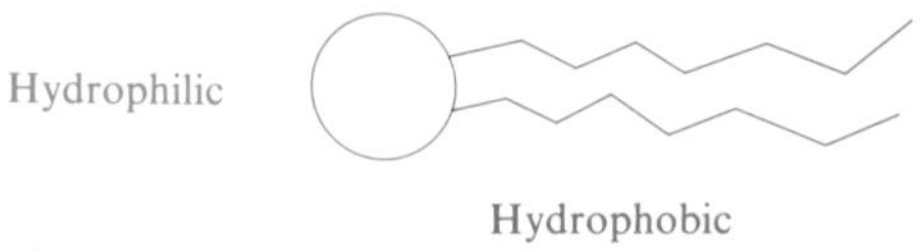

Hydrophilic

Hydrophobic

lipid bilayer

By stacking these lipids together, a basic membrane is formed. This structure is known as a **lipid bilayer**. It has the necessary properties of a membrane—a hydrophobic barrier and a hydrophilic surface.

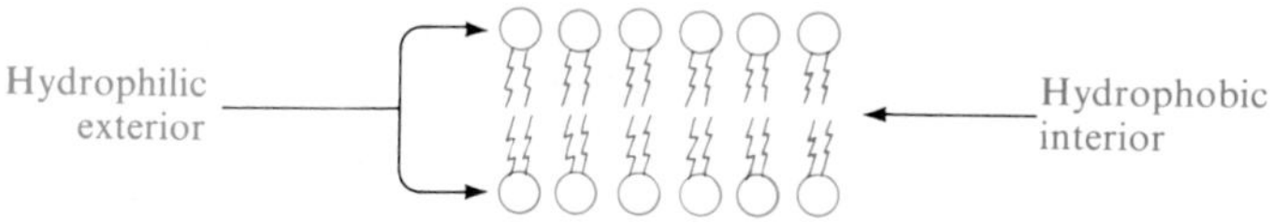

Hydrophilic exterior

Hydrophobic interior

Lipids give this barrier an oily or fluid appearance. The more unsaturated fatty acids in the membrane, the more fluid it will be. Other lipids, most importantly cholesterol, cause the membrane to be less fluid.

Membrane fluidity can have significant effects on cell function. It is thought that general anesthetics (for example, ether, halothane) are effective partly because they dissolve in membranes, altering the fluidity of the lipid bilayer. During severe cirrhosis of the liver, red cells are forced to take abnormally large amounts of cholesterol into their membranes, causing these membranes to be less fluid. The red cells become more rigid, have greater difficulty passing through narrow capillaries, and are destroyed more easily.

liposomes

Artificial lipid bilayers have important medical applications. When membrane lipids like phospholipids are specially mixed with aqueous solutions, small spheres of lipid bilayers form. These **liposomes** enclose an aqueous core into which solutes can be placed. Because of the barrier properties of the bilayer, the

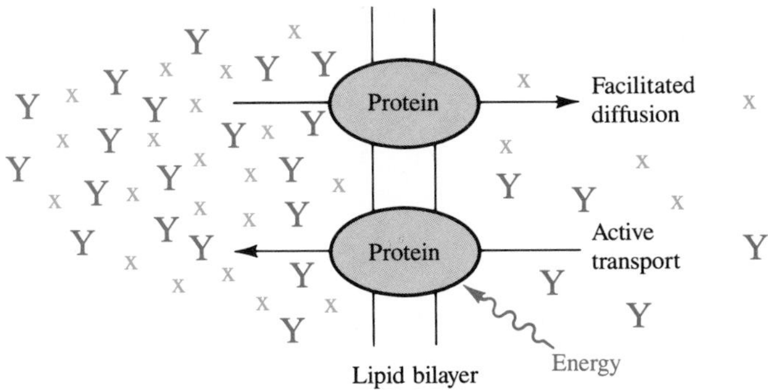

◄ **FIGURE 11.6**
How membrane transport is aided by proteins: Molecules or ions (symbolized by Y and x) can move from high concentration to low concentration without energy (facilitated diffusion), but movement in the reverse direction requires energy (active transport).

interior solute is completely separated from the external solution. Such liposome packages are being developed for drug delivery; even though the patient is injected with the drug, the drug is not exposed until the liposome reaches its particular target cell or organ. (The liposome bilayer is designed to be recognized, bound and absorbed *only* by the target cells.) Ideally, the drug does not affect other parts of the body.

The lipid bilayer acts as a barrier to water and hydrophilic molecules because of its hydrophobic interior. Because a cell is surrounded by a lipid bilayer, most charged or polar molecules have difficulty entering the cell. But the cell must have nutrients, so it is faced with a dilemma. How can it selectively allow some hydrophilic molecules to cross the lipid bilayer while excluding others?

Proteins in the fluid bilayer solve this dilemma. These proteins allow specific molecular transport through the hydrophobic interior. (For a general discussion of proteins, see Chapter 12.) They recognize specific molecules on the exterior of a cell membrane and shuttle these molecules into the cell. This process may be as simple as providing a tunnel through the membrane for selected nutrients. If the protein helps (facilitates) transport without using energy, the process is called **facilitated diffusion**. Some transport requires energy, such as when molecules are moved from areas of low concentration to areas of high concentration (the opposite direction from that of diffusion). This energy requiring transport is termed **active transport** (see Figure 11.6).

facilitated diffusion

active transport

Other proteins are located in the lipid bilayer to allow special reactions to occur. These special reactions, which often could be harmed by water, are enclosed in the hydrophobic interior of the lipid bilayer. Much of the cellular energy production (oxidation–reduction) occurs in this environment.

Thus a complete cellular membrane must have both lipid and protein. A typical membrane includes about 60% protein, 25% phospholipid, 10% cholesterol, and 5% sphingolipid. The fluid lipid bilayer is studded with many solid proteins. The proteins form a random pattern on the outer surface of the oily lipid. This general membrane is called the **fluid-mosaic model** (see Figure 11.7). Proteins that are primarily inside the lipid bilayer are termed *intrinsic membrane proteins*, and those on the surface are named *extrinsic membrane proteins*.

fluid-mosaic model

Chemistry in Action

The Myelin Sheath and Nerve Transmission

Human nerve tissue is a good example of the importance of membranes. Nerves coordinate many of the body processes, allowing life to continue. Their ability to function depends primarily on the characteristics of their membranes.

Examine the human motor neuron shown below. Notice the thickness of the axon (long cylindrical portion). The membranes of the axon are so important that two cells join together to provide them; the outer wrapping from one cell is the myelin sheath, and the thin inner neuronal membrane is from the other cell.

The neuronal membrane transmits electrical nerve impulses. To accomplish this task the neuron, using energy, slowly concentrates potassium ions inside the cell while expelling sodium ions (active transport shown in the diagram above). Throughout life, proteins within the neuronal membranes constantly pump these ions. When a neuron transmits a signal, membrane proteins allow a small portion of the potassium ions to flow rapidly out of the cell while sodium ions flow in. The sodium and potassium ions now flow from areas of high concentration to areas of low concentration without using energy. This is an example of facilitated diffusion. The rapid ion movement is an electrical nerve impulse.

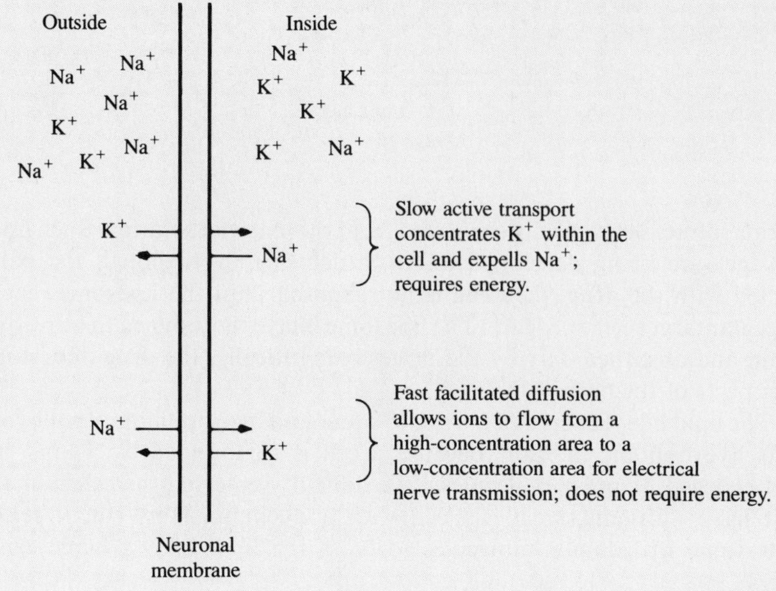
Outside
Inside
Na^+
K^+
Slow active transport concentrates K^+ within the cell and expels Na^+; requires energy.
Fast facilitated diffusion allows ions to flow from a high-concentration area to a low-concentration area for electrical nerve transmission; does not require energy.
Neuronal membrane

Scanning electron micrograph of motor nerve end plates in muscle. ▼

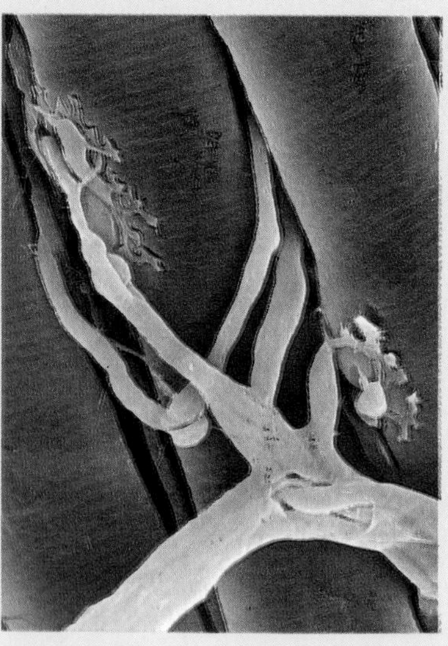

The myelin sheath serves as insulation for electrical nerve transmission (like the insulation around a copper wire). It is made up of concentric wrappings of a membrane that is high in lipid but low in protein (about 30% protein and 70% lipid). Remember that a lipid bilayer impedes movement of hydrophilic groups such as ions. The major function of the myelin sheath is to act as a barrier.

If the myelin sheath is removed, nerve transmission is faulty. Multiple sclerosis is a disease that causes destruction of the myelin sheath in portions of the central nervous system. The cause of this crippling disease is not completely understood. As the myelin disappears, the affected person experiences vision impairment, muscle weakness, and lack of coordination. These nerve-based symptoms arise because of poor nerve electrical transmission.

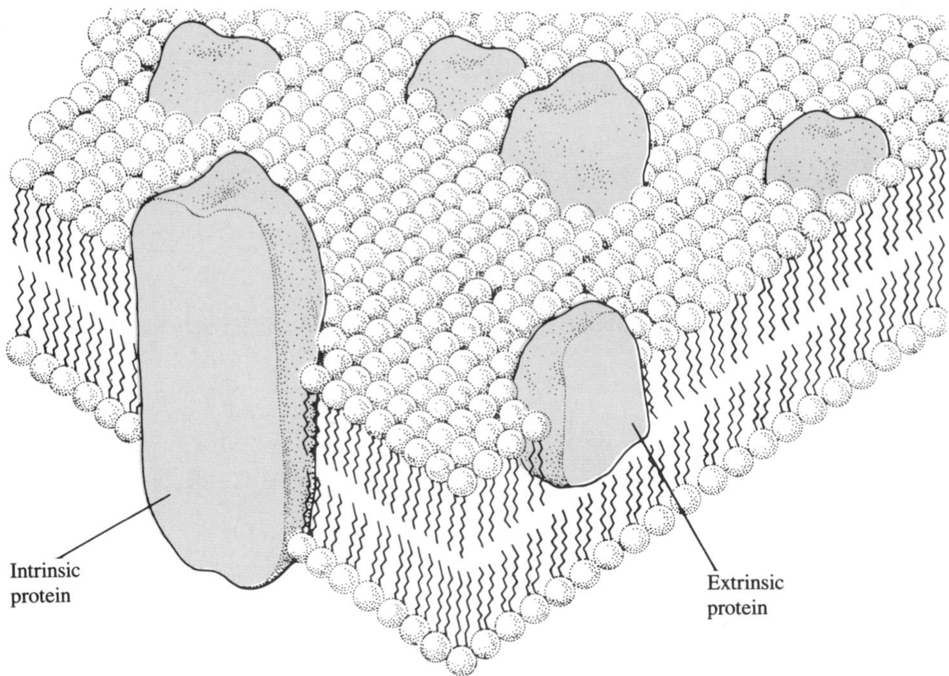

◄ FIGURE 11.7
The fluid-mosaic model of a membrane.

CONCEPTS IN REVIEW

1. Describe several general features of lipid structures.
2. Describe the classes of lipids and their functions.
3. Briefly explain why fatty acids are hydrophobic.
4. State which fatty acids commonly occur in fats and oils.
5. State which fatty acids are essential to human diets.
6. Explain why unsaturated fatty acids have lower melting points than the corresponding saturated fatty acids.
7. Briefly discuss the biological importance of eicosanoids.
8. Define the major biological function of waxes.
9. Describe the general structural makeup of phospholipids.
10. Describe the similarities between phospholipids and sphingolipids.
11. Draw the structural feature common to all steroids.
12. Draw the structures for cholesterol and several other common steroids.
13. Describe the biochemical relationships between common steroid hormones.
14. Discuss various components of the steroid distribution system.
15. Discuss atherosclerosis and the factors that affect it.
16. Draw a schematic of a lipid bilayer.

17. Discuss some important characteristics of a membrane lipid.
18. Describe two forms of membrane transport.
19. Explain how myelin helps electrical nerve transmission.

Equations in Review

Reaction Between an Alcohol (Glycerol or Sphingosine) and a Fatty acid (example)

$$\begin{array}{l} CH_2{-}O{-}\boxed{H + H{-}O}{-}C(=O){-}R_1 \\ | \\ CH{-}O{-}\boxed{H + H{-}O}{-}C(=O){-}R_2 \\ | \\ CH_2{-}O{-}\boxed{H + H{-}O}{-}C(=O){-}R_3 \end{array} \longrightarrow \begin{array}{l} CH_2{-}O{-}C(=O){-}R_1 \\ | \\ CH{-}O{-}C(=O){-}R_2 \\ | \\ CH_2{-}O{-}C(=O){-}R_3 \end{array} + 3\,H_2O$$

Glycerol Fatty acids A triacylglycerol

Exercises

1. Why are the lipids, which are dissimilar substances, classified as a group?
2. Briefly explain why caproic acid is more water-soluble than stearic acid.
3. Write the structural formula of a triacylglycerol that contains one unit each of palmitic, stearic, and oleic acids. How many other triacylglycerols are possible, each containing one unit of each of these acids?
4. Draw formulas for the products of a hydrolysis reaction involving a triacylglycerol that contains palmitic acid, oleic acid, and linoleic acid.
5. What are the three essential fatty acids? What are the consequences of their being absent from the diet?
6. Briefly explain why arachidonic acid is of special biological importance.
7. List two reasons why fats contain more biochemical energy than carbohydrates.
8. How is aspirin thought to relieve inflammation?
9. Wax serves a protective function on many types of leaves. How does it do this?
10. What two properties must a membrane lipid possess?
11. In what organ in the body are phospholipids mainly produced?
12. Lecithins and cephalins are both derivatives of phosphatidic acid. Indicate how they differ from each other.
13. Draw the structure of phosphatidyl serine.
14. In what ways is sphingosine similar to a glycerol molecule that has been esterified to one fatty acid?
15. Show the structure of a glucocerebroside.
16. What two structural features allow sphingomyelin to serve as a membrane lipid?
17. What common structural feature is possessed by all steroids? Write the structural formulas of two steroids.
18. List the four classes of eicosanoids.
19. How does a diet that contains a large amount of fish possibly decrease the risk of a heart attack?
20. Why are waxes generally the most solid of the lipids?
21. What is atherosclerosis? How is it produced and what are its symptoms?
22. Why is dietary cholesterol intake potentially critical in controlling high serum cholesterol levels?

23. Briefly describe the body's cholesterol distribution system.
24. Why is HDL a potential aid in controlling serum cholesterol levels?
25. Draw the structure of a membrane lipid.
26. Why can a lipid bilayer be described as a barrier?
27. What advantage does a liposome provide as a vehicle for drug delivery?
28. Why is the myelin sheath known as an insulator?
29. Would you expect an intrinsic protein to be hydrophobic? Explain.
30. Distinguish active transport from facilitated diffusion.
31. Which of these statements are correct? Rewrite each incorrect statement to make it correct.
(a) A lipid will dissolve in water.
(b) Lipids are often small molecules.
(c) A triacylglycerol is high in biochemical energy because it contains many oxidized carbons.
(d) Linoleic acid has a lower melting point than stearic acid.
(e) Phosphatidyl choline is also known as lecithin.
(f) A sphingolipid always contains carbohydrate.
(g) Cholesterol is often found in membranes.
(h) Movement of potassium ion into a nerve cell is an example of facilitated diffusion.
(i) A lipid bilayer has a hydrophilic interior.
(j) The "fluid" in the fluid-mosaic model refers to the lipid bilayer.
(k) Estradiol is the precursor of testosterone.
(l) Cortisone blocks inflammation by limiting the release of arachidonic acid from membranes.
(m) Cells that need cholesterol are able to absorb the low density lipoprotein.
(n) Thromboxane formation may be a factor in heart disease.

12 Amino Acids, Polypeptides, and Proteins

◀ CHAPTER OPENING PHOTO: **This Olympic weight lifter uses muscles composed of long chains of proteins.**

The word "protein" derives from the Greek word *proteios* meaning "first." When these chemicals were discovered, they were placed first in biological importance. Although biochemists now take a more balanced view of the importance of proteins, think of the startling properties provided us by these molecules. Spider-web protein is many times stronger than the toughest steel; hair, feathers, and hooves are all made from one related group of proteins; another protein provides the glass clear lens material needed for vision. If very small quantities (milligram amounts) of some proteins are missing, a person's metabolic processes may be out of control. Juvenile-onset diabetes mellitus results from a lack of the insulin protein. Dwarfism can arise when the growth hormone protein is lacking. A special "antifreeze" blood protein allows Antarctic fish to survive at body temperatures below freezing.

This list could go on and on, but what is perhaps most amazing is that this great variety of proteins is made from the same, relatively small, group of amino acids. By using various amounts of these amino acids in different sequences, nature has created proteins to serve the many tasks needed to sustain life.

12.1 THE STRUCTURE–FUNCTION CONNECTION

Proteins are present in every living cell. Their very name, derived from the Greek word *proteios*, which means holding first place, signifies the importance of these substances. Proteins are one of the three major classes of foods. The other two, carbohydrates and fats, are needed for energy; proteins are needed for growth and maintenance of body tissue. Some common foods with high (over 10%) protein content are fish, beans, nuts, cheese, eggs, poultry, and meat. These foods tend to be scarce and relatively expensive. Proteins are, therefore, the class of foods that is least available to the undernourished people of the world. Hence, the question of how to secure an adequate supply of high-quality protein for an ever-increasing population is one of our more critical problems (see Chapter 15).

Proteins function as structural materials and as enzymes (catalysts) that regulate the countless chemical reactions taking place in every living organism, including the reactions involved in the decomposition and synthesis of proteins.

All proteins are polymeric substances that yield amino acids on hydrolysis. Those that yield only amino acids when hydrolyzed are classified as **simple proteins**; those that yield amino acids and one or more additional products are

simple proteins

conjugated proteins

classified as **conjugated proteins**. There are approximately 200 different known amino acids in nature. Some are found in only one particular species of plant or animal, others in only a few life forms. But 20 of these amino acids are found in almost all proteins. Furthermore, these same 20 amino acids are used by all forms of life in the synthesis of proteins.

All proteins contain carbon, hydrogen, oxygen, and nitrogen. Some proteins contain additional elements, usually sulfur, phosphorus, iron, copper, or zinc. The significant presence of nitrogen in all proteins sets them apart from carbohydrates and lipids. The average nitrogen content is about 16%.

Proteins are highly specific in their functions. The amino acid units in a given protein molecule are arranged in a definite sequence. An amazing fact about proteins is that in some cases if just one of the hundreds or thousands of amino acid units is missing or out of place, the biological function of that protein is seriously damaged or destroyed. The sequence of amino acids in a protein establishes the function of that protein.

This relationship between structure and function contrasts sharply with that for other classes of biochemicals. For example, carbohydrates can provide cellular energy because they contain one particular type of atom, reduced carbon, that is readily oxidizable. This important function does not depend directly on the sequence in which the atoms are arranged. On the other hand, an appropriate sequence of amino acids produces a protein strong enough to form a horse's hoof, a different sequence produces a protein capable of absorbing oxygen in the lungs and releasing it to needy cells; yet another sequence produces a hormone capable of directing carbohydrate metabolism for an entire organism. As will be seen, full understanding of the function of a protein requires that the structure of that protein be understood.

12.2 The Nature of Amino Acids

Each amino acid has two functional groups, an amino group ($-NH_2$) and a carboxyl group ($-COOH$). The amino acids that are found in proteins are called alpha (α) amino acids because the amino group is attached to the first or alpha carbon atom adjacent to the carboxyl group. The beta (β) position is the next adjacent carbon; the gamma (γ) position the next carbon; and so on. The following formula represents an alpha (α) amino acid:

$$\overset{\gamma}{C}H_3\overset{\beta}{C}H_2\overset{\alpha}{C}HCOOH \quad (NH_2 \text{ on } C_\alpha)$$

α-Amino butyric acid

Alpha amino acids are represented by this general formula:

$$\boxed{R}-\underset{\boxed{NH_2}}{\overset{H}{\underset{|}{\overset{|}{C}}}}-\boxed{COOH}$$

Variable group (R); Carboxyl group (COOH); Amino group (NH_2)

The portion of the molecule designated R is commonly referred to as the *amino acid side chain.* It is not restricted to alkyl groups and may contain (a) open chain, cyclic, or aromatic hydrocarbon groups; (b) additional amino or carboxyl groups; (c) hydroxyl groups; or (d) sulfur-containing groups.

Amino acids are divided into three groups: neutral, acidic, and basic. They are classified as neutral amino acids when their molecules have the same number of amino and carboxyl groups, as acidic when their molecules have more carboxyl groups than amino groups, or as basic when their molecules have more amino groups than carboxyl groups.

The names, formulas, and abbreviations of the common amino acids are given in Table 12.1. Two of these, aspartic acid and glutamic acid, are classified as acidic; three—lysine, arginine, and histidine—as basic; the remainder are classified as neutral amino acids.

TABLE 12.1 Common Amino Acids Derived from Proteins

Name	Abbreviation	Formula
Alanine	Ala	$CH_3CH(NH_2)COOH$
Arginine	Arg	$NH_2{-}C({=}NH){-}NH{-}CH_2CH_2CH_2CH(NH_2)COOH$
Asparagine	Asn	$NH_2C({=}O){-}CH_2CH(NH_2)COOH$
Aspartic acid	Asp	$HOOCCH_2CH(NH_2)COOH$
Cysteine	Cys	$HSCH_2CH(NH_2)COOH$
Glutamic acid	Glu	$HOOCCH_2CH_2CH(NH_2)COOH$
Glutamine	Gln	$NH_2C({=}O)CH_2CH_2CH(NH_2)COOH$
Glycine	Gly	$HCH(NH_2)COOH$
Histidine	His	imidazole ring (N=CH, HC, C, N–H) $C{-}CH_2CH(NH_2)COOH$
Isoleucine[a]	Ile	$CH_3CH_2CH(CH_3){-}CH(NH_2)COOH$

(continued)

Table 12.1 (*continued*)

Name	Abbreviation	Formula
Leucine[a]	Leu	$(CH_3)_2CHCH_2CHCOOH$ $\vert$ NH_2
Lysine[a]	Lys	$NH_2CH_2CH_2CH_2CH_2CHCOOH$ $\vert$ NH_2
Methionine[a]	Met	$CH_3SCH_2CH_2CHCOOH$ $\vert$ NH_2
Phenylalanine[a]	Phe	C_6H_5—$CH_2CHCOOH$ $\vert$ NH_2
Proline	Pro	(pyrrolidine ring) N—COOH $\vert$ H
Serine	Ser	$HOCH_2CHCOOH$ $\vert$ NH_2
Threonine[a]	Thr	CH_3CH—$CHCOOH$ $\vert$ $\vert$ OH NH_2
Tryptophan[a]	Trp	(indole ring: C—$CH_2CHCOOH$, ‖ CH, N—H) $\vert$ NH_2
Tyrosine	Tyr	HO—C_6H_4—$CH_2CHCOOH$ $\vert$ NH_2
Valine[a]	Val	$(CH_3)_2CHCHCOOH$ $\vert$ NH_2

[a] Amino acids essential in human nutrition.

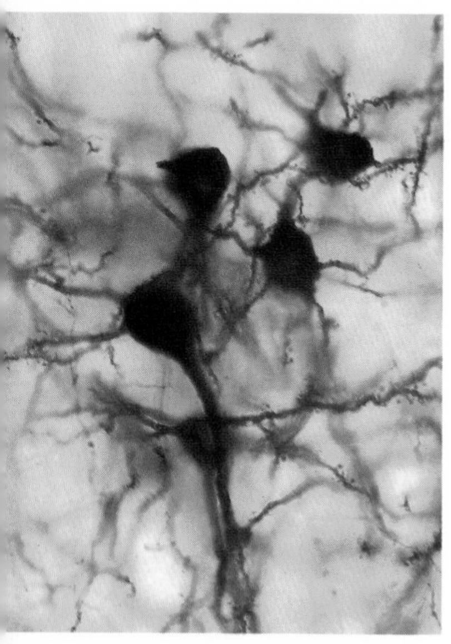

▲ **Cerebrum nerve synapse magnified 1200 times. Neurotransmitters cross these synapses to send messages between cells.**

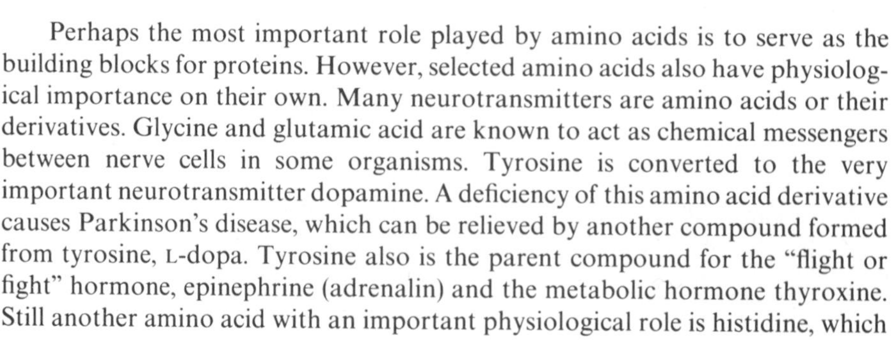

Perhaps the most important role played by amino acids is to serve as the building blocks for proteins. However, selected amino acids also have physiological importance on their own. Many neurotransmitters are amino acids or their derivatives. Glycine and glutamic acid are known to act as chemical messengers between nerve cells in some organisms. Tyrosine is converted to the very important neurotransmitter dopamine. A deficiency of this amino acid derivative causes Parkinson's disease, which can be relieved by another compound formed from tyrosine, L-dopa. Tyrosine also is the parent compound for the "flight or fight" hormone, epinephrine (adrenalin) and the metabolic hormone thyroxine. Still another amino acid with an important physiological role is histidine, which is converted in the body to histamine. This derivative causes the stomach lining to secrete HCl but probably is best known for causing many of the symptoms associated with tissue inflammation and colds and is the reason antihistamines are such important over-the-counter medications.

12.3 ESSENTIAL AMINO ACIDS

Dietary protein is broken down during digestion into its constituent amino acids, which supply much of the body's need for amino acids (see Chapter 15). Eight of the amino acids are **essential amino acids**. These amino acids—isoleucine, leucine, lysine, methionine, phenylalanine, threonine, tryptophan, and valine—are essential to the functioning of the human body. Since the body is not capable of synthesizing them, they must be supplied in our diets if we are to enjoy normal health. It is known that some other animals require amino acids in addition to those listed for humans. Rats, for example, require two additional amino acids—arginine and histidine—in their diets.

essential amino acids

On a nutritional basis, proteins are classified as *complete* or *incomplete*. A complete protein supplies all the essential amino acids; an incomplete protein is deficient in one or more essential amino acids. Many proteins, especially those from vegetable sources, are incomplete. For example, protein from corn (maize) is deficient in lysine. The nutritional quality of such vegetable proteins can be greatly improved by supplementing them with the essential amino acids that are lacking, if these can be synthesized at reasonable costs. Lysine, methionine, and tryptophan are being sold at present for enriching human food and livestock feed. This is another way to extend the world's limited supply of high-quality food protein. In still another approach to the problem of obtaining more high-quality protein, plant breeders have developed maize varieties with greatly improved lysine content. Genetic engineering may hold the key to further significant improvements in plant protein quality.

12.4 D-AMINO ACIDS AND L-AMINO ACIDS

All amino acids, except glycine, have at least one asymmetric carbon atom. For example, two stereoisomers of alanine are possible:

$$\begin{array}{c} COOH \\ | \\ H{-}C{-}NH_2 \\ | \\ CH_3 \end{array} \qquad \begin{array}{c} COOH \\ | \\ H_2N{-}C{-}H \\ | \\ CH_3 \end{array}$$

D-(−)-Alanine   L-(+)-Alanine

Projection formulas illustrate well the D and L configurations of amino acids in the same way as the configurations of D- and L-glyceraldehyde (Section 10.2). The —COOH group is written at the top of the projection formula, and the

D configuration is indicated by writing the alpha $—NH_2$ to the right of carbon 2. The L configuration is indicated by writing the alpha $—NH_2$ to the left of carbon 2. Although some D-amino acids occur in nature, only L-amino acids occur in proteins. The (+) and (−) signs in the name indicate the direction of rotation of plane-polarized light by the amino acid. Most amino acids have relatively complex structures making use of the projection formula difficult. Thus, unless stereochemical information is explicitly considered, amino acids will be shown using a condensed, structural formula in this chapter.

12.5 AMPHOTERISM

Amino acids are *amphoteric* (or *amphiprotic*); that is, they can react either as an acid or as a base. For example, with a strong base such as sodium hydroxide, alanine reacts as an acid, as shown in equation (1); with a strong acid such as HCl, alanine reacts as a base as shown in equation (2).

$$\underset{\text{Alanine}}{CH_3\underset{\substack{|\\NH_2}}{C}HCOOH} + NaOH \longrightarrow \underset{\text{Sodium alanate}}{CH_3\underset{\substack{|\\NH_2}}{C}HCOO^-\,Na^+} + H_2O \qquad (1)$$

$$CH_3\underset{\substack{|\\NH_2}}{C}HCOOH + HCl \longrightarrow \underset{\text{Alanyl ammonium chloride}}{CH_3\underset{\substack{|\\NH_3^+\,Cl^-}}{C}HCOOH} \qquad (2)$$

zwitterions

Even in neutral biological solutions, amino acids do not actually exist in the molecular form shown in equations (1) and (2). Instead, they exist mainly as dipolar ions called **zwitterions**. Again using alanine as an example, the proton on the carboxyl group transfers to the amino group, forming a zwitterion by an acid—base reaction within the molecule:

$$\underset{\text{Alanine molecule}}{CH_3\underset{\substack{|\\H_2N:}}{C}HCOO\,(H)} \longrightarrow \underset{\text{Alanine zwitterion}}{CH_3\underset{\substack{|\\NH_3^+}}{C}HCOO^-}$$

On an ionic basis, the reaction of alanine with NaOH and HCl is

$$\underset{\text{Alanine zwitterion}}{CH_3\underset{\substack{|\\NH_3^+}}{C}HCOO^-} + OH^- \longrightarrow \underset{\text{Alanate anion}}{CH_3\underset{\substack{|\\NH_2}}{C}HCOO^-} + H_2O \qquad (3)$$

$$\underset{\text{Alanine zwitterion}}{CH_3\underset{\substack{|\\NH_3^+}}{C}HCOO^-} + H^+ \longrightarrow \underset{\text{Alanyl ammonium cation}}{CH_3\underset{\substack{|\\NH_3^+}}{C}HCOOH} \qquad (4)$$

Other amino acids behave like alanine. Together with protein molecules that contain $—COOH$ and $—NH_2$ groups, they help to buffer or stabilize the pH of the blood at about 7.4. The pH is maintained close to 7.4 because any excess acid or base in the blood is neutralized by reactions such as shown in equations (3) and (4).

$$\underset{\substack{\text{Cation form}\\ \text{II}}}{\underset{|\atop NH_3^+}{RCHCOOH}} \underset{OH^-}{\overset{H^+}{\rightleftharpoons}} \underset{\substack{\text{Zwitterion form}\\ \text{I}}}{\underset{|\atop NH_3^+}{RCHCOO^-}} \underset{OH^-}{\overset{H^+}{\rightleftharpoons}} \underset{\substack{\text{Anion form}\\ \text{III}}}{\underset{|\atop NH_2}{RCHCOO^-}} \qquad (5)$$

isoelectric point

When an amino acid in solution has equal positive and negative charges, as in formula I of equation (5), it is electrically neutral and does not migrate toward either the positive or negative electrode when placed in an electrolytic cell. The pH at which there is no migration toward either electrode is called the **isoelectric point** (see Table 12.2). If acid (H^+) is added to an amino acid at its isoelectric point, the equilibrium is shifted toward formula II, and the cation formed migrates toward the negative electrode. When base (OH^-) is added, the anion formed (formula III) migrates toward the positive electrode. Differences in isoelectric points are important in isolating and purifying amino acids and proteins, since their rates and directions of migration can be controlled in an electrolytic cell by adjusting the pH. This method of separation is called *electrophoresis*.

Amino acids are classified as basic, neutral, or acidic depending on whether the ratio of $—NH_2$ to $—COOH$ groups in the molecules is greater than 1:1, equal to 1:1, or less than 1:1, respectively. Furthermore, this ratio differs from 1:1 only if the amino acid side chain (R—) contains an additional amino or carboxyl group. For example, if the side chain contains a carboxyl group, the amino acid is considered acidic. Thus, the R— group determines whether an amino acid is classified as basic, neutral, or acidic.

Isoelectric points are found at pH values ranging from 7.8 to 10.8 for basic amino acids, 4.8 to 6.3 for neutral amino acids, and 2.8 to 3.3 for acidic amino acids. It is logical that a molecule such as glutamic acid, with one amino group and two carboxyl groups, would be classified as acidic and that its isoelectric point would be at a pH lower than 7.0. It might also seem that the isoelectric point of an amino acid that is classified as neutral, such as alanine, with one amino and one carboxyl group, would have an isoelectric point of 7.0. However, the isoelectric point of alanine is 6.0, not 7.0. This is because the carboxyl group and the amino group are not equally ionized. The carboxyl group of alanine ionizes to a greater degree as an acid than the amino group ionizes as a base.

TABLE 12.2 Isoelectric Points of Selected Amino Acids

Amino acid	pH at isoelectric point	Amino acid	pH at isoelectric point
Arginine	10.8	Serine	5.7
Lysine	9.7	Glutamic acid	3.2
Alanine	6.0	Aspartic acid	2.9
Glycine	6.0		

EXAMPLE 12.1 Draw the structure of L-serine in a strongly acidic solution.

SOLUTION First, draw the structure for L-serine as the molecule would exist in a neutral solution. The α-amino and carboxylic acid groups form a zwitterion.

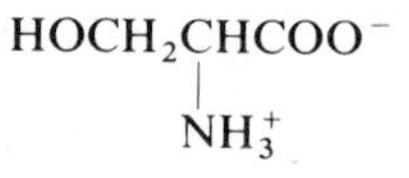

$$\underset{\displaystyle NH_3^+}{HOCH_2\overset{}{C}HCOO^-}$$

When the solution is made acidic (the concentration of hydrogen ions is increased), the amine group is unaffected because it is already protonated. However, the carboxylate anion bonds to a hydrogen ion, resulting in an L-serine structure with a net positive charge.

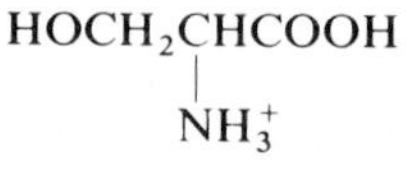

$$\underset{\displaystyle NH_3^+}{HOCH_2CHCOOH}$$

PRACTICE Draw the structure of L-valine in a strongly basic solution.
Answer: $(CH_3)_2CHCH_2\underset{\displaystyle NH_2}{C}HCOO^-$

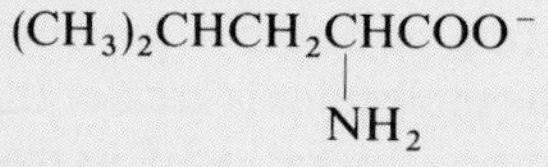

12.6 FORMATION OF POLYPEPTIDES

peptide linkage

Proteins are polyamides consisting of amino acid units joined through amide structures. If we react two glycine molecules, with the elimination of a molecule of water, we form a compound containing the amide structure, also called the **peptide linkage**, or peptide bond. The elimination of water occurs between the carboxyl group of one amino acid and the α-amino group of a second amino acid (see Section 6.6). The product formed from two glycine molecules is called glycylglycine (abbreviated Gly-Gly). Because it contains two amino acid units, it is called a dipeptide.

$$H_2N\text{—}CH_2\text{—}C(=O)\text{—}OH + H\text{—}NH\text{—}CH_2\text{—}C(=O)\text{—}OH \longrightarrow \underset{NH_2}{CH_2}\text{—}C(=O)\text{—}\underset{H}{N}\text{—}CH_2\text{—}C(=O)\text{—}OH + H_2O$$

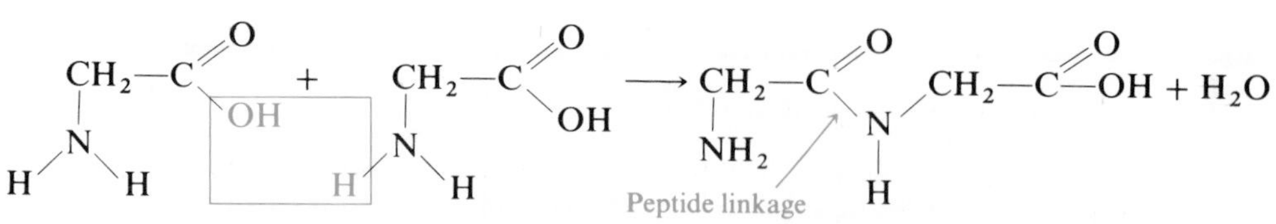

Peptide linkage

Glycylglycine
(Gly-Gly)

polypeptide

If three amino acid units are included in a molecule, it is a tripeptide; if four, a tetrapeptide; if five, a pentapeptide; and so on. Peptides containing up to about 40–50 amino acid units in a chain are called **polypeptides**. The units making up the peptide are amino acids less the elements of water and are referred to as *amino acid residues* or, simply, residues. Still larger chains of amino acids are known as proteins.

When amino acids form a polypeptide chain, a carboxyl group and an α-amino group are involved in each peptide bond (amide bond). While these groups are joined in peptide bonds, they cannot ionize as acids or bases. Consequently, the physico-chemical properties of a polypeptide/protein are determined to a large extent by the side chains of the amino acid residues.

In linear peptides one end of the chain has a free amino group and the other end a free carboxyl group. The amino-group end is called the *N-terminal residue* and the other end the *C-terminal residue*:

1 2 3 4 5 6 7
Ala-Pro-Tyr-Met-Gly-Lys-Gly

N-Terminal residue (Ala, 1) — C-Terminal residue (Gly, 7)

The sequence of amino acids in a chain is numbered starting with the N-terminal residue, which is written to the left with the C-terminal residue at the right. Any segment of the sequence that is not specifically known is placed in parentheses. Thus in the heptapeptide above, if the order of tyrosine and methionine were not known, the structure would be written as

Ala-Pro-(Met, Tyr)-Gly-Lys-Gly

Peptides are named as acyl derivatives of the C-terminal amino acid with the C-terminal unit keeping its complete name. The *ine* ending of all but the C-terminal amino acid is changed to *yl*, and these are listed in the order in which they appear, starting with the N-terminal amino acid.

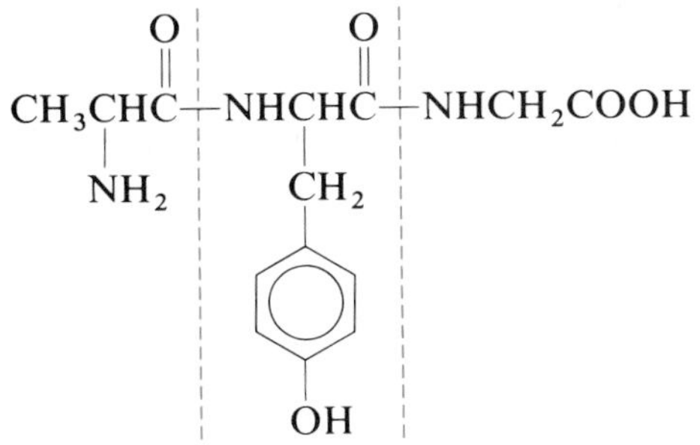

$$CH_3CH(NH_2)C(=O)\text{—}NHCH(CH_2C_6H_4OH)C(=O)\text{—}NHCH_2COOH$$

Alanyl | Tyrosyl | Glycine

Ala-Tyr-Gly

Thus Ala-Tyr-Gly is called alanyltyrosylglycine. The name of Arg-Gln-His-Ala is arginylglutamylhistidylalanine.

Alanine and glycine can form two different dipeptides, Gly-Ala and Ala-Gly, using each amino acid only once:

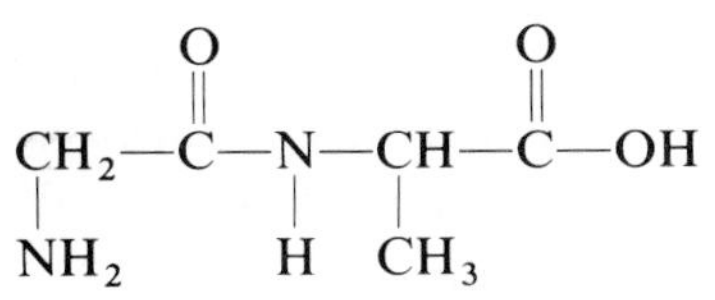

$$\underset{NH_2}{CH_2}\text{—}\overset{O}{\overset{\|}{C}}\text{—}\underset{H}{N}\text{—}\underset{CH_3}{CH}\text{—}\overset{O}{\overset{\|}{C}}\text{—}OH \quad \text{and} \quad CH_3\underset{NH_2}{CH}\text{—}\overset{O}{\overset{\|}{C}}\text{—}\underset{H}{N}\text{—}CH_2\text{—}\overset{O}{\overset{\|}{C}}\text{—}OH$$

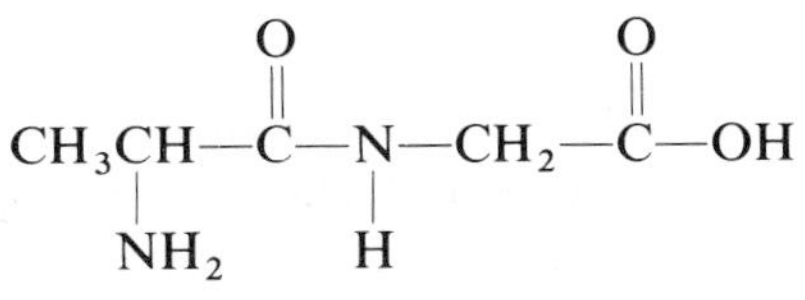

Glycylalanine (Gly-Ala) — Alanylglycine (Ala-Gly)

TABLE 12.3 **Primary Structures and Functions of Some Biological Polypeptides**[a]

Name	Primary structure	General biological function
Substance P	Arg-Pro-Lys-Pro-Gln-Gln-Phe-Phe-Gly-Leu-Met-NH_2	Is a pain-producing agent
Bradykinin	Arg-Pro-Pro-Gly-Phe-Ser-Pro-Phe-Arg	Affects tissue inflammation and blood pressure
Angiotensin II	Asp-Arg-Val-Tyr-Val-His-Pro-Phe	Maintains water balance and blood pressure
Leu-enkephalin Met-enkephalin	Tyr-Gly-Gly-Phe-Leu Tyr-Gly-Gly-Phe-Met	Relieves pain, produces sense of well-being
Vasopressin	Cys-Tyr-Phe-Gln-Asn-Cys-Pro-Arg-Gly-NH_2 (S—S bridge between the two Cys)	Increases blood pressure, decreases kidney water excretion
Oxytocin	Cys-Tyr-Ile-Gln-Asn-Cys-Pro-Leu-Gly-NH_2 (S—S bridge between the two Cys)	Initiates childbirth labor, causes mammary gland milk release, affects kidney excretion of water and sodium

[a] Where —NH_2 is indicated at the end of the sequence, the C-terminal amino acid has an amide structure rather than a free —COOH.

If three different amino acids react—for example, glycine, alanine, and threonine–six tripeptides in which each amino acid appears only once are possible.

Gly-Ala-Thr	Ala-Thr-Gly	Thr-Ala-Gly
Gly-Thr-Ala	Ala-Gly-Thr	Thr-Gly-Ala

The number of possible peptides rises very rapidly as the number of amino acid units increases. For example, there are 120 ($1 \times 2 \times 3 \times 4 \times 5 = 120$) different ways to combine five different amino acids to form a pentapeptide, using each amino acid only once in each molecule. If the same constraints are applied to 15 different amino acids, the number of possible combinations is greater than 1 trillion (10^{12})! Since a protein molecule may contain several hundred amino acid units, with individual amino acids occurring several times, the number of possible combinations from 20 amino acids is simply beyond imagination.

There are a number of small, naturally occurring polypeptides with significant biochemical functions. In general these substances serve as hormones or nerve transmitters. Their functions range from controlling pain and pleasure responses in the brain to controlling smooth muscle contraction or kidney fluid excretion rates (see Table 12.3). The amino acid sequence and chain length give a polypeptide its biological effectiveness and specificity.

For example, recent research has shown that the effects of opiates (opium derivatives) on the brain are also exhibited by two naturally occurring pentapeptides, Leu-enkephalin (Tyr-Gly-Gly-Phe-Leu) and Met-enkephalin (Tyr-Gly-Gly-Phe-Met). These two polypeptides are natural painkillers. Alterations of the amino acid sequence—which alters the side-chain characteristics—cause drastic changes in the analgesic effects of these pentapeptides. The substitution of L-alanine for either of the glycine residues in these compounds (simply changing one side-chain group from —H to —CH_3) causes an approximately 1000-fold decrease in effectiveness as a painkiller! The substitution of L-tyrosine for L-phenylalanine causes a comparable loss of activity. Even the substitution of D-tyrosine for the L-tyrosine residue causes a considerable loss in the analgesic effectiveness of the pentapeptides.

It is clearly evident that a particular sequence of amino acid residues is essential for proper polypeptide function. This sequence aligns the side-chain characteristics (large or small; polar or nonpolar; acidic, basic, or neutral) in the proper positions for a specific polypeptide function.

Oxytocin and vasopressin are similar nonapeptides, differing only at two positions in their primary structure (see Table 12.3). Yet their biological functions differ dramatically. Oxytocin controls uterine contractions during labor in childbirth and also causes contraction of the smooth muscles of the mammary glands, resulting in milk excretion. Vasopressin in high concentration raises the blood pressure and has been used in treatment of surgical shock for this purpose. Vasopressin is also an antidiuretic, regulating the excretion of fluid by the kidneys. The absence of vasopressin leads to diabetes insipidus. This condition is characterized by excretion of up to 30 liters of urine per day, but can be controlled by administration of vasopressin or its derivatives.

The isolation and synthesis of oxytocin and vasopressin was accomplished by Vincent du Vigneaud (1901–1978) and co-workers at Cornell University. Du Vigneaud was awarded the Nobel prize in chemistry in 1955 for this work. Synthetic oxytocin is indistinguishable from the natural material. It is available commercially and is used for the induction of labor in the late stages of pregnancy.

EXAMPLE 12.2

Write the structure of the tripeptide Ser-Gly-Ala.

SOLUTION

First, write the structures of the three amino acids in this tripeptide.

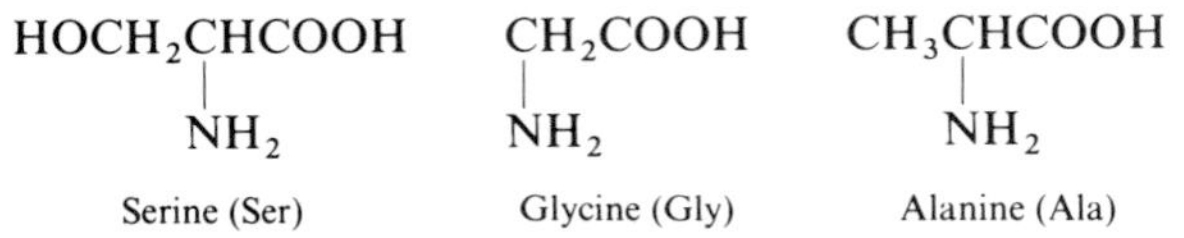

$$\underset{\text{Serine (Ser)}}{HOCH_2\underset{\displaystyle NH_2}{\underset{|}{C}}HCOOH} \qquad \underset{\text{Glycine (Gly)}}{\underset{\displaystyle NH_2}{\underset{|}{C}}H_2COOH} \qquad \underset{\text{Alanine (Ala)}}{CH_3\underset{\displaystyle NH_2}{\underset{|}{C}}HCOOH}$$

By convention, the amino acid residue written at the left end of the tripeptide has a free amino group while the residue at the right end has a free carboxylic acid group. When the amino acids are connected by peptide linkages the following structure results:

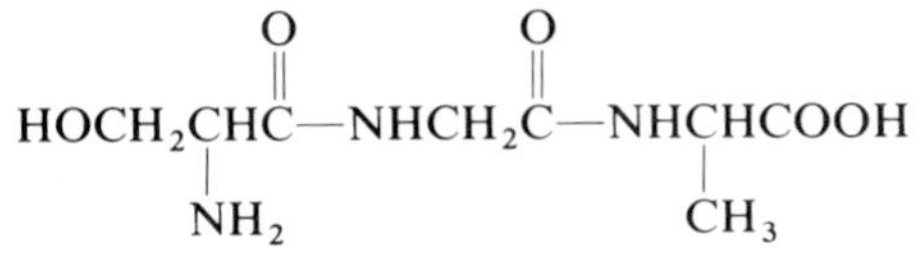

$$HOCH_2\underset{\displaystyle NH_2}{\underset{|}{C}}H\overset{\displaystyle O}{\overset{\|}{C}}—NHCH_2\overset{\displaystyle O}{\overset{\|}{C}}—NH\underset{\displaystyle CH_3}{\underset{|}{C}}HCOOH$$

PRACTICE Write the structure of the pentapeptide Gly-Leu-Asp-Ser-Cys.

Answer:

```
      O          O          O          O
      ‖          ‖          ‖          ‖
 CH2C—NHCHC—NHCHC—NHCHC—NHCHCOOH
  |         |          |          |          |
 NH2       CH2        CH2        CH2        CH2
            |          |          |          |
            CH        COOH       OH         SH
           /  \
        CH3  CH3
```

12.7 PROTEIN STRUCTURE

By 1940 a great deal of information concerning proteins had been assembled. Their elemental composition was known, and they had been carefully classified according to solubility in various solvents. Proteins were known to be polymers of amino acids, and the different amino acids had, for the most part, been isolated and identified. Protein molecules were known to be very large in size, with molar masses ranging from several thousand to several million.

Knowledge of protein structure could help to answer many chemical and biological questions. But for a while the task of determining the actual structure of molecules of such colossal size appeared to be next to impossible. Then Linus Pauling (b. 1901), at the California Institute of Technology, attacked the problem by a new approach. Using X-ray diffraction techniques, Pauling and his collaborators painstakingly determined the bond angles and dimensions of amino acids and of dipeptides and tripeptides. After building accurate scale models of the dipeptides and tripeptides, they determined how these could be fitted into likely polypeptide configurations. Based on this work, Pauling and R. B. Corey proposed in 1951 that two different conformations—the *α-helix* and the *β-pleated-sheet*—were the most probable stable polypeptide chain configurations of protein molecules. These two macromolecular structures are illustrated in Figure 12.1. Within a short time it was established that many proteins do have structures corresponding to those predicted by Pauling and Corey. This work was a very great achievement. Pauling received the 1954 Nobel prize in chemistry for this work on protein structure. Pauling's and Corey's work provided the inspiration for another great biochemical breakthrough—the concept of the double-helix structure for deoxyribonucleic acid, DNA (see Section 14.6).

Proteins are very large molecules. But just how many amino acid units must be present for a substance to be a protein? There is no universally agreed upon answer to this question. Some authorities state that a protein must have a molar mass of at least 6000 or contain about 50 amino acid units. Smaller amino acid polymers, containing from 5 to 50 amino acid units, are classified as polypeptides and are not proteins. In reality, there is no clearly defined lower limit to the molecular size of proteins. The distinction is made to emphasize (1) that proteins often serve structural or enzymatic functions, whereas polypeptides often serve hormone related functions and (2) that the three-dimensional conformation of proteins is directly related to function, whereas the relation is not so clear-cut with polypeptides.

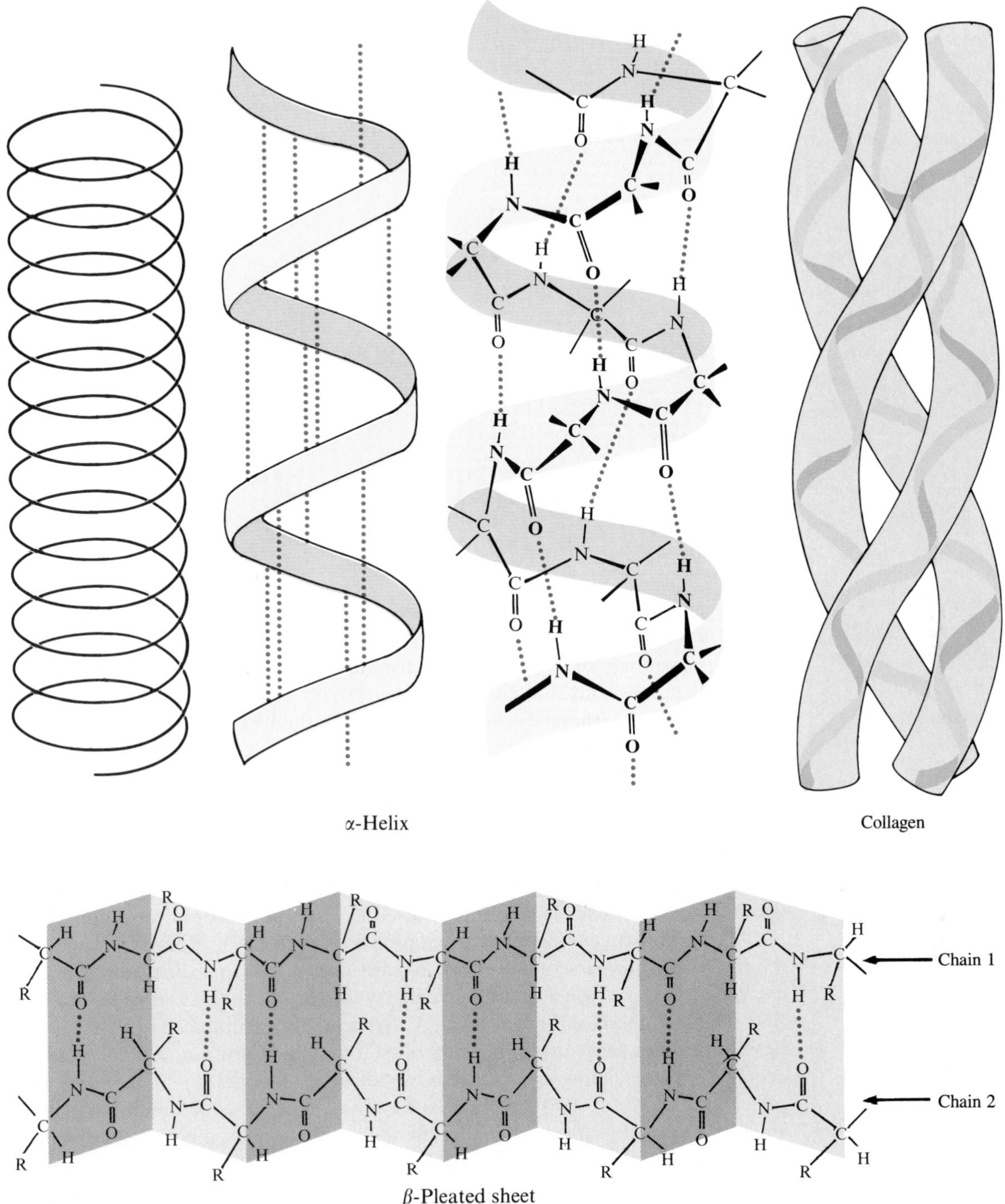

▲

FIGURE 12.1

α-Helix, β-pleated-sheet, and the special collagen protein structures. Collagen is composed of three helical protein chains wound together in a three-stranded helix. As the most abundant protein in the animal world, collagen's function in the body is mainly as connective tissue.

FIGURE 12.2 ▶ Amino acid sequence of beef insulin.

15 Gln—Leu—Glu—Asn—Tyr—Cys 20—Asn 21
Tyr
Leu
Ser
Cys—Val 10
S S
Ser
Ala
S
1 Gly—Ile—Val—Glu—Gln 5—Cys—Cys
Chain A
S
S
S
Cys—Gly 20
Val
Leu
Tyr
15 Leu
Ala
Glu
Glu
Arg
Gly
Phe
Phe 25
Tyr
1 Phe—Val—Asn—Gln—His 5—Leu—Cys—Gly—Ser—His 10—Leu—Val
Chain B
Thr
Pro
Lys
Ala 30

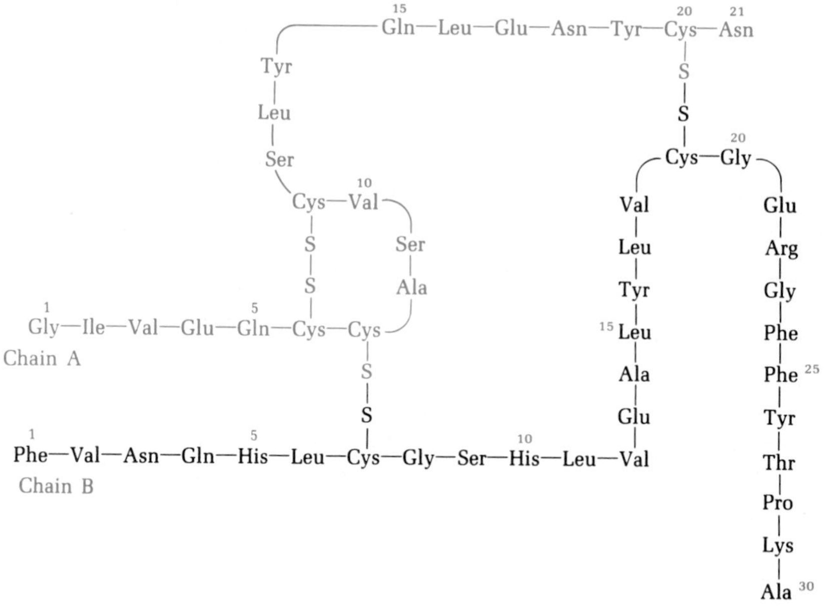

In general, if a protein molecule is to perform a specific biological function, it must have a closely defined overall conformation, or shape. This overall conformation consists of (1) a primary structure, (2) a secondary structure, (3) a tertiary structure, and sometimes (4) a quaternary structure.

primary structure

The **primary structure** of a protein is established by the number, kind, and sequence of amino acid units composing the polypeptide chain or chains making up the molecule. The primary structure determines the alignment of side-chain characteristics, which, in turn, determines the three-dimensional shape into which the protein folds. In this sense the amino acid sequence is of primary importance in establishing protein shape.

Determining the sequence of the amino acids in even one protein molecule was a formidable task. The amino acid sequence of beef insulin was announced in 1955 by the British biochemist Frederick Sanger (b. 1918). This determination required several years of effort by a team under Sanger's direction. He was awarded the 1958 Nobel prize in chemistry for this work. Insulin is a hormone that regulates the blood-sugar level. A deficiency of insulin leads to the condition of diabetes. Beef insulin consists of 51 amino acid units in two polypeptide chains. The two chains are connected by disulfide linkages (—S—S—) of two cysteine residues at two different sites. The primary structure is shown in Figure 12.2. Insulins from other animals, including humans, differ slightly by one, two, or three amino acid residues in chain A.

secondary structure

The **secondary structure** of proteins can be characterized as a regular, three-dimensional structure held together by hydrogen bonding between the oxygen of the $\rangle C{=}O$ and the hydrogen of the $H{-}N\langle$ groups in the polypeptide chains:

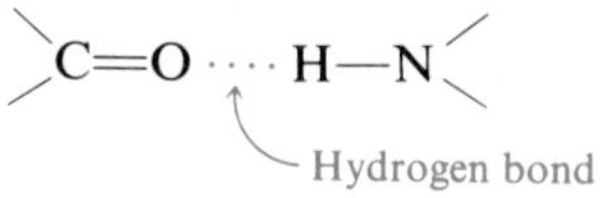

$$\rangle C{=}O \cdots H{-}N\langle$$

Hydrogen bond

The α-helical and β-pleated-sheet structures of Pauling and Corey are two examples of secondary structure. As shown in Figure 12.1, essentially every peptide bond is involved in at least one hydrogen bond in these structures. Proteins having α-helical or β-pleated-sheet secondary structures are strongly held in particular conformations by virtue of the large number of hydrogen bonds.

The fibrous proteins are an important class of proteins that contain highly developed secondary structures. Because these structures provide strength, these proteins tend to function in support roles. For example, collagen in the form of a three-stranded helix (see Figure 12.1) is the principal protein in connective tissues. The α-keratins depend on the α-helix for strength and to provide support for such diverse structures as hair, fingernails, feathers, and hooves. The silk protein, fibroin, is folded into a β-pleated-sheet structure. In each case the repeating secondary structure with its multitude of hydrogen bonds provides the protein with strength and some degree of rigidity.

tertiary structure

The **tertiary structure** of a protein refers to the distinctive and characteristic conformation, or shape, of a protein molecule. This overall three-dimensional conformation is held together by a variety of interactions between amino acid side chains. These interactions include (1) hydrogen bonding, (2) ionic bonding, and (3) disulfide bonding. For example,

1. Glutamic acid–tyrosine hydrogen bonding

$$\text{Protein}—CH_2CH_2\overset{\displaystyle OH}{\overset{|}{C}}{=}O \cdots HO—\langle\bigcirc\rangle—\text{Protein}$$

2. Glutamic acid–lysine ionic bonding

$$\text{Protein}—CH_2CH_2\overset{\displaystyle O}{\overset{\|}{C}}—O^-\ H_3N^+—CH_2CH_2CH_2CH_2—\text{Protein}$$

3. Cysteine–cysteine disulfide bonding

$$\text{Protein}—CH_2—S—S—CH_2—\text{Protein}$$

The tertiary structure depends on the number and location of these interactions, variables that are fixed when the primary structure is synthesized. Thus, the tertiary structure depends on the primary structure. For example, there are three locations in the insulin molecule (Figure 12.2) where the primary sequence permits disulfide bonding. This, in turn, has an obvious bearing on the shape of insulin.

Hair is especially rich in disulfide bonds. These can be broken by certain reducing agents and restored by an oxidizing agent. This fact is the key to "cold" permanent waving of hair. Some of the disulfide bonds are broken by applying a reducing agent to the hair. The hair is then styled with the desired curls or waves. These are then permanently set by using an oxidizing agent to reestablish the disulfide bonds at different points.

▲ **Frederick Sanger (1918–).**

$$\left.\middle|\!-CH_2-S-S-CH_2-\middle|\right. \xrightarrow[\text{agent}]{\text{Reducing}}$$

Bonds in normal hair

$$\left|-CH_2-S-H\ H-S-CH_2-\right| \xrightarrow[\text{agent}]{\text{Oxidizing}} \left|-CH_2-S-S-CH_2-\right|$$

Broken bonds of "reduced" form

Reestablished bonds of permanently waved hair

If Table 12.1 is examined closely it can be concluded that most of the amino acids have side chains that cannot form hydrogen bonds nor ionic bonds nor disulfide bonds. What then do the majority of amino acids do to hold together the tertiary structure of a protein? This is an important question and leads to an equally important answer. *The uncharged relatively nonpolar amino acids form the center or core of most proteins.* These amino acids have side chains that don't bond very well to water; they are like saturated hydrocarbons or lipids and are hydrophobic. When a protein is synthesized, the uncharged, nonpolar amino acids turn inward toward each other, excluding water and forming the core of the protein structure.

Myoglobin, a small oxygen-carrying protein of the muscle, was the first protein for which a three-dimensional structure was determined (see Figure 12.3). It can be described as having a folded-sausage structure, each section of the sausage representing a segment of the α-helix. Under normal conditions the folds of the myoglobin structure are held firmly in place by interactions between amino acid side chains. The conformation of myoglobin closely accommodates an organically bound iron atom (in the heme group, shown in Figure 12.3 by the rectangular solid), which allows myoglobin to store and transport oxygen in the muscles. The oxygen transport and storage function is determined by myoglobin's specific primary, secondary, and tertiary structures. It is worth noting that myoglobin is a *conjugated* protein—that is, a protein that contains groups other than amino acid residues.

Many proteins, including myoglobin and molecules of a much larger size, have an overall structure which is supported by a basic framework. This framework is composed of pieces of strong, secondary structure. For example, each short α-helical section in myoglobin is relatively rigid because of its many hydrogen bonds. These rigid cylinders then form a cage around the heme group, holding it firmly in place so that it can bind oxygen in the appropriate way.

Like myoglobin, larger proteins also have a skeleton made up of secondary structure, primarily α-helix and β-pleated sheet. Often these bigger molecules are folded into a number of units, each about the same size as myoglobin, which are called **protein domains**. In this way, a larger protein is like several myoglobin-sized proteins connected together. A protein domain has its own secondary skeleton and often serves a discrete task in a protein's overall function. In fact, if selected peptide bonds are broken carefully, domains can actually be isolated and separated.

protein domains

To learn more about these domains and how secondary structure serves as a protein skeleton, scientists have developed a simplified means of visualizing complex proteins. Several proteins are illustrated in Figure 12.4. These simplified structures only sketch the position of the protein chain and leave out the loca-

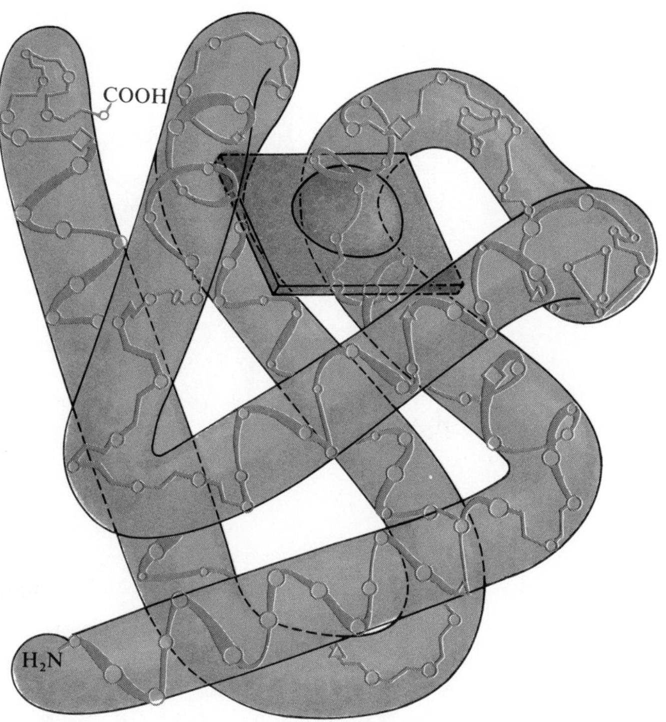

Myoglobin

◀ **FIGURE 12.3**
Tertiary structure of a protein, represented by myoglobin. The blue portion represents a heme group.

tion of the amino acid side chains. The α-helix is shown with a curling line while each strand of β-pleated sheet is a broader line with an arrowhead at its end to show which way the protein chain is running (from the amino end toward the carboxyl terminus). These pictures are sometimes referred to as "ribbon structures" based on the appearance of the protein strand.

Proteins share common skeletal structures just as various animal species have a common bone structure (see Figure 12.4). Some proteins use the α-helix like myoglobin. Spiral tubes are twisted around to support the bulk of these protein domains. In other proteins the β-pleated sheet is configured to provide a rigid protein framework. Some proteins have a fan of β-pleated sheet (or twisted sheet) while for other molecules the β-pleated sheet has wrapped around on itself to form a barrel. As the structures of more and more proteins are examined, it is apparent that there are at least several common protein skeletons. The twisted sheet and β-barrel are forms taken by the β-pleated sheet while the α-helix often is found on the outside of the β-pleated sheet or in bundles of four, Figure 12.5 (page 305).

Note that these ribbon structures make it easy to follow the protein chain and to see how the secondary structure is arranged, *but* they do not provide a true picture of a protein. In reality proteins are solid, as shown with the space-filling model of an enzyme (phosphoglycerate kinase) in Figure 12.6 (page 306). The hydrophobic amino acids tend to form the interior with the charged and polar amino acids on the surface where they can interact with water. Notice that this protein has two domains connected through a relatively narrow center.

quaternary structure

A fourth type of structure, called **quaternary structure**, is found in some complex proteins. These proteins are made up of two or more smaller protein subunits (polypeptide chains). Nonprotein components may also be present. The

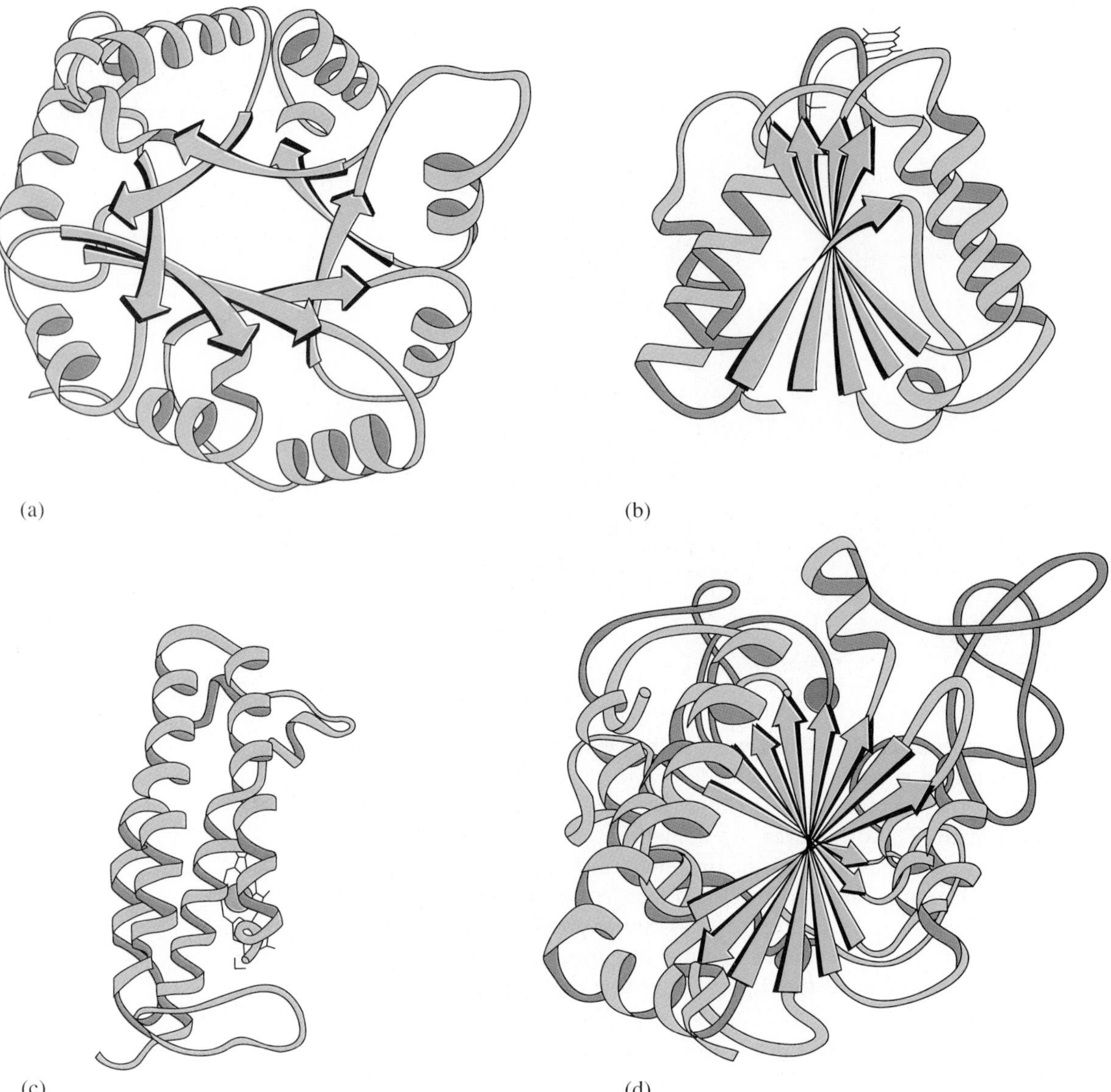

▲
FIGURE 12.4
Ribbon structures of several proteins. (a) Triose phosphate isomerase, an enzyme used in glucose metabolism; (b) flavodoxin, a conjugated protein found in some bacteria; (c) cytochrome c′, a conjugated protein which contains a heme group and is important in cellular energy metabolism; (d) carboxypeptidase, an enzyme used in the digestion of proteins.

quaternary structure refers to the shape of the entire complex molecule and is determined by the way in which the subunits are held together by *noncovalent* bonds—that is, by hydrogen bonding, ionic bonding, and so on.

Quaternary structure is commonly important in proteins that are involved in the control of metabolic processes. For example, hemoglobin, the oxygen transport protein of the blood, is composed of four subunits (see Figure 12.7, page 306). Each subunit is similar to myoglobin in that a set of helical segments surround the oxygen-binding heme group. Of course, the important structural difference is that hemoglobin has a quaternary structure. This leads to an equally important functional difference. Whereas myoglobin always binds and releases oxygen in the same way, hemoglobin changes its oxygen-binding characteristics depending on the available O_2. When hemoglobin binds oxygen on one subunit,

FIGURE 12.5 ▶ Common protein skeletal structures. (a) Twisted sheet of β-pleated sheet; (b) β-barrel of β-pleated sheet; (c) bundle of four α-helices.

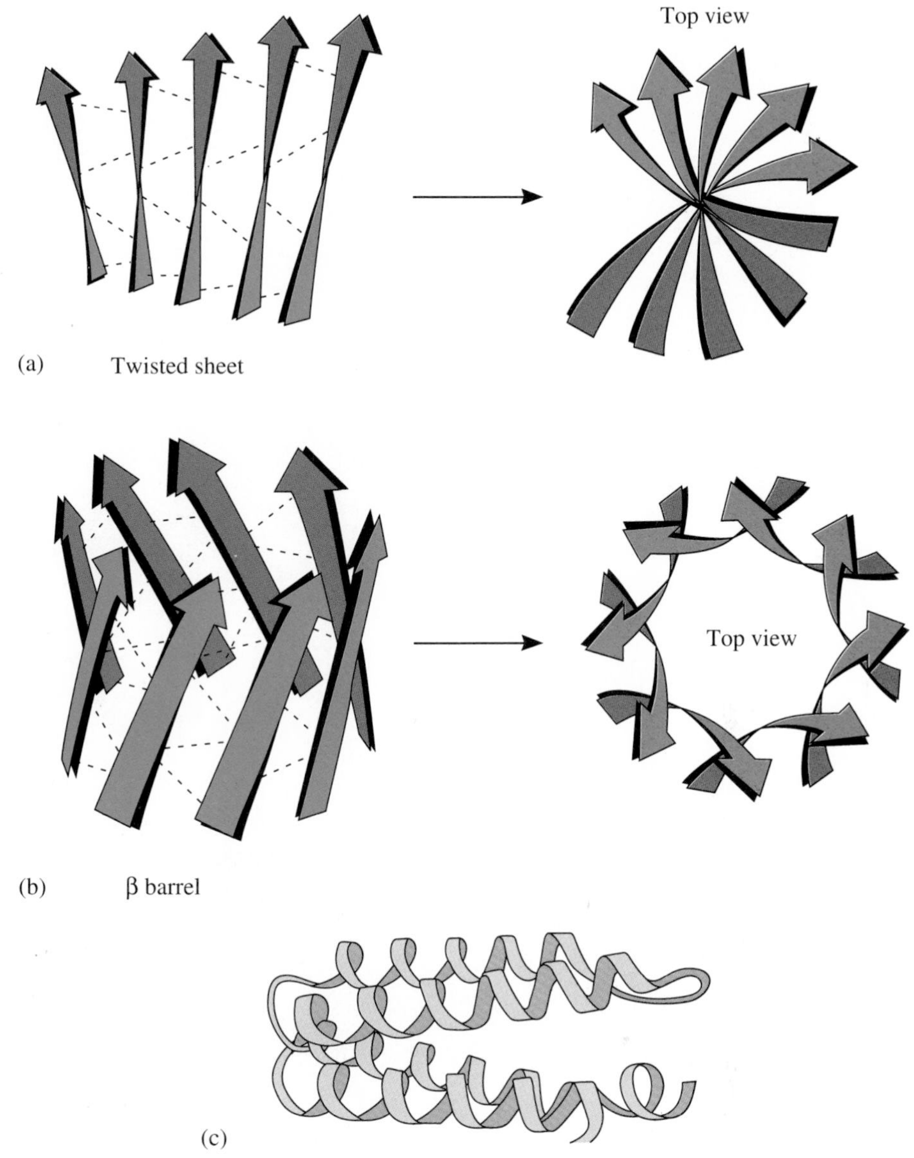

the protein's conformation changes to facilitate the binding of three additional oxygen molecules (see Figure 12.8, page 307). The oxygen binding is said to be *cooperative*—that is, the binding of an oxygen at one site promotes oxygen binding on the other three sites. In an oxygen-rich environment, hemoglobin becomes saturated with oxygen.

Conversely, the loss of one oxygen from hemoglobin facilitates the release of oxygen from the other sites. As hemoglobin moves to the oxygen-needy body tissues, its oxygen is cooperatively released. The presence of a quaternary structure allows the binding or removal of one oxygen molecule to control the binding or removal of three other oxygen molecules. Hence, the oxygen transport effectiveness of hemoglobin is multiplied by the quaternary structure.

FIGURE 12.6 ►
Space-filling model of the enzyme phosphoglycerate kinase. Note the two protein domains separated by the narrow central region.

FIGURE 12.7 ►
Quaternary structure of a protein, represented by hemoglobin: A set of axes has been drawn through the molecule to help visualize the position of each protein chain. The heme groups are symbolized by rectangular solids located in the middle of each protein chain.

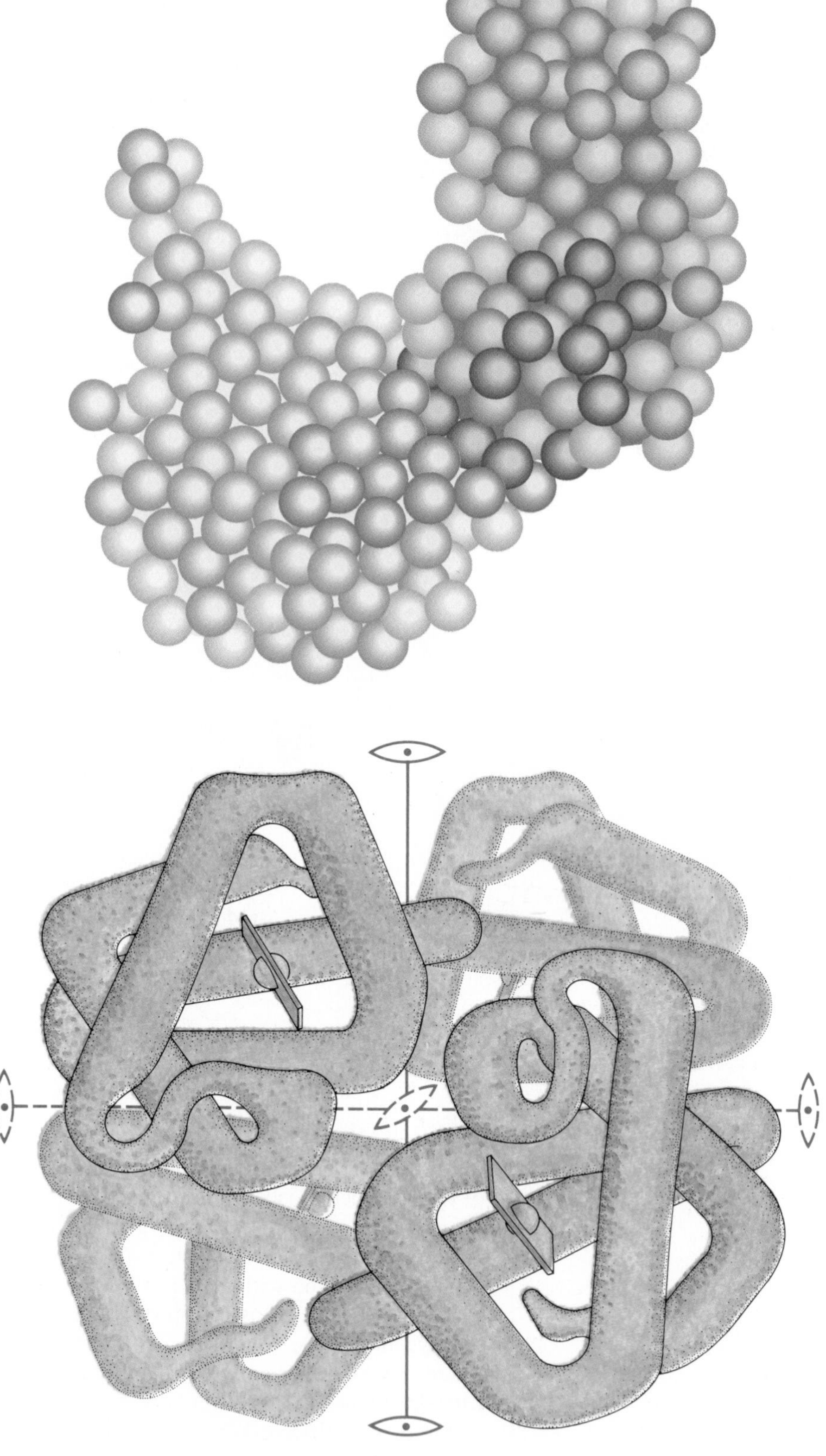

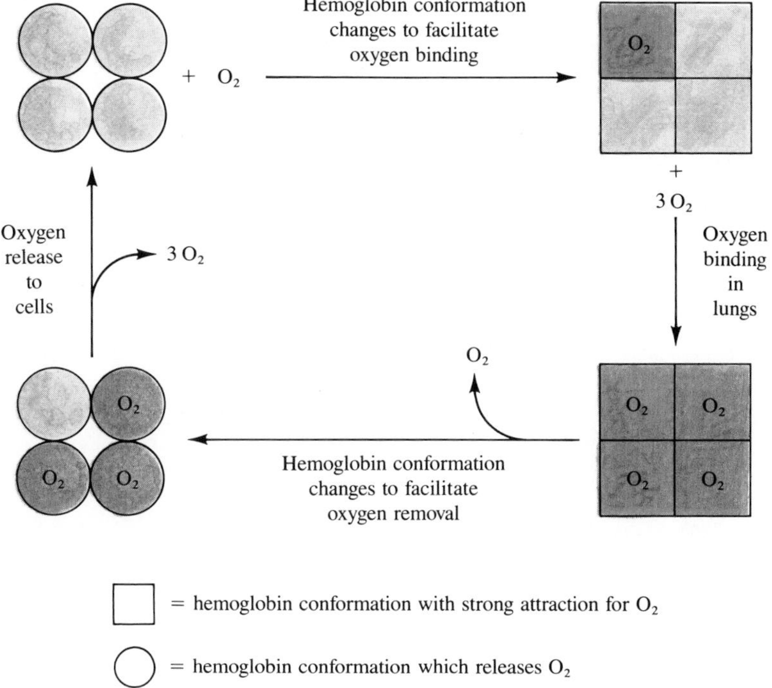

◀ **FIGURE 12.8**
A schematic representation of the oxygen–hemoglobin binding process. The circles and the squares represent two different conformations of the hemoglobin molecule. Oxygen binding or release causes hemoglobin to change its conformation.

Even minor alterations in primary structure may have drastic effects on the three-dimensional structural function of a protein. A graphic example of this fact is provided by sickle-cell anemia. This crippling genetic disease is due to red blood cells assuming a sickle shape. Sickled cells have impaired vitality and function. Sickle-cell anemia has been traced to a small change in the primary structure, or amino acid residue sequence, of hemoglobin. Normal hemoglobin molecules contain four polypeptide subunits—two identical α-polypeptide chains and two identical β-polypeptide chains. Sickle-cell and normal β-polypeptide chains of hemoglobin each contain 146 amino acid residues and differ only in the residue at the sixth position. In the sickle-cell hemoglobin chain, a glutamic acid residue has been replaced by a valine residue in this position. This change is sufficient, under some circumstances, to cause hemoglobin to aggregate into long filaments—a different quaternary structure. Large amounts of hemoglobin are present in red blood cells, and the changed quaternary structure causes sickling of the cell and greatly diminishes cell vitality (see Figure 12.9). This cell affliction has led to the premature deaths of many affected individuals.

To summarize, there are four classes of protein structure, and each has a different function.

1. Primary structure is defined by the amino acid residue sequence of the polypeptide chain. This sequence determines the shapes, or conformations, into which a protein can be arranged.
2. Secondary structure is a regular, repeating three-dimensional conformation held together by hydrogen bonding between components of the amide bonds of the primary chain. Hydrogen bonding can be between bonds in the same chain (for instance, the α-helix) or between bonds in

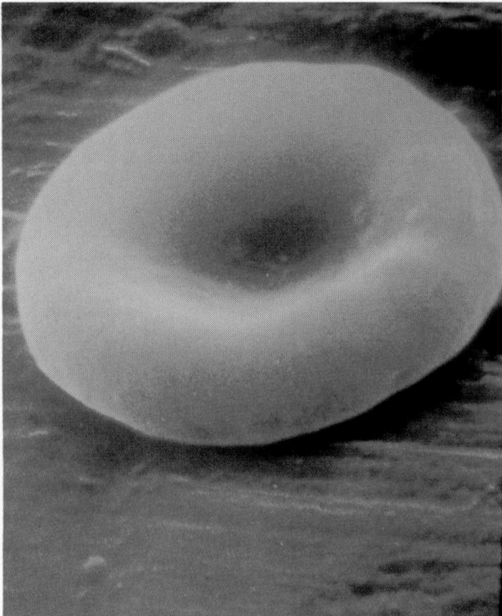

Figure 12.9 ► **Scanning electron micrograph of sickled red blood cell (left) and normal red blood cell (right).**

adjacent chains (for instance, the β-pleated sheet). The secondary structure imparts strength to proteins.

3. Tertiary structure is the overall three-dimensional structural conformation of the protein molecule. Various kinds of bonding interactions between components of the amino acid side chains stabilize the tertiary structure. The biological function of a protein is ultimately determined by the tertiary structure.
4. Quaternary structure, present in some proteins, describes the three-dimensional arrangement of subunits linked together by noncovalent bonds. The subunits have their own primary, secondary, and tertiary structures. Quaternary structure is often a prerequisite for proteins involved in the control of metabolic processes.

12.8 Functions of Proteins

Proteins serve a variety of very important biological functions as dictated by their diverse structures. A listing of general protein functions includes (1) structural, (2) catalytic, (3) hormonal, and (4) binding. The catalytic function is perhaps the most important and will be discussed in Chapter 13. However, each of the other functions is also vital to life. In the next several paragraphs, important examples of each function will be discussed. Note how each protein's structure critically determines its function.

Collagen, an example of a structural protein, is the most abundant protein in the body. It forms the bone matrix around which the calcium phosphate mineral can crystallize. Ligaments, tendons, and skin are composed of a large proportion of collagen. The structure of this protein allows it to provide a strong framework for each of these tissues. As shown in Figure 12.1, collagen is a long

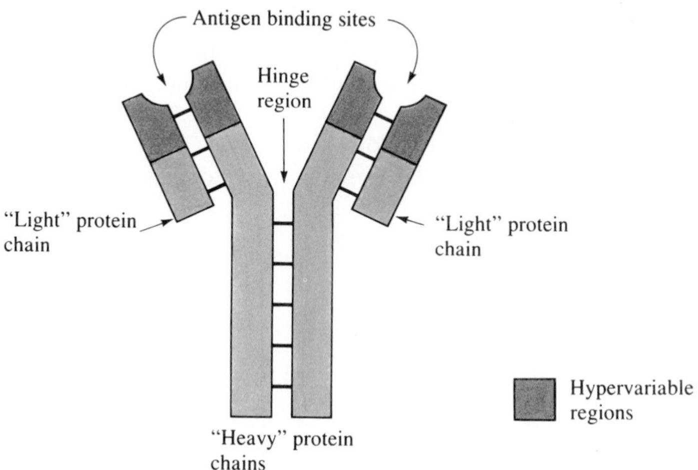

◀ **FIGURE 12.10 Diagrammatic shape of a typical immunoglobulin G protein.**

slender protein whose three strands are wrapped one around another as a rope would be woven, and, like a rope, the finished product is much stronger than a single strand. These triple helices are in turn stacked together like cordwood to form collagen fibers. The resulting tough material can be aligned to form tendons or deposited as a network to form a bone or skin structure. Next time you take a stride, recognize the force exerted on your Achilles tendon and how important the strength of collagen is to life.

Binding proteins serve a multitude of functions from transport of oxygen (by hemoglobin) to transport of vital nutrients across the intestinal membranes to binding of invading bacteria via the immune response. In each case, the protein structure is designed to efficiently accomplish its function. For example, consider the immunoglobulins (antibodies), proteins responsible for binding molecules foreign to the body. A successful immunological response requires that our bodies be prepared with a protein whose binding site is closely complementary to each of millions of different invading molecules (antigens). Just how our body accomplishes this feat can be described starting with the shape of a typical immunoglobulin G (Figure 12.10). Antigen binding regions are located at the ends of two arms. These are hinged together so that the distance between binding sites can vary with the size of the invading particle. The immunoglobulin protein chains are endowed with special hypervariable regions; every different immunoglobulin has a distinct amino acid sequence in its antigen binding sites and, therefore, has sites of unique size and shape. The body ensures that there will be immunoglobulins for many different antigens by producing millions of proteins with different hypervariable regions. Note that two different protein chains make up the antigen binding site. Since each chain has a hypervariable region that can be changed independently, the body has the ability to produce upwards of 10^{10} (ten billion) immunoglobulins with different binding sites, more than enough to handle exposure to invading particles.

Proteins or polypeptides that function as hormones are first synthesized in the cell as larger precursor molecules. Because these proteins are designed to be exported into the bloodstream, their structures share a common polypeptide segment, called a *signal peptide*. This amino acid sequence causes proteins to be moved into the endoplasmic reticulum, where they can be modified to become hormonally active. Bovine insulin, for example, starts out as a protein 107 amino acids long. When it arrives in the endoplasmic reticulum, the signal peptide (23 amino acids) is removed because it is no longer needed. Then a middle section of the protein is removed (33 amino acids), leaving the active form of insulin as two chains bonded together by three disulfide bonds (see Figure 12.2). Even the small polypeptide hormones like vasopressin or oxytocin are derived from much larger precursors; these 9-amino-acid-long peptides are derived from proteins of 215 and 160 amino acids, respectively.

12.9 Loss of Protein Structure

denaturation

Because protein structure is so important to life's functions, the loss of protein structure can be crucial. If a protein loses only its native three-dimensional conformation, the process is referred to as **denaturation**. In contrast, hydrolysis of peptide bonds ultimately converts proteins into their constituent amino acids. Often denaturation precedes hydrolysis.

Denaturation involves alteration or disruption of the secondary, tertiary, or quaternary—but not primary—structure of proteins (see Figure 12.11). Because a protein's function depends on its natural conformation, biological activity is lost with denaturation. This process may involve changes ranging from the subtle and reversible alterations caused by a slight pH shift to the extreme alterations involved in tanning a skin to form leather.

Environmental changes may easily disrupt natural protein structure, which is held together predominantly by noncovalent, relatively weak bonds. As gentle an act as pouring a protein solution can cause denaturation. Purified proteins must often be stored under ice-cold conditions because room temperature denatures them. It is not surprising that a wide variety of chemical and physical agents also can denature proteins. To name a few: strong acids and strong bases, salts (especially those of heavy metals), certain specific reagents such as tannic acid and picric acid, alcohol and other organic solvents, detergents, mechanical action such as whipping, high temperature, and ultraviolet radiation. Denatured proteins are generally less soluble than native proteins and often coagulate or precipitate from solution. Cooks have taken advantage of this for many years. When egg white, which is a concentrated solution of egg albumin protein, is stirred vigorously (as with an egg beater), an unsweetened meringue forms; the albumin denatures and coagulates. A cooked egg solidifies partially because egg proteins including albumin are denatured by heat.

In clinical laboratories the analysis of blood serum for small molecules such as glucose and uric acid is hampered by the presence of serum protein. This problem is resolved by first treating the serum with an acid to denature and precipitate the protein. The precipitate is removed and the protein-free liquid is then analyzed.

Loss of protein structure also occurs with hydrolysis of the peptide bonds to produce free amino acids. This chemical reaction destroys the protein's primary structure. Proteins can be hydrolyzed by boiling in a solution containing a strong acid such as HCl or a strong base such as NaOH. At ordinary temperatures proteins can be hydrolyzed using enzymes (see Chapter 13). These molecules, called proteolytic enzymes, are themselves proteins that function to

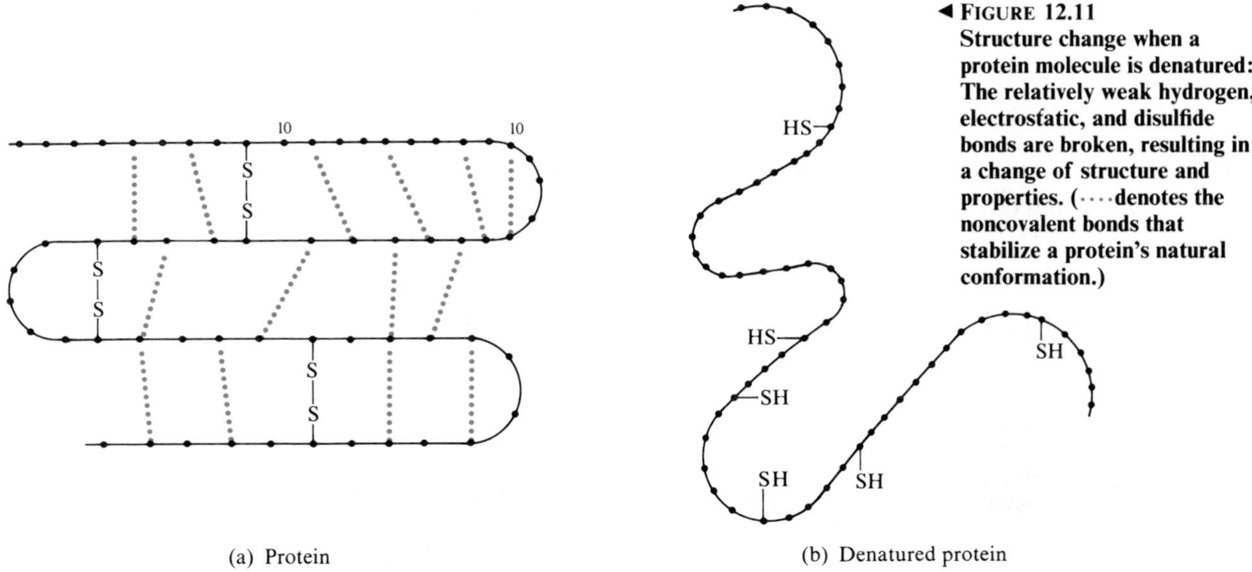

◀ **FIGURE 12.11**
Structure change when a protein molecule is denatured: The relatively weak hydrogen, electrostatic, and disulfide bonds are broken, resulting in a change of structure and properties. (····denotes the noncovalent bonds that stabilize a protein's natural conformation.)

catalyze or speed up the hydrolysis reaction. The essential reaction of hydrolysis is the breaking of a peptide linkage and the addition of the elements of water:

Peptide linkage in protein chain

$$\begin{array}{ccccccccccccccccccccc}
 & H & & R & & O & & & & H & & & & & & & H & & R & & O & & & & & & H & & \\
 & | & & | & & \| & & & & | & & & & & & & | & & | & & \| & & & & & & | & & \\
\sim & N & - & C & - & C & - & N & - & C & - & C\sim & + H_2O \longrightarrow & \sim & N & - & C & - & C & - & OH & + & H_2N & - & C & - & C\sim \\
 & & & | & & & & | & & | & & \| & & & & & | & & & & & & & & | & & \| \\
 & & & H & & & & H & & R & & O & & & & & H & & & & & & & & R & & O
\end{array}$$

(∿∿ = the rest of the protein chain)

Any molecule with one or more peptide bonds, from the smallest dipeptide to the largest protein molecule, can be hydrolyzed. During hydrolysis, proteins are broken down into smaller and smaller fragments until all component amino acids are liberated.

Dietary protein must have its structure completely destroyed before it can provide nutrition for the body. Thus, digestion involves both the processes of denaturation and hydrolysis. Stomach acid causes most proteins to denature. Then, proteolytic enzymes in the stomach and the small intestine hydrolyze the proteins to smaller and smaller fragments until the free amino acids are formed and can be absorbed through the intestinal membranes into the bloodstream.

12.10 TESTS FOR PROTEINS AND AMINO ACIDS

Many tests have been devised for detecting and distinguishing among amino acids, peptides, and proteins. Some examples are described here.

Xanthoproteic Reaction Proteins containing a benzene ring—for example, the amino acids phenylalanine, tryptophan, and tyrosine—react with concentrated nitric acid to give yellow reaction products. Nitric acid on skin produces a positive xanthoproteic test, as skin proteins are modified by this reaction.

Biuret Test A violet color is produced when dilute copper(II) sulfate is added to an alkaline solution of a peptide or protein. At least two peptide bonds must be present, as the color change occurs only when peptide bonds can surround the Cu^{2+} ion. Thus, amino acids and dipeptides do not give a positive biuret test.

Ninhydrin Test Triketohydrindene hydrate, generally known as *ninhydrin*, is an extremely sensitive reagent for amino acids:

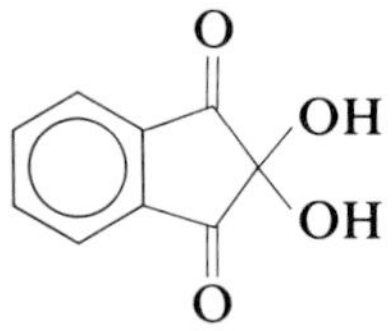

O OH OH O

Ninhydrin

All amino acids, except proline and hydroxyproline, give a blue solution with ninhydrin. Proline and hydroxyproline produce a yellow solution. Less than 1 μg (10^{-6} g) of an amino acid can be detected with ninhydrin.

Chromatographic Separation

Complex mixtures of amino acids are readily separated by thin layer, paper, or column chromatography. In chromatographic methods the components of a mixture are separated by means of differences in their distributions between two phases. Separation depends on the relative tendencies of the components to remain in one phase or the other. In *thin-layer chromatography* (TLC), for example, a liquid and a solid phase are used. The procedure is as follows: A tiny drop of a solution containing a mixture of amino acids (obtained by hydrolyzing a protein) is spotted on a strip (or sheet) coated with a thin layer of dried alumina or some other adsorbant. After the spot has dried, the bottom edge of the strip is put into a suitable solvent. The solvent ascends the strip (by diffusion), carrying the different amino acids upward at different rates. When the solvent front nears the top, the strip is removed from the solvent and dried. The locations of the different amino acids are established by spraying the strip with ninhydrin solution and noting where colored spots appear. The pattern of colored spots is called a chromatogram. The identities of the amino acids in an unknown mixture can be established by comparing the chromatogram of the mixture with a chromatogram produced by known amino acids. A typical chromatogram of amino acids is shown in Figure 12.12.

Since proteins tend to denature during thin-layer chromatography, they are often separated by column chromatography. In this technique a solution containing a mixture of proteins (liquid phase) is allowed to percolate through a column packed with beads of a suitable polymer (solid phase). Separation of the mixture is accomplished as the proteins partition between the solid and liquid phases. The separated proteins move at different rates and are collected as they leave the column. Unlike amino acid chromatography, mild conditions must be

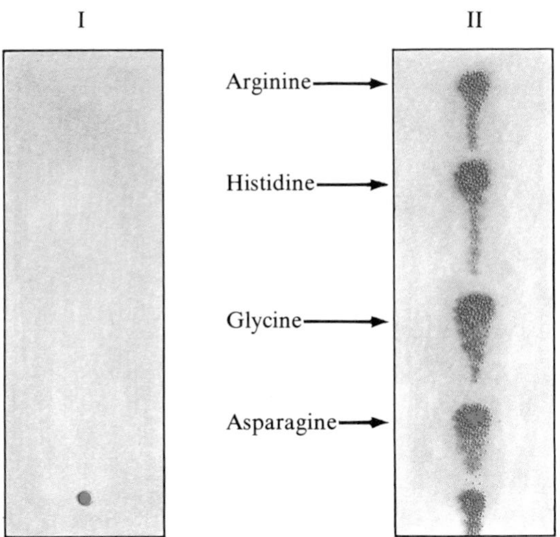

FIGURE 12.12 Chromatogram showing separation of selected amino acids. On the left, spotted on the chromatographic strip, is an amino acid mixture containing arginine, histidine, glycine, and asparagine. On the right is the developed chromatogram showing the separated amino acids after treatment with ninhydrin. The solvent is a 250:60:250 volume ratio of 1-butanol–acetic acid–water.

maintained to limit protein denaturation. In the past it was not uncommon for a protein column chromatography to take from 6 to 12 hours. Recent developments in the field of high-performance liquid chromatography (HPLC) have shortened this time to minutes.

12.11 Determination of the Primary Structure of Polypeptides

Sanger's Reagent The pioneering work of Frederick Sanger gave us the first complete primary structure of a protein, insulin, in 1955. He used specific enzymes to hydrolyze insulin into smaller peptides and amino acids, then separated and identified the hydrolytic products by various chemical reactions.

Sanger's reagent, 2-4-dinitrofluorobenzene (DNFB), reacts with the α-amino group of the N-terminal amino acid of a polypeptide chain. The carbon–nitrogen bond between the amino acid and the benzene ring is more resistant to hydrolysis than are the remaining peptide linkages. Thus, when the substituted polypeptide is hydrolyzed, the terminal amino acid remains with the dinitrobenzene radical and can be isolated and identified. The remaining peptide chain is hydrolyzed to free amino acids in the process. This method marked an important step in the determination of the amino acid sequence in a protein. The reaction of Sanger's reagent is illustrated in the following equations:

$$\underset{\text{DNFB}}{O_2N\text{-}C_6H_3(NO_2)\text{-}F} + \underset{\text{Polypeptide chain}}{H\text{—}NH\text{—}CHR\text{—}CO\text{—}NH\text{—}CHR\text{—}CO\text{—}}$$

$$\xrightarrow{\text{Alkaline}} \underset{\text{DNFB polypeptide derivative}}{O_2N\text{-}C_6H_3(NO_2)\text{—}NH\text{—}CHR\text{—}CO\text{—}NH\text{—}CHR\text{—}CO\text{—}}$$

$$\xrightarrow{\text{Acid hydrolysis}} \underset{\text{DNFB-terminal amino acid derivative}}{O_2N\text{-}C_6H_3(NO_2)\text{—}NH\text{—}CHR\text{—}COOH} + \underset{\text{Mixture of amino acids}}{H_3N^+\text{—}CHR\text{—}COOH}$$

From the DNFB hydrolysis, Sanger learned which amino acids were present in insulin. By less drastic hydrolysis, he split the insulin molecule into peptide fragments consisting of two, three, four, or more amino acid residues. After analyzing vast numbers of fragments utilizing the N-terminal method, he pieced them together in the proper sequence by combining fragments with overlapping structures at their ends, finally elucidating the entire insulin structure. As an example, consider the overlap that occurs between the hexapeptide and heptapeptide shown below:

Gly-Glu-Arg-	Gly-Phe-Phe		Hexapeptide
	Gly-Phe-Phe-	Tyr-Thr-Pro-Lys	Heptapeptide
Gly-Glu-Arg-	Gly-Phe-Phe-	Tyr-Thr-Pro-Lys	Decapeptide

The three residues Gly-Phe-Phe at the end of the hexapeptide match the three residues at the beginning of the heptapeptide. By using these three residues in common, the structure of the decapeptide shown, which occurs in chain B of insulin (residues 20–29), is determined. (See Figure 12.2, which shows the amino acid sequence of insulin.)

Edman Degradation More recently, the Edman degradation method has been developed to split off amino acids one at a time from the N-terminal end of a polypeptide chain. In this procedure the reagent, phenylisothiocyanate, is first added to the N-terminal amino group. The N-terminal amino acid–phenylisothiocyanate addition product is then cleaved from the polypeptide chain. The resultant substituted phenylthiohydantoin is then isolated and identified. The shortened polypeptide chain is then ready to undergo another Edman degradation. By repeating this set of reactions, one can determine directly the amino acid sequence of a polypeptide. A machine, the protein sequenator, which carries out protein sequencing by Edman degradation automatically, is now available.

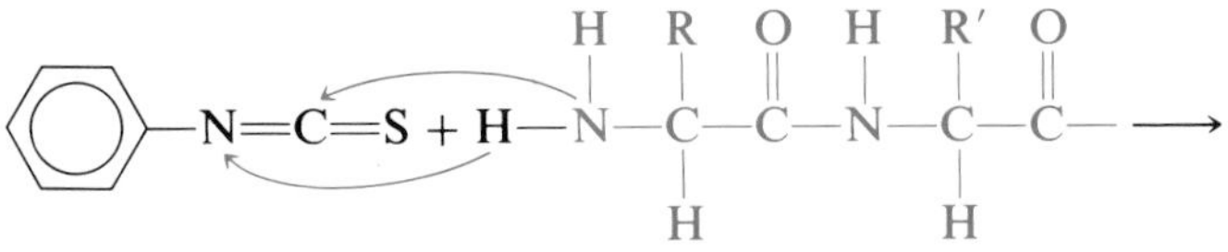

Phenylisothiocyanate

Polypeptide chain

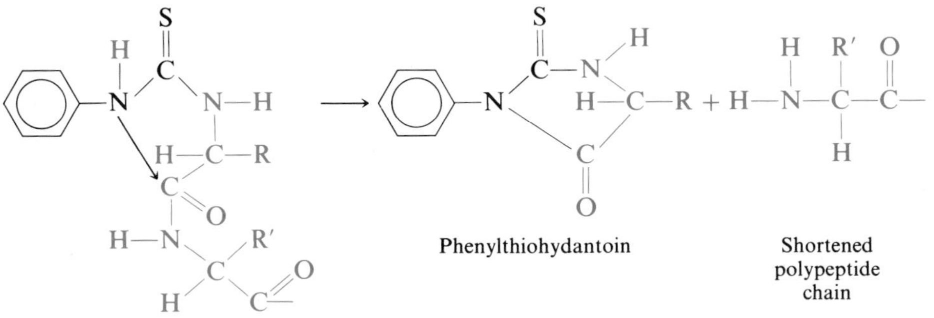

Phenylthiohydantoin

Shortened polypeptide chain

12.12 Synthesis of Peptides and Proteins

Since each amino acid has two functional groups, it is not difficult to form dipeptides or even fairly large polypeptide molecules. As mentioned in Section 12.6, glycine and alanine react to form two different dipeptides, glycylalanine and alanylglycine. If threonine, alanine, and glycine react, six tripeptides, each made up of three different amino acids, are obtained. By reacting a mixture of several amino acids, polypeptides are produced that contain a random arrangement of the amino acid units. This fact makes it clear that even a small protein like insulin could not be produced by simply reacting a mixture of the required amino acids. When such a large polypeptide is synthesized, it is formed by joining amino acids one by one in the proper sequence. Within cells, the proper sequence is maintained by careful genetic control (see Section 14.10).

When a polypeptide chain of known primary structure is synthesized *in vitro* (synthesis in "glass" without the aid of living tissue), the process must be controlled so that only one particular amino acid is added at each stage. Remarkable progress has been made in developing the necessary techniques. Amino acids are used in which either the amino or carboxylic acid group has been inactivated or blocked with a suitable *blocking agent*. The blocked amino or carboxylic acid group is reactivated by removing the blocking agent in the next stage of the synthesis. For example, if the tripeptide Thr-Ala-Gly is to be made, amino-blocked threonine is reacted with carboxyl-blocked alanine to make the doubly blocked Thr-Ala dipeptide. The carboxyl-blocked alanine end of the dipeptide can then be reactivated and reacted with carboxyl-blocked glycine to make the blocked Thr-Ala-Gly tripeptide. The free tripeptide can then be obtained by removing the blocking agents from both ends. Using [B] to designate the blocking agents, this synthesis is represented in schematic form as follows:

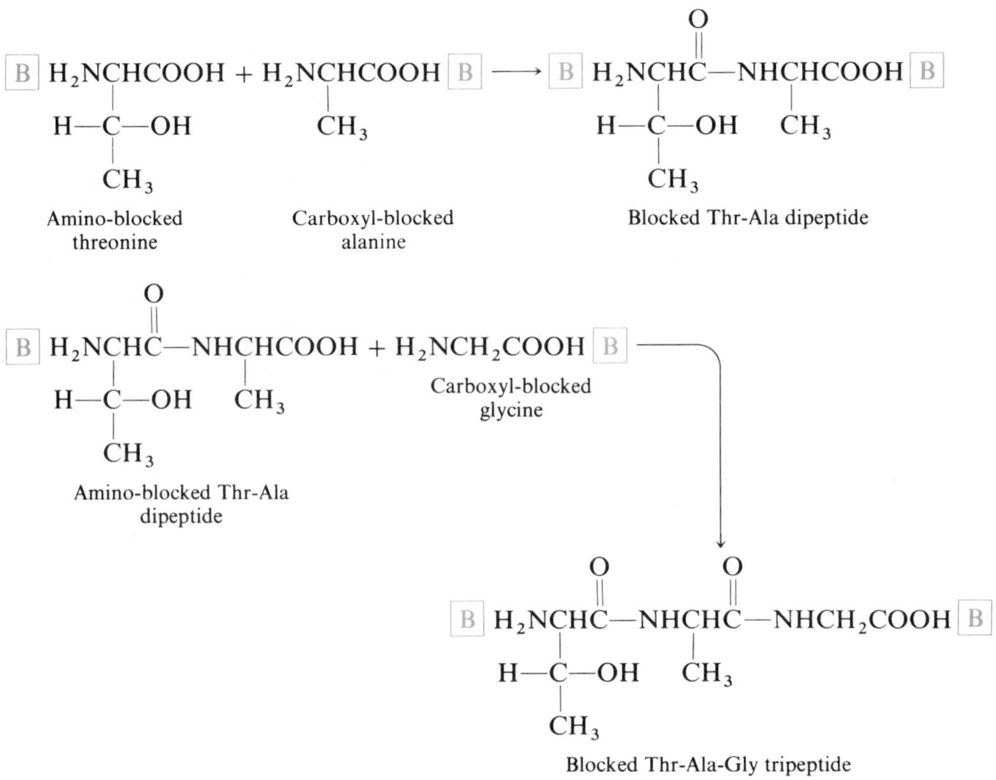

```
                                                                    O
                                                                    ‖
[B] H2NCHCOOH + H2NCHCOOH [B] ⟶ [B] H2NCHC—NHCHCOOH [B]
        |              |                |       |
     H—C—OH           CH3            H—C—OH    CH3
        |                               |
       CH3                             CH3
```

Amino-blocked threonine — Carboxyl-blocked alanine — Blocked Thr-Ala dipeptide

```
           O
           ‖
[B] H2NCHC—NHCHCOOH + H2NCH2COOH [B] ──┐
        |       |                       │
     H—C—OH    CH3                      │
        |                               │
       CH3                              ↓
                                    O        O
                                    ‖        ‖
                          [B] H2NCHC—NHCHC—NHCH2COOH [B]
                                  |      |
                               H—C—OH   CH3
                                  |
                                 CH3
```

Amino-blocked Thr-Ala dipeptide — Carboxyl-blocked glycine

Blocked Thr-Ala-Gly tripeptide

Longer polypeptide chains of specified amino acid sequence can be made by this general technique. The procedure is very tedious. The synthesis of insulin required an effort equivalent to one person working steadily for several years.

It is not necessary to prepare an entire synthetic protein polypeptide chain by starting at one end and adding amino acids one at a time. Previously prepared shorter polypeptide chains of known structure can be joined to form a longer polypeptide chain. This method was used in making synthetic insulin. The insulin molecule, shown in Figure 12.2, consists of two polypeptide chains bonded together by two disulfide bonds. A third disulfide bond, between two amino acids in one chain, makes a small loop in that chain. Once the two chains had been assembled from fragments, a seemingly formidable problem remained—how to form the disulfide bonds in the correct positions. As it turned out, it was necessary only to bring the two chains together, with the cysteine side chains in the reduced condition, and to treat them with an oxidizing agent. Disulfide bonds formed at the right places, and biologically active insulin molecules were obtained.

In the mid-1960s a machine capable of automatically synthesizing polypeptide chains of known amino acid sequence was designed by R. B. Merrifield of Rockefeller University. The starting amino acid is bonded to a plastic surface (polystyrene bead) in the reaction chamber of the apparatus. Various reagents needed for building a chain of predetermined structures are automatically delivered to the reaction chamber in a programmed sequence. Twelve reagents and about 100 operations are needed to lengthen the chain by a single amino acid residue. But the machine is capable of adding residues to the chain at the rate of six a day. Such a machine makes it possible to synthesize complex molecules like insulin in a few days. The first large polypeptide (pancreatic ribonuclease), containing 124 amino acid residues, was synthesized by this method in 1969. More recently a human growth hormone (HGH) containing 188 amino acid residues was synthesized using this technique.

Over the past ten years, techniques have been developed to use biological systems to create and produce new proteins. These procedures start with genetic material which codes for the protein of interest. Then this material is properly modified and introduced into rapidly growing cells that are treated to overproduce this foreign protein. The result can be a harvest of much needed protein, such as the human insulin used by diabetics or the human growth hormone used to treat dwarfism. These procedures constitute a part of genetic engineering and will be discussed in more detail in Chapter 14. The advantages of these new techniques can be realized by comparing the rate of biological protein synthesis with that achieved by the machine designed by Merrifield. If a bacterium such as *E. coli* is used to produce a human protein such as growth hormone, one amino acid residue can be added every 0.01 second; a growth hormone molecule can be produced every 10 to 20 seconds. In contrast, the same growth hormone would take days to produce in the chemistry laboratory.

▲
Production of a cloned protein. The technician is holding a container with cultured cells in a nutrient medium.

Concepts in Review

1. List five foods that are major sources of proteins.
2. List the elements that are usually contained in proteins.
3. Write formulas for and know the abbreviations for the common amino acids.
4. Write the zwitterion formula of an amino acid and know how it behaves in a dilute acidic and in a dilute basic solution.
5. Understand why a protein in solution at its isoelectric pH does not migrate in an electrolytic cell.
6. Combine amino acids into polypeptide chains.
7. Understand how peptide chains are named and numbered.
8. Understand what is meant by the N-terminal and C-terminal residues of a peptide chain.
9. Briefly explain the primary, secondary, and tertiary structure of a protein.
10. Explain the meaning of the statement, "The primary structure helps establish a protein's three-dimensional structure."
11. Define quaternary structure and explain its importance in the function of hemoglobin.
12. Understand the bonding in the α-helical and β-pleated-sheet structure of a protein.
13. Give an example of a structural protein.
14. Explain the role cysteine plays in the structure of polypeptides and proteins.
15. Describe how the α-helix and β-pleated sheet are important in the structure of protein domains.

16. List the most important protein functions.
17. Relate the structure of collagen to its biological function.
18. Discuss the role of the immunoglobulins in the body's defense mechanisms and identify important structural elements of these proteins.
19. Explain the importance of peptide bond cleavage in the formation of protein and peptide hormones.
20. Describe Sanger's work on determining the primary structure of proteins.
21. Reconstruct a peptide chain from a knowledge of its hydrolysis products.
22. Explain how Edman degradation allows the primary structure to be determined.
23. Describe chromatographic methods of separating amino acids.
24. State the physical evidence observed in a positive reaction in the (a) xanthoproteic reaction, (b) biuret test, and (c) ninhydrin test.
25. Know what is meant by denaturation and the various methods by which proteins can be denatured.

Equations in Review

Ionization of Amino Acids

$$\underset{\substack{\text{Cation form}\\ \text{II}}}{\underset{\displaystyle NH_3^+}{\underset{|}{RCHCOOH}}} \underset{OH^-}{\overset{H^+}{\rightleftharpoons}} \underset{\substack{\text{Zwitterion form}\\ \text{I}}}{\underset{\displaystyle NH_3^+}{\underset{|}{RCHCOO^-}}} \underset{H^+}{\overset{OH^-}{\rightleftharpoons}} \underset{\substack{\text{Anion form}\\ \text{III}}}{\underset{\displaystyle NH_2}{\underset{|}{RCHCOO^-}}}$$

(Similar reactions may occur on the R groups of specific amino acids.)

Reaction Between Amino Acids to Form a Peptide Linkage

$$\underset{\displaystyle NH_2}{\underset{|}{RCHCOOH}} + \underset{\displaystyle NH_2}{\underset{|}{RCHCOOH}} \longrightarrow \underset{\displaystyle NH_2}{\underset{|}{RCH}}\overset{\displaystyle O}{\overset{\|}{C}}{-}NH{-}\overset{\displaystyle R}{\overset{|}{C}}HCOOH + H_2O$$

Hydrolysis of the Peptide Linkage in Proteins

Peptide linkage in protein chain

$$\sim N(H){-}C(H)(R){-}C(=O){-}N(H){-}C(H)(R){-}C(=O)\sim + H_2O \longrightarrow \sim N(H){-}C(H)(R){-}C(=O){-}OH + H_2N{-}C(H)(R){-}C(=O)\sim$$

($\sim$ = rest of protein chain)

EXERCISES

1. List four foods that are major sources of proteins.
2. Why are the amino acids of proteins called α-amino acids?
3. What elements are present in amino acids and proteins?
4. Why are proteins from some foods of greater nutritional value than others?
5. Write the names of the amino acids that are essential to humans.
6. What two general methods are now available for improving the nutritional value of corn protein?
7. Which amino acids contain a heterocyclic ring?
8. Write the structural formulas for D-serine and L-serine. Which form is found in proteins?
9. Why are the amino acids amphoteric? Why are they optically active?
10. Write the structural formula representing threonine at its isoelectric point.
11. For phenylalanine write:
    (a) The molecular formula
    (b) The zwitterion formula
    (c) The formula in 0.1 M H_2SO_4
    (d) The formula in 0.1 M NaOH
12. Write ionic equations to show how alanine acts as a buffer toward:
    (a) H^+ ion (b) OH^- ion
13. (a) At what pH will arginine not migrate to either electrode in an electrolytic cell?
    (b) In what pH range will it migrate toward the positive electrode?
14. What can you say about the number of positive and negative charges on a protein molecule at its isoelectric point?
15. At what pH will the following amino acids be at their isoelectric points?
    (a) Histidine (c) Glutamic acid
    (b) Phenylalanine
16. Write out the full structural formula of the two dipeptides containing glycine and phenylalanine. Indicate the location of the peptide bonds.
17. Write structures for:
    (a) Glycylglycine
    (b) Glycylglycylalanine
    (c) Leucylmethionylglycylserine
18. Using amino acid abbreviations, write all the possible tripeptides containing one unit each of glycine, phenylalanine, and leucine.
19. How many dipeptides containing glycine can be written using the 20 amino acids from Table 12.1?
20. Explain what is meant by (a) the primary structure, (b) the secondary structure, and (c) the tertiary structure of a protein.
21. What special role does the sulfur-containing amino acid cysteine have in protein structure?
22. How do myoglobin and hemoglobin differ in structure and function?
23. Briefly describe the protein skeletal shapes formed by the β-pleated sheet.
24. How do amino acids like alanine and leucine help stabilize the three-dimensional structure of a protein?
25. Ribonuclease is a protein that is slightly smaller than myoglobin. How many protein domains would you predict for the structure of ribonuclease?
26. List four general functions performed by proteins.
27. How are the hypervariable regions in immunoglobulin chains important to this protein's function?
28. Protein hormones are often modified before they become active. What is a signal peptide, and how is it important in protein modification?
29. Suggest a reason why proteins tend to be easily denatured.
30. Explain how hydrolysis of a protein differs from denaturation.
31. What chemical change occurs when a protein is hydrolyzed to amino acids?
32. What is the visible evidence observed in a positive reaction for the following tests?
    (a) Xanthoproteic reaction
    (b) Biuret test
    (c) Ninhydrin test
33. Would Thr-Ala-Gly react with each of the following?
    (a) Sanger's reagent
    (b) Concentrated HNO_3 to give a positive xanthoproteic test
    (c) Ninhydrin
34. Which amino acids give a positive xanthoproteic test?
35. (a) What is thin-layer chromatography?
    (b) Describe how amino acids are separated using this technique.
    (c) What reagent is used to locate the amino acids in the chromatogram?
36. Briefly describe protein column chromatography.
37. Threonine has two asymmetric centers. Write

Fischer projection formulas for its stereoisomers.

38. Show the reactants and products for one complete cycle of the Edman degradation on the tripeptide Ala-Leu-Gly.

39. What is the amino acid sequence of heptapeptides A and B, which upon hydrolysis yield these tripeptides:
(A) Gly-Phe-Leu, Phe-Ala-Gly, Leu-Ala-Tyr
(B) Phe-Gly-Tyr, Phe-Ala-Ala, Ala-Leu-Phe
Both A and B contain one residue each of Gly, Leu, and Tyr and two residues each of Ala and Phe.

40. A nonapeptide is obtained from blood plasma by treatment with the enzyme trypsin. Analysis showed that both terminal amino acids are arginine. Total hydrolysis of this peptide yielded Gly, Ser, 2 Arg, 2 Phe, 3 Pro. Partial hydrolysis gave Phe-Ser, Phe-Arg, Arg-Pro, Pro-Pro, Pro-Gly-Phe, Ser-Pro-Phe. What is the amino acid sequence of the nonapeptide?

41. One hundred grams (100.0 g) of a food product was analyzed and found to contain 6.0 g of nitrogen. If protein contains an average of 16% nitrogen, what percentage of the food is protein?

42. Human hemoglobin contains 0.33% iron. If each hemoglobin molecule contains four iron atoms, what is the molar mass of hemoglobin?

43. Which of these statements are correct? Rewrite each incorrect statement to make it correct.
(a) Proteins, like fats and carbohydrates, are primarily for supplying heat and energy to the body.
(b) Proteins differ from fats and carbohydrates in that they contain a large amount of nitrogen.
(c) A complete protein is one that contains all the essential amino acids.
(d) Except for glycine, amino acids that are found in proteins have the L-configuration.
(e) All amino acids have an asymmetric carbon atom and are therefore optically active.
(f) The amide linkages by which amino acids are joined together are called peptide linkages.
(g) Two different dipeptides can be formed from the amino acids glycine and phenylalanine.
(h) The compound Ala-Phe-Tyr has two peptide bonds and is therefore known as a dipeptide.
(i) A zwitterion is a dipolar ion form of an amino acid.
(j) The primary structure of a protein is the α-helical or β-pleated-sheet form that it takes.
(k) The tertiary structure of a protein determines that protein's primary structure.
(l) The amino acid residues in a peptide chain are numbered beginning with the C-terminal amino acid.
(m) Insulin contains two polypeptide chains, one with 21 amino acids and the other with 30 amino acids.
(n) Amino acids are often removed from protein hormones to activate them.
(o) Collagen is an example of a binding protein.
(p) α-helices cluster into a "twisted sheet" conformation to form part of many protein skeletons.
(q) A protein structure with hinged arms provides binding flexibility for the immunoglobulins.
(r) When a protein is denatured, the polypeptide bonds are broken, liberating the amino acids.
(s) Irreversible coagulation or precipitation of proteins is called denaturation.
(t) Sanger's reagent reacts with peptide chains, isolating the N-terminal amino acid.

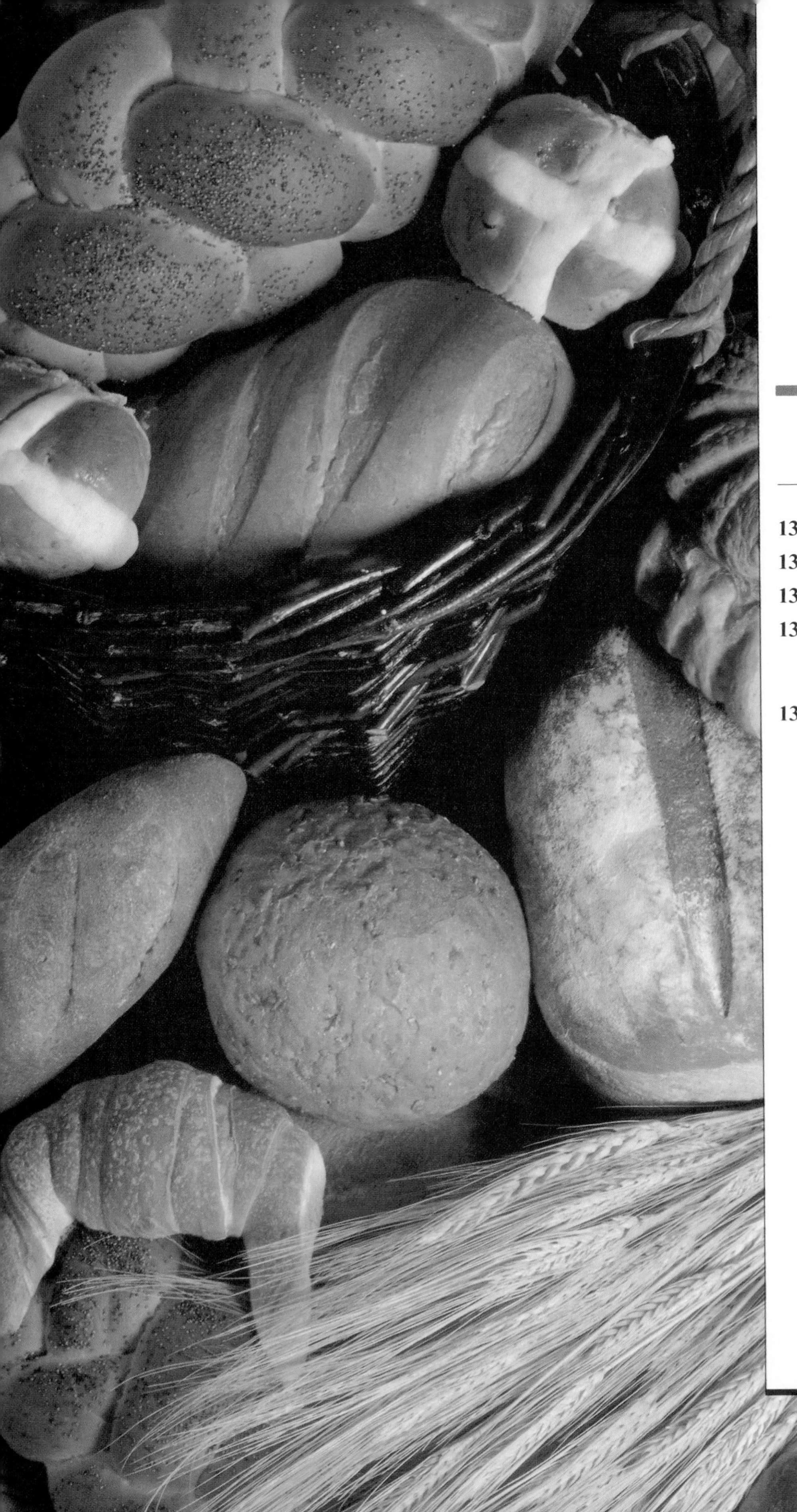

13

Enzymes

◀ Chapter Opening Photo: **Yeast provides the enzymes necessary to make bread rise.**

Perhaps you have seen laundry detergents advertised as "containing enzymes." These molecules are added to detergents in order to clean especially hard-to-remove spots. In life as well, enzymes take on the "tough" metabolic tasks—in fact, life cannot continue in the absence of enzymes.

Enzymes are important because they can accelerate a chemical reaction by one million to one-hundred million times. Imagine what would happen if some of our tasks were accelerated by that amount! A two-hour daily homework assignment would be completed in about one-thousandth of a second. A flight from Los Angeles to New York would take about one-hundredth of a second. The building of Hoover Dam, a monumental task requiring five years of earth moving and complex steel and concrete work, would require only about thirty seconds.

Scientists now understand the general characteristics of enzymes. And, as we will see in this chapter, these molecules achieve almost miraculous results by following some very basic chemical principles.

13.1 Molecular Accelerators

enzymes

Enzymes are the catalysts of biochemical reactions. Enzymes catalyze nearly all of the myriad reactions that occur in living cells. Uncatalyzed reactions that require hours of boiling in the presence of a strong acid or a strong base can occur in a fraction of a second in the presence of the proper enzyme at room temperature and nearly neutral pH. The catalytic functions of enzymes are directly dependent on their three-dimensional structures. It was generally believed until quite recently that all enzymes were proteins. However, research under way since about 1980 has shown that certain ribonucleic acids (RNAs, see Chapter 14) also function as enzymes.

Louis Pasteur was one of the first scientists to study enzyme catalyzed reactions. He believed that living yeasts or bacteria were required for these reactions, which he called *fermentations*—for example, the conversion of glucose to alcohol by yeasts. In 1897 Eduard Büchner (1860–1917) made a cell-free filtrate that contained enzymes prepared by grinding yeast cells with very fine sand. The enzymes in this filtrate converted glucose to alcohol, thus proving that the presence of living cells was not required for enzyme activity. For this work Büchner received the Nobel prize in chemistry in 1907.

It is important to realize that enzymes are essential to life. The critical biochemical reactions go too slowly for life to be maintained in the absence of enzymes. The typical biochemical reaction occurs more than a million times faster when catalyzed by an enzyme. For example, we know that the reduced carbons of carbohydrates can react with oxygen to produce carbon dioxide and energy. Yet the sucrose in the sugar bowl at home never reacts significantly with the oxygen in the air. These sucrose molecules must overcome an energy barrier (activation energy) before reaction can occur (see Figure 13.1). In the sugar bowl, the energy barrier is too large. But in the cell, enzymes lower the activation energy and enable sucrose to react rapidly enough to provide the energy needed for life processes.

Each organism contains thousands of enzymes. Some are simple proteins consisting only of amino acid units. Others are conjugated and consist of a protein part, or *apoenzyme*, and a nonprotein part, or *coenzyme*. Both parts are essential, and a functioning enzyme consisting of both the protein and nonprotein parts is called a *holoenzyme*:

Apoenzyme + Coenzyme = Holoenzyme

▲ **Fermentation of glucose.**

Often the coenzyme is derived from a vitamin, and one coenzyme may be associated with many different enzymes.

For some enzymes an inorganic component such as a metal ion (for example, Ca^{2+}, Mg^{2+}, or Zn^{2+}) is required. This inorganic component is an *activator*. From the standpoint of function, an activator is analogous to a coenzyme, but inorganic components are not called coenzymes.

Another remarkable property of enzymes is their specificity of reaction; that is, a certain enzyme catalyzes the reaction of a specific type of substance. For example, the enzyme maltase catalyzes the reaction of maltose and water to form glucose. Maltase has no effect on the other two common disaccharides, sucrose and lactose. Each of these sugars requires a specific enzyme—sucrase to hydrolyze sucrose, lactase to hydrolyze lactose. These reactions are indicated by the following equations:

$$\underset{\text{Maltose}}{C_{12}H_{22}O_{11}} + H_2O \xrightarrow{\text{Maltase}} \underset{\text{Glucose}}{C_6H_{12}O_6} + \underset{\text{Glucose}}{C_6H_{12}O_6}$$

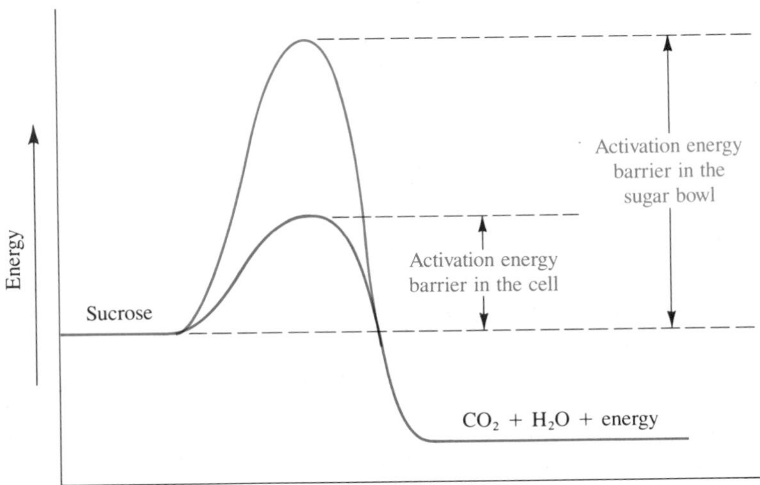

◀ FIGURE 13.1
A typical reaction energy profile: The lower activation energy in the cell is due to the catalytic effect of enzymes.

$$\underset{\text{Sucrose}}{C_{12}H_{22}O_{11}} + H_2O \xrightarrow{\text{Sucrase}} \underset{\text{Glucose}}{C_6H_{12}O_6} + \underset{\text{Fructose}}{C_6H_{12}O_6}$$

$$\underset{\text{Lactose}}{C_{12}H_{22}O_{11}} + H_2O \xrightarrow{\text{Lactase}} \underset{\text{Glucose}}{C_6H_{12}O_6} + \underset{\text{Galactose}}{C_6H_{12}O_6}$$

The substance acted on by an enzyme is called the *substrate*. Sucrose is the substrate of the enzyme sucrase. Enzymes have been named by adding the suffix *-ase* to the root of the substrate name. Note the derivations of maltase, sucrase, and lactase from maltose, sucrose, and lactose. Many enzymes, especially digestive enzymes, have common names such as pepsin, rennin, trypsin, and so on. These names have no systematic significance.

In the International Union of Biochemistry (IUB) System, enzymes are assigned to one of six classes, the names of which clearly describe the nature of the reaction they catalyze. Each of the classes has several subclasses. In this system the name of the enzyme has two parts; the first gives the name of the substrate, and the second, ending in *-ase*, indicates the type of reactions catalyzed by all enzymes in the group. The six main classes of enzymes are

1. *Oxidoreductases:* Enzymes that catalyze the oxidation–reduction between two substrates.
2. *Transferases:* Enzymes that catalyze the transfer of a functional group between two substrates.
3. *Hydrolases:* Enzymes that catalyze the hydrolysis of esters, carbohydrates, and proteins (polypeptides).
4. *Lyases:* Enzymes that catalyze the removal of groups from substrates by mechanisms other than hydrolysis.
5. *Isomerases:* Enzymes that catalyze the interconversion of stereoisomers and structural isomers.
6. *Ligases:* Enzymes that catalyze the linking together of two compounds with the breaking of a pyrophosphate bond in adenosine triphosphate (ATP, see Chapter 14).

Because the systematic name is usually long and often complex, working or practical names are used for enzymes. For example, adenosine triphosphate creatine phosphotransferase is called creatine kinase, and acetylcholine acylhydrolase is called acetylcholine esterase.

13.2 Enzyme Catalysis

Enzymes catalyze biochemical reactions and, thus, increase the rate of these chemical reactions—but how does this process take place? To answer this question, we must first consider some general properties of a chemical reaction.

Every chemical reaction starts with at least one reactant and finishes with a minimum of one product. As the reaction proceeds, the reactant concentration decreases and the product concentration increases. Often these changes are plotted as a function of time, as shown in Figure 13.2 for the hypothetical conversion of reactant A into product B. A reaction rate is defined as a change in concentration with time.

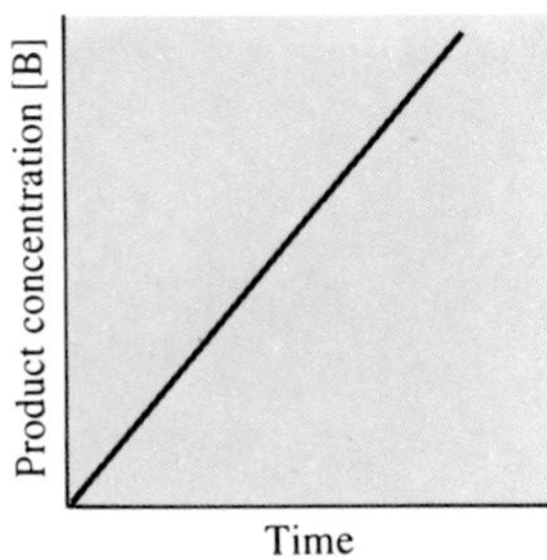

◀ FIGURE 13.2
The change in product concentration [B] as a function of time. The reaction rate is determined by measuring the slope of this line.

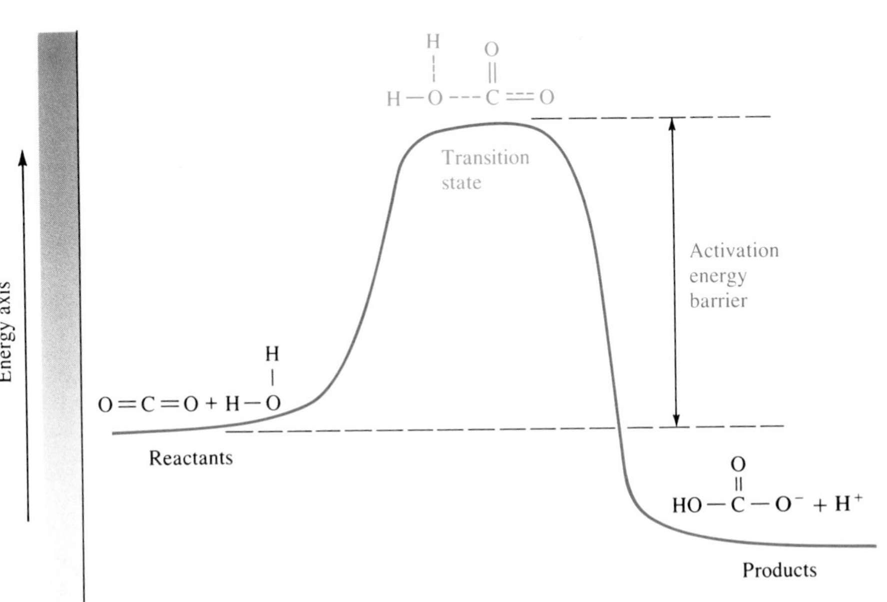

◀ FIGURE 13.3
An energy profile for the reaction between water and carbon dioxide: The dashed lines show bonds that are being formed or broken in the transition state.

transition state

The reactant must pass through a high-energy **transition state** in order to be converted into a product. This transition state is an unstable structure with characteristics of both the reactant and the product. The energy necessary to move a reactant to the transition state is termed the activation energy.

For example, carbon dioxide can be reacted with water to yield bicarbonate. Yet, as shown in Figure 13.3, energy is required to align the water at its appropriate position and to rearrange the bonds within the carbon dioxide. Once the transition state is created, the remainder of the process proceeds easily. As with almost all chemical reactions, reaching the transition state is difficult and limits the rate at which reactants are converted to products.

There are three common ways of increasing a reaction rate (see Figure 13.4):

1. *Increasing the reactant concentration:* When the total reactant concentration is made larger, the number of reactant molecules with the necessary activation energy also increases. For simple reactions in the absence

FIGURE 13.4 ▶
Energy profiles illustrating three ways to increase a reaction rate. Reactant molecules are represented by square symbols. The triangular symbols represent the number of transition state molecules that are converted to products.

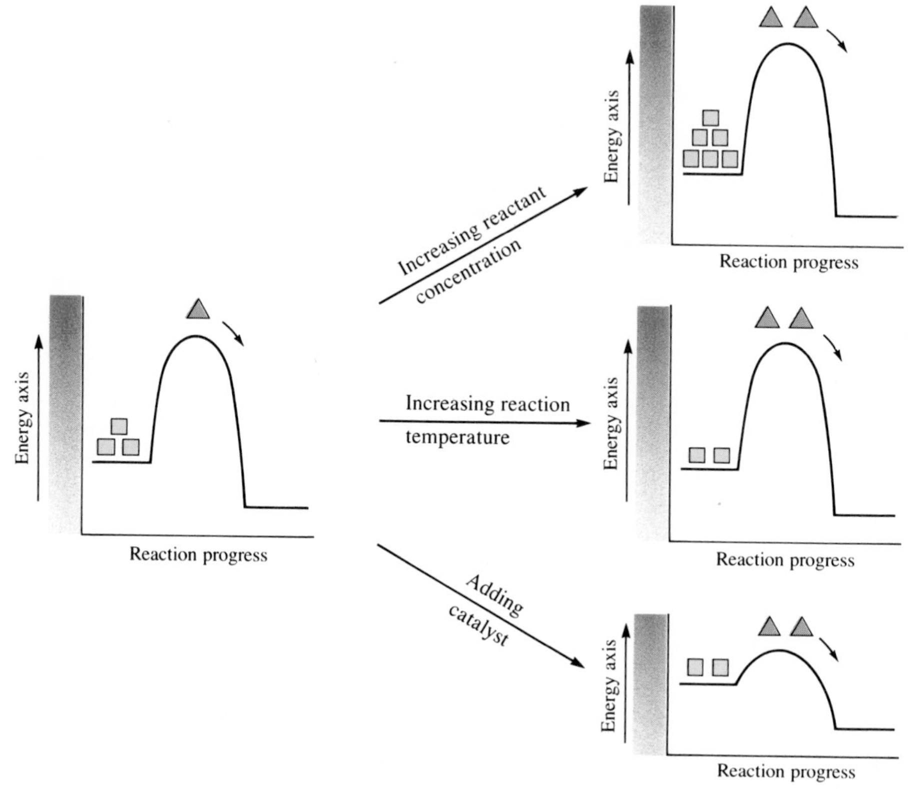

of a catalyst, the reaction rate increases in a linear way with reactant concentration.

2. *Increasing the reaction temperature:* An increase in temperature generally means that each reactant molecule becomes more energetic. A larger fraction of the reactants have the activation energy necessary to be converted to products, and the reaction rate increases.
3. *Adding a catalyst:* A catalyst lowers the activation energy by allowing a new, lower energy transition state. Since this new process has a lower activation energy, more reactants have the energy to become products. The reaction rate increases.

Biological systems can rarely change reactant concentration or temperature upon demand. Thus, to alter reaction rates, life has evolved a set of superb catalysts—the enzymes. How these protein catalysts work has been a subject of study for many years.

In 1913, two German researchers, Leonor Michaelis (1875–1949) and Maud Menten, measured enzyme-catalyzed reaction rates as a function of substrate (reactant) concentration. They observed that most enzyme-catalyzed reactions show an increasing rate with increasing substrate concentration *but* only to a specific maximum velocity (V_{max}; Figure 13.5). A graph like that in Figure 13.5 is often called a Michaelis–Menten plot.

Scientists have learned much about the nature of enzymes by studying the Michaelis–Menten plot. First, because the rate approaches a maximum, it can be concluded that enzymes have a limited catalytic ability. Once these enzymes are operating at a maximum, a further increase in substrate (reactant) concentration does not change the reaction rate. By analogy, an enzyme shuttles reac-

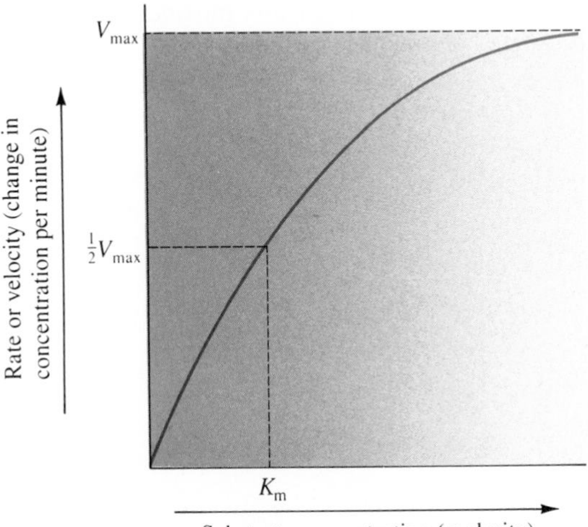

◄ **FIGURE 13.5**
A Michaelis–Menten plot showing the rate of an enzyme-catalyzed reaction as a function of substrate concentration. The shaded portion of the graph approximately marks the area where a change in substrate concentration causes a significant rate change.

tants to the transition state (and on to products) like an usher seating patrons at a theater. No matter how many people arrive at the entrance, a conscientious usher can only lead the ticket holders to their places at a set pace. Similarly, each specific enzyme has a set, maximum catalytic rate.

The V_{max} that can be determined from a Michaelis–Menten plot is one measure of an enzyme's maximum catalytic efficiency. Perhaps a more useful measure, called the **turnover number**, is calculated from the V_{max}. A turnover number measures how many substrate molecules one enzyme can react or "turn over" in a given time span. For example, a particular enzyme might have a turnover number of 1000 s^{-1}, which would mean one enzyme molecule can react 1000 substrate molecules per second.

turnover number

The Michaelis–Menten plot also shows that enzymes are responsive and most useful to the cell only within a specific substrate concentration range. Physiological reactions generally need to change as their environment changes. That is, reaction rates should increase when there are more reactants and decrease when there are less reactants. Figure 13.5 shows such changes only over a limited substrate concentration range. It is within this range that an enzyme is most useful for the cell.

The **Michaelis constant, K_m**, is a numerical measure of the effective substrate concentration range for an enzyme. This constant is defined as the substrate concentration needed for an enzyme to operate at one-half of its maximum rate. Thus, the K_m is poised at the approximate midpoint of the effective concentration range. Perhaps the most direct way to derive K_m is shown in Figure 13.5; after identifying $\frac{1}{2}V_{max}$ a line can be extrapolated to the abscissa (x-axis) and the numerical value for K_m determined.

Michaelis constant, K_m

EXAMPLE 13.1

The enzyme carbonic anhydrase is responsible for catalyzing the reaction between water and carbon dioxide:

$$CO_2 + H_2O \rightleftarrows HCO_3^- + H^+$$

This enzyme is important to the body because it allows carbon dioxide produced by body tissues to dissolve quickly in the bloodstream for transport to the lungs. In addition, this enzyme quickly converts bicarbonate to carbon dioxide for the lungs to exhale. Based on the following Michaelis–Menten plot, estimate both the V_{max} and K_m for carbonic anhydrase.

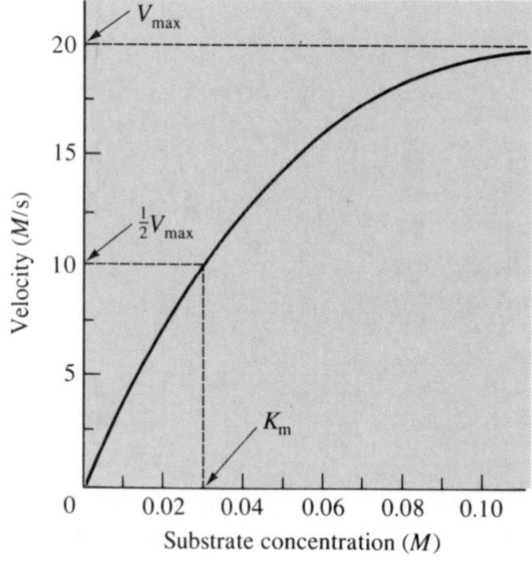

SOLUTION

The V_{max} can be estimated by reading the y-axis where the graphed line becomes horizontal. For this data, carbonic anhydrase has a V_{max} of 20.0 M/s. The K_m can be estimated by first finding a value on the y-axis that is equal to $\frac{1}{2}$ V_{max} (10.0 M/s). From this value extrapolate over to the graphed line and down to the x-axis. The value on the x-axis is the Michaelis constant and is equal to 0.03 M.

PRACTICE Find the K_m and V_{max} for the digestive enzyme, pepsin, from the following graph:

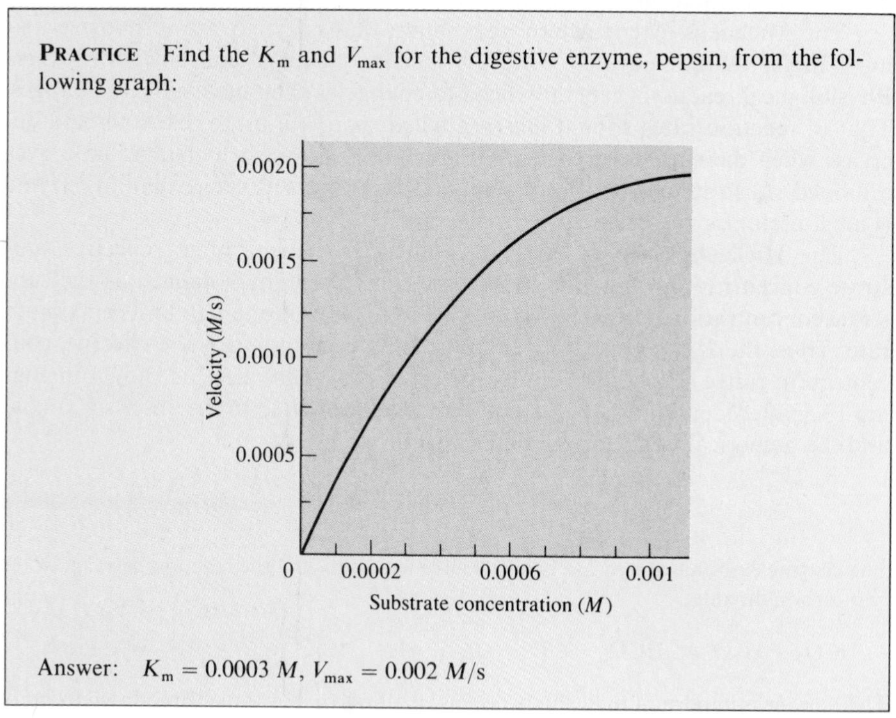

Answer: $K_m = 0.0003\ M$, $V_{max} = 0.002\ M/s$

Scientists believe that each specific enzyme's catalytic abilities are tailored to fit a specific metabolic need. Some enzymes work well at low substrate concentrations, whereas others require much higher concentrations before they operate efficiently. Some enzymes catalyze reactions very quickly while others fit a biochemical need by reacting much more slowly. Several examples will illustrate these concepts.

There are two common mammalian enzymes that begin glucose metabolism, hexokinase and glucokinase. Both enzymes catalyze the same reaction, an addition of a phosphate group to glucose, but hexokinase has a K_m of about 0.0001 M while glucokinase has a K_m of about 0.005 M. These two enzymes differ in their effective concentration range; at low glucose concentrations only the hexokinase catalyzes the reaction while at higher glucose concentrations both hexokinase and glucokinase react. Thus, the difference in K_ms means that hexokinase has first priority to use the available glucose. This is important because hexokinase is found in all tissues, where glucose is used for energy, while glucokinase is found only in the liver, where glucose is stored as glycogen. When energy is needed, hexokinase uses the glucose. If there is some excess glucose, the glucokinase enzyme starts converting this sugar to glycogen. The difference in K_ms helps shunt the glucose to where it can best be used.

We have considered how the Michaelis' constant is important; now let us compare the turnover numbers for several enzymes. Catalase is responsible for destroying the cellular toxin, hydrogen peroxide, before it can do biological damage. This enzyme has a large turnover number of 10,000,000 s^{-1}; one catalase enzyme can destroy 10 million hydrogen peroxide molecules per second. This very large turnover number minimizes the danger posed by hydrogen peroxide. In contrast, the enzyme chymotrypsin has a much smaller turnover number of about 0.2 s^{-1} (two reactants are converted to products every 10 seconds by one chymotrypsin molecule). This enzyme digests protein as it moves slowly through the small intestine. Since the digestive process is slow, chymotrypsin is not required to react as quickly as catalase. In many cases it appears that an enzyme's turnover number matches the speed required for a biological process.

EXAMPLE 13.2

Two enzymes are studied under identical conditions. Enzyme A is found to have a turnover number of 1500 s^{-1} and a K_m of 0.01 M whereas enzyme B shows a turnover number of 500 s^{-1} and a K_m of 0.005 M. Compare (a) the catalytic efficiency of the two enzymes and (b) their respective effective substrate concentration ranges.

SOLUTION

(a) The turnover number is a measure of catalytic efficiency. Under identical conditions, the larger the turnover number, the more efficient an enzyme is as a catalyst. Because enzyme A has a larger turnover number than enzyme B, enzyme A is a more efficient catalyst.

(b) The K_m is a measure of the effective substrate concentration range for an enzyme. A lower K_m value means that an enzyme works well at lower substrate concentrations. Enzyme B is effective at a lower substrate concentration range than enzyme A.

PRACTICE Under optimum conditions, the digestive enzyme pepsin has a turnover number of about 30 min^{-1} while a second digestive enzyme, trypsin, has a turnover number of 12 min^{-1}. Both of these enzymes digest proteins. Which would you judge to be the more efficient?

Answer: Under these conditions, pepsin is the more efficient because it has the larger turnover number, converting 30 reactant molecules to products per minute.

13.3 ENZYME ACTIVE SITE

Catalysis takes place on a small portion of the enzyme structure called the *enzyme active site*. Often this is a crevice or pocket on the enzyme representing only 1–5% of the total surface area. For example, Figure 13.6 shows a space-filling model of the enzyme hexokinase, which catalyzes a first step in the breakdown of glucose to provide metabolic energy. Notice that the active site is located in a crevice. Glucose can enter this site and is bound. The enzyme then must change shape before the reaction takes place. Thus, although catalysis occurs at the small active site, the entire three-dimensional structure of the enzyme is important.

By examining values such as the turnover number and the K_m, scientists have gained a basic understanding of what takes place at an enzyme active site. To function effectively an enzyme must attract and bind the substrate. Once the substrate is bound, a chemical reaction is catalyzed. This two-step process is described by the following general sequence. Enzyme (E) and substrate (S) combine to form an enzyme–substrate intermediate (E–S). This intermediate decomposes to give the product (P) and regenerate the enzyme:

$$\mathrm{E + S \xrightarrow[\text{Binding}]{} E{-}S \xrightarrow[\text{Catalysis}]{} E + P}$$

For the hydrolysis of maltose by the enzyme maltase, the sequence is

$$\underset{\mathrm{E}}{\text{Maltase}} + \underset{\mathrm{S}}{\text{Maltose}} \longrightarrow \underset{\mathrm{E{-}S}}{\text{Maltase–Maltose}}$$

$$\underset{\mathrm{E{-}S}}{\text{Maltase–Maltose}} + \mathrm{H_2O} \longrightarrow \underset{\mathrm{E}}{\text{Maltase}} + \underset{\mathrm{P}}{\text{2 Glucose}}$$

Each different enzyme has its own unique active site whose shape determines, in part, which substrates can bind. Enzymes are said to be stereospecific; that is, each enzyme catalyzes reactions for only a limited number of different reactant structures. For example, maltase binds to maltose (two glucose units linked by a α-1,4-glycosidic bond) but not to lactose (galactose coupled to glucose). In fact, this enzyme can even distinguish maltose from cellobiose (glucose coupled to glucose by a β-1,4-linkage), in which only the glycosidic linkage is different. Enzyme stereospecificity is a very important means by which the cell controls its biochemistry.

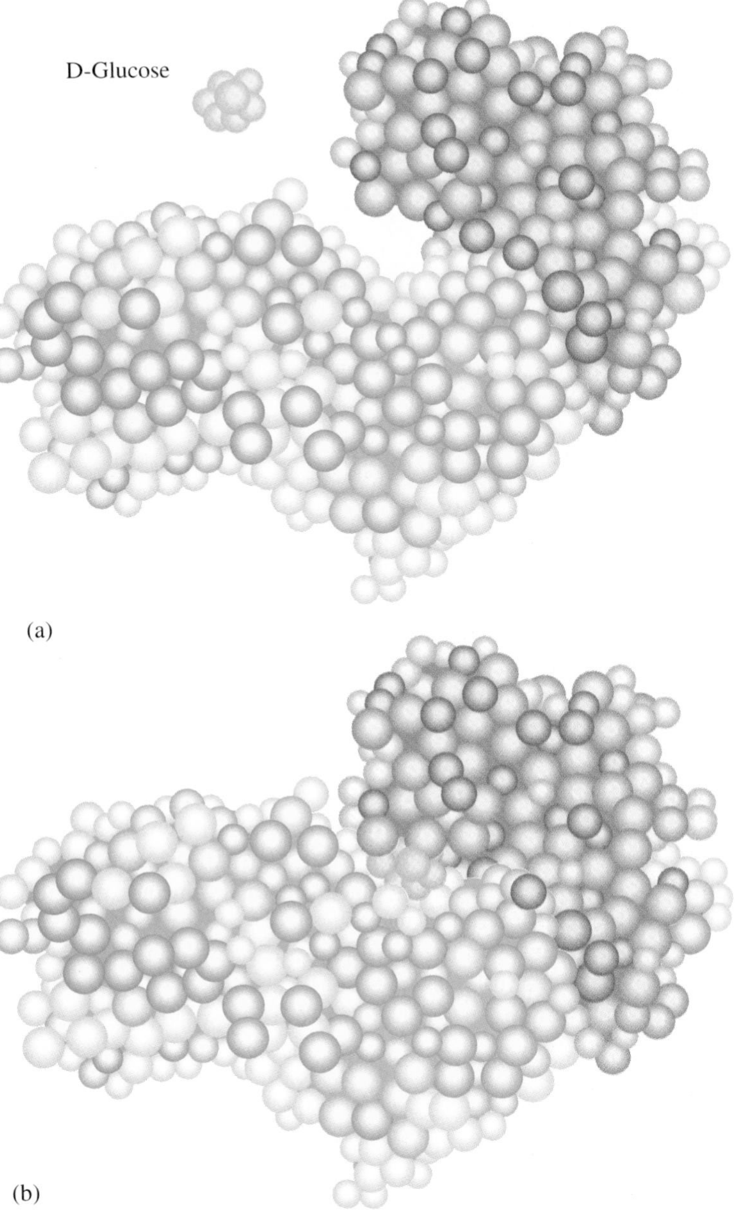

◀ **FIGURE 13.6**
A space-filling model of the enzyme, hexokinase, before (a) and after (b) it binds to the substrate, glucose: Note the two protein domains for this enzyme which are colored differently.

Enzyme specificity is partially due to a complementary relationship between the active site and substrate structures. This **lock-and-key hypothesis** envisions the substrate as a key that fits into the appropriate active site, the lock. Although this hypothesis describes a fundamental property of enzyme–substrate binding, it has been known for some time that enzyme active sites are not rigid as a lock would be. Instead, the active site bends to a certain degree when the appropriate substrate binds. The **induced-fit model** proposes that the active site adjusts its structure in order to prepare the substrate–enzyme complex for catalysis. Enzyme stereospecificity is thus explained in terms of an active site having

lock-and-key hypothesis

induced-fit model

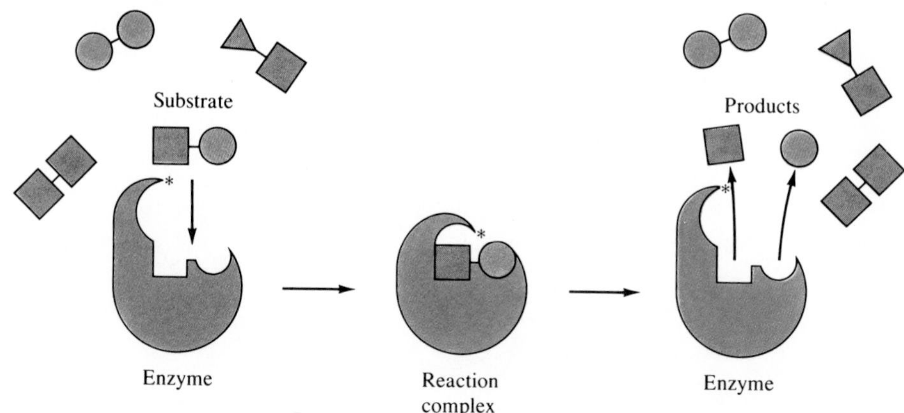

FIGURE 13.7 ► Enzyme-substrate interaction illustrating both the lock-and-key hypothesis and the induced-fit model. The correct substrate (■—●) fits the active site (lock-and-key hypothesis). This substrate also causes an enzyme conformation change which positions a catalytic group (*) to cleave the appropriate bond (induced-fit model).

a somewhat flexible shape. This shape is rigid enough to exclude very dissimilar substrates (lock-and-key hypothesis) but flexible enough to accommodate (induced-fit model) and allow catalysis of appropriate substrates (see Figure 13.7).

The fact that an enzyme is flexible can help to explain enzyme binding specificity and also how the enzyme converts reactants into products. *An enzyme is a dynamic catalyst.* As the enzyme attracts the substrate into the active site, the enzyme's shape and the reactant's shape both begin to change. Note the change in hexokinase structure when glucose is bound (Figure 13.6). This alteration of enzyme shape aids the transformation of the reactant into the product. Figure 13.7 schematically depicts an enzyme where a shape change leads to catalysis. This only exemplifies the numerous alterations that can be brought about by enzymes, for example, bonds broken or formed, charges moved, and new molecular substituents added or removed.

An actual metabolic reaction will illustrate some of the basic features of enzyme catalysis. For example, let us take the enzyme hexokinase, which catalyzes the transformation of glucose to glucose-6-phosphate.

$$\text{glucose } ({}^6CH_2OH) \xrightarrow[\text{Mg}^{2+},\ \text{ATP}]{\text{Hexokinase}} \text{glucose-6-phosphate } ({}^6CH_2OPO_3^{2-})$$

glucose glucose-6-phosphate

Like many enzymes, hexokinase requires a second reactant. In this case, adenosine-5′-triphosphate (ATP) supplies the phosphate group that is transferred to the glucose. ATP is a very important molecule within the cell because it often transfers energy as well as phosphate groups from enzyme to enzyme (see Chapter 14). Additionally, the metal ion, Mg^{2+}, is required as an activator

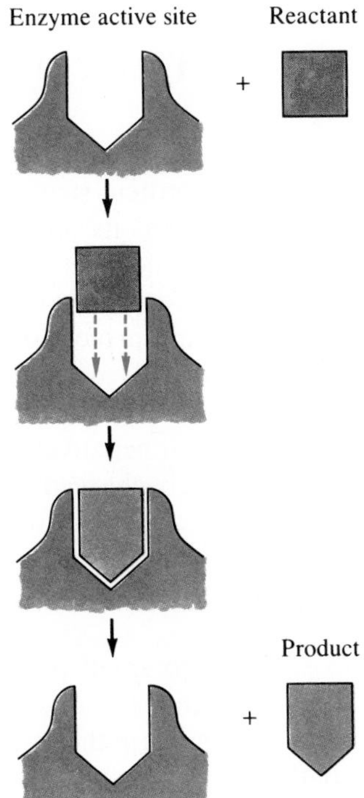

◀ **FIGURE 13.8 Schematic showing the substrate being forced toward the product shape by enzyme binding.**

in this reaction. With all of these components present, the enzyme can start the catalytic process.

When glucose binds, the hexokinase shape changes to bring the ATP close to the C-6 of the glucose, thus forcing the transfer of phosphate to this specific carbon. Hexokinase speeds this reaction in several ways. First, this enzyme acts to bring the reactants close together, a process termed **proximity catalysis**. Second, hexokinase positions the reactants so the proper bonds will form or be broken. (The enzyme ensures that a phosphate is added to C-6 of glucose and not at one of the other carbons.) This is often termed the **productive binding hypothesis**, because reactants are bound/oriented in such a way that products result. Hexokinase is a successful catalyst—glucose reacts with ATP 10 billion (10^{10}) times faster than it would in the absence of this enzyme. Increases in reaction rate of this magnitude are essential to life. In fact, without enzymes, cellular reactions are too slow to keep the cells alive.

proximity catalysis

productive binding hypothesis

Biotechnologists have made use of our understanding of enzyme catalysis to design (with nature's help) completely new enzymes. Antibodies (immunoglobulin proteins) are produced that bind tightly to a molecule like the transition state. Thus, the antibody binding site is not complementary to the shape of the reactant but rather to a shape more like the product. When these antibodies bind reactant molecules, the strong attractive forces "strain" the reactants as illustrated in Figure 13.8. The reactant molecule is impelled to change shape to fit the binding site. Catalysis occurs, and these antibodies act as enzymes! Scientists have termed this mode of catalysis the **strain hypothesis**, and it is thought to be important in many natural enzymes as well as these "antibody enzymes." In the not-too-distant future, such artificial enzymes may serve important industrial and medical applications.

strain hypothesis

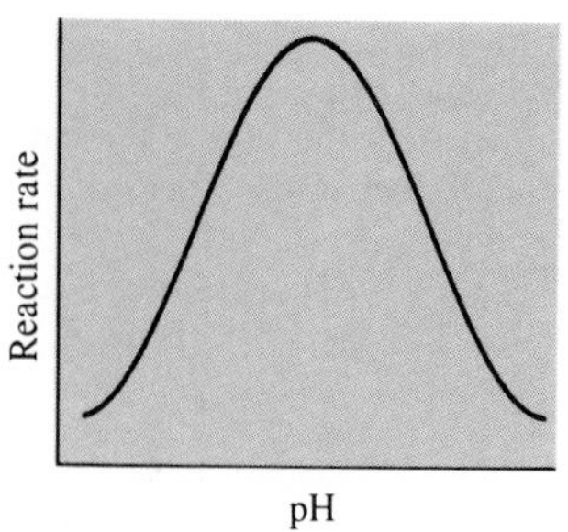

▲
FIGURE 13.9
A typical plot of the enzyme-catalyzed rate as a function of pH.

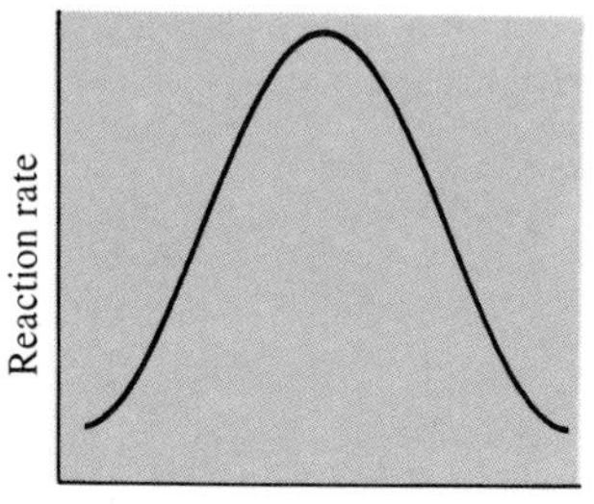

▲
FIGURE 13.10
A plot showing the typical temperature dependence of an enzyme-catalyzed rate.

13.4 Temperature and pH Effects on Enzyme Catalysis

Essentially any change that will affect protein structure will affect an enzyme's catalytic function. If an enzyme is denatured, its activity will be lost. Thus, strong acids and bases, organic solvents, mechanical action, and high temperature are examples of treatments that may decrease an enzyme-catalyzed rate of reaction.

Even slight changes in the pH can have profound effects on enzyme catalysis. Remember that some of the amino acids that make up enzymes have side chains whose charge depends on pH. For example, side chains with carboxylic acid functional groups may be either neutral or negatively charged; those with amino groups may be either neutral or positively charged. Thus, as the pH is changed the charges on an enzyme, or more specifically at the active site of an enzyme, also change. Enzyme catalysis is affected. For each enzyme there is an optimum pH; shifts to more acidic or more basic conditions decrease the enzyme activity as shown in Figure 13.9.

Because enzymes are so sensitive to small pH changes, our bodies have developed elaborate mechanisms to control the amount of acid and base present in cellular fluids. The kidneys and lungs share the responsibility for maintaining blood acid and base levels. If the blood pH shifts outside of the narrow range 6.8–7.8, death often results. The body's metabolic processes can no longer maintain life partially because of a pH-induced change in enzyme activities.

Body temperature is also carefully controlled partially because enzyme activities are particularly temperature-sensitive. A typical plot of temperature versus enzyme activity is shown in Figure 13.10. At very low temperatures, few reactant molecules have enough energy to overcome the activation energy barrier and the reaction occurs slowly. As the temperature increases, more reactants have the necessary activation energy and the rate increases. But a point is reached where the high temperature causes enzyme denaturation, and the rate of reaction starts to decrease. Thus, both low and high temperatures cause slow reaction rates, and, as with pH, there is an optimum temperature for each enzyme. Not surprisingly, the optimum temperature for many human enzymes is approximately body temperature (about 37°C).

13.5 Enzyme Regulation

Since enzymes are vital to life, enzyme catalysis is under careful cellular control. The cell uses a variety of mechanisms to change the rate of substrate conversion to product. Sometimes a new group of atoms is covalently joined to the enzyme in a process called *covalent modification*. In other cases, another molecule is noncovalently bound to the enzyme. The protein structural change that results may cause a decrease in enzyme activity, **enzyme inhibition**, or an increase in activity, **enzyme activation**.

enzyme inhibition

enzyme activation

To learn about enzyme control, scientists have carefully studied both inhibition and activation. They have found that an enzyme's catalytic abilities may be changed by changing its K_m or its turnover number. For example, an enzyme may be inhibited by making it bind to its substrate more weakly (increasing its K_m) or by decreasing its catalytic efficiency (decreasing its turnover number or V_{max}). Reversing these changes causes enzyme activation. A Michaelis–Menten plot illustrates this point for inhibition (see Figure 13.11). Note that a decrease in V_{max} causes the curve to rise less while an increase in K_m results in a curve with a shallower slope.

Hexokinase is an example of an enzyme that is under cellular control. Because this enzyme begins the breakdown of glucose to yield cellular energy, the hexokinase-catalyzed reaction is often not needed when cellular energy levels are high. Control occurs in the following way: (1) if glucose no longer is needed for cellular energy, the glucose-6-phosphate concentration increases; (2) this compound binds to the hexokinase enzyme and inhibits the enzyme activity. Because glucose-6-phosphate is a product of the reaction, this form of enzyme control is called **product inhibition**. Hexokinase responds to the overall cellular energy state and does not use more glucose than needed.

product inhibition

Feedback inhibition and **feedforward activation** are two other common forms of enzyme control. To understand these mechanisms, visualize the various cellular processes as assembly lines with a different enzyme at each step from raw material to finished product. Feedback inhibition affects enzymes at the beginning of the molecular assembly line. A final product acts as "feedback" and inhibits an enzyme from using too many molecular starting materials. In contrast, feedforward activation often controls enzymes at the end of the molecular assembly line. If there is an excess of starting materials, these molecules will "feedforward" and activate enzymes, which in turn cause the whole process to move faster. As with other control mechanisms, both feedback inhibition and feedforward activation serve to coordinate enzyme processes within the cell.

feedback inhibition

feedforward activation

A variety of drug therapies make use of enzyme control to selectively affect target cells. Careful drug design can create a molecule which binds to only one type of enzyme. By binding, the drug blocks normal catalysis and causes enzyme inhibition. In each of the following examples, a specific enzyme is inhibited, which in turn causes a selective metabolic change.

1. Methotrexate is an anticancer drug because it is similar in structure to, but cannot function like, the coenzyme dihydrofolate. This coenzyme is needed to reproduce cellular genetic material. When methotrexate replaces dihydrofolate, an enzyme is inhibited and genetic replication is slowed. Since rapid cell growth requires genetic replication, rapidly growing cancer cells are selectively impacted by methotrexate treatment.
2. AZT (3′-azido-3′-deoxythymidine) was the first drug approved in the United States for treatment of the viral disease, acquired immune deficiency syndrome (AIDS). This drug is structurally similar to a reactant needed to make genetic material for the AIDS virus. When AZT binds to a specific enzyme (reverse transcriptase), the formation of new viral genetic material is inhibited. Virus reproduction is impeded and the progression of AIDS is slowed.

These examples of drug therapy illustrate a very important principle: Because biological processes depend on enzymes, enzyme control often has a major impact on life.

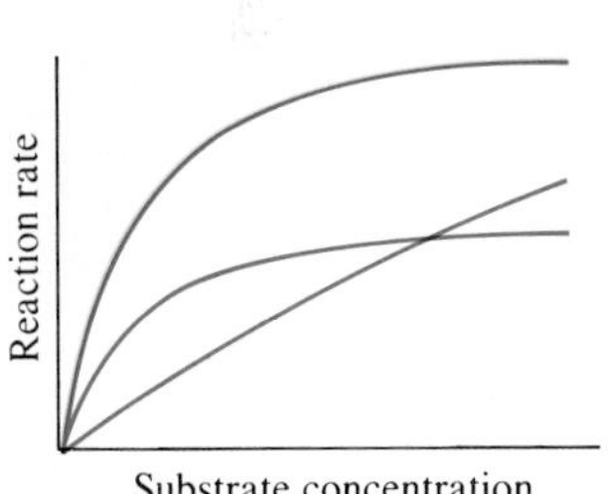

▲ FIGURE 13.11
A Michaelis–Menton plot for an unregulated enzyme (green), the same enzyme inhibited by a decrease in V_{max} (blue) and the enzyme inhibited by an increase in K_m (red)

Chemistry in Action

Industrial Strength Enzymes

Not only are enzymes important in biology, but these proteins also are becoming increasingly important in industry. Enzymes offer two major advantages to manufacturing processes and in commercial products: first, enzymes cause very large increases in reaction rates even at room temperature; second, enzymes are relatively specific and can be used to target selected reactants. Perhaps the biggest disadvantage to industrial enzymes is their relative short supply (and, therefore, higher cost as compared to traditional chemical treatments). Recent developments in biotechnology offer supplies of less expensive enzymes through genetic engineering.

Enzymes have long been used in food processing. The citrus industry has recently perfected a process to remove peel from oranges or grapefruits by using the enzyme pectinase. The pectinase penetrates the peel in a vacuum infusion process. There it dissolves the albedo (the white stringy material) that attaches the peel to the fruit. When the fruit is removed from the solution, the skin can be peeled easily by machine or hand. The industry is now marketing pre-peeled citrus to hospitals, airlines, and restaurants (see photo below).

About 25% of all industrial enzymes are used to convert cornstarch into syrups that are equivalent in sweetness and in calories to ordinary table sugar. More than 5 billion pounds of such syrups are produced annually. The process uses three enzymes: the first, α-amylase, catalyzes the liquefaction of starch to dextrins; the second, a glucoamylase, catalyzes the breakdown of dextrins to glucose; the third, glucose isomerase, converts glucose to fructose.

$$\text{Starch} \xrightarrow{\alpha\text{-Amylase}} \text{Dextrins}$$

$$\text{Dextrins} \xrightarrow{\text{Glucoamylase}} \text{Glucose}$$

$$\text{Glucose} \xrightarrow[\text{isomerase}]{\text{Glucose}} \text{Fructose}$$

The product is a high-fructose syrup equivalent in sweetness to sucrose. One of these syrups, sold commercially since 1968, contains by dry weight about 42% fructose, 50% glucose, and 8% other carbohydrates.

Industrial enzymes offer solutions to environmental pollution problems for some manufacturers. For example, the paper industry, like other industries that use chemicals, is concerned with minimizing processes that produce potentially hazardous waste. Paper is produced from wood chips by first digesting the cellulose structure with calcium sulfite and then bleaching the pulp with chlorine to obtain a bright white paper. An excess of chlorine must be used because the pulp is not completely broken down. This excess creates a significant disposal problem as chlorine is environmentally hazardous. Recent developments in biotechnology offer a potential solution. The enzymes needed to complete wood fiber digestion (cellulase and hemicellulase) have been produced in larger quantities via genetic engineering. With such enzymes to finish degrading the wood pulp, paper manufacturers may be able to markedly decrease the amount of chlorine used as bleach.

Consumer goods are increasingly impacted by enzyme technology. Many detergents are better cleansing agents because they contain enzymes; fully 40% of all industrially produced enzymes are used in this way. Meat tenderizers often contain papain, an enzyme which breaks down protein molecules. Even clothing manufacturers are finding uses for newly available enzymes. More and more denim products are en-

(*continued*)

(*continued*)
zyme-treated to replace stonewashing, a process in which the material is washed with pumice to soften the fabric's appearance and remove some of the dye. Because this abrasion may weaken the fabric as well, some manufacturers now use "biostoning." The denim is treated with the enzyme, cellulase, which changes the fabric's appearance without weakening the fabric structure.

The ability to produce large quantities of purified enzymes has raised a number of potential medical applications. For genetic diseases characterized by the loss of a specific enzyme, a treatment known as enzyme-replacement therapy may be useful. For example, a lysosomal storage disease, such as Tay–Sachs disease, leads to the accumulation of excess intracellular polysaccharides because specific digestive enzymes are unavailable. Polysaccharide buildup can lead to mental retardation, paralysis, blindness, and death. Current research is aimed at developing an appropriate microcapsule package that will transport additional digestive enzymes to the affected cells. Such enzyme-replacement therapy has also been proposed for removing toxic substances from the bloodstream.

Concepts in Review

1. Briefly explain why living cells need catalysts.
2. List the six main classes of enzymes and their functions.
3. Compare a simple, uncatalyzed reaction with an enzyme-catalyzed process.
4. Define the symbols K_m and V_{max} and relate them to the Michaelis–Menten plot.
5. Discuss the relationship between the reaction rate and the enzyme concentration.
6. Describe an enzyme active site.
7. Tell what is meant by the specificity of an enzyme.
8. List several ways that an enzyme can facilitate the conversion of substrate to product.
9. Summarize the effects of pH and temperature on an enzyme-catalyzed reaction.
10. Describe how inhibition and activation are important in enzyme control.
11. Discuss the potential role of enzymes in medicine and industry.

Equations in Review

Enzyme-Catalyzed Conversion of Substrate to Product

$$\mathrm{E + S \xrightarrow[\text{Binding}]{} E\text{–}S \xrightarrow[\text{Catalysis}]{} E + P}$$

EXERCISES

1. What is the activation energy and how is this energy affected by enzymes?
2. What is the general role of enzymes in the body?
3. Distinguish between a coenzyme and an apoenzyme.
4. Give the names of enzymes that catalyze the hydrolysis of (a) sucrose, (b) lactose, and (c) maltose.
5. What are six general classes of enzymes?
6. By drawing a Michaelis–Menten plot, define the V_{max}.
7. Why are K_m s reported in units of concentration, for example, molarity?
8. The digestive enzyme chymotrypsin breaks peptide bonds adjacent to the amino acids L-tryptophan and L-phenylalanine. This enzyme has a K_m for a specific L-tryptophan–containing substrate of 0.08 millimolar (m*M*) and a K_m for a specific L-phenylalanine–containing substrate of 1.30 m*M*. Which substrate do you think binds more tightly to the enzyme? Briefly explain.
9. Chymotrypsin has a turnover number for a glycine-containing substrate of 0.05 s^{-1} and a turnover number for an L-tyrosine–containing substrate of 200 s^{-1}. For which substrate is chymotrypsin a more efficient catalyst? Briefly explain.
10. A catalyst increases the rate of a chemical reaction. List two other means of increasing reaction rates.
11. An enzyme reacts 0.02 moles per liter of substrate every 8 minutes. What is the reaction rate in units of molar per minute?
12. Pepsin, a digestive enzyme found in the stomach, has a turnover number of 0.5 s^{-1} for a specific protein substrate. How many proteins can be digested by one pepsin molecule in 5 minutes?
13. A scientist studies two enzymes which catalyze the same reaction. Enzyme A has a turnover number of 225 s^{-1} and a K_m of 0.03 *M* whereas enzyme B has a turnover number of 120 s^{-1} and a K_m of 0.15 *M*. The scientist concludes that enzyme B is more effective than enzyme A. Do you agree? Briefly explain.
14. Differentiate between the lock-and-key hypothesis and the induced-fit model for enzyme function.
15. Two enzymes are being studied; the first enzyme uses *n*-butyl alcohol as a substrate while the second enzyme uses *t*-butyl alcohol as a substrate. Based on the lock-and-key hypothesis, how might the shapes for the enzyme active sites differ?
16. List one important way in which the induced-fit model is important in the hexokinase catalyzed reaction.
17. If the K_m for an enzyme is decreased, would you predict activation or inhibition? Briefly explain.
18. Why does an enzyme catalyzed reaction rate decrease at high temperatures?
19. Feedback inhibition is an important form of enzyme regulation. Based on what you know about this control mechanism, how might a different process, "feedback activation," cause regulatory *problems* for a cell?
20. List three ways that substrate binding to the active site helps the reactants convert to products.
21. How does an enzyme inhibitor differ from an enzyme substrate?
22. Describe briefly how an artificial enzyme that is produced from an immunoglobulin helps substrates react to form products.
23. Which of the following statements are correct? Rewrite the incorrect ones to make them correct.
    - (a) Enzymes are proteins.
    - (b) Enzymes increase the activation energy for a reaction.
    - (c) An enzyme active site is where catalysis occurs.
    - (d) The product of an enzyme catalyzed reaction is called the substrate.
    - (e) Doubling the reactant concentration always doubles the rate of an enzyme catalyzed reaction.
    - (f) An enzyme with a small K_m can bind at low substrate concentrations.
    - (g) The substrate concentration that gives a rate of $\frac{1}{4}$ V_{max} is equal to the K_m.
    - (h) The turnover number is a measure of an enzyme's catalytic ability.
    - (i) The lock-and-key hypothesis requires a flexible enzyme.
    - (j) The productive binding hypothesis states that an enzyme binds to and orients the reactants so that products can form most easily.
    - (k) Inhibition occurs if an enzyme's K_m is increased.
    - (l) Feedforward activation increases the rate for enzymes at or close to the end of a metabolic process ("assembly line").
    - (m) Denaturation decreases an enzyme catalyzed reaction rate.
    - (n) Enzyme treatment can allow manufacturers to avoid more harsh chemical and physical processes.

14 Nucleic Acids and Heredity

14.1 Molecules of Heredity—A Link

14.2 Bases and Nucleosides

14.3 Nucleotides: Phosphate Esters

14.4 High-Energy Nucleotides

14.5 Polynucleotides; Nucleic Acids

14.6 Structure of DNA

14.7 DNA Replication

14.8 RNA: Genetic Transcription

14.9 The Genetic Code

14.10 Biosynthesis of Proteins

14.11 Mutations

◀ CHAPTER OPENING PHOTO: **This model shows the double helix structure of DNA.**

The plight of Doctor Frankenstein's monster touches a chord in all of us. An evil scientist has given this monster life but cannot control his creation. The monster is "unnatural" and, as such, the story leads to tragedy.

The advent of genetic engineering has raised a similar fear of a tragic ending. Genetic engineers work with the molecules that code life—the nucleic acids. By changing the code, new life forms can be produced. Already bacteria have been altered to make needed human proteins. Recently, both cows and goats have been genetically engineered to produce a human protein in their milk.

The scientists involved in these initial programs have followed careful protocols and have produced valued medicines. However, the day may soon be with us when we must decide whether humans should be made smarter, stronger, etc., via genetic engineering. How this decision will be made is open to discussion. However, an understanding of the biochemistry of nucleic acids has given us the power to consider such decisions.

14.1 MOLECULES OF HEREDITY—A LINK

The question of how hereditary material duplicates itself was for a long time one of the most baffling problems of biology. For many years biologists attempted in vain to solve this problem and also to find an answer to the question "Why are the offspring of a species undeniably of that species?" Many thought the chemical basis for heredity lay in the structure of the proteins. But no one was able to provide evidence showing how protein could reproduce itself. The answer to the heredity problem was finally found in the structure of the nucleic acids.

nucleoprotein

nucleic acids

The unit structure of all living things is the cell. Suspended in the nuclei of cells are chromosomes, which consist largely of proteins and nucleic acids. A simple protein bonded to a nucleic acid is called a **nucleoprotein**. There are two types of **nucleic acids**—those that contain the sugar deoxyribose and those that contain the sugar ribose. Accordingly, they are called deoxyribonucleic acid (DNA) and ribonucleic acid (RNA). DNA was discovered in 1869 by the Swiss physiologist Friedrich Miescher (1844–1895), who extracted it from the nuclei of cells.

14.2 Bases and Nucleosides

Nucleic acids are complex chemicals that combine several different classes of smaller molecules. As with many complex structures, it is easier to understand the whole by first studying its component parts. We will start the examination of nucleic acids by learning about a critical part of these molecules, two classes of heterocyclic bases, the purines and the pyrimidines:

Purine, $C_5H_4N_4$ Pyrimidine, $C_4H_4N_2$

These parent compounds are related in structure, the pyrimidine being a six-membered heterocyclic ring while the purine contains both a five- and six-membered ring. The nitrogen atoms cause these compounds to be known as heterocycles (the rings are made up of more than just carbon atoms) and also as bases. Like the ammonia nitrogen, these heterocycles react with hydrogen ions to make a solution more basic.

There are five major bases commonly found in nucleic acids—two purine bases (adenine and guanine) and three pyrimidine bases (cytosine, thymine, and uracil). Figure 14.1 gives one stable form for each compound. Note that the bases differ one from another in their ring substituents. Each base has a lowermost nitrogen, which is bonded to a hydrogen as well as two carbons. This specific >N—H shares chemical similarities with an alcohol (—OH) group. Just as two sugars can be linked together when an alcohol of one monosaccharide reacts with a second monosaccharide (see Chapter 10), so a purine or pyrimidine can be bonded to a sugar by a reaction with the —NH group.

A **nucleoside** is formed when either a purine or pyrimidine base is linked to a sugar molecule, usually D-ribose or D-2′-deoxyribose. nucleoside

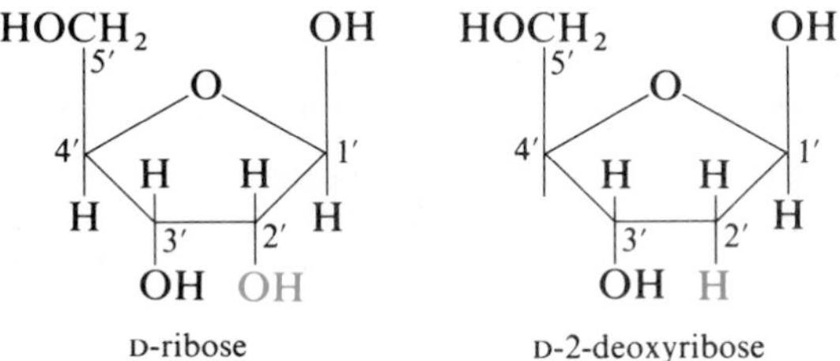

D-ribose D-2-deoxyribose

The base and sugar are bonded together between carbon 1′ of the sugar and either the purine nitrogen at position 9 or the pyrimidine nitrogen at position 1. Typical structures of nucleosides are shown in Figure 14.2. A prime is added to the position number to differentiate the sugar numbering system from the purine or pyrimidine numbering system.

The name of each nucleoside emphasizes the importance of the base to the chemistry of the molecule. Thus, adenine and D-ribose react to yield adenosine, whereas cytosine and D-2′-deoxyribose yield deoxycytidine. The root of the nucleoside name derives from the purine or pyrimidine name. The compositions of the common ribonucleosides and the deoxyribonucleosides are given in Table 14.1.

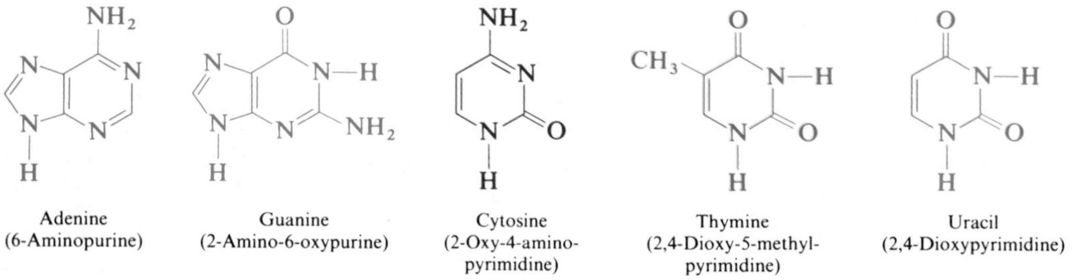

Adenine (6-Aminopurine) | Guanine (2-Amino-6-oxypurine) | Cytosine (2-Oxy-4-amino-pyrimidine) | Thymine (2,4-Dioxy-5-methyl-pyrimidine) | Uracil (2,4-Dioxypyrimidine)

▲ **FIGURE 14.1 Purine and pyrimidine bases found in living matter.**

FIGURE 14.2 ► Typical structures of ribonucleosides and deoxyribonucleosides.

Adenosine | Deoxyadenosine

Cytidine | Deoxycytidine

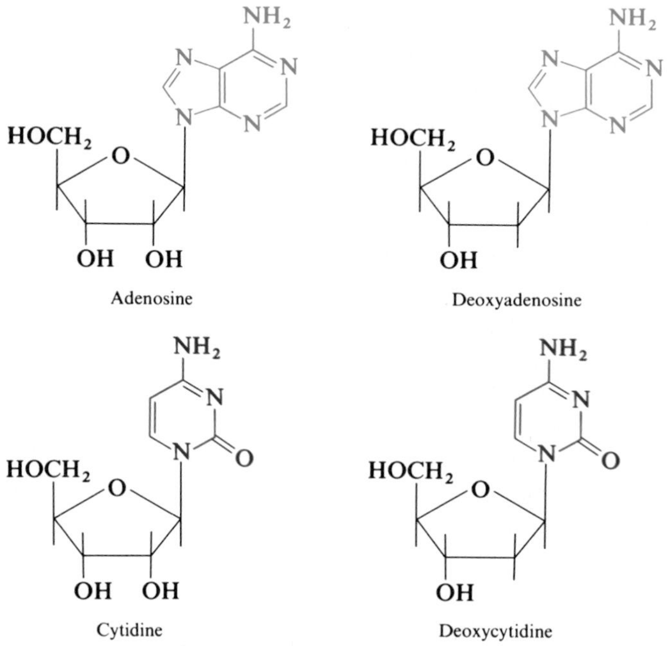

TABLE 14.1 Composition of Ribonucleosides and Deoxyribonucleosides

Name	Composition	Abbreviation
Adenosine	Adenine–ribose	A
Deoxyadenosine	Adenine–deoxyribose	dA
Guanosine	Guanine–ribose	G
Deoxyguanosine	Guanine–deoxyribose	dG
Cytidine	Cytosine–ribose	C
Deoxycytidine	Cytosine–deoxyribose	dC
Thymidine	Thymine–ribose	T
Deoxythymidine	Thymine–deoxyribose	dT
Uridine	Uracil–ribose	U
Deoxyuridine	Uracil–deoxyribose	dU

14.3 Nucleotides: Phosphate Esters

A more complex set of biological molecules is formed by linking phosphate groups to nucleosides. Phosphate esters of nucleosides are termed **nucleotides**. These molecules consist of a purine or a pyrimidine base linked to a sugar, which in turn is bonded to at least one phosphate group.

nucleotides

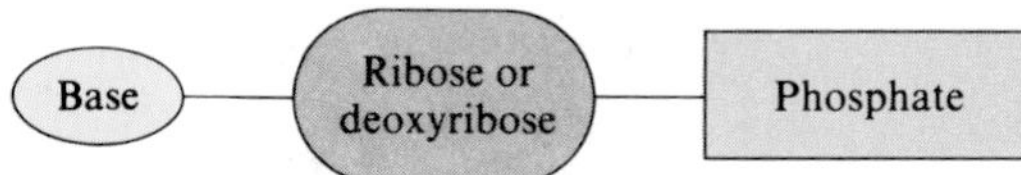

The ester may be a monophosphate, a diphosphate, or a triphosphate. When two or more phosphates are linked together, a high-energy phosphate anhydride bond is formed (see Section 14.4). The ester linkage may be to the hydroxyl group of position 2′, 3′, or 5′ of ribose or of position 3′ or 5′ of deoxyribose. Examples of nucleotide structures are shown in Figure 14.3. The abbreviations for the five nucleosides containing D-ribose are

Adenosine	A
Guanosine	G
Cytidine	C
Thymidine	T
Uridine	U

The letters MP (monophosphate) can be added to any of these to designate the corresponding nucleotide. Thus GMP is guanosine monophosphate. A lowercase d is placed in front of GMP if the nucleotide contains the deoxyribose sugar (dGMP). When the letters such as AMP or GMP are given, it is generally understood that the phosphate group is attached to position 5′ of the ribose unit (5′-AMP). If attachment is elsewhere, it will be designated, for example, 3′-AMP.

Two other important adenosine phosphate esters are adenosine diphosphate (ADP) and adenosine triphosphate (ATP). Note that the letters DP are used for diphosphate and TP for triphosphate. In these molecules the phosphate groups

Adenosine-5′-monophosphate (AMP)

Deoxyadenosine-5′-monophosphate (dAMP)

◄ **Figure 14.3 Examples of nucleotides.**

FIGURE 14.4 ► Structures of ADP and ATP.

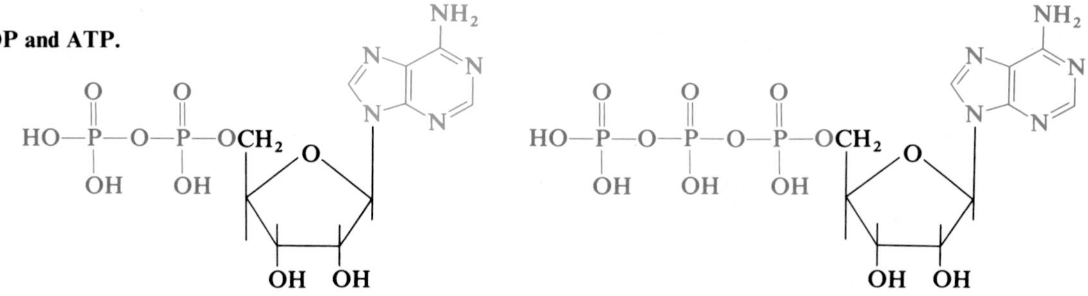

Adenosine-5′-diphosphate (ADP)

Adenosine-5′-triphosphate (ATP)

are linked together. The structures are similar to AMP except that they contain two and three phosphate residues, respectively (see Figure 14.4). All the nucleosides form mono-, di-, and triphosphate nucleotides.

14.4 HIGH-ENERGY NUCLEOTIDES

The nucleotides have a central role in the energy transfers in many metabolic processes. ATP and ADP are especially important in these processes. The role of these two nucleotides is to store and release energy to the cells and tissues. The source of energy is the foods we eat, particularly carbohydrates and fats. Energy is released as the carbons from these foods are oxidized (see Chapter 16). Part of this energy is used to maintain body temperature, and part is stored in the phosphate anhydride bonds of such molecules as ADP and ATP. Because a relatively large amount of energy is stored in these bonds, they are known as high-energy phosphate anhydride bonds.

High-energy phosphate anhydride bonds (ATP)

High-energy anhydride bond (ADP)

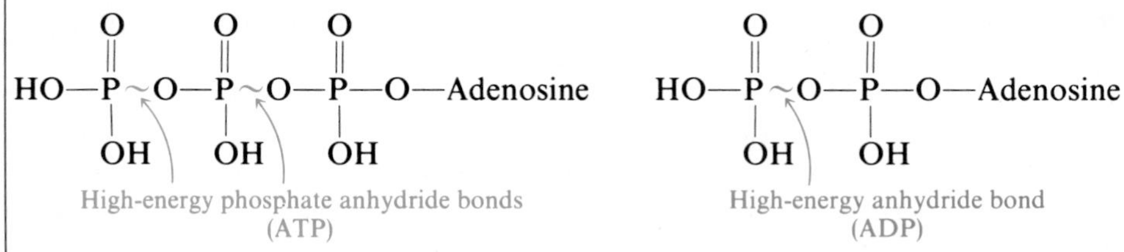

Chemical energy is needed for many of the complex reactions that are essential to life processes. This energy is obtained from the hydrolysis of high-energy phosphate anhydride bonds in ADP and ATP. In the hydrolysis, ATP forms ADP and inorganic phosphate (P_i) with the release of about 35 kJ of energy per mole of ATP:

$$\text{ATP} + \text{H}_2\text{O} \underset{\text{Energy storage}}{\overset{\text{Energy utilization}}{\rightleftharpoons}} \text{ADP} + \text{P}_i + \sim 35 \text{ kJ}$$

The hydrolysis reaction is reversible, with ADP being converted to ATP by still higher energy molecules. In this manner, energy is supplied to the cells from

ATP, and energy is stored by the synthesis of ATP from ADP and AMP. Processes such as muscle movement, nerve sensations, vision, and even the maintenance of our heartbeats are all dependent on energy from ATP.

14.5 Polynucleotides; Nucleic Acids

Starting with two nucleotides, a dinucleotide is formed by splitting out a molecule of water between the —OH of the phosphate group of one nucleotide and the —OH on C-3′ of the ribose or deoxyribose of the other nucleotide. Then another and another nucleotide can be added in the same manner until a polynucleotide chain is formed. Each nucleotide is linked to its neighbors by phosphate ester bonds (see ester formation in Section 6.6).

Two series of polynucleotide chains are known, one containing D-ribose and the other D-2′-deoxyribose. One polymeric chain consists of the monomers AMP, GMP, CMP, and UMP and is known as a polyribonucleotide. The other chain contains the monomers dAMP, dGMP, dCMP, and dTMP is known as a polydeoxyribonucleotide:

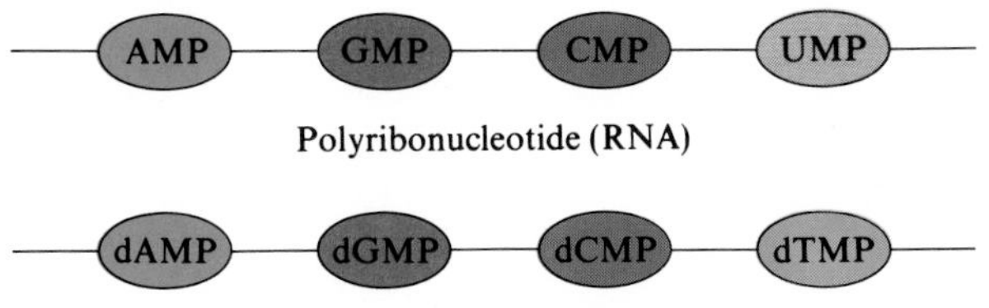

Polyribonucleotide (RNA)

Polydeoxyribonucleotide (DNA)

The nucleic acids DNA and RNA are polynucleotides. **Ribonucleic acid (RNA)** is a polynucleotide that upon hydrolysis yields ribose, phosphoric acid, and the four purine and pyrimidine bases adenine, guanine, cytosine, and uracil. **Deoxyribonucleic acid (DNA)** is a polynucleotide that yields D-2′-deoxyribose, phosphoric acid, and the four bases adenine, guanine, cytosine, and thymine. Note that RNA and DNA contain one different pyrimidine nucleotide. RNA contains uridine, whereas DNA contains thymidine. A segment of a ribonucleic acid chain is shown in Figure 14.5. As will be described later, RNA and DNA also commonly differ in function: DNA serves as the storehouse for genetic information; RNA aids in expressing genetic characteristics.

ribonucleic acid (RNA)

deoxyribonucleic acid (DNA)

14.6 Structure of DNA

Deoxyribonucleic acid (DNA) is a polymeric substance made up of the four nucleotides dAMP, dGMP, dCMP, and dTMP. The size of the DNA polymer varies with the complexity of the organism; more complex organisms tend to have larger DNAs. For example, simple bacteria like *Escherichia coli* have about 8 million nucleotides in their DNA while a human DNA contains up to about 500 million nucleotides. The order in which these nucleotides occur varies in

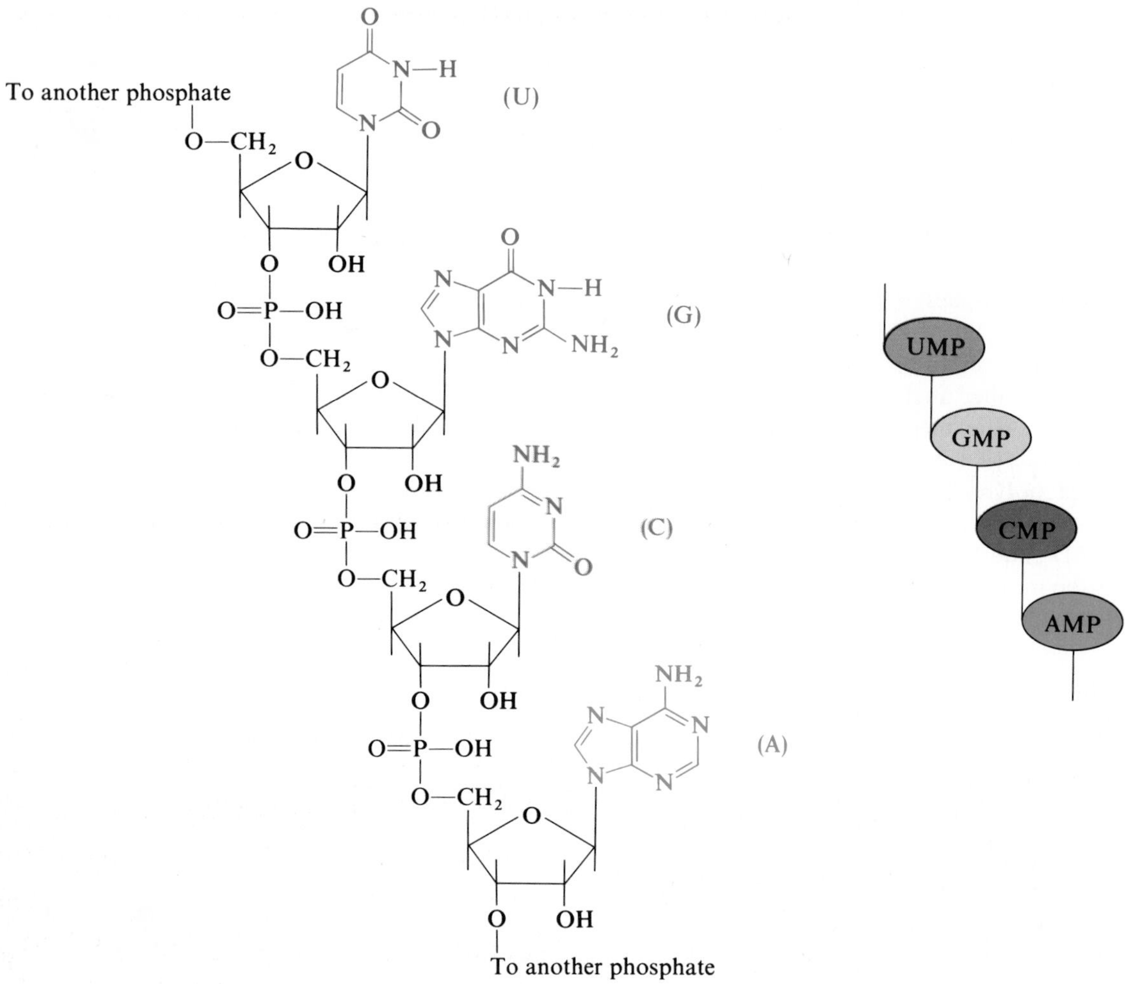

▲
FIGURE 14.5
A segment of ribonucleic acid (RNA) consisting of the four nucleotides adenosine monophosphate, cytidine monophosphate, guanosine monophosphate, and uridine monophosphate.

different DNA molecules, and it is within this order that the genetic information in a cell is stored.

Scientists have tried to understand DNA structure by determining the nucleotide composition of this molecule from many different sources. For a long time it was thought that the four nucleotides occurred in equal amounts in DNA. However, more refined analyses showed that the amounts of purine and pyrimidine bases varied in different DNA molecules. Surprisingly, careful consideration of these data also showed that the ratios of adenine to thymine and guanine to cytosine were always essentially 1:1. This observation served as an important key to unraveling the structure of DNA. The analyses of DNA from several species are shown in Table 14.2.

A second important clue to the special configuration and structure of DNA came from X-ray diffraction studies. Most significant was the work of Maurice H. F. Wilkins (b. 1916) of Kings College of London. Wilkins's X-ray pictures implied that the nucleotide bases were stacked one on top of another like a stack

TABLE 14.2 Relative Amounts of Purines and Pyrimidines in Samples of DNA

Source	Adenine	Thymine	Ratio A/T	Guanine	Cytosine	Ratio G/C
Beef thymus	29.0	28.5	1.02	21.2	21.2	1.00
Beef liver	28.8	29.0	0.99	21.0	21.1	1.00
Beef sperm	28.7	27.2	1.06	22.2	22.0	1.01
Human thymus	30.9	29.4	1.05	19.9	19.8	1.00
Human liver	30.3	30.3	1.00	19.5	19.9	0.98
Human sperm	30.9	31.6	0.98	19.1	18.4	1.04
Hen red blood cells	28.8	29.2	0.99	20.5	21.5	0.96
Herring sperm	27.8	27.5	1.01	22.2	22.6	0.98
Wheat germ	26.5	27.0	0.98	23.5	23.0	1.02
Yeast	31.7	32.6	0.97	18.3	17.4	1.05
Vaccinia virus	29.5	29.9	0.99	20.6	20.0	1.03
Bacteriophage T_2	32.5	32.6	1.00	18.2	18.6	0.98

of saucers. From his work as well as that of others, the American biologist James D. Watson (b. 1928) and British physicist Francis H. C. Crick (b. 1916), working at Cambridge University, designed and built a scale model of a DNA molecule. In 1953 Watson and Crick announced their now famous double-stranded helical structure for DNA. This was a milestone in the history of biology, and in 1962 Watson, Crick, and Wilkins were awarded the Nobel prize in medicine and physiology for their studies of DNA.

▲ **Francis Crick (1916–) and James Watson (1928–).**

The structure of DNA, according to Watson and Crick, consists of two polymeric strands of nucleotides in the form of a double helix, with both nucleotide strands coiled around the same axis (see Figure 14.6). Along each strand are alternate phosphate and deoxyribose units with one of the four bases adenine, guanine, cytosine, or thymine attached to deoxyribose as a side group. The double helix is held together by hydrogen bonds extending from the base on one strand of the double helix to a complementary base on the other strand. The structure of DNA has been likened to a ladder that has been twisted into a double helix, with the rungs of the ladder kept perpendicular to the twisted railings. The phosphate and deoxyribose units alternate along the two railings of the ladder, and two nitrogen bases form each rung of the ladder.

In the Watson–Crick model of DNA, the two polynucleotide strands fit together best when a purine base is adjacent to a pyrimidine base. Although this allows for four possible base pairings, A–T, A–C, G–C, and G–T, only the adenine–thymine and guanine–cytosine base pairs can effectively hydrogen-bond together. Under normal conditions, **an adenine on one polynucleotide strand is paired with a thymine on the other strand; a guanine is paired with a cytosine** (see Figure 14.7). This pairing results in A:T and G:C ratios of 1:1, as substantiated by the data in Table 14.2. The hydrogen bonding of complementary base pairs is shown in Figure 14.8. Note that if the sequence of one strand is known, the sequence of the other strand can be determined. The two DNA polymers are said to be *complementary* to each other. As will be discussed in Section 14.7, the cell can chemically "read" one strand in order to synthesize its complementary partner.

FIGURE 14.6 ▶ Double-stranded helical structure of DNA. (···· denotes a hydrogen bond between adjoining bases.)

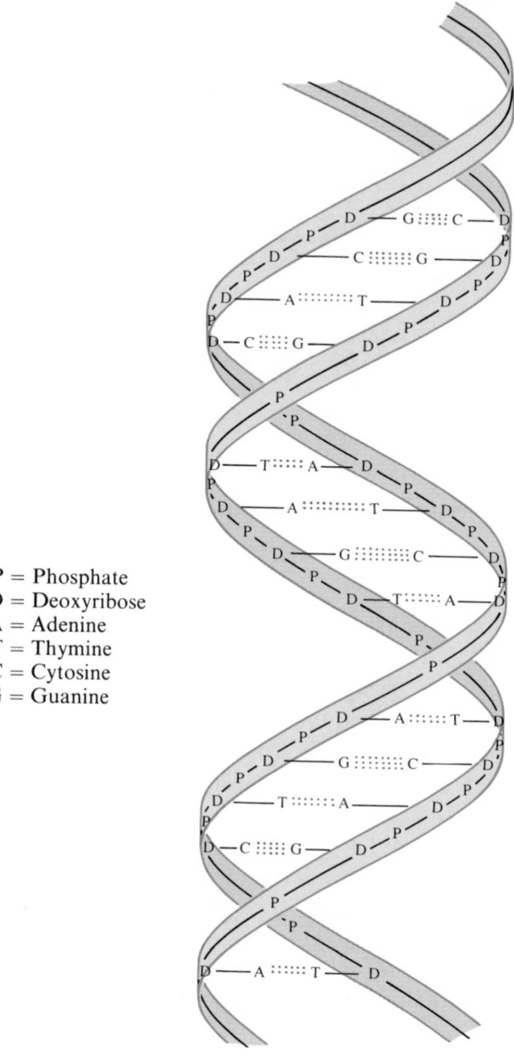

The double helix is an important part of DNA structure. It does not explain how the very large DNA can be packed into a cell or the even smaller cell nucleus. For example, a human DNA molecule can be extended to almost 10 centimeters in length and yet is contained in a nucleus with a diameter about a hundred thousand times smaller. To begin the necessary packing, the DNA is looped around small aggregates of positively charged histone proteins. Hundreds of these aggregates are associated with each DNA molecule so that the DNA is foreshortened and has the appearance of a string of pearls. Further condensation is achieved by wrapping this structure into a tight coil called a solenoid, as shown in Figure 14.9. Finally, the solenoid nucleoprotein complex is wound around a protein scaffold within the nucleus. By following this complete procedure, human DNA can be taken to a length of about 10 μm in condensed chromosomes. Like a high-density computer disk, DNA takes up only a little space relative to the large amount of genetic information it contains.

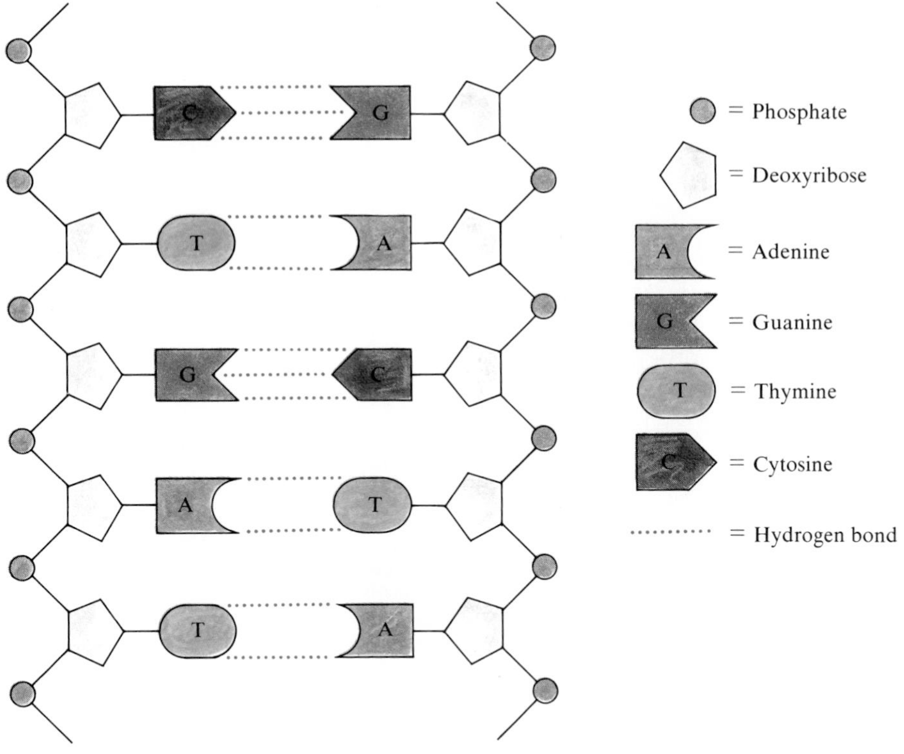

◀ **FIGURE 14.7**
Schematic diagram of a DNA segment showing phosphate, deoxyribose, and complementary base pairings held together by hydrogen bonds.

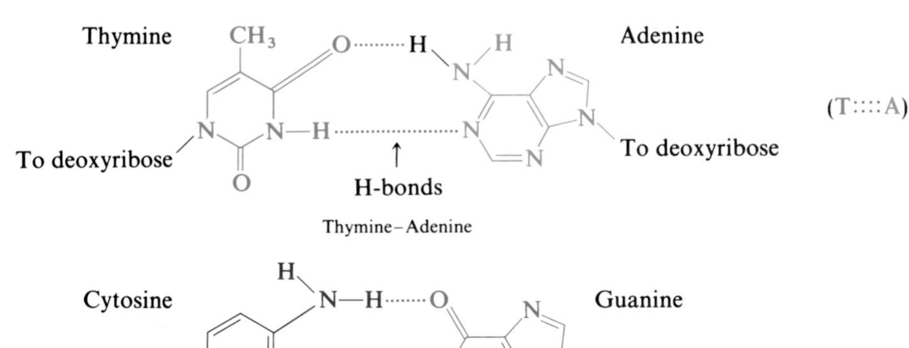

◀ **FIGURE 14.8**
Hydrogen bonding between the complementary bases thymine and adenine (T::::A) and cytosine and guanine (C::::G). Note that one pair of bases has two hydrogen bonds and the other pair has three hydrogen bonds.

14.7 DNA Replication

The foundations of our present concepts of heredity and evolution were laid within the span of a decade. Charles Darwin (1809–1882), in *The Origin of Species* (1859), presented evidence supporting the concept of organic evolution

FIGURE 14.9 ▶ Condensed form of DNA: After the DNA polymer is wrapped twice around the histone protein aggregates (shown as round balls), it is coiled around a central axis to form a solenoid structure.

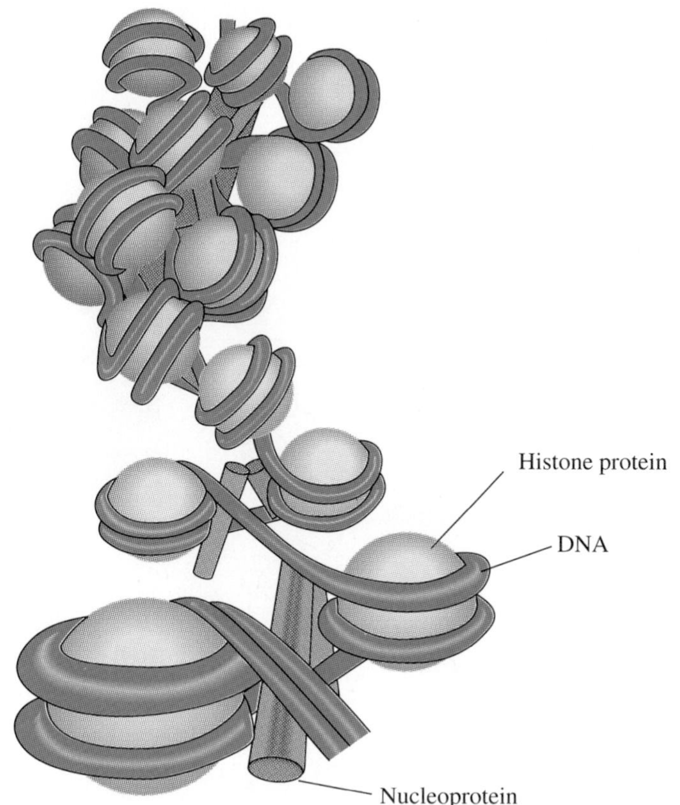

and his theory of natural selection. Gregor Johann Mendel (1822–1884) discovered the basic laws of heredity in 1866, and Friedrich Miescher discovered nucleic acid in 1869. Although Darwin's views were widely discussed and generally accepted by biologists within a few years, Mendel's and Miescher's work went unnoticed for many years.

Mendel's laws were rediscovered about 1900 and led to our present understanding of heredity and the science of genetics. Interest in nucleic acids lagged until nearly the 1950s, when chemical and X-ray data provided the basis for the suggestion by Watson and Crick that DNA exists in a double helix and that DNA has the possible copying mechanism for genetic material.

Heredity is the process by which the physical and mental characteristics of parents are transferred to their offspring. In order for this to occur, it is necessary for the material responsible for genetic transfer to be able to make exact copies of itself. The polymeric DNA molecule is the chemical basis for heredity. The genetic information needed for transmittal of a species' characteristics is coded along the polymeric chain. Although the chain is made from only four different nucleotides, the information content of DNA resides in the sequence of these nucleotides.

genome

The **genome** is the sum of all hereditary material contained in a cell. Within the eucaryotic genome are chromosomes, which are long, threadlike bodies composed of nucleic acids and proteins that contain the fundamental units of heredity, called genes. A **gene** is a segment of the DNA chain that controls formation of a molecule of RNA. In turn, many RNAs determine the amino acid

gene

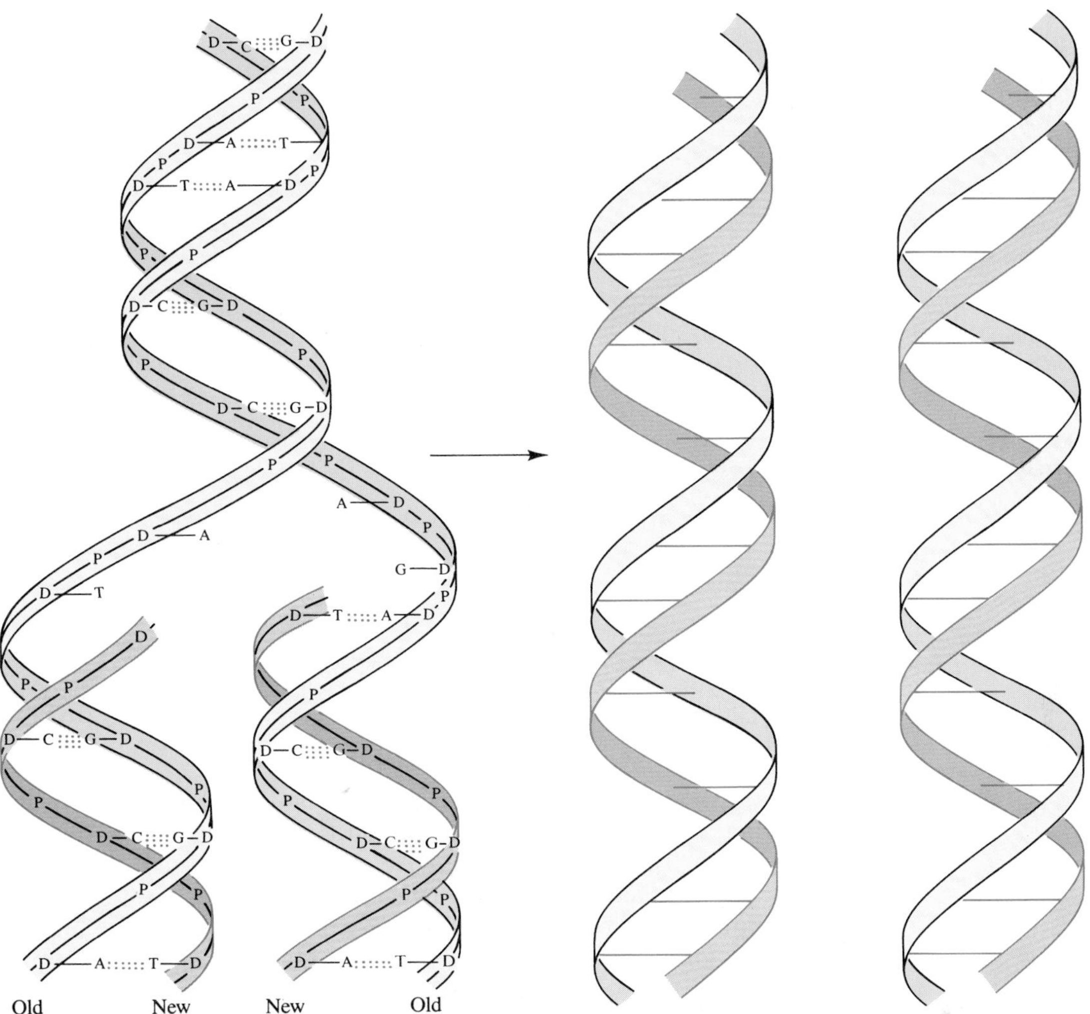

▲
FIGURE 14.10
Method of replication of DNA: The two helices unwind, separating at the hydrogen bonds. Each strand then serves as a template, recombining with the proper nucleotides to form a new double-stranded helix. The newly synthesized DNA strands are shown in color with arrows showing the direction of synthesis.

sequences for specific polypeptides or proteins. One gene commonly directs the synthesis of only one polypeptide or protein molecule. The cell has the capability of producing a multitude of different proteins because each DNA molecule contains a large number of different genes.

replication

For life to continue relatively unchanged, genetic information must be reproduced exactly each time a cell divides. **Replication**, as the name implies, is the biological process for duplicating the DNA molecule. The DNA structure of Watson and Crick holds the key to replication; because of the complementary nature of DNA's nitrogen bases, adenine bonds only to thymine and guanine only to cytosine. Nucleotides with complementary bases can hydrogen-bond to each single strand of DNA and hence be incorporated into a new DNA double helix. Every double-stranded DNA molecule that is produced contains one template strand and one newly formed, complementary strand. This form of DNA synthesis, known as *semiconservative* replication, is illustrated in Figure 14.10.

Replication is one of the most complicated enzyme-catalyzed processes in life. Enzymes are required to unwind the DNA before replication and to repackage the DNA after synthesis. The two template strands are copied differently.

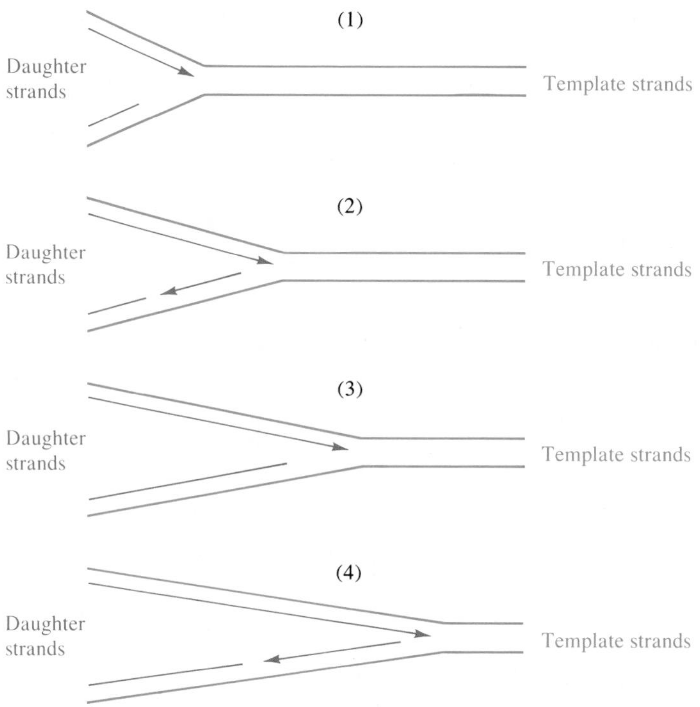

FIGURE 14.11 ▶ Diagram showing the basic replication process. Arrows indicate the direction of DNA synthesis. In going from schematic 1 to schematic 2, the template DNA strands unwind and some synthesis occurs for both daughter strands. Moving to schematic 3, the DNA fragments are connected on one daughter strand while DNA synthesis continues on the other strand and the template strands unwind further. DNA synthesis again takes place for both daughter strands in schematic 4.

One daughter strand grows directly toward the point at which the templates are unwinding while the other daughter strand is synthesized away from this point. In this way, the same enzyme catalyzed reaction can be used for synthesis of both strands. However, the one daughter strand that has been created in small fragments must be connected before replication is complete. So, while one DNA strand is formed by continuous synthesis, the other new strand is formed by a repetition of fragment synthesis followed by a coupling reaction (see Figure 14.11).

Other processes "proofread" the new polymers to check for errors. Amazingly, replication is so carefully coordinated that a mistake is passed on to the new strands only one in about 10^9 times. Of course this important fact means that new cells retain the genetic characteristics of their parents.

The DNA content of cells doubles just before the cell divides, and one-half of the DNA goes to each daughter cell. After cell division is completed, each daughter cell contains DNA and the full genetic code that was present in the original cell. This process of ordinary cell division is known as **mitosis** and occurs in all the cells of the body except the reproductive cells.

mitosis

As we have indicated before, DNA is an integral part of the chromosomes. Each species carries a specific number of chromosomes in the nucleus of each of its cells. The number of chromosomes varies with different species. Humans have 23 pairs, or 46 chromosomes. The fruit fly has 4 pairs, or 8 chromosomes. Each chromosome contains DNA molecules. Mitosis produces cells with the same chromosomal content as the parent cell. However, in the sexual reproductive cycle, cell division occurs by a different process known as meiosis.

In sexual reproduction, two cells, the sperm cell from the male and the egg cell (or ovum) from the female, unite to form the cell of the new individual.

If reproduction took place with mitotic cells, the normal chromosome content would double when two cells united. However, in **meiosis** the cell splits in such a way as to reduce the number of chromosomes to one-half of the number normally present (23 in humans). The sperm cell carries half of the chromosomes from its original cell, and the egg cell also carries half of the chromosomes from its original cell. When the sperm and the egg cells unite during fertilization, the cell once again contains the correct number of chromosomes and the hereditary characteristics of the species. Thus, the offspring derives half its genetic characteristics from the father and half from the mother.

meiosis

14.8 RNA: Genetic Transcription

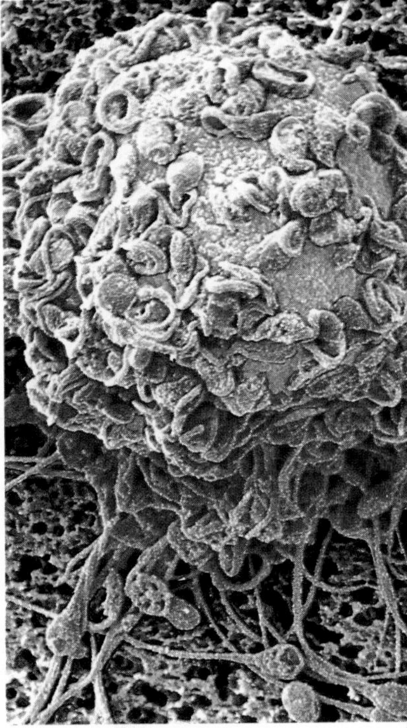

▲ The sperm and egg each provide half the chromosomes as they join during the fertilization process.

One of the main functions of DNA is to direct the synthesis of ribonucleic acids (RNAs). RNA differs from DNA in the following ways: (1) it consists of a single polymeric strand of nucleotides rather than a double helix; (2) it contains the pentose D-ribose instead of D-2′-deoxyribose; (3) it contains the pyrimidine base uracil instead of thymine; and (4) some types of RNA have a significant fraction of unusual bases in addition to the common four. RNA also differs functionally from DNA. Whereas DNA serves as the storehouse of genetic information, RNA is used to process this information into proteins. Three types of RNA are needed to produce proteins: ribosomal RNA (rRNA), messenger RNA (mRNA), and transfer RNA (tRNA).

More than 80% of the cellular RNA is ribosomal RNA. It is found in the ribosomes, where it is associated with protein in proportions of about 60–65% protein to 30–35% rRNA. Ribosomes are the sites for protein synthesis.

Messenger RNA carries genetic information from DNA to the ribosomes. It is a template made from DNA and carries the code that directs the synthesis of proteins. The size of mRNA varies according to the length of the polypeptide chain it will encode.

The primary function of tRNA is to bring amino acids to the ribosomes for incorporation into protein molecules. Consequently there exists at least one tRNA for each of the 20 amino acids required for proteins. Transfer RNA molecules have a number of structural features in common. The end of the chain of all tRNA molecules terminates in a CCA nucleotide sequence to which is attached the amino acid to be transferred to a protein chain. The primary structure of tRNA allows extensive folding of the molecule such that complementary bases are hydrogen-bonded to each other to form a structure that appears like a cloverleaf. The cloverleaf model of tRNA has an anticodon loop consisting of seven unpaired nucleotides. Three of these nucleotides make up an anticodon (see Figure 14.12). The anticodon is complementary to, and hydrogen-bonds with, three bases on an mRNA. The other two loops in the cloverleaf structure enable the tRNA to bind to the ribosome and other specific enzymes during protein synthesis (see Section 14.10.)

transcription

The making of RNA from DNA is called **transcription**. The verb *transcribe* literally means to copy, often into a different format. When the nucleotide sequence of one strand of DNA is transcribed into a single strand of RNA, genetic information is copied from DNA to RNA. This transcription occurs in a complementary fashion and depends upon hydrogen bonded pairing between

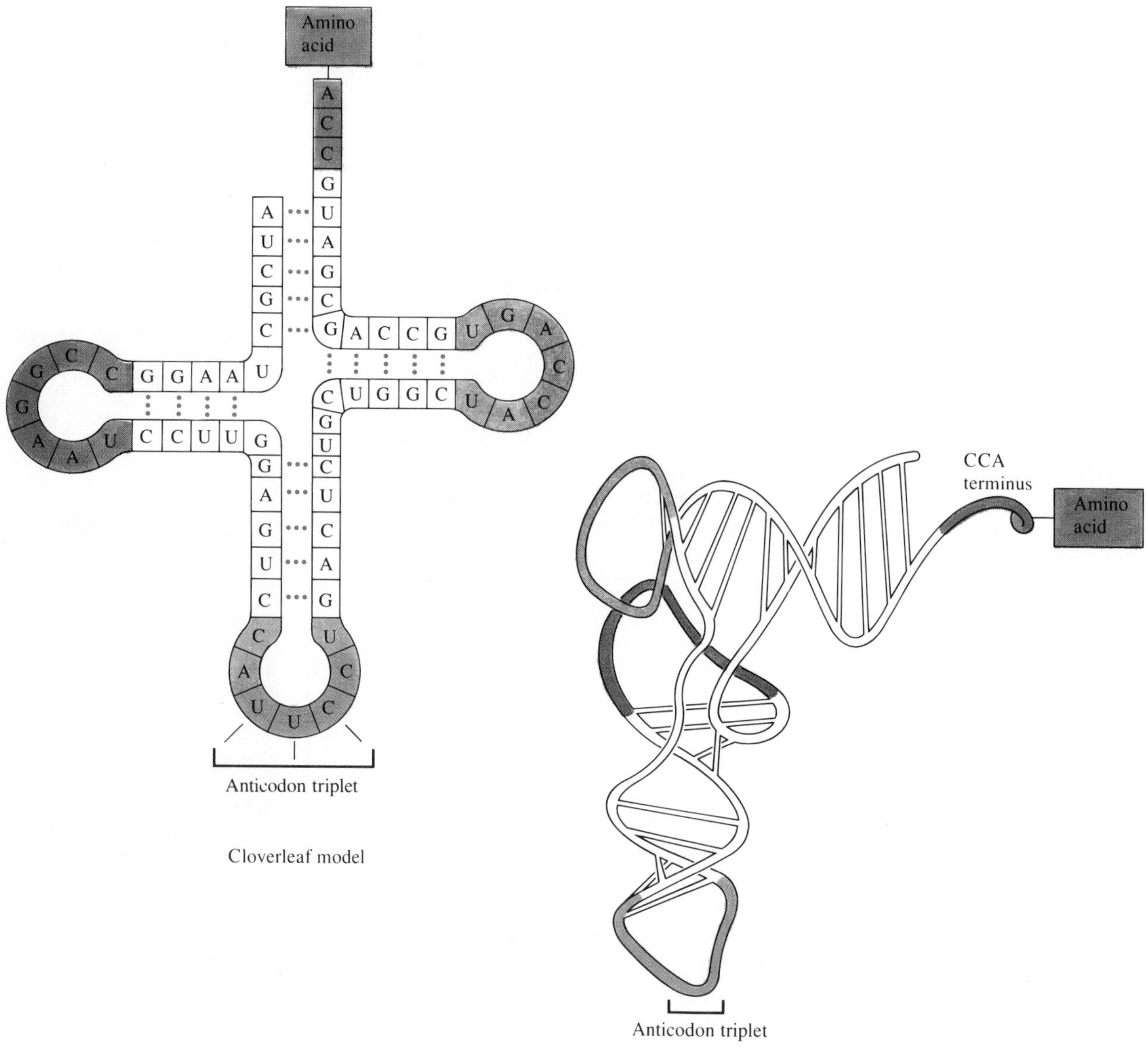

▲
FIGURE 14.12
Cloverleaf model and three dimensional representations of tRNA. The anticodon triplet (CCU) located at the lower loop is complementary to GAA (which is the code for glutamic acid) on mRNA.

appropriate bases (see Figure 14.13). Where there is a guanine base in DNA, a cytosine base will occur in RNA. Cytosine is transcribed to guanine, thymine to adenine, and adenine to uracil (the thymine-like base which is found in RNA).

Because transcription is the initial step in the expression of genetic information, this process is under stringent cellular control. Only a small fraction of the total information stored in DNA is used at any one time. In procaryotic cells (see Section 16.5), related genes are often located together so that they can be transcribed in concert. The control of eucaryotic gene expression is more complex.

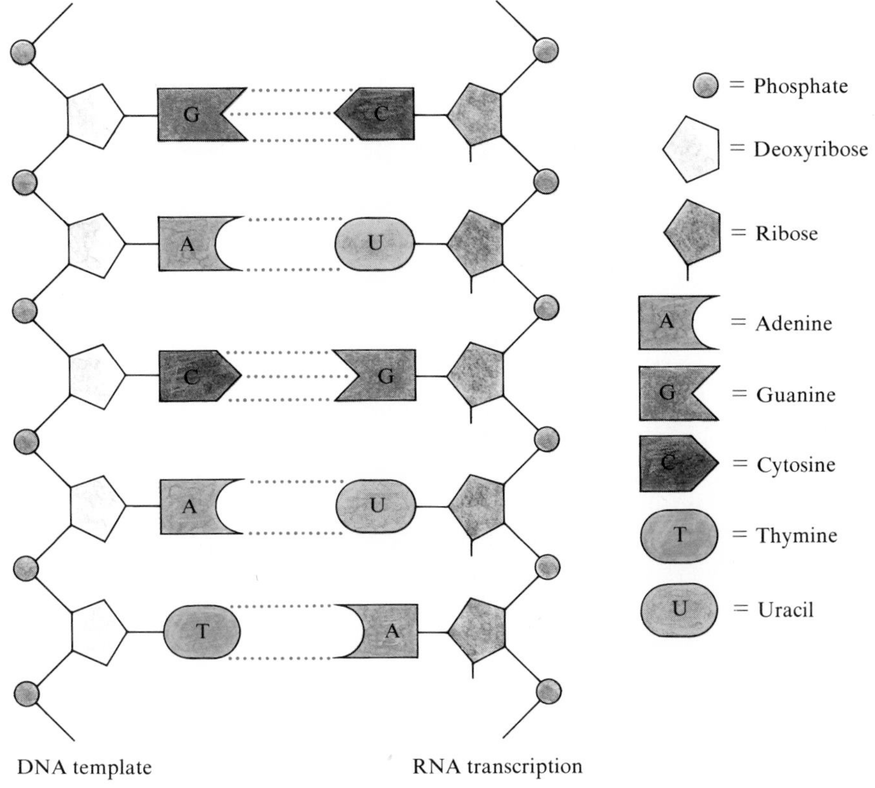

◄ FIGURE 14.13 **Transcription of RNA from DNA. The sugar in RNA is ribose. The complementary base of adenine is uracil. After transcription is complete, the new RNA separates from its DNA template and travels to another location for further use. (.... denotes a hydrogen bond between adjoining bases.)**

The importance of transcription control is illustrated by the recently discovered oncogenes. These genes, which cause cells to become malignant or cancerous, were originally discovered as part of the genome of cancer causing viruses. To the surprise of many investigators, it was also found that these same oncogenes are present in many normal mammalian cells. The cells carry on their normal and necessary functions, and are not cancerous, as long as the oncogenes are under control. But control can be lost due to, for example, a virus infection or exposure to a chemical carcinogen. Then the oncogenes are transcribed too often, and the cell becomes cancerous.

Following transcription, the RNA molecules that are produced from DNA often are modified before they are put to use. Ribosomal RNA and tRNA molecules are formed as larger precursors and are then trimmed to the correct size. After transcription, many of the bases in tRNA are modified by methylation, saturation of a double bond, or by isomerization of the ribose-base linkage. This post-transcriptional modification or processing changes the information content of the RNA.

Eucaryotic mRNA may undergo considerable alteration before the message that it carries is ready to guide protein synthesis. These changes may include the elimination of portions of the mRNA molecule, the splicing together of two or more mRNA molecules, or the addition of new bases to one end of the mRNA. During this processing, the message encoded in the mRNA molecule is apparently refined so that it can be correctly read by the ribosome.

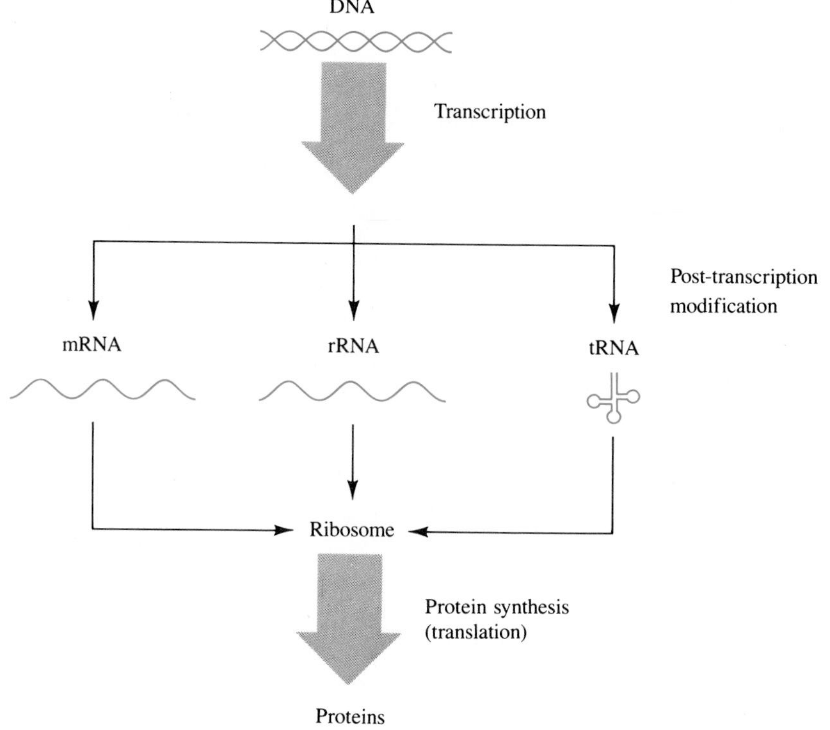

FIGURE 14.14 ► A flow diagram representing the processing of cellular genetic information.

Figure 14.14 summarizes the processes by which genetic information is transferred within a cell. These steps culminate in the conversion of a coded nucleotide message into a protein amino acid sequence.

14.9 THE GENETIC CODE

For a long time after the structure of DNA was elucidated, scientists struggled with the problem of how the information stored in DNA could specify the synthesis of so many different proteins. Since the backbone of the DNA molecule contains a regular structure of repeated and identical phosphate and deoxyribose units, the key to the code had to lie with the four bases—adenine, guanine, cytosine, and thymine.

The code, using only the four nucleotides A, G, C, and T, must be capable of coding at least for the 20 amino acids that occur in proteins. If each nucleotide coded one amino acid, only four amino acids could be represented. If the code used two nucleotides to specify an amino acid, 16 (4×4) combinations would be possible—still not enough. Using three nucleotides we can have 64 ($4 \times 4 \times 4$) possible combinations—which is more than enough to specify the 20 common amino acids in proteins. It has now been determined that each code word requires a sequence of three nucleotides. The code is therefore a triplet code. Each triplet of three nucleotides is called a **codon**, and, in general, each codon specifies one

codon

◀ This table shows the sequence of nucleotides in the triplet codons of messenger RNA that specify a given amino acid. For example, UUU or UUC is the codon for Phe, UCU is the codon for Ser; CAU or CAC is the codon for His.

TABLE 14.3 The Genetic Code for Messenger RNA

First nucleotide	Second nucleotide				Third nucleotide
	U	C	A	G	
U	Phe	Ser	Tyr	Cys	U
	Phe	Ser	Tyr	Cys	C
	Leu	Ser	TC[a]	TC[a]	A
	Leu	Ser	TC[a]	Trp	G
C	Leu	Pro	His	Arg	U
	Leu	Pro	His	Arg	C
	Leu	Pro	Gln	Arg	A
	Leu	Pro	Gln	Arg	G
A	Ile	Thr	Asn	Ser	U
	Ile	Thr	Asn	Ser	C
	Ile	Thr	Lys	Arg	A
	Met	Thr	Lys	Arg	G
G	Val	Ala	Asp	Gly	U
	Val	Ala	Asp	Gly	C
	Val	Ala	Glu	Gly	A
	Val	Ala	Glu	Gly	G

[a] Termination or nonsense codons.

amino acid. Thus, to describe a protein containing 200 amino acid units, a gene containing at least 200 codons, or 600 nucleotides, is required.

In the sequence of biological events, the code from a gene in DNA is first transcribed to a coded RNA, which, in turn, is used to direct the synthesis of a protein. The 64 possible codons for mRNA are given in Table 14.3. In this table a three-letter sequence (first nucleotide–second nucleotide–third nucleotide) specifies a particular amino acid. For example, the codon CAC (cytosine–adenine–cytosine) is the code for the amino acid histidine (His). You will note that three codons in the table, marked TC, do not encode any amino acids. These are called *nonsense* or *termination codons.* They act as signals to indicate where the synthesis of a protein molecule is to end. The other 61 codons identify 20 amino acids. Methionine and tryptophan have only one codon each. For the other amino acids, the code is redundant; that is, each amino acid is specified by at least two, and sometimes by as many as six, codons.

It is believed that the genetic code is a universal code for all living organisms; that is, the same nucleotide triplet specifies a given amino acid regardless of whether that amino acid is synthesized by a bacterial cell, a pine tree, or a human being.

Recently scientists have developed a machine that automates the sequencing of DNA. Whereas a researcher might manually sequence about 140 bases per day, the machine can chemically "read" about 10,000 bases per day. This rapid decoding of genetic information is essential if scientists finally hope to

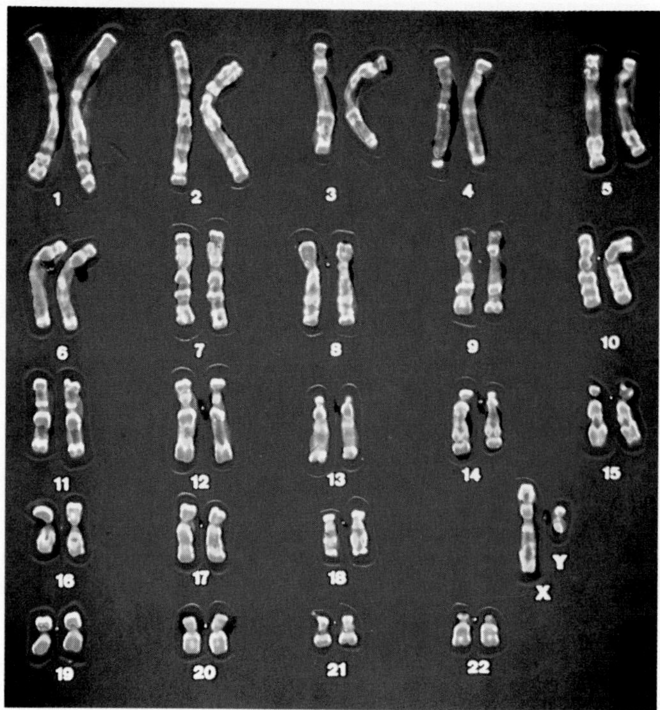

A karyotype of a normal ▶ male showing all the pairs of chromosomes. This information can be used in genetic counseling to identify possible genetic abnormalities in offspring.

understand the human genome, which contains about 3 billion bases. Just such a major collaborative research project, called the Human Genome Project, is in progress. Because one laboratory would take about 1000 years to decode the human genome even with a sequencing machine, the Human Genome Project involves many research laboratories across the United States. The first few years of this project have resulted in identification of the chromosomal location of the genes causing muscular dystrophy, Huntington's disease, and cystic fibrosis. Scientists project that within 20 years they will have the information to diagnose and treat the large number of genetic disorders which afflict humankind.

14.10 Biosynthesis of Proteins

translation

The biosynthesis of proteins is extremely complex, and the following is only a cursory description of the overall process. The production of a polypeptide using an mRNA template is called **translation**. This term is used because it literally means a change from one language to another. The genetic code is *translated* into the primary structure of a polypeptide or a protein.

The biosynthesis of proteins begins when messenger RNA leaves the cellular nucleus and travels to the cytoplasm. Each mRNA is then bound to five or more ribosomes, the bodies responsible for protein synthesis. Amino acids must also be transferred to the ribosomes. To accomplish this step, cellular energy in the form of ATP is used to couple amino acids to tRNAs to form aminoacyl–tRNA complexes that can bind to the ribosomes.

$$\mathrm{R{-}CH(NH_2){-}\overset{\displaystyle O}{\overset{\|}{C}}{-}OH + tRNA + ATP \xrightarrow[\text{synthetase}]{\text{Aminoacyl-tRNA}}}$$

$$\mathrm{R{-}CH(NH_2){-}\overset{\displaystyle O}{\overset{\|}{C}}{-}tRNA + AMP + HO{-}\overset{\displaystyle O}{\overset{\|}{P}}(OH){-}O{-}\overset{\displaystyle O}{\overset{\|}{P}}(OH){-}OH}$$

Aminoacyl-tRNA

A different specific enzyme is utilized for binding each of the 20 amino acids to a corresponding tRNA. Although only 20 amino acids are involved, there are about 60 different tRNA molecules in the cells. In summary the function of tRNA is to bring amino acids to the ribosome synthesis site.

Initiation The next step in the process is the initiation of polypeptide synthesis. Two codons signal for the start of protein synthesis, AUG and GUG (AUG being the more common). As shown in Table 14.3, these codons also code for incorporation of the amino acids methionine and valine. Most mRNAs have more than one AUG and GUG, and the ribosome must choose at which codon to begin. It appears that the ribosome uses information in addition to the AUG or GUG triplet to choose the correct starting codon for protein synthesis.

Once the correct starting point has been identified, a special initiator tRNA binds to the ribosome. This specific tRNA carries an *N*-formyl methionine in procaryotic cells:

$$\mathrm{CH_3{-}S{-}CH_2CH_2\underset{}{CH}(NH{-}HC{=}O){-}\overset{\displaystyle O}{\overset{\|}{C}}{-}tRNA}$$

N-formyl methionine-tRNA

Because of the attached formyl group (CHO), a second amino acid will react only with the carboxyl group of methionine, the correct direction for protein synthesis. In eucaryotic cells, the initiator tRNA carries a methionine group.

Elongation The next stage involves the elongation or growth of the peptide chain, which is assembled one amino acid at a time. After the initiator tRNA is attached to the mRNA codon, the elongation of the polypeptide chain involves the following steps (see Figure 14.15):

1. The next aminoacyl-tRNA enters the ribosome and becomes attached to mRNA through the hydrogen bonding of the tRNA anticodon to the mRNA codon.
2. The peptide bond between the two amino acids is formed by the transfer of the amino acid from the initial aminoacyl-tRNA to the incoming aminoacyl-tRNA. In this step, which is catalyzed by the enzyme peptidyl

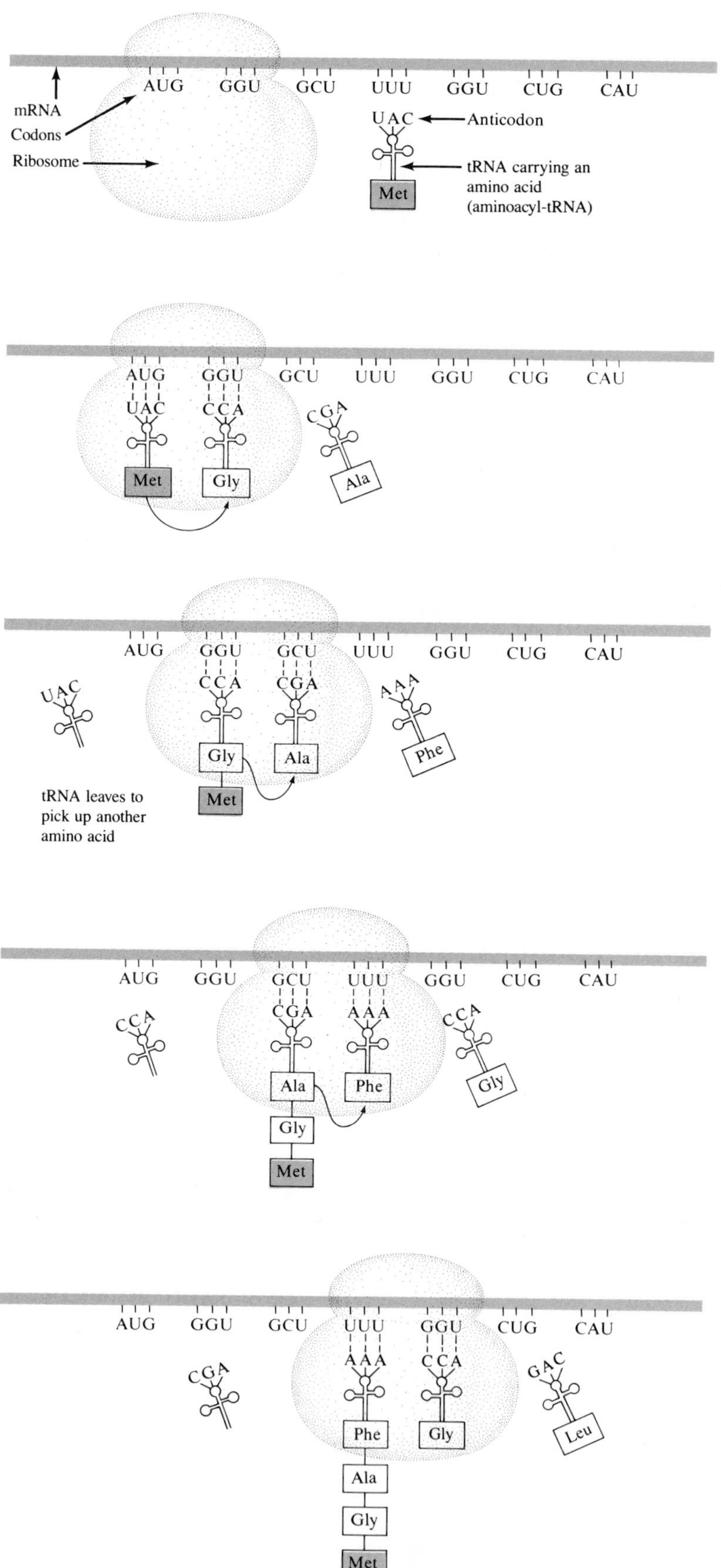

FIGURE 14.15 ▶ Biosynthesis of proteins: mRNA from DNA enters and complexes with the ribosomes. tRNA carrying an amino acid (aminoacyl-tRNA) enters the ribosome and attaches to the mRNA at its complementary anticodon. The peptide chain elongates when another aminoacyl-tRNA enters the ribosome and attaches to the mRNA. The peptide bond is then formed by the transfer of the peptide chain from the initial to the incoming aminoacyl-tRNA. The sequence is repeated until a termination codon appears in mRNA.

transferase, the carboxyl group of the first amino acid separates from its tRNA and forms a peptide bond with the free amino group of the incoming aminoacyl-tRNA.

3. The tRNA carrying the peptide chain (now known as a peptidyl-tRNA) moves over in the ribosome, the free tRNA is ejected, and the next aminoacyl-tRNA enters the ribosome.

The peptide chain is transferred to the incoming amino acid and the sequence is repeated over and over again as the mRNA moves through the ribosome, just like a tape delivering its message. In each step the entire peptide chain is transferred to the incoming amino acid.

The initiation and elongation of polypeptide chains requires cellular energy. The primary source of this energy is the nucleotide guanosine-5′-triphosphate (GTP). At various steps in the growth of the protein chain, a high-energy GTP phosphate anhydride bond is hydrolyzed, yielding GDP and a phosphate group. The energy that is released drives protein synthesis. This reaction is analogous to that involving ATP (see Section 14.4).

Termination The termination of the polypeptide chain occurs when a nonsense or termination codon appears. In normal cells there are no tRNAs that have complementary anticodons to the termination codons. Because there is no new aminoacyl-tRNA to bind to the ribosome, the peptidyl-tRNA is hydrolyzed, and the free polypeptide (protein) is released. All of these amazing, coordinated steps are accomplished at a high rate of speed—about 1 minute for a 150 amino acid chain in hemoglobin and 10–20 seconds for a 300–500 amino acid chain in the bacterium *Escherichia coli* (*E. coli*). This mechanism of protein synthesis is illustrated in Figure 14.15.

14.11 Mutations

It is known that from time to time a new trait appears in an individual that is not present in either parents or ancestors. These traits, which are generally the result of genetic or chromosomal changes, are called **mutations**. Some mutations are beneficial, but most are harmful. Because mutations are genetic, they may be passed on to the next or future generations. mutation

Mutations can occur spontaneously or can be caused by chemical agents or various types of radiation such as X rays, cosmic rays, and ultraviolet rays. The agent that causes the mutation is called a **mutagen**. Exposure to mutagens may produce changes in the DNA of the sperm or ova. The likelihood of such changes is increased by the intensity and length of exposure to the mutagen. Mutations may then show up as birth defects in the next generation. Common types of genetic alterations include the substitution of one purine or pyrimidine for another during DNA replication. Such a substitution is a change in the genetic code and causes misinformation to be transcribed from the DNA. A mutagen also may alter genetic material by causing a chromosome or chromosome fragment to be added or removed. mutagen

There is clear evidence that many mutagens are also carcinogens. When these chemicals alter the genome, they may also change genetic controls, causing a cell to become cancerous. Bruce Ames, an American biochemist, made use of this

(continued on page 364)

Chemistry in Action

Genetic Engineering

Almost since life first evolved, genetic material has been manipulated and changed to achieve specific goals. Nature has its own genetic engineers, the viruses. These small particles commonly carry only a few genes surrounded by a protein coat. Viruses are not living cells but exist as parasites within host cells. The virus invades a cell, adds its genetic material to that of the cell, and forces the cell to produce viral genes and proteins.

For example, the virus that causes the acquired immune deficiency syndrome (AIDS) acts by invading and altering the transcription of cells that are part of the body's immune system (lymphocytes). Within the cell the virus releases viral RNA and the enzyme *reverse transcriptase*. The viral RNA acts as a template and the enzyme synthesizes viral DNA, which then inserts into the cell DNA. New viral RNAs and proteins are produced. The cell has now lost control of its normal transcription and reproductive ability. Progressive damage to the immune system occurs as immune cells produce new viruses and then die.

In recent years laboratory techniques for the controlled production of genetic changes have been developed. These techniques are known as *genetic engineering* and have already been responsible for considerable progress in medicine and biology. Genetic engineering holds the promise of revolutionary advances in medicine, agriculture, the manufacture of pharmaceuticals, and

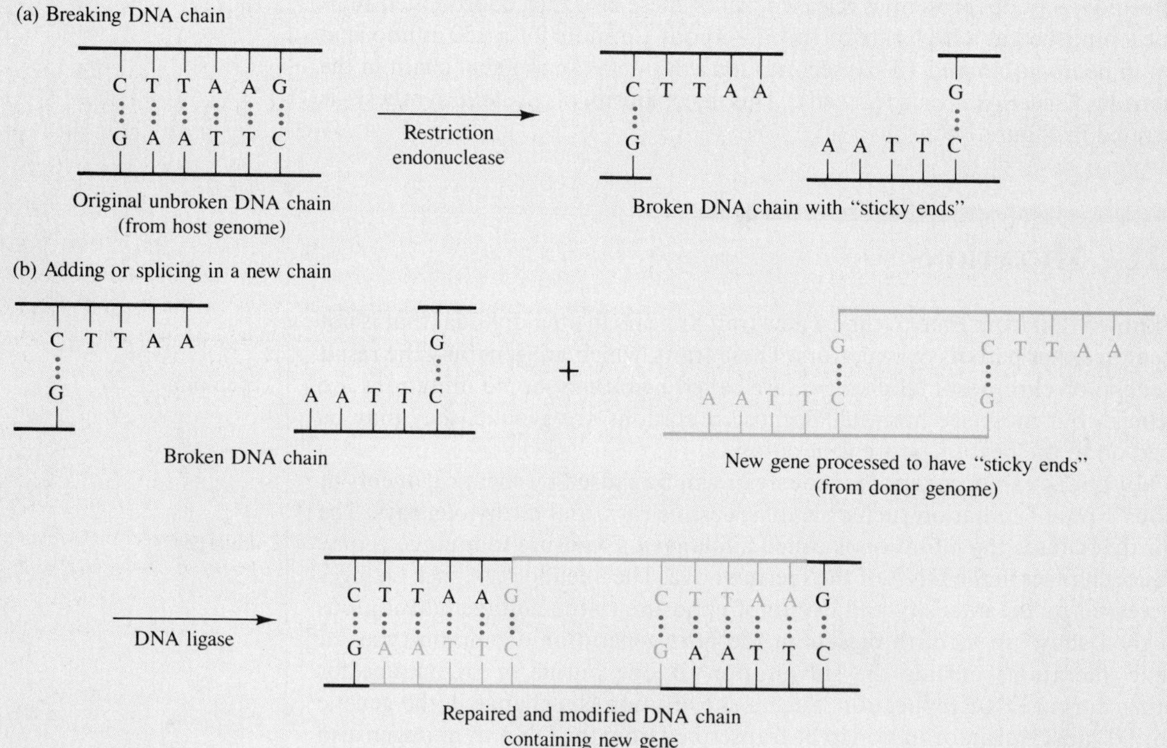

▲
Schematic diagram showing (a) breaking of double-stranded DNA chain to obtain "sticky ends" and (b) adding or splicing in a new gene previously processed to have matching sticky ends. Only the nitrogen bases involved in the sticky ends are shown.

(continued)

(*continued*)
other fields. Using techniques similar to those used by the viruses, the genetic engineer inserts specific genes into the genome of a host cell. The host cell is thus programmed to produce new or different proteins that may benefit humankind.

Genetic engineering has been made possible by several basic advances in nucleic acid biochemistry. First, scientists have gained the ability to isolate, identify, and then synthesize multiple copies of specific genetic messages. Often the gene of interest is present in only one copy in every million genes—this first step is difficult and yet is of critical importance for the genetic engineer.

A recent discovery, the DNA polymerase chain reaction, has considerably improved the success rate for this first process. DNA polymerase is an enzyme that replicates DNA when supplied a starting fragment (the primer) and a DNA strand to copy (the template). By supplying the appropriate primer, the polymerase can be induced to synthesize a specific gene, even in the presence of a wide variety of other genetic material. What makes this reaction especially valuable is that the polymerase can use the newly synthesized DNA as a template for further replication. Thus, after 20 synthetic cycles, almost a million copies of the original gene can be produced. Like a radioactive chain reaction, the polymerase chain reaction leads to an explosion in the number of copied genes.

Once the number of copies of a specific gene has been increased, this gene may be identified, studied, and ultimately perhaps transferred to another DNA molecule. Gene identification has proved valuable in prenatal diagnosis as well as forensic medicine. The polymerase chain reaction allows diagnosis in less than one day of such genetic diseases as phenylketonuria, muscular dystrophy, and cystic fibrosis. Because the DNA from one cell can be analyzed with this technique, fertilized eggs can be grown through several cell divisions and tested for potential fatal genetic diseases before being implanted in the womb. Again the sensitivity of the polymerase chain reaction is important in allowing forensic chemists to compare a suspect's DNA with a small amount of cellular material found at the scene of a crime.

A second important process in genetic engineering is the insertion of genetic material into a "foreign" genome. Special enzymes, the *restriction endonucleases*, have provided a key step during gene insertion. These enzymes split double-stranded DNA at very specific locations. Often the newly formed break has what is termed "sticky ends"; that is, one end of the break can stick to the end of another break via hydrogen bonding between complementary bases (see diagram on page 362). When both a gene and a "foreign" genome are processed in this way, they bond together. Then, with the aid of other enzymes (ligases), the gene can be covalently bonded into place. The resultant modified and repaired "foreign" genome now contains a new gene. The result of this process is a form of recombinant DNA. The term *recombinant DNA* refers to DNA whose genes have been rearranged to contain new or different hereditary information. The process of gene addition to DNA is shown in the diagram on page 864.

Genetic engineering is progressing in a variety of areas. Bacteria have been modified to produce proteins that are relatively scarce. Human insulin and human growth hormone are now synthesized by microorganisms. Bovine rennin, an enzyme needed in large amounts during cheese production, is now partially supplied by genetically modified bacteria.

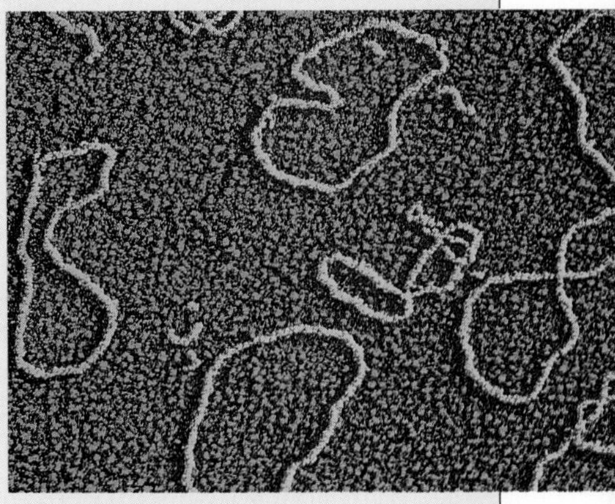

▲ **Electron micrograph of plasmids of bacterial DNA from *E. Coli* bacterium.**

Presently, natural proteins can be altered to improve specific properties by genetic engineering. For example, the proteolytic enzymes used in detergents are being modified to improve their stability when exposed to bleach and high pH (conditions that often exist during a laundry cycle). Lipid digestive enzymes (lipases) are being modified to convert inexpensive oils into the more expensive triacylglycerols.

Genetic engineering is also used to alter the properties of living organisms. An immunity to specific weed killers is being incorporated into plants of commercial importance in order to aid growers. Organisms are being developed that can metabolize and therefore clean up toxic wastes. Thus, in the future it is likely that genetic engineering will have a major impact on our way of life.

information to develop a sensitive and easy test for potential carcinogens. The Ames test uses specific strains of bacteria that lack some necessary enzymes due to mutation. These bacteria are exposed to a possible cancer causing substance. If the bacteria regain their missing enzymes, the substance tested has been proved to be a mutagen. By quickly identifying mutagens, this test helps scientists recognize potential carcinogens.

The average person is exposed to many mutagens every day. Yet the frequency of mutation is relatively low. This seeming contradiction can be understood with the knowledge that each cell contains enzymes for repairing damaged DNA. For example, a simple walk on a sunny day exposes the skin cells to ultraviolet radiation, which chemically alters a few of the thymine bases in the DNA. If these changes were allowed to remain, the DNA could not be replicated correctly and a mutation would occur. Fortunately, cellular enzymes locate the damaged DNA, excise the altered thymines, and rebuild the correct nucleotide sequence. Similar repair processes are occurring continuously for most normal cells.

In some cases mutations have weakened the cellular DNA repair machinery. Patients suffering from *xeroderma pigmentosum* lack the enzyme that recognizes chemically altered thymines. For these people sunlight becomes a real danger. Exposure to only small amounts of ultraviolet radiation causes skin ulceration and eventual formation of multiple skin cancers. Although this disease occurs only rarely, it has been estimated that about 1% of all humans are carriers of these mutations.

Concepts in Review

1. Write the structural formulas for the two purine and three pyrimidine bases found in nucleotides.
2. Distinguish between ribonucleotides and deoxyribonucleotides.
3. List the compositions, abbreviations, and structures for the ten nucleotides in DNA and RNA.
4. Write the structural formulas for ADP and ATP.
5. Identify where energy is stored in ADP and ATP.
6. Write a structural formula of a segment of a polynucleotide that contains four nucleotides.
7. Describe the double-helix structure of DNA according to Watson and Crick.
8. Explain the concept of complementary bases.
9. Describe and illustrate the replication process of DNA.
10. Understand how heredity factors are stored in DNA molecules.
11. Distinguish between mitosis and meiosis.
12. Understand how the genetic code is used in the synthesis of proteins.
13. Describe a potential cause of cancer involving an oncogene.
14. Explain the genetic code.
15. State the functions of the three different kinds of RNA.

16. Describe the transcription of the genetic code from DNA to RNA.
17. Describe the biosynthesis of proteins.
18. Understand how mutations are caused.
19. Describe the Ames test.
20. Briefly describe genetic engineering.

Equations in Review

Reaction Between a High-Energy Phosphate Bond of ATP and Water

$$\text{ATP} + H_2O \underset{\text{Energy storage}}{\overset{\text{Energy utilization}}{\rightleftharpoons}} \text{ADP} + P_i + \sim 35\text{ kJ}$$

Use of ATP Energy to Bond an Amino Acid to a Transfer RNA

$$\text{R—CH(NH}_2\text{)—C(=O)—OH} + \text{tRNA} + \text{ATP} \xrightarrow[\text{synthetase}]{\text{Aminoacyl-tRNA}}$$

$$\text{R—CH(NH}_2\text{)—C(=O)—tRNA} + \text{AMP} + \text{HO—P(=O)(OH)—O—P(=O)(OH)—OH}$$

Exercises

1. Write the names and structural formulas for the five nitrogen bases found in nucleotides.
2. What is the difference between a nucleoside and a nucleotide?
3. Identify the compounds represented by the following letters:
   (a) A, AMP, ADP, ATP
   (b) G, GMP, GDP, GTP
4. What are the three units that make up a nucleotide?
5. Write structural formulas for the substances represented by
   (a) A (c) ADP (e) dGTP
   (b) AMP (d) ATP (f) CDP
6. What is the major function of ATP in the body?
7. What are the principal structural differences between DNA and RNA?
8. Draw the structure for a three nucleotide segment of RNA.
9. Show by structural formulas the hydrogen bonding between adenine and uracil.
10. Briefly describe the structure of DNA as proposed by Watson and Crick.
11. What is meant by the term *complementary bases*?
12. Explain why the ratio of thymine to adenine in DNA is 1:1, but the ratio of thymine to guanine is not necessarily 1:1.
13. Why is DNA considered to be the genetic substance of life?
14. Briefly describe the process of DNA replication.
15. What is the role of DNA in the genetic process?
16. What is the genetic code?
17. Why are at least three nucleotides needed for one unit of the genetic code?
18. List the three kinds of RNA and identify the role of each.
19. What is an oncogene?
20. What is a codon? An anticodon?

21. Explain the relationship between codons and anticodons.
22. There are 146 amino acid residues in the β-polypeptide chain of hemoglobin. How many nucleotides in mRNA are needed to designate this chain? (See Figure 12.7 to review the β-chain.)
23. In RNA does the guanine content have to be equal to the cytosine content? Explain. Do they have to be equal in DNA? Explain.
24. Starting with DNA, briefly outline the biosynthesis of proteins.
25. Explain the role of *N*-formylmethionine in procaryotic protein synthesis.
26. A segment of a DNA strand consists of GCTTAGACCTGA.
    (a) What is the nucleotide order in the complementary mRNA?
    (b) What is the anticodon order in tRNA?
    (c) What is the sequence of amino acids coded by the DNA?
27. What will the anticodon be in tRNA if the codon in mRNA is the following?
    (a) GUC (d) UUU
    (b) ACC (e) CCA
    (c) CGA
28. Complete hydrolysis of RNA would yield what compounds?
29. What is mutation?
30. Why do mutations occur?
31. Briefly describe the Ames test.
32. Does DNA damage always result in a mutation? Explain.
33. Briefly list the basic steps that are often employed in genetic engineering.
34. Which of these statements are correct? Rewrite each incorrect statement to make it correct.
    (a) Adenine and guanine are both purine bases and are found in both DNA and RNA.
    (b) The ratio of adenine to thymine and guanine to cytosine in DNA is about 1:1.
    (c) DNA and RNA are responsible for transmitting genetic information from parent to daughter cells.
    (d) DNA is a polymer made from nucleotides.
    (e) Codons are combinations of the base units in a tRNA molecule.
    (f) The double-helix structure of DNA is held together by peptide linkages.
    (g) Amino acids are linked to tRNA by an ester bond.
    (h) The nucleotide adenosine monophosphate contains adenine, D-ribose, and a phosphate group.
    (i) The letters ATP stand for adenine triphosphate.
    (j) Thymine and uracil are both complementary bases to adenine.
    (k) Messenger RNA is a transcribed section of DNA.
    (l) The ratio of adenine to guanine and thymine to cytosine is 1:1 in DNA.
    (m) Genetic information is based on the nucleotide sequence in DNA.
    (n) Humans have 46 pairs of chromosomes.
    (o) In mitosis the sperm cell and the egg cell, each with 23 chromosomes, unite to give a new cell containing 46 chromosomes.
    (p) The genetic code consists of triplets of nucleotides; each triplet codes an amino acid.
    (q) Transfer RNA carries the code for the synthesis of proteins.
    (r) ADP and ATP contain high energy phosphate anhydride bonds.
    (s) On hydrolysis, DNA yields ribose, phosphoric acid, and the bases adenine, guanine, cytosine, and thymine.
    (t) DNA has a double-helix conformation, whereas all RNAs have a single-helix conformation.

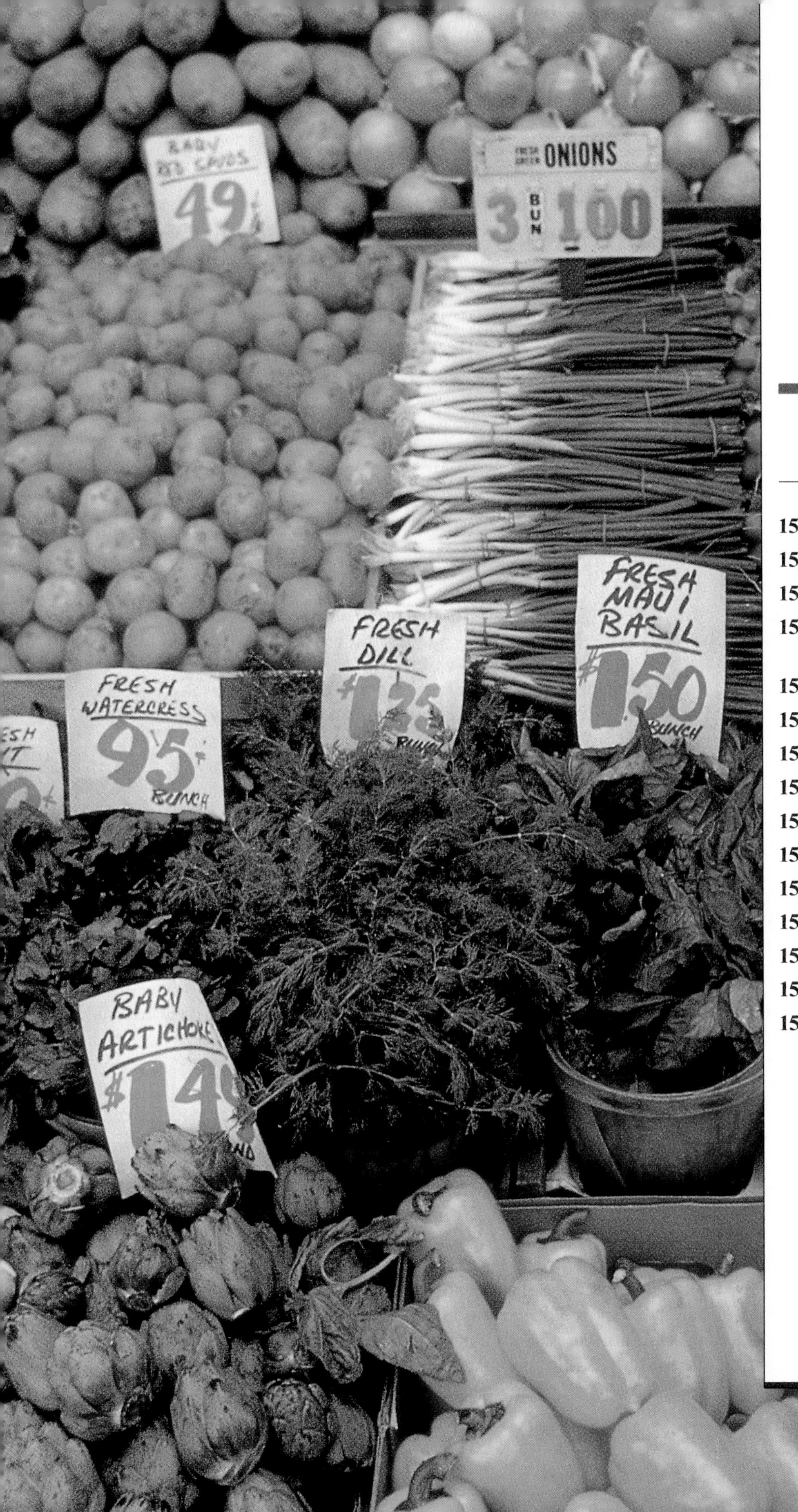

15

Nutrition

◀ **CHAPTER OPENING PHOTO: A healthy assortment of fresh vegetables is necessary to provide adequate nutrition.**

Jack Sprat could eat no fat,
his wife could eat no lean,
yet twixt the two of them,
they licked the platter clean.

—*Mother Goose*

For hundreds of years it has been known that diet is important to good health and that diets may need to vary from one individual to another. Yet only in recent years have we been able to understand nutritional needs on a molecular level. In the nursery rhyme, Jack Sprat was clearly on a low-fat diet. Today, we can point to evidence that fat intake (especially saturated fat) may be related to heart disease. Fat molecules accumulate on the blood vessel walls, which leads to hardening of the arteries.

An understanding of nutrition and digestion is closely coupled with an understanding of biochemistry. As more is learned about how diet impacts health, we as consumers can make better choices concerning which foods to purchase and eat.

15.1 NUTRIENTS

Nutrition is a science of practical importance. Every person is concerned with diet. As a child you may have heard "Finish your milk" or "Please eat your vegetables." Do you remember being told that chocolate will cause complexion problems? How many of your friends are watching their weight?

The need for choosing the right diet has given rise to the science of nutrition, the study of nutrients—how they are digested, absorbed, metabolized, and excreted. **Nutrients** are components of the food we eat that provide for body growth, maintenance, and repair. Milk is a food, but the calcium from that milk is a nutrient. We eat meat, a food, for protein, a nutrient.

nutrient

As you study biochemistry, you learn about molecules that are required for life. In future chapters, you will learn how the cell uses and produces these molecules. Unfortunately, our cells are not self-sufficient. They require a constant input of energy, a source of carbon and nitrogen, as well as a variety of minerals and special molecules. Cells can synthesize many molecules, but they need starting materials. In addition, most cells require some molecules that they cannot synthesize. Nutrients, when digested, provide the building blocks that allow cells to make carbohydrates, lipids, proteins, and nucleic acids, as well as providing the energy for life.

Nutritionists divide nutrients into six broad classes: (1) carbohydrates, (2) lipids, (3) proteins, (4) vitamins, (5) minerals, and (6) water. The first three classes—carbohydrates, lipids, and proteins—are the major sources of the building materials, replacement parts, and energy needs of the cells. The next three classes of nutrients—water, minerals, and vitamins—have functions other than as sources of energy or building materials. Nevertheless they have vital roles in nutrition. Water is absolutely essential to every diet, because most biochemical reactions occur in aqueous solution. Minerals are required to maintain specific concentrations of certain inorganic ions in the cellular and extracellular fluids. They are also utilized in a variety of other ways—for example, calcium and phosphorus in bones and teeth and iron in hemoglobin. Vitamins are components of some enzyme systems that are vital to the cells.

Nutrients supply the needs of the body's many different cells. For example, red blood cells must produce hemoglobin and thus need iron. Muscle cells produce muscle fibers and need much protein. As they do their jobs, cells wear out and must be replaced. Red blood cells, on an average, are renewed every six weeks, whereas the cells lining the digestive tract must be replaced every three days.

The six classes of nutrients provide the basis for a healthy diet. This chapter will describe briefly (1) the relationship between diet and nutrition, (2) some characteristics of each nutrient category, and (3) the processes by which these nutrients are digested.

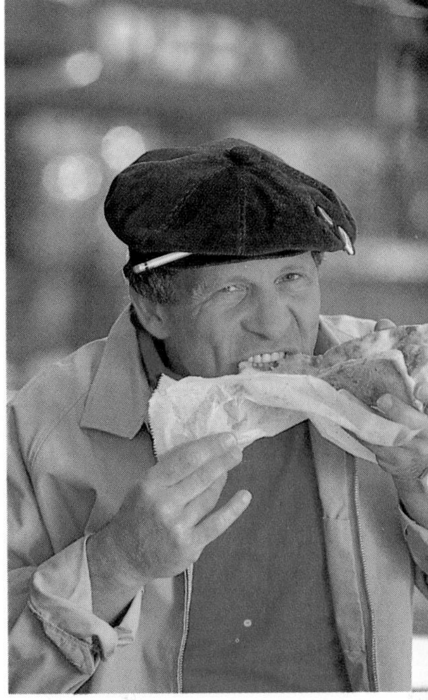

▲
"Fast foods" make up a large portion of many peoples daily diet.

15.2 Diet

diet

Diet is the food and drink that we consume. Our choice of meals determines the nutrients available to our bodies. Thus, our health depends directly on our diet.

Unfortunately, some dietary choices are not clear. Controversy surrounds many food selections. Are "fast foods" unhealthy? Should we avoid food additives? What are "natural" foods? To make an intelligent decision, we must understand the role of the food nutrients in maintaining good health.

Many nutrients are contained in each foodstuff. For example, a McDonalds' Big Mac contains 13% protein, 16% fat, and 20% carbohydrate. An order of french fries adds primarily carbohydrate (38%) with some fat (18%) and protein (4%). Such a meal might be supplemented with a chocolate shake (23% carbohydrate, 3% fat, 3% protein). These foods provide a variety of nutrients, but does this represent a healthful or an unhealthful diet?

Nutritionists face this difficult problem of deciding the kinds of nutrients that should be in a diet. They often establish dietary need by correlating physical well-being with nutrient consumption. James Lind (1716–1794), a physician in the British Navy during the middle of the 18th century, was one of the first to use this approach. In a study of scurvy, a disease that afflicted sailors on long voyages, he placed seamen who suffered from scurvy on various diets, some of which contained citrus fruits. By observing changes in the conditions of the seamen, Lind was able to conclude that citrus fruits provide a nutrient that prevents scurvy. This and later work eventually led to the requirement of limes and lemons in the diets of the British Merchant Marine (1765) and the British Navy (1795). Scurvy is now recognized as a deficiency disease caused by a lack of vitamin C, ascorbic acid.

recommended dietary allowance

As scientists like Lind discovered and studied more nutrients, they also found that the minimum quantities needed for good health varied from person to person. Thus, rather than establishing uniform minimum requirements, nutritionists have established a standard called the recommended dietary allowance. The **recommended dietary allowance** (RDA) for a nutrient is an average value that has been shown to maintain health for large groups of people. Although there is considerable variation in the dietary needs of individuals, RDAs are useful yardsticks in judging healthful diets. RDAs for a variety of nutrients are shown in Table 15.1.

15.3 Energy in the Diet

An important component of every diet is the energy allowance which derives primarily from the energy-containing nutrients, the carbohydrates, lipids, and proteins. These molecules have in common that they are a rich source of reduced carbons. As we will see in Chapter 16, almost all of the energy for life is derived from reactions in which cells oxidize carbon compounds. Energy is released as each carbon is ultimately converted to carbon dioxide. Nutrients that supply energy contain carbons that can be oxidized to release energy.

The dietary energy allowance varies with activity, body size, age, and sex (see Table 15.1). Thus a 65-kg male office worker requires a diet that furnishes 2700 kcal/day, whereas a man of similar weight working as a carpenter requires about 3000 kcal/day. Women generally use less energy than men, and energy use decreases with age. [Many nutritionists still use the kilocalorie unit or its synonym, the large Calorie (Cal). Remember, there are 4.184 kilojoules per kilocalorie (or Calorie).]

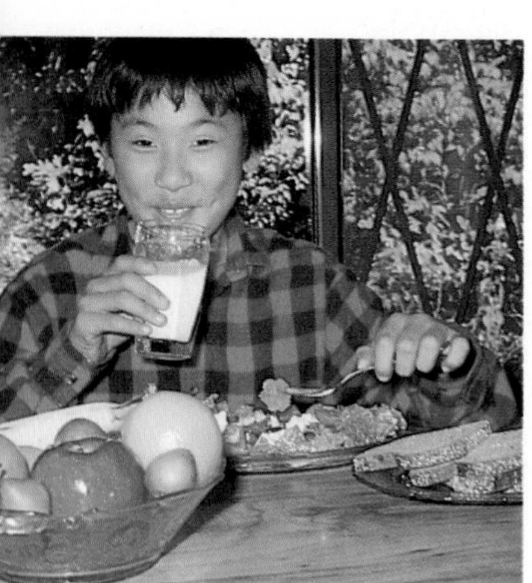

▲ A "balanced" diet includes food from each of the major groups in proper proportion.

The balance between energy needs and the energy allowance is of vital importance. Calorie deficiency leads to a condition called *marasmus*, which affects many of the world's poor, particularly children. Marasmus is a wasting disease due to starvation. People suffering from this disease have limited diets that often consist of bulky, carbohydrate-containing foods—for example, sweet potatoes (32% carbohydrate, 1% fat, 2% protein). These foods are not energy-rich (about 160 kcal for a medium-size sweet potato). Children, with their small stomachs, have difficulty consuming enough to satisfy their energy requirements. It is estimated that 15–20% of the people in underdeveloped countries suffer from malnutrition due to insufficient calories.

In contrast, many people in developed countries consume far more calories than they need for health and well-being. Food is available in abundance, much of it rich in energy. For example, the lunch described previously consisting of a Big Mac (563 kcal), french fries (220 kcal), and a chocolate shake (383 kcal) would supply nearly one-half of the daily energy allowance for an adult male. Excess, accumulated calories lead to a condition called *obesity*, which is characterized by an overabundance of fatty tissue and by many attendant health problems.

TABLE 15.1 Recommended Daily Dietary Allowances[a] (revised 1989)

	Age (years)	Weight (kg)	Weight (lb)	Height (cm)	Height (in.)	Protein (g)	Fat-soluble vitamins: Vitamin A (μg RE)[b]	Vitamin D (μg)[c]	Vitamin E (mg α-TE)[d]	Water-soluble vitamins: Vitamin C (mg)	Thiamin (mg)	Riboflavin (mg)	Niacin (mg)	Vitamin B_6 (mg)	Folic acid (μg)	Vitamin B_{12} (μg)	Minerals: *Ca* (mg)	*P* (mg)	*Mg* (mg)	*Fe* (mg)	*Zn* (mg)	*I* (μg)
Infants	0.0–0.5	6	13	61	24	13	375	7.5	3	30	0.3	0.4	5	0.3	25	0.3	400	300	40	6	5	40
	0.5–1.0	9	20	71	28	14	375	10	4	35	0.4	0.5	6	0.6	35	0.5	600	500	60	10	5	50
Children	1–3	13	29	90	35	16	400	10	6	40	0.7	0.8	9	1.0	50	0.7	800	800	80	10	10	70
	4–6	20	44	112	44	24	500	10	7	45	0.9	1.1	12	1.1	75	1.0	800	800	120	10	10	90
	7–10	28	62	132	52	28	700	10	7	45	1.0	1.2	13	1.1	100	1.4	800	800	120	10	10	120
Males	11–14	45	99	157	62	45	1000	10	10	50	1.3	1.5	17	1.7	150	2.0	1200	1200	270	12	15	150
	15–18	66	145	176	69	59	1000	10	10	60	1.5	1.8	20	2.0	200	2.0	1200	1200	400	12	15	150
	19–24	73	160	177	70	58	1000	10	10	60	1.5	1.7	19	2.0	200	2.0	1200	1200	350	10	15	150
	25–50	79	174	176	70	63	1000	5	10	60	1.5	1.7	19	2.0	200	2.0	800	800	350	10	15	150
	51+	77	170	173	68	63	1000	5	10	60	1.2	1.4	15	2.0	200	2.0	800	800	350	10	15	150
Females	11–14	46	101	157	62	46	800	10	8	50	1.1	1.3	15	1.4	150	2.0	1200	1200	280	15	12	150
	15–18	55	120	163	64	49	800	10	8	60	1.1	1.3	15	1.5	180	2.0	1200	1200	300	15	12	150
	19–24	58	128	164	65	46	800	10	8	60	1.1	1.3	15	1.6	180	2.0	1200	1200	280	15	12	150
	25–50	63	138	163	64	50	800	5	8	60	1.0	1.3	15	1.6	180	2.0	800	800	280	15	12	150
	51+	65	143	160	63	50	800	5	8	60	1.0	1.2	13	1.6	180	2.0	800	800	280	10	12	150
Pregnant						50	800	10	10	70	1.5	1.6	17	2.2	400	2.2	1200	1200	320	30	15	175
Lactating						55	1200	10	11	90	1.6	1.8	20	2.1	260	2.6	1200	1200	350	15	17	200

Reference: *Recommended Dietary Allowances*, 10th ed. Food and Nutrition Board, National Research Council–National Academy of Sciences.

[a] The allowances are intended to provide for individual variations among most normal persons as they live in the United States under usual environmental stresses. Diets should be based on a variety of common foods in order to provide other nutrients for which human requirements have been less well defined.

[b] Retinol equivalents. 1 retinol equivalent = 1 μg retinol or 6 μg β-carotene.

[c] As cholecaliciferol. 10 μg cholecalciferol = 400 IU of vitamin D.

[d] α-Tocopherol equivalents. 1 mg α-tocopherol = 1 α-TE.

Each pound of body fat contains about 3500 kcal of energy, or between one and two days' total RDA for energy. Because fat contains so much energy, it is normally accumulated only slowly. Unfortunately, for the same reason, fat is also very difficult to lose. To lose 1 lb of fat, a 65-kg man would have to swim nonstop for about 10 hours, play tennis continuously for about 8 hours, or run for 4 hours. Exercise alone is generally not sufficient to cure obesity without a change in diet as well.

Thus, many people in the affluent, developed countries find it necessary to choose a restricted-calorie diet (to "diet"). The difficulties associated with selecting a restricted-calorie diet have led to the creation of numerous fad diets that fail to provide sound nutrition. Yet nutritionists counsel that successful and nutritionally sound dieting can be accomplished by following these simple guidelines: (1) Reduce calorie intake by only a moderate amount (a 500 kcal/day reduction causes a loss of 1 lb of fat per week) and be prepared to continue the diet for a long time; (2) carefully select foods so that the diet contains adequate amounts of all nutrients. The primary function of any diet is to maintain good health.

15.4 Carbohydrates in the Diet

Carbohydrates are a good source of usable reduced carbon atoms, which makes them important sources of dietary energy. About half of the average daily calorie requirement derives from carbohydrates. These molecules are perhaps the most easily metabolized (see Chapter 17) of the energy-supplying nutrients and can be used for energy under both aerobic and anaerobic conditions. Additionally, carbons from carbohydrates are used to build other cellular molecules—amino acids, nucleic acids, as well as other carbohydrates. Excess dietary carbohydrate is most often converted to fat.

Dietary carbohydrates are primarily the polysaccharides starch and cellulose, the disaccharides lactose and sucrose, and the monosaccharides glucose and fructose. Seeds are the most common source of starch, grains being about 70% by mass starch, whereas dried peas and beans contain about 40%. A second major source of starch is tuber and root crops such as potatoes, yams, and cassava. The disaccharide lactose is an important component of milk, and sucrose is usually consumed as refined sugar (derived from sugar beets or sugar cane). The monosaccharides are often found in fruits.

The polysaccharides, also termed *complex carbohydrates*, are difficult to digest because of their complex structures (see Section 10.14). Starch is digested only slowly, enabling the body to control distribution of this energy nutrient. Cellulose is not digested by humans; however, it is a major source of *dietary fiber*. As cellulose passes through the digestive tract, it absorbs water and provides dietary bulk. This bulk acts to prevent constipation and diverticulosis, a weakening of the intestinal walls. Many nutritionists recommend a daily fiber intake of 15–30 g, supplied by such foods as whole-wheat bread (1.8 g/slice) and bran cereals (7.5 g/0.5 cup).

Although no RDA has been set for carbohydrate, many nutritionists recommend that a minimum of about 500 kcal/day be derived from this source. In the

American diet most of these calories are derived from starch, although in recent years an increasing amount has been coming from sucrose.

The high sucrose content of many modern diets is due primarily to the large amounts of sucrose in commercially prepared foods. In 1900 an American consumed an average of about 20 lb of sucrose annually in prepared foods and beverages; by 1971 this figure had risen to about 70 lb annually. This large increase was caused mainly by (1) increased consumption of prepared foods and (2) an increased percentage of sucrose added to these foods by the manufacturers in attempts to gain larger shares of the market. (It is well known that many people, especially children, have a preference for sweet foods.) Some breakfast cereals on the market today contain more than 40% sucrose!

The increase in sucrose consumption has troubled many nutritionists for several reasons. First, sucrose is a prime factor in the incidence of dental caries. Because it is readily used by oral bacteria, sucrose promotes growth of the microorganisms that cause tooth decay. Second, ingested sucrose is rapidly hydrolyzed to monosaccharides, which are promptly absorbed from the intestine, leading to a rapid increase in blood-sugar levels. Wide variations in the blood-sugar level may stress the body's hormonal system for controlling blood sugar. Finally, sucrose is said to provide "empty calories." This means that sucrose supplies metabolic energy (calories) but lacks other nutrients. Nutritionists often recommend starch over sucrose as a major source of dietary carbohydrate.

15.5 Fats in the Diet

Fat is a more concentrated source of dietary energy than carbohydrate. Not only does fat contain more carbons per unit mass, but the carbons in fats are more reduced. As an energy source fats provide about 9 kcal/g, whereas carbohydrates provide only about 4 kcal/g. Energy can only be obtained from fat when oxygen is present as we will see in Chapter 18; fat metabolism is strictly aerobic in humans. The carbons from fats can be used to synthesize amino acids, nucleic acids, and other fats, but our bodies cannot achieve a net synthesis of carbohydrate from fat. Thus, fats tend not to be as versatile a nutrient as the carbohydrates, although fats are a more concentrated source of energy.

Fats contribute much of the dietary energy of many foods. For example, french fries contain about 18% fat, yet this fat provides about 40% of the calories in this food. A cup of whole milk has 170 kcal, but only 80 kcal comes from a cup of skim (nonfat) milk. Many nutritionists counsel that the best way to reduce calorie intake is to eat foods containing less fat.

In a diet, both the kind and the amount of fat are important. Fatty acids from meat and dairy products are relatively saturated, whereas those from plant sources are generally more unsaturated. Because there is a probable link between high consumption of saturated fats and atherosclerosis, the U. S. Department of Agriculture and other agencies concerned with nutrition have recommended that American diets should contain about equal portions of polyunsaturated and saturated fatty acids. Two ways of increasing polyunsaturated fats in the diets are to (1) cook with vegetable oils such as corn or peanut oil and (2) use soft margarine, which usually contains more unsaturated fats than hard or stick margarine or butter.

Polyunsaturated fats generally also contain three essential fatty acids—linoleic acid, linolenic acid, and arachidonic acid:

$$CH_3(CH_2)_4CH{=}CHCH_2CH{=}CH(CH_2)_7CO_2H$$

Linoleic acid

$$CH_3CH_2CH{=}CHCH_2CH{=}CHCH_2CH{=}CH(CH_2)_7CO_2H$$

Linolenic acid

$$CH_3(CH_2)_4CH{=}CHCH_2CH{=}CHCH_2CH{=}CHCH_2CH{=}CH(CH_2)_3CO_2H$$

Arachidonic acid

Each of these nutrients has been shown to relieve the deleterious physiological changes, such as poor growth, skin lesions, kidney damage, and impaired fertility, that result from a totally fat-free diet. One essential biochemical function of these fatty acids is as precursors for prostaglandin synthesis.

15.6 Proteins in the Diet

The third energy supplying nutrient is protein with an average energy yield of about 4.2 kcal/g. This energy is derived primarily from reduced carbons. However, recall that proteins also contain a large number of nitrogen atoms; in fact, protein is the primary source of nitrogen in our diets. As discussed in Chapter 18, perhaps the most important function of dietary protein is to provide for synthesis of nitrogen containing molecules such as nucleic acids, enzymes and other proteins, nerve transmitters, and many hormones. Because these materials are critical for human growth, protein malnutrition, or *kwashiorkor*, is a particularly serious problem. Unlike carbohydrates and fats (excluding the essential fatty acids), a specific RDA has been established for dietary protein (see Table 15.1).

Kwashiorkor can occur even when calorie intake is sufficient and, thus, is an especially insidious form of malnutrition. In many poverty ridden areas of the world, the only reliable source of protein for children is mother's milk. After weaning, the children eat a protein-poor grain diet. Although the calorie intake is sufficient, these children show the stunted growth, poor disease resistance, and general body wasting that are characteristic of kwashiorkor.

Proteins are obtained from animal sources such as meat, milk, cheese, and eggs, and from plant sources such as cereals, nuts, and legumes (peas, beans, and soybeans). Animal proteins have nutritive values that are generally superior to those of vegetable proteins in that they supply all of the 20 amino acids that the body uses. In contrast, a single vegetable source often lacks several amino acids. This deficiency is critical, because humans cannot synthesize the group of amino acids called the *essential amino acids* (see Section 12.3; Table 15.2). The eight essential amino acids must be obtained from the diet.

Nutritionists often speak of a dietary source (or sources) of complete protein. A **complete protein** is one that supplies all of the essential amino acids. An-

complete protein

Table 15.2 Common Dietary Amino Acids

Essential	Essential	Nonessential	Nonessential
Isoleucine	Tryptophan	Alanine	Glutamine
Leucine	Valine	Arginine	Glycine
Lysine		Asparagine	Histidine
Methionine		Aspartic acid	Proline
Phenylalanine		Cysteine	Serine
Threonine		Glutamic acid	Tyrosine

imal products are, in general, sources of complete proteins. However, by either choice or necessity, animal protein is seldom consumed by a significant fraction of the world's population. Besides the moral, ethical, and religious reasons given for limiting consumption of animal protein, these proteins are relatively expensive sources of amino acids. Thus, most of the people of the underdeveloped countries subsist primarily on vegetable protein. A constant danger inherent in a vegetarian diet is that the source of vegetable protein may be deficient in several of the essential amino acids; that is, the protein may be incomplete. For this reason nutritionists recommend that several sources of vegetable protein be included with each meal in a vegetarian diet. As an example, soybeans, which are rich in lysine, might supplement wheat, which is lysine deficient.

15.7 Vitamins

vitamin

Vitamins are a group of naturally occurring organic compounds that are essential for good nutrition and must be supplied in the diet. Whereas the energy supplying nutrients are digested and metabolized extensively, vitamins are often used after only minimal modification. Some of the vitamins necessary for humans are listed in Table 15.3. Note that vitamins are often classified according to their solubility, those that are fat soluble and those that are water soluble. The structural formulas of several vitamins are shown in Figure 15.1.

A prolonged lack of vitamins in the diet leads to vitamin deficiency diseases such as beriberi, pellagra, pernicious anemia, rickets, and scurvy. Left uncorrected, a vitamin deficiency ultimately results in death. Even when supplementary amounts of vitamins are provided, impaired growth due to a vitamin deficiency may be irreversible. For example, it is difficult to correct the distorted bone structures resulting from a childhood lack of vitamin D. Thus, it is especially important that children receive sufficient vitamins for proper growth and development.

Although vitamins are required in only small amounts (see the RDAs in Table 15.1), the biochemistry of life cannot continue without them. Each vitamin serves at least one specific purpose for an organism. The water soluble compounds are generally involved in cellular metabolism of the energy supplying nutrients. For example, thiamin is required to achieve a maximum energy yield

TABLE 15.3 Some of the Most Important Vitamins

Vitamin	Important dietary sources	Some deficiency symptoms
FAT SOLUBLE		
Vitamin A (Retinol)	Green and yellow vegetables, butter, eggs, nuts, cheese, fish liver oil	Poor teeth and gums, night blindness
Vitamin D (Ergocalciferol, D_2; cholecalciferol, D_3)	Egg yolk, milk, fish liver oils; formed from provitamin in the skin when exposed to sunlight	Rickets (low blood-calcium level, soft bones, distorted skeletal structure)
Vitamin E (α-Tocopherol)	Meat, egg yolk, wheat germ oil, green vegetables; widely distributed in foods	Not definitely known in humans
Vitamin K (Phylloquinone, K_1; menaquinone, K_2)	Eggs, liver, green vegetables; produced in the intestines by bacterial reactions	Blood is slow to clot (antihemorrhagic vitamin)
WATER SOLUBLE		
Vitamin B_1 (Thiamin)	Meat, whole-grain cereals, liver yeast, nuts	Beriberi (nervous system disorders, heart disease, fatigue)
Vitamin B_2 (Riboflavin)	Meat, cheese, eggs, fish, meat products, liver	Sores on the tongue and lips, bloodshot eyes, anemia
Vitamin B_6 (Pyridoxine)	Cereals, liver, meat, fresh vegetables	Skin disorders (dermatitis)
Vitamin B_{12} (Cyanocobalamin)	Meat, eggs, liver, milk	Pernicious anemia
Vitamin C (Ascorbic acid)	Citrus fruits, tomatoes, green vegetables	Scurvy (bleeding gums, loose teeth, swollen joints, slow healing of wounds, weight loss)
Niacin (Nicotinic acid and amide)	Meat, yeast, whole wheat	Pellagra (dermatitis, diarrhea, mental disorders)
Biotin (Vitamin H)	Liver, yeast, egg yolk	Skin disorders (dermatitis)
Folic acid	Liver extract, wheat germ, yeast, green leaves	Macrocytic anemia, gastrointestinal disorders

from carbohydrates, and pyridoxine is of central importance in protein metabolism (see Chapters 17 and 18). Niacin and riboflavin are key components in almost all cellular redox reactions. The fat soluble vitamins often serve very specialized functions. Vitamin D acts as a regulator of calcium metabolism. One function of vitamin A is to furnish the pigment that makes vision possible, while vitamin K enables blood clotting to occur normally.

Because some vitamin functions are not well understood, miraculous properties have been ascribed to these substances, such as vitamins C and E. In the absence of conclusive scientific studies, it is difficult to judge the merits of some of these claims.

◀ **Figure 15.1**
The structures of selected vitamins.

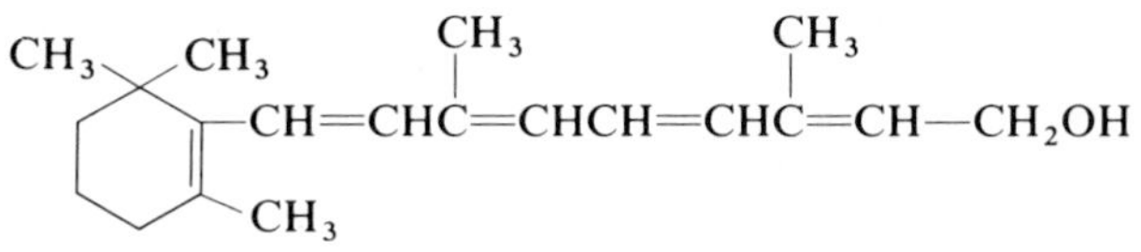

Vitamin A
(Retinol)

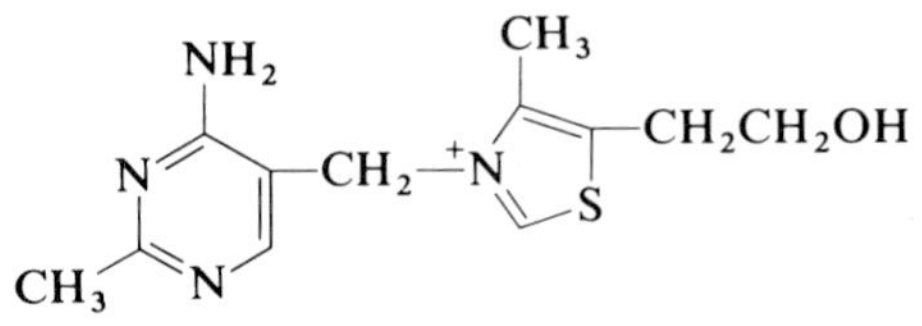

Vitamin B_1
(Thiamin)

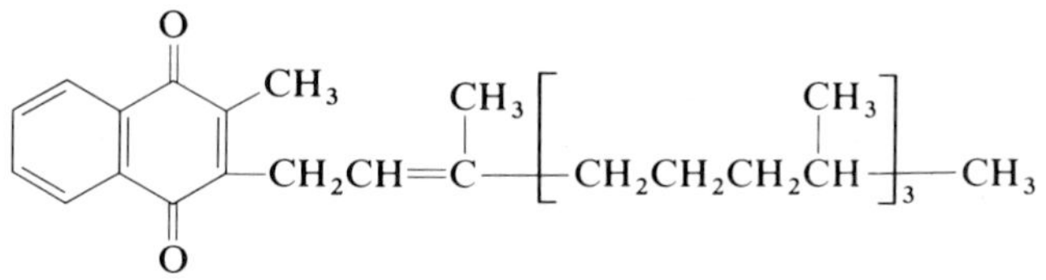

Vitamin K_1
(Phylloquinone)

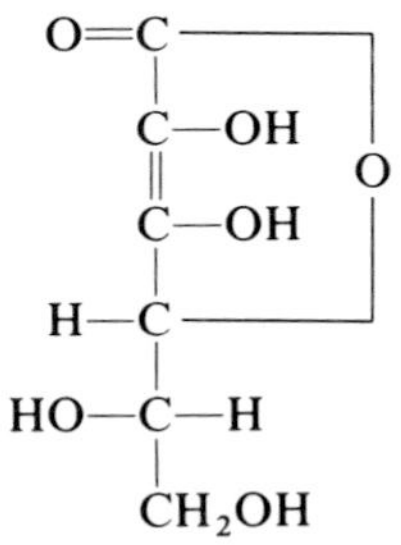

Vitamin C
(Ascorbic acid)

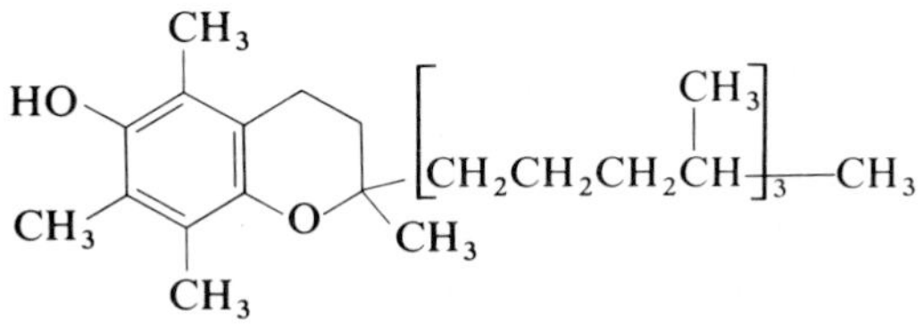

Vitamin E
(α-Tocopherol)

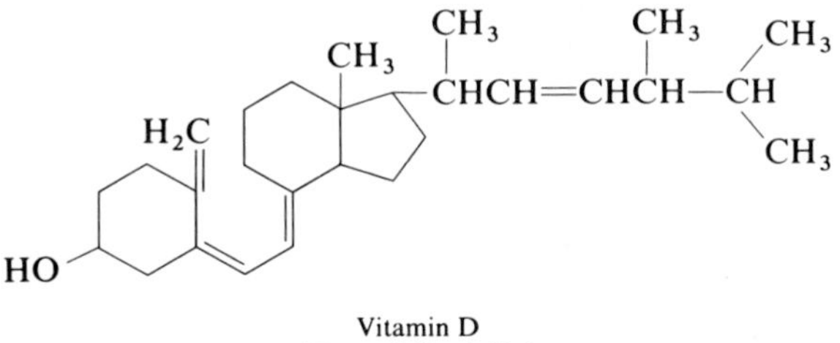

Vitamin D
(Ergocalciferol, D_2)

Although vitamins are required only in small quantities, their natural availability is also low. Nutritionists caution that a diet should be balanced to include adequate sources of vitamins. As you can see from Table 15.3, the dietary sources of vitamins are varied. In general, fruits, vegetables, and meats are rich sources of the water soluble vitamins; and eggs, milk products, and liver are good sources of the fat soluble vitamins.

A seemingly balanced diet may be deficient in vitamins due to losses incurred in food processing, storing, and cooking. As much as 50–60% of the water soluble vitamins in vegetables can be lost during cooking. Vitamin C, for example, can be destroyed by exposure to air. Removal of the outside hull from grains drastically decreases their B vitamin content. Thus, when polished rice became a dietary staple in the Orient, beriberi (the thiamin-deficiency disease) grew to epidemic proportions.

15.8 MINERALS

A number of inorganic ions are needed in the diet for good health. Those that must be ingested in relatively large amounts, the *major elements*, include sodium, potassium, chloride, calcium, magnesium, and phosphate (phosphorus). Elements in a second group, the *trace elements*, are required in only small amounts. As scientific studies of the body's mineral requirements proceed, the list of needed trace elements constantly lengthens. A recent compilation of these trace elements is given in Table 15.4.

Mineral nutrients differ from organic nutrients in that the body, in general, uses minerals in the ionic form in which they are absorbed. Although these elements are required for good health, they can also be toxic if ingested in quan-

TABLE 15.4 Essential Trace Elements

Element	Function	Human deficiency signs
Fluorine	Structure of teeth, possibly of bones; possible growth effect	Increased incidence of dental caries; possibly risk factor for osteoporosis
Silicon	Calcification; possible function in connective tissue	Not known
Vanadium	Not known	Not known
Chromium	Efficient use of insulin	Relative insulin resistance, impaired glucose tolerance, elevated serum lipids
Manganese	Mucopolysaccharide metabolism, superoxide dismutase enzyme	Not known
Iron	Oxygen and electron transport	Anemia
Cobalt	Part of vitamin B_{12}	Only as vitamin B_{12} deficiency
Nickel	Interaction with iron absorption	Not known
Copper	Oxidative enzymes; interaction with iron; cross-linking of elastin connective protein	Anemia, changes of ossification; possibly elevated serum cholesterol
Zinc	Numerous enzymes involved in energy metabolism and in transcription and translation	Growth depression, sexual immaturity, skin lesions, depression of immunocompetence, change of taste acuity
Arsenic	Not known	Not known
Selenium	Glutathione peroxidase; interaction with heavy metals	Endemic heart problems conditioned by selenium deficiency
Molybdenum	Xanthine, aldehyde and sulfide oxidase enzymes	Not known
Iodine	Constituent of thyroid hormones	Goiter, depression of thyroid function, cretinism

tities that are too large. Nutritionists have established RDAs for some of these minerals and warn against excess intake.

The major minerals—sodium, potassium, and chloride—are responsible for maintaining the appropriate salt levels in body fluids. Many enzyme reactions require an optimum salt concentration of 0.1 to 0.3 *M*. In addition, individual elements serve specific functions; nerve transmission, for example, requires a supply of extracellular sodium and intracellular potassium. Although there is no RDA for these two elements, 2–4 g/day represents an average NaCl consumption. But because high levels of NaCl can contribute to high blood pressure, many nutritionists advise using salt in moderation.

Calcium and magnesium serve many roles in the body, including being required by some enzymes. Fully 90% of all body calcium and an important percentage of the magnesium are found in the bones and teeth. Calcium also is needed for nerve transmission and blood clotting.

Trace elements are similar to vitamins in that (1) they are required in small amounts and (2) food contains only minute quantities of them. Usually a normal diet contains adequate quantities of all trace elements. The exact function of many trace elements remains unknown.

The most notable exception to the foregoing generalizations is iron. This element is part of hemoglobin, the oxygen-binding protein of the blood. (Iron is also a critical component of some enzymes.) Relatively large amounts of iron are required for hemoglobin replenishment. Unfortunately, many foods are not rich enough in iron to provide the necessary RDA. This is especially true for the higher iron RDA for women. Therefore nutritionists sometimes recommend a daily iron dietary supplement.

15.9 Water

Water is the solvent of life. As such it carries nutrients to the cells, allows biochemical reactions to proceed, and carries waste from the cells. Water makes up approximately 55–60% of the total body mass.

Our bodies are constantly losing water via urine (700–1400 mL/day), feces (150 mL/day), sweat (500–900 mL/day), and expired air (400 mL/day). If dehydration is to be prevented, this water output must be offset by water intake. In the normal diet, liquids provide about 1200–1500 mL of water per day. The remaining increment is derived from food (700–1000 mL/day) and water formed by biochemical reactions (metabolic water; 200–300 mL/day). Water losses vary and depend on the intake and the activity of the individual.

A proper water balance is maintained by control of water intake and water excretion. The kidney is the center for control of water output. Water intake is controlled by the thirst sensation. We feel thirsty when one or both of the two following events occur: (1) As the body's water stores are depicted, the salt concentration rises. Specific brain cells monitor this salinity and initiate the thirst feeling. (2) As water is drawn away from the salivary glands, the mouth feels dry; this event also leads to the sensation of thirst.

15.10 Processed Foods

Nearly all of the foods available in a supermarket today have been processed to various degrees. The processing may be very extensive with items such as luncheon meats, TV dinners, breakfast cereals, and so on. Loss of nutrients is a common risk associated with processing.

The short history of flour milling is an apt illustration of the risks of too much processing: In 1840 bread had a rough consistency and the color characteristic of stone-ground wheat flour. Over the years vast improvements in milling technology were made. In 1940 bread had a soft, smooth consistency and the white color characteristic of flour made from only the starchy portion of wheat. Consumers generally preferred this bread over the coarse and sometimes gritty product of previous centuries. It was discovered about this time (1940) that the bread had a very low vitamin content and needed vitamin enrichment. Furthermore, in the early 1970s, it was found that the amount of dietary fiber in bread can be greatly increased by less selective milling of the wheat. Excessive processing or milling of the wheat had decreased the nutritive value of bread. The most nutritious bread being baked today is very similar to that made from the minimally processed flour of 1840.

Advocates of "natural," "organic," or "health" foods argue that foods should be minimally affected by modern technology to ensure maximum nutrition. They correctly point out the dangers of nutrient loss during food processing. Yet in the eyes of many consumers in today's busy world, the convenience of ready-prepared foods greatly outweighs any possible nutritional risks associated with their use.

Nutritionists have faced this dilemma by establishing procedures for monitoring nutritional values of processed foods. If a food contains an added nutrient (as do most processed foods) or if a food makes a nutritional claim, then the package must contain a nutritional information panel using the following format:

—Serving or portion size
—Servings or portions per container
—Calorie content per serving
—Protein, grams per serving
—Carbohydrate, grams per serving
—Fat, grams per serving
—Proteins, vitamins, and minerals as percentages of the USRDA.

By using this information, together with a basic knowledge of the nutrients needed for good health, the consumer can make educated choices among processed foods.

15.11 Food Additives

Various substances or chemicals may be added to foods during processing. In fact, more than 3000 of these *food additives* have been given the "generally recognized as safe" (GRAS) rating by the U.S. Food and Drug Administration.

TABLE 15.5 Some Common Food Additives

Food additive	Purpose
Sodium benzoate Calcium lactate Sorbic acid	Prevention of food spoilage (antimicrobials)
BHA (Butylated hydroxyanisole) BHT (Butylated hydroxytoluene) EDTA (Ethylenediaminetetraacetic acid)	Prevention of changes in color and flavor (antioxidants)
Calcium silicate Silicon dioxide Sodium silicoaluminate	Keeps powders and salt free-flowing (anticaking agents)
Carrageenan Lecithin	Aids even distribution of suspended particles (emulsifiers)
Pectin Propylene glycol	Imparts body and texture (thickeners)
MSG (Monosodium glutamate) Hydrolyzed vegetable protein	Supplements or modifies taste (flavor enhancers)

The purpose of these food additives varies. Some additives enhance the nutritional value of a food, such as when a food is vitamin-enriched. Other additives serve as preservatives. For example, sodium benzoate is used to inhibit bacterial growth. BHA (butylated hydroxyanisole) and BHT (butylated hydroxytoluene) are used as antioxidants. Still other additives may be used to improve the appearance and flavor of a food—for example, emulsifiers, thickeners, anticaking agents, flavors, flavor enhancers, nonsugar sweeteners, and colors (see Table 15.5).

There has been and continues to be a great deal of controversy concerning the use of food additives. Due to the nature and complexity of the subject, there is no doubt that this debate will continue into the foreseeable future. Controversy centers around the problem of balancing the benefit derived from an additive against the risk to consumers. The use of at least some additives is a necessity in the preparation of many foods. To discover that there is a risk and to assess the degree of risk for an additive requires long, difficult, and expensive research. As a case in point, salting and smoking were used in curing meats for centuries before there was any knowledge that these processes might involve a hazard. Research has shown that both processes involve risks to at least some consumers: Salt aggravates certain cardiovascular conditions, and smoke produces carcinogens in the meat. Yet in the eyes of many consumers, these risks are outweighed by the benefits to be had from salted and smoked meats. On the other hand, there would be few consumers, indeed, who would wish to have a compound known to be very carcinogenic used as an additive in their ice cream, even though that compound could improve the flavor of the ice cream remarkably!

Owing to the technical nature of the task, the consumer must rely largely on the judgment and integrity of the professional people who have been assigned the responsibility of protecting our food supply. Consumers also should (1) inform themselves as fully as possible concerning the nature, purpose, and possible hazards of the additives that are used or proposed for us in our foods and (2) as responsible citizens make sure that our government provides adequate support to professionals charged with protecting our food.

15.12 A Balanced Diet

To summarize the preceding sections, carbohydrates, fats, and proteins are a major group of nutrients in our diets. These nutrients supply the molecules that are needed for energy, growth, and maintenance. A typical adult diet includes about 100–200 g each of carbohydrate, fat, and protein daily.

A second group of nutrients—vitamins, minerals, and water—is not used for energy but is nevertheless essential to our existence. Vitamins provide organic molecules that cannot be made in the body; and minerals provide the inorganic ions needed for life. Water is the solvent in which most of the chemical reactions essential to life occur. Vitamins and minerals are required only in small amounts, from a few micrograms to a few milligrams per day. But water must be consumed in large quantities, 2 to 3 liters per day.

For health and well-being, each of six groups of nutrients must be in our diet to satisfy the RDAs given in Table 15.1. With the variety of foods that are available, how can we make sure that our diets contain enough of all the needed nutrients? The answer "Eat a balanced diet" leads to another question, "How can we make sure that our diet is balanced?"

To answer this question, nutritionists have divided foods into six groups: (1) milk products, (2) vegetables, (3) fruits, (4) cereal products, (5) meats, and (6) fatty foods. Each group is a good source of one or more nutrients. To obtain a balanced mixture of carbohydrate, fat, and protein, a diet should contain food from several classes. A balanced diet also assures an adequate supply of essential minerals and vitamins.

A balanced diet must include several food groups, even though each food may contain many nutrients. For example, compare the three breakfasts in Figure 15.2, each of which supplies about 600 kcal of food energy. By choosing only doughnuts (cereal food group) and coffee, the consumer would gain some nutrients but only in small quantities. A breakfast of cold cereal (cereal group) and milk (milk group), toast (cereal group) with margarine (fatty food group) and jelly, and coffee includes more food groups. Still more food groups are found in a breakfast of orange juice (fruit group), a fried egg (meat group), pancakes (cereal group) with margarine (fatty food group) and syrup, milk (milk group) and coffee. Many other breakfasts could be chosen instead, yet an important generalization can be drawn from these three examples: The nutritional value of a meal improves if at least several food groups are included. The third breakfast in this illustration is the most balanced and provides the best nutrition. Although the consumer often does not know the nutrient content of a specific food, overall nutrition can be ensured by choosing a balanced diet.

After the food composing a balanced diet is eaten, it must be digested, absorbed, and transported in order for the proper nutrients to reach the cells.

◄ **FIGURE 15.2**
A comparison of nutritional values for three breakfast. (No RDA has been established for carbohydrates and fats.)

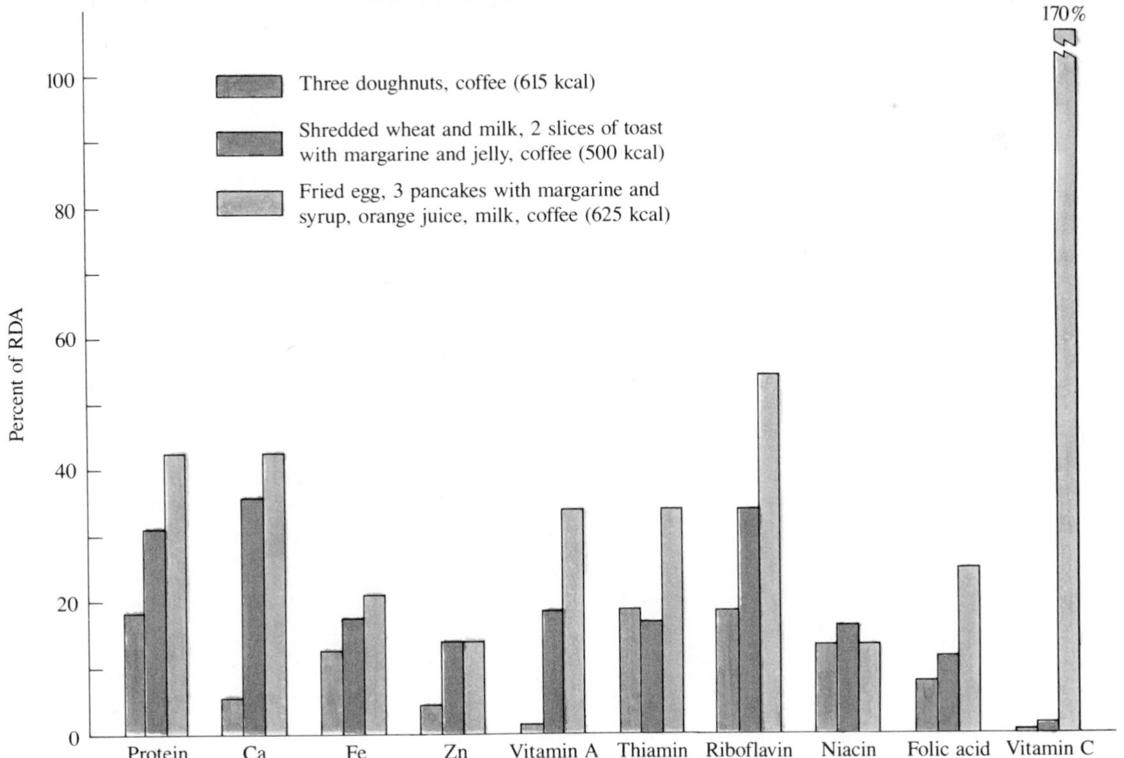

Eating puts food into the alimentary canal (which includes the mouth, esophagus, stomach, small intestine, and large intestine). In a sense this canal is an extension of our external environment; that is, until food is broken down and processed, it cannot enter our internal environment to reach the cells. After digestion and absorption, the nutrients are transported to the cells by the blood and lymph systems. The liver has a vital role in controlling nutrient levels in the blood and neutralizing toxic substances.

15.13 Human Digestion

digestion

The human digestive tract is shown diagrammatically in Figure 15.3. Although food is broken up mechanically by chewing and by a churning action in the stomach, digestion is a chemical process. **Digestion** is a series of enzyme-catalyzed reactions by which large molecules are hydrolyzed to molecules small enough to be absorbed through the intestinal membranes. Foods are digested to smaller

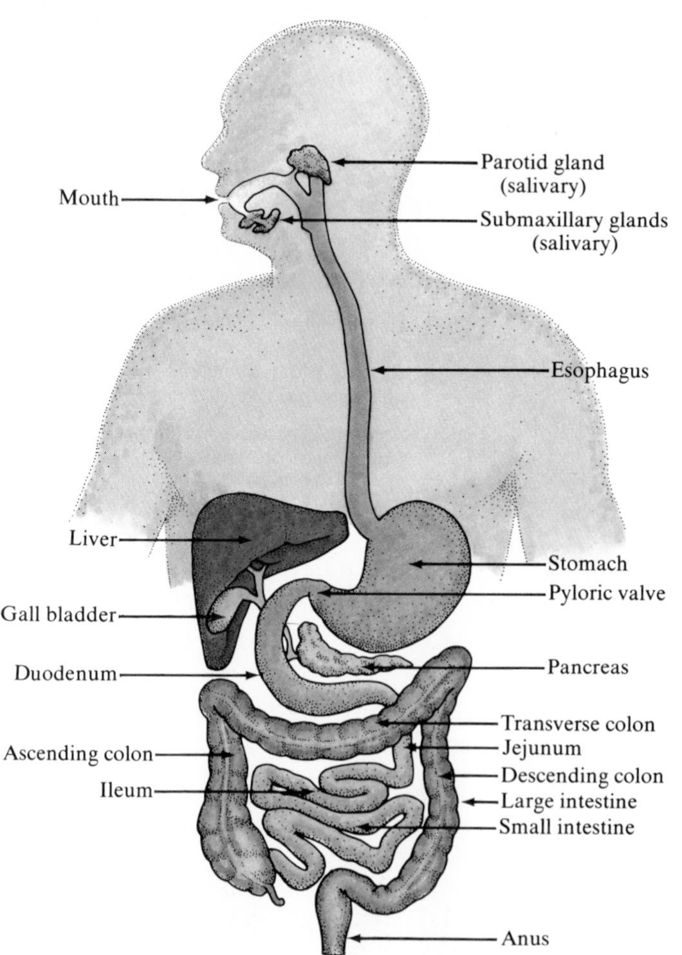

Figure 15.3 ▶ The human digestive tract.

molecules according to this general scheme:

Carbohydrates ⟶ Monosaccharides

Fats ⟶ { Fatty acids; Glycerol; Mono- and diesters of glycerol }

Proteins ⟶ { Amino acids; Dipeptides; Tripeptides }

Food passes through the human digestive tract in this sequence:

Mouth ⟶ esophagus ⟶ stomach ⟶ small intestine (duodenum, jejunum, and ileum) ⟶ large intestine (see Figure 15.3).

Five principal digestive juices (or fluids) enter the digestive tract at various points:

1. Saliva from three pairs of salivary glands in the mouth
2. Gastric juice from glands in the walls of the stomach
3. Pancreatic juice, which is secreted by the pancreas and enters the duodenum through the pancreatic duct
4. Bile, which is secreted by the liver and enters the duodenum via a duct from the gall bladder
5. Intestinal juice from intestinal mucosal cells

The main functions and principal enzymes found in each of these fluids are summarized in Table 15.6. The important digestive enzymes occur in gastric, pancreatic, and intestinal juices. An outline of the digestive process follows. (Detailed accounts of the various stages of digestion are to be found in biochemistry and physiology texts.)

Salivary Digestion Food is chewed (masticated) and mixed with saliva in the mouth, and the hydrolysis of starch begins. The composition of saliva depends on many factors—age, diet, condition of teeth, time of day, and so on. Normal saliva is about 99.5% water. Saliva also contains mucin (a glycoprotein); a number of mineral ions such as K^+, Ca^{2+}, Cl^-, PO_4^{3-}, SCN^-; and one enzyme, salivary amylase (ptyalin). The pH of saliva ranges from slightly acidic to slightly basic, with the optimum pH about 6.6–6.8.

Mucin acts as a lubricant and facilitates the chewing and swallowing of food. The enzyme salivary amylase catalyzes the hydrolysis of starch to maltose:

$$\text{Starch} + \text{Water} \xrightarrow[\text{amylase}]{\text{Salivary}} \text{Maltose}$$

Salivary amylase is inactivated at a pH of 4.0, so it has very little time to act before the food reaches the highly acidic stomach juices.

Saliva is secreted continuously, but the rate of secretion is greatly increased by the sight and odor, or even the thought, of many foods. The mouth-watering effect of the sight or thought of pickles is familiar to most of us. This is an example of a *conditioned reflex*.

TABLE 15.6 Digestive Fluids

Fluid (volume produced daily)	Source	Principal enzymes and/or function
Saliva (1000–1500 mL)	Salivary glands	Lubricant, aids chewing and swallowing; also contains salivary amylase (ptyalin), which begins the digestion of starch
Gastric juice (2000–3000 mL)	Glands in stomach wall	Pepsin, gastric lipase; pepsin catalyzes partial hydrolysis of proteins to proteoses and peptones in the stomach
Pancreatic juice (500–800 mL)	Pancreas	Trypsinogen, chymotrypsinogen, procarboxypeptidase (converted after secretion to trypsin, chymotrypsin, and carboxypeptidase, respectively, which continue protein digestion); amylopsin (α-amylase, a starch-digestive enzyme), steapsin (a lipase)
Bile (500–1000 mL)	Liver	Contains no enzymes; but contains bile salts, which aid digestion by emulsifying lipids; serves to excrete cholesterol and bile pigments derived from hemoglobin
Intestinal juice	Intestinal mucosal cells	Contains a variety of finishing enzymes: sucrase, maltase, and lactase for carbohydrates; aminopolypeptidase and dipeptidase for final protein breakdown; intestinal lipase; nucleases and phosphatase for hydrolysis of nucleic acids

Gastric Digestion When food is swallowed, it passes through the esophagus to the stomach. In the stomach, mechanical action continues; food particles are reduced in size and are mixed with gastric juices until a material of liquid consistency, known as *chyme*, is obtained.

Gastric juice is a clear, pale yellow, acidic fluid having a pH of about 1.5–2.5. It contains hydrochloric acid; the mineral ions Na^+, K^+, Cl^-, and some phosphates; and the digestive enzymes pepsin and lipase. The flow of gastric juice is accelerated by conditioned reflexes and by the presence of food in the stomach. The secretion of the hormone *gastrin* is triggered by food entering the stomach. This hormone, which is produced by the gastric glands, is absorbed into the bloodstream and returned to the stomach wall where it stimulates the secretion of additional gastric juice. Control of gastric secretion by this hormone is an example of one of the many chemical control systems that exist in the body.

The chief digestive function of the stomach is the partial digestion of protein. The principal enzyme of gastric juice is pepsin, which digests protein. The enzyme is secreted in an inactive form called pepsinogen, which is activated by hydrochloric acid to pepsin. Pepsin catalyzes the hydrolysis of proteins to fragments called proteoses and peptones, which are still fairly large molecules. Pepsin splits the peptide bonds adjacent to only a few amino acid residues, particularly tyrosine and phenylalanine:

$$\text{Protein} + \text{Water} \xrightarrow{\text{Pepsin}} \text{Proteoses} + \text{Peptones}$$

The second enzyme in the stomach, gastric lipase, is a fat digesting enzyme. Its action in the stomach is slight because the acidity is too high for lipase activity. Food may be retained in the stomach for as long as 6 hours. It then passes through the pyloric valve into the duodenum.

Intestinal Digestion The next section of the digestive tract, the small intestine, is where most of the digestion occurs. The stomach contents are first made alkaline by secretions from the pancreatic and bile ducts. The pH of the pancreatic juice is 7.5–8.0, and the pH of bile is 7.1–7.7. The shift in pH is necessary because the enzymes of the pancreatic and intestinal juices are active only in an alkaline medium. Enzymes that digest all three kinds of food—carbohydrates, fats, and proteins—are secreted by the pancreas. Pancreatic secretion is stimulated by hormones that are secreted into the bloodstream by the duodenum and the jejunum.

The enzymes occurring in the small intestine include pancreatic amylases (diastase) that hydrolyze most of the starch to maltose, and carbohydrases (α-amylase, maltase, sucrase, and lactase) that complete the hydrolysis of disaccharides to monosaccharides. The proteolytic enzymes trypsin and chymotrypsin attack proteins, proteoses, and peptones, hydrolyzing them to dipeptides. Then the peptidases—carboxypeptidase, aminopeptidase, and dipeptidase—complete the hydrolysis of proteins to amino acids. Pancreatic lipases catalyze the hydrolysis of almost all fats. Fats are split into fatty acids, glycerol, and mono- and diesters of glycerol by these enzymes.

The liver is another important organ in the digestive system. A fluid known as bile is produced by the liver and stored in the gall bladder, a small organ located on the surface of the liver. When food enters the duodenum, the gall bladder contracts, and the bile enters the duodenum through a duct that is also used by the pancreatic juice. In addition to water, the major constituents of the bile are bile acids (as salts), bile pigments, inorganic salts, and cholesterol. The bile acids are steroid monocarboxylic acids, two of which are shown below:

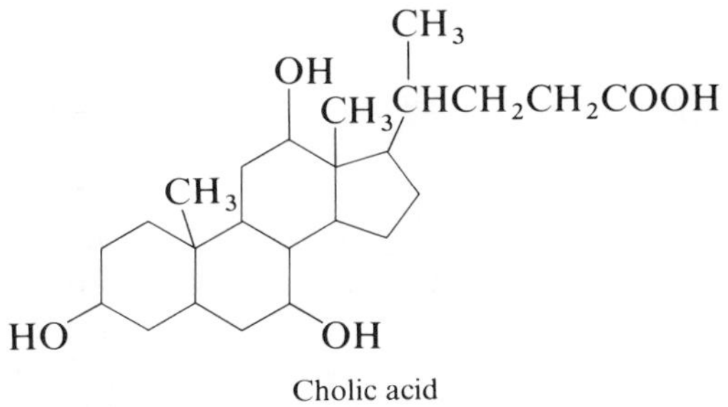

Cholic acid

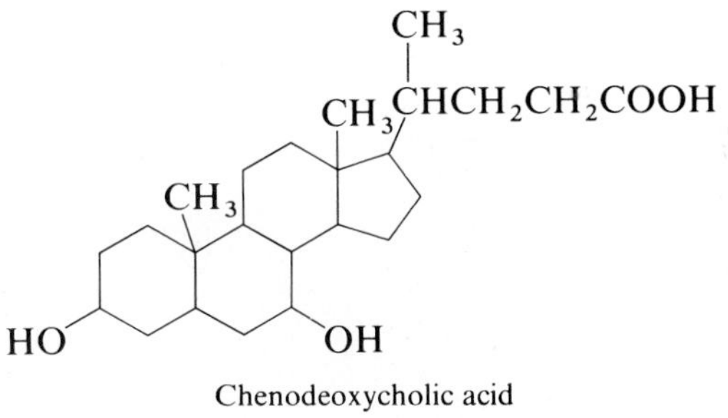

Chenodeoxycholic acid

The bile acids are synthesized in the liver from cholesterol, which is also synthesized in the liver. The presence of bile in the intestine is important for the digestion and absorption of fats. When released into the duodenum, the bile acids emulsify the fats, allowing them to be hydrolyzed by the pancreatic lipases. About 90% of the bile salts are reabsorbed in the lower part of the small intestine and are transported back to the liver and used again.

Most of the digested food is absorbed from the small intestine. Undigested and indigestible material passes from the small intestine to the large intestine, where it is retained for varying periods of time before final elimination as feces. Additional chemical breakdown, sometimes with the production of considerable amounts of gases, is brought about by bacteria (or rather by bacterial enzymes) in the large intestine. For a healthy person this additional breakdown is not important from the standpoint of nutrition since absorption of nutrients does not occur from the large intestine. However, large amounts of water, partly from digestive juices, are absorbed from the large intestine so that the contents become more solid before elimination.

15.14 ABSORPTION

absorption

For digested food to be utilized in the body, it must pass from the intestine into the blood and lymph systems. The process by which digested foods pass through the membrane linings of the small intestine and enter the blood and lymph is called **absorption**. Absorption is complicated, and we shall consider only an overview of it.

After the food you have eaten is digested, the body must absorb billions upon billions of nutrient molecules into the bloodstream. The absorption system is in the membranes of the small intestine, which, upon microscopic inspection, are seen to be wrinkled into hundreds of folds. These folds are covered with thousands of small projections called *villi*. Each projection is itself covered by many minute folds called *microvilli*. The small intestine's wrinkles, folds, and projections increase the surface area available for absorption. The average small intestine is about 4 meters (13.3 ft) long and is estimated to contain about 8360 square meters (90,000 sq ft) of absorbing surface.

The inner surface of the small intestine is composed of mucosal cells that produce many enzymes, such as disaccharidases, aminopeptidases, and dipepti-

Absorption of digested food ▶ occurs in the small intestine through the villi and microvilli shown here.

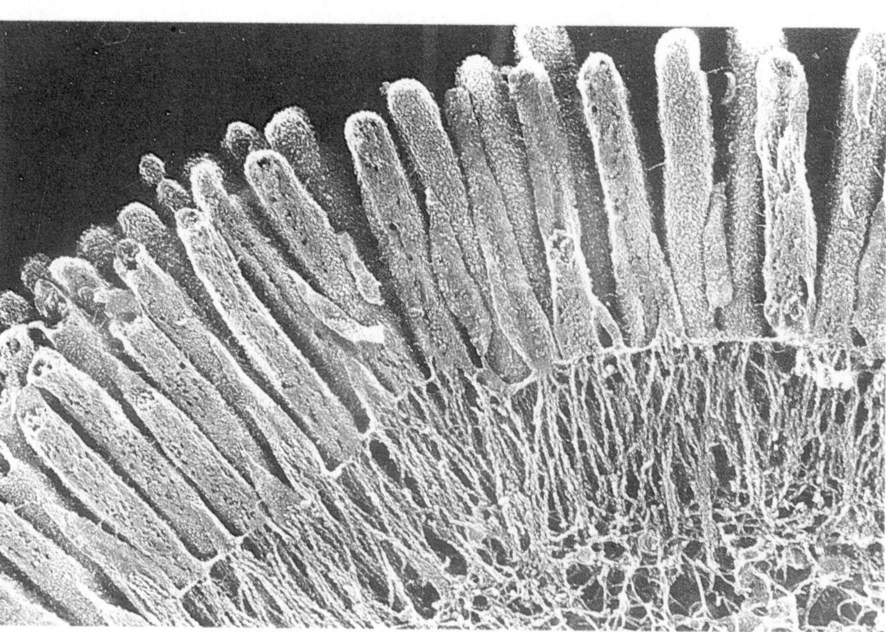

dases, needed to complete the digestive process. As digestion is completed, the resulting nutrient molecules are absorbed by the mucosal cells and transferred to the blood and lymph systems. Water soluble nutrients such as monosaccharides, glycerol, short chain fatty acids, amino acids, and minerals enter directly into the bloodstream. Fat soluble nutrients such as long chain fatty acids and monoacylglycerols first enter the lymph fluid and then enter the bloodstream where the two fluids come together.

An important factor in the absorption process is that the membranes of the intestine are selectively permeable; that is, they prevent the passage of most large molecules but allow the passage of smaller molecules. For example, polysaccharides, disaccharides, and proteins are not ordinarily absorbed, but generally monosaccharides and amino acids are.

15.15 Liver Function

The liver is the largest organ in the body and performs several vital functions. Two of these functions are (1) the regulation of the concentrations of organic nutrients in the blood and (2) the removal of toxic substances from the blood.

The concentration of blood sugar (glucose) is controlled and maintained by processes that occur in the liver. After absorption, excess glucose and other monosaccharides are removed from the blood and converted to glycogen in the liver. The liver is the principal storage organ for glycogen. As glucose is used in other cells, the stored liver glycogen is gradually hydrolyzed to maintain the appropriate blood-glucose concentration. Liver function is under sensitive hormonal control, as are most vital body functions. This regulation will be discussed further in Chapter 17.

A second major function of the liver is the detoxification of harmful and potentially harmful substances. This function apparently developed as higher vertebrates appeared in the evolutionary time scale. The liver is able to deal with most of the toxic molecules that occur in nature. For example, ethanol is oxidized in the liver and nitrogenous metabolic waste products are converted to urea for excretion.

Organic chemists have learned to synthesize new substances that have no counterparts in the biological world. They are used as industrial chemicals, insecticides, drugs, and food additives. When these potentially toxic substances are ingested, even in small amounts, the body is faced with the difficult challenge of metabolizing or destroying substances that are unlike any found in nature.

The liver is actually able to meet this challenge and deal with most of these foreign molecules through an oxidation system located on the endoplasmic reticulum. Bound to these intracellular membranes are enzymes that can catalyze reactions between oxygen and the foreign molecules. As these molecules are oxidized, they become more polar and water soluble. Finally, the oxidation products of the potential toxins are excreted in the urine or bile fluid.

For example, most automobile antifreeze solutions contain ethylene glycol, a toxic substance. Even though this compound does not occur naturally, the liver can metabolize ethylene glycol. When small amounts are ingested accidentally, the following chemical changes occur:

$$\underset{\text{Ethylene glycol}}{\mathrm{H{-}C(OH)(H){-}C(OH)(H){-}H}} \xrightarrow{\text{Oxidation}} \underset{\text{Glyoxal}}{\mathrm{H{-}C(OH)(H){-}C({=}O){-}H}} \xrightarrow{\text{Oxidation}} \underset{\text{Glycolate}}{\mathrm{H{-}C(OH)(H){-}C({=}O){-}O^-}} \xrightarrow{\text{Oxidation}}$$

$$\underset{\text{Glyoxalate}}{\mathrm{H{-}C({=}O){-}C({=}O){-}O^-}} \xrightarrow{\text{Oxidation}} \underset{\text{Formate}}{\mathrm{H{-}C({=}O){-}O^-}} + \underset{\text{Bicarbonate}}{\mathrm{HO{-}C({=}O){-}O^-}}$$

Thus ethylene glycol is converted by oxidation to two more polar (charged) acid anions that are easily eliminated from the body.

Unfortunately oxidation is not effective for some compounds. Halogenated hydrocarbons, which are particularly inert to oxidation, accumulate in fatty tissue or in the liver itself. Examples of halogenated hydrocarbons are carbon tetrachloride, hexachlorobenzene, DDT, dioxins, and polychlorinated biphenyls (PCBs). Some compounds become more toxic after oxidation. For example, polycyclic hydrocarbons (which can be formed when food is barbecued) become carcinogenic upon partial oxidation. Methanol becomes particularly toxic because it is converted by oxidation to formaldehyde. One of the most serious dangers of environmental pollution lies in the introduction of compounds that the liver cannot detoxify.

In a sense the liver is the final guardian along the pathway by which nutrients pass to the cells. This pathway starts with a balanced diet. Once foods are digested and absorbed, the liver adjusts nutrient levels and removes potential toxins. The blood can then provide nutrients for the cellular biochemistry that constitutes life.

Concepts in Review

1. Distinguish a nutrient from a food.
2. Describe the difference between a minimum dietary requirement and a recommended dietary allowance.
3. Summarize the importance of nutrients in metabolism.
4. Briefly describe the general differences between carbohydrate and fat metabolism.
5. Briefly discuss the major functions of dietary protein.
6. Discuss the dangers of kwashiorkor.
7. Explain why fats are a more concentrated source of metabolic energy than carbohydrates.

8. List some of the dangers of a high-sucrose diet.
9. Briefly describe the importance of dietary fiber.
10. List the essential fatty acids and essential amino acids.
11. Discuss a major danger inherent in a vegetarian diet.
12. Summarize some of the functions of the water soluble vitamins.
13. Discuss some of the functions of the fat soluble vitamins.
14. State, in a general way, the results of vitamin deficiencies.
15. List the major mineral elements.
16. Compare the similarities between trace mineral elements and vitamins.
17. Briefly discuss the importance of water in the diet.
18. List four purposes served by food additives.
19. Briefly discuss food additives and their effect on nutrition.
20. List the five principal digestive juices and where they originate in the body.
21. List the principal enzymes of the various digestive juices.
22. Give the main digestive functions of each of the five principal digestive juices.
23. List the classes of products formed when carbohydrates, fats, and proteins are digested.
24. Briefly describe the absorption of nutrients from the digestive tract into the lymph and blood.
25. Discuss the role of the liver in maintaining blood glucose levels.
26. Explain how the liver metabolizes potentially toxic compounds.

Equations in Review

Hydrolysis of Carbohydrates During Digestion (example)

$$\text{Starch} + \text{Water} \xrightarrow{\text{amylase}} \text{Maltose}$$
$$\text{Maltose} + \text{Water} \xrightarrow{\text{maltase}} \text{Glucose}$$

Hydrolysis of Proteins During Digestion

$$\text{Protein} + \text{Water} \xrightarrow{\text{enzyme}} \text{Proteoses} + \text{Peptones}$$
$$\text{Proteoses} + \text{Peptones} + \text{Water} \xrightarrow{\text{enzyme}} \text{Dipeptides}$$
$$\text{Dipeptides} + \text{Water} \xrightarrow{\text{enzyme}} \text{Amino acids}$$

Hydrolysis of Fats During Digestion (example)

$$\text{Triacylglycerols} + \text{Water} \longrightarrow \text{Fatty acids} + \text{Glycerol} + \text{Monoacylglycerols} + \text{Diacylglycerols}$$

Exercises

1. Milk is a food. List four nutrients that can be obtained from milk.
2. List the three classes of nutrients that do *not* commonly supply energy for the cell.
3. What is meant by the term *energy allowance*?
4. How does marasmus differ from kwashiorkor?
5. You are told that a new diet will cause you to lose 9 kg (20 lb) of fat in one week. Is this reasonable? Explain.
6. What is meant by the statement that candy provides empty calories?
7. Why is cellulose important in the diet?
8. Explain why a tablespoon of butter (a fatty food) approximately doubles the calorie content of a medium-size baked potato (a carbohydrate food).
9. What is meant by the term *essential fatty acid*?
10. What chemical characteristics do the essential fatty acids have in common?
11. List the essential amino acids.
12. How do animal proteins differ from vegetable proteins?
13. Which vitamins are water soluble? Which are fat soluble?
14. Why does cooking affect the B-complex vitamin content of vegetables?
15. List three different functions that can be attributed to vitamins.
16. Distinguish the major elements from the trace elements.
17. List two major biological functions for calcium.
18. In what ways are the trace elements similar to vitamins? How do they differ?
19. What percentage of the average water consumption comes from solid foods? How much from liquids?
20. A fruit drink label claims that the juice contains 100% of the RDA for vitamin C. Because of this nutrition claim, what information must be printed on the label by law?
21. List five common categories of food additives.
22. Which federal agency is responsible for regulating the use of food additives?
23. Why must the food of higher animals be digested before it can be utilized?
24. What are the five principal digestive juices?
25. What is chyme?
26. What is the approximate pH of each of the following?
    (a) Saliva (c) Pancreatic juice
    (b) Gastric juice (d) Bile
27. What enzymes are present in each of the digestive juices?
28. In what parts of the digestive system are each of the following digested?
    (a) Carbohydrates (b) Fats (c) Proteins
29. In what part of the digestive tract does the absorption of food occur?
30. What are the end products of carbohydrate digestion? List the specific compounds that are formed.
31. What is the digestive function of the liver?
32. List the principal digestive enzymes that act on proteins.
33. How do the intestinal mucosal cells aid digestion?
34. How does the liver metabolize toxic compounds and remove them from the bloodstream?
35. Which of these statements are correct? Rewrite each incorrect statement to make it correct.
    (a) Water is an essential nutrient.
    (b) Most vegetable proteins are complete proteins.
    (c) Oleic acid is an essential fatty acid.
    (d) A dietary supply of glycine is not needed.
    (e) Of the three classes of energy nutrients, an RDA has been established only for proteins.
    (f) Vitamins are inorganic nutrients.
    (g) Most foods contain a variety of nutrients.
    (h) Calcium is an important trace element.
    (i) The functions of most trace elements are not well understood.
    (j) The main purpose of digestion is to hydrolyze large molecules to smaller ones that can be absorbed through the intestinal membranes.
    (k) Most of the digestion of food occurs in the stomach.
    (l) Gastric juice contains hydrochloric acid and has a pH of 1.5–2.5.
    (m) Digestion in the small intestine occurs in an alkaline medium.
    (n) The function of bile acids is to emulsify carbohydrates; this allows them to be hydrolyzed to monosaccharides.
    (o) The liver functions to reduce potentially toxic compounds.

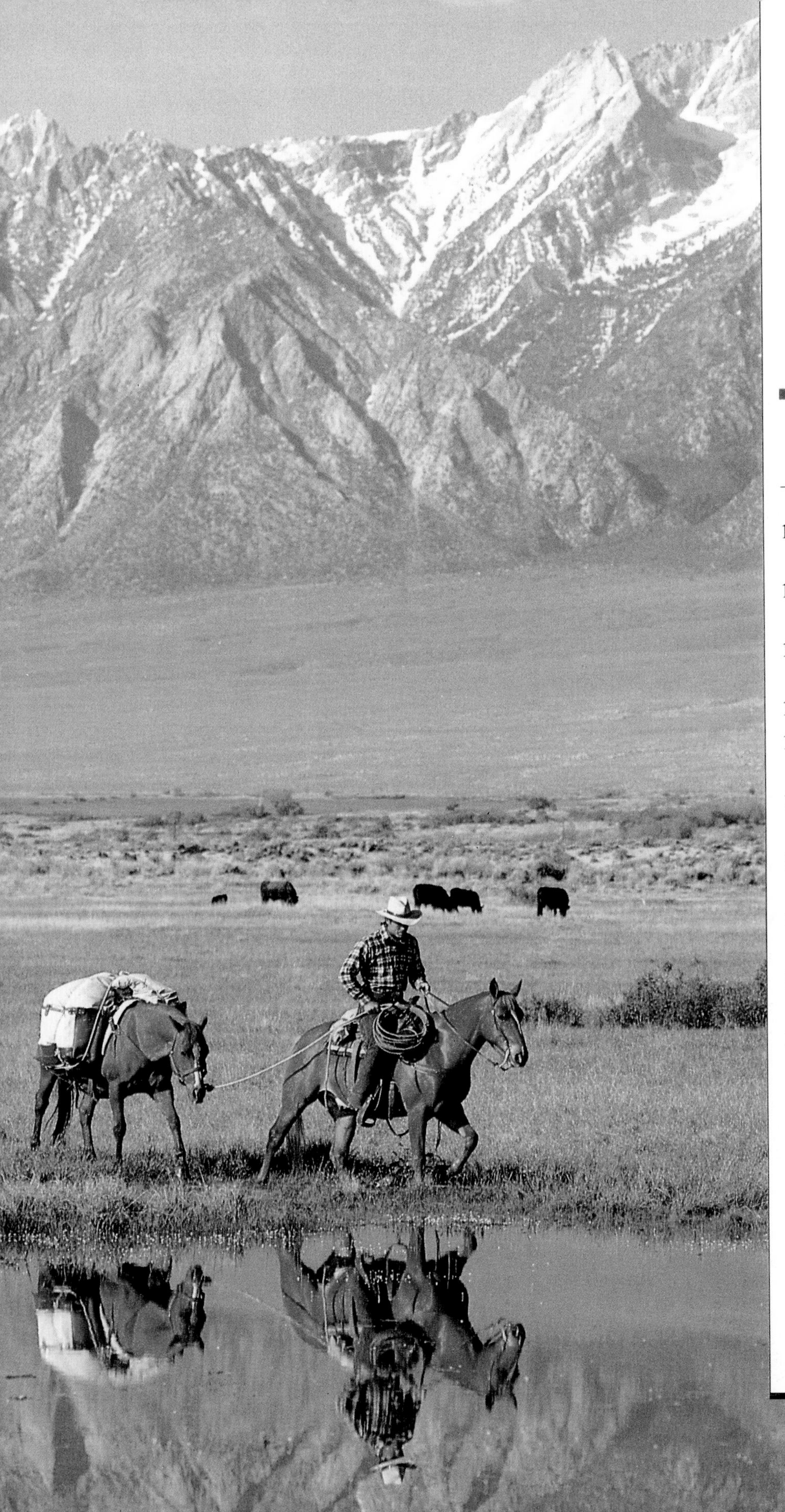

16

Bioenergetics

◀ **Chapter Opening Photo: The energy for life begins with the sun, flows through the grass, the cattle, and continues up the food chain.**

If you are traveling through the midwestern United States on a warm night in early summer, you might notice small yellow lights dancing through the fields. This beautiful sight is evidence that the fireflies, or lightning bugs, have returned. Their flickering light does not arise from a small fire or electrical discharge but rather from a chemical reaction. Bioenergetics are at work.

The monarch butterfly is a very striking insect with a wing span of several inches. As it flies, it is buffeted by the wind, first one direction and then another. Clearly, the monarch is light and not a powerful flier. Yet, this small creature makes an annual migration from the San Francisco Bay area to Mexico and Central America, a distance of about 2000 miles. Chemical reactions in each of the insects' cells make energy available for this arduous trip. Again, bioenergetics are at work.

While you have been reading these paragraphs, fully 20 percent of the oxygen you breathed has been used by your brain. Chemical processes have reacted this oxygen with blood glucose, yielding the energy needed to comprehend your reading. This is another example of bioenergetics—the chemical processes directly related to energy needs and uses in life.

16.1 Energy Changes in Living Organisms

bioenergetics

For life to exist, energy must be available. The part of biochemistry that deals with the transformation, distribution, and utilization of energy by living organism is called **bioenergetics**. Thus, when our muscles undergo physical activity, bioenergetics must have an important role. Let us follow some of the biochemical changes during fairly intense work—for example, cutting grass with a hand-propelled mower on a warm day—as a means of introduction to bioenergetics.

For the most part, bioenergetics occurs inside cells. Consequently, cells must take in needed chemicals from and return waste products to the surrounding fluids. Because of this exchange process, the chemical changes in the fluid surrounding working muscle cells provide important clues concerning the principles of bioenergetics.

As lawn mowing progresses, breathing accelerates; oxygen is taken in and carbon dioxide expelled more rapidly. These gases are transported by the bloodstream between the muscles, where bioenergetics is active, and the lungs. In fact, the blood is an important intermediary in bioenergetics.

◄ **In order to move and live we must transform and use chemical energy. The field of bioenergetics involves the study of these energy interrelationships at a cellular level.**

16.2 Oxygen/Carbon Dioxide Exchange

Muscles must have an adequate oxygen supply, especially when a person is pushing a lawn mower or doing any other work. About 5 g of oxygen (4 L at 25°C and 1 atm) is required for every minute of strenuous activity by a young adult. The necessary oxygen is supplied to the muscle cells by oxygenated arterial blood. Waste carbon dioxide from the muscle cells is removed by oxygen-deficient venous blood.

Normally the partial pressure of oxygen is about 100 torr in the lungs and 35 torr in the cells. Because gases move spontaneously from regions of higher pressure to regions of lower pressure, oxygen moves toward the cells. But the body must move oxygen at rates far faster than can be attained by simple diffusion. Red blood cells, which contain the oxygen transport protein hemoglobin (Hb) (see Section 12.7), increase the oxygen transport rate by 80–90 times that obtained by simple diffusion.

The amount of oxygen bound by hemoglobin changes as the partial pressure of oxygen changes. Figure 16.1 graphically shows the oxygen-binding characteristics of hemoglobin in the form of a steeply sloped **S**-shaped curve, known as a *sigmoidal curve*. The solid line represents the behavior of hemoglobin when the body is resting. The steep portion of the curve is in the 35–40 torr partial pressure range of oxygen found in the fluid surrounding the cell. In this steep portion of the curve, a small change in the partial pressure of oxygen causes a relatively large change in the oxygen bound to hemoglobin. The lowering of the partial pressure of oxygen as hemoglobin moves from the lungs to resting muscle tissue causes the release of about 70% of the hemoglobin-bound oxygen.

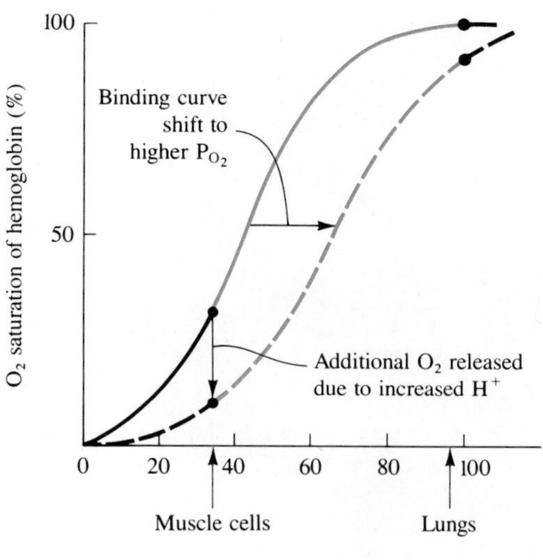

FIGURE 16.1 ▶ The oxygen binding curve for hemoglobin under approximate physiological conditions: As the partial pressure of oxygen is increased, more O_2 binds to hemoglobin. The colored portion of each curve highlights changes in O_2 saturation of hemoglobin as the blood circulates between the lungs and the muscle cells.

When the strenuous work of lawn mowing begins, the muscle cells must have more oxygen to generate the needed energy. The rate of oxygen flow to the cells is speeded up by an increase in the pulse and respiration rates of the person doing the mowing. But more subtle, and very effective, biochemical changes also occur.

First, in hard-working muscle tissue where bioenergetics proceeds rapidly, the partial pressure of oxygen may drop to 10 torr. This decrease in P_{O_2} from 35 torr to 10 torr is small. But because the hemoglobin–oxygen binding curve is steep, the amount of additional oxygen released is large. Hemoglobin may release up to 90% of its oxygen under these conditions.

Second, hydrogen ions are formed as the muscles work (see Section 16.3). These ions bind to oxygenated hemoglobin (HbO_2) and stimulate the release of additional oxygen.

$$H^+ + HbO_2 \longrightarrow HbH^+ + O_2 \qquad (1)$$

This acid effect is represented graphically by a shift of the oxygen binding curve toward higher partial pressures of oxygen, as shown in Figure 16.1. This shift, shown by the dashed line, means that more O_2 is released in the muscles. When muscle cells increase bioenergetics and need more oxygen, the acid produced by this activity triggers the release of more oxygen from HbO_2.

When oxygen is used in the muscle cells, carbon dioxide is produced. This metabolic product must be removed from the cells. The partial pressure of carbon dioxide is highest in the muscle cells, decreases in the venous blood, and is lowest in the lungs. Thus, carbon dioxide tends to move from the cells toward the lungs. But as with oxygen, carbon dioxide must be moved at a faster rate than can be attained by simple diffusion.

For the most part the rapid, efficient removal of carbon dioxide is effected by two methods. In the first method hemoglobin acts as a carrier molecule. Carbon dioxide reacts with amino groups on the hemoglobin molecule to form carbamino ion groups and H^+ ions:

$$Hb{-}NH_2 + CO_2 \longrightarrow \underset{\text{Carbamino ion}}{Hb{-}NH{-}CO_2^-} + H^+ \quad (2)$$

In the second method of removal, carbon dioxide reacts with water to form highly soluble bicarbonate and hydrogen ions:

$$CO_2 + H_2O \rightleftharpoons H_2CO_3 \rightleftharpoons H^+ + HCO_3^- \quad (3)$$

Reactions (2) and (3) occur in the fluid surrounding the muscles. The hydrogen ions produced by these reactions stimulate the further release of oxygen in the muscle tissue by the reaction shown in equation (1).

The hemoglobin carbamino ions, bicarbonate ions, and excess hydrogen ions are transported to the lungs via the venous blood. There the exhalation of carbon dioxide enables the reaction of equations (2) and (3) to reverse, as shown in these equations:

$$Hb{-}NH{-}CO_2^- + H^+ \longrightarrow Hb{-}NH_2 + CO_2 \quad (4)$$

$$HCO_3^- + H^+ \rightleftharpoons H_2CO_3 \rightleftharpoons H_2O + CO_2 \quad (5)$$

These reversible reactions serve not only to eliminate CO_2 but also to consume the excess H^+ ions that were formed in the muscle tissue.

As shown in equations (1) to (5), acid (H^+) has an important role in both the delivery of O_2 and the removal of CO_2. In muscle, CO_2 and H^+ are formed. This acid (H^+) causes HbO_2 to release the additional O_2 needed to continue the bioenergetics. In the lungs, CO_2 is exhaled and the blood becomes less acidic, causing Hb to bind more O_2. The overall interrelationships of oxygen, carbon dioxide, and acid can be summarized in this way:

Energy use at the muscle	**Gas balance restored at the lungs**
O_2 used	O_2 inhaled
CO_2 formed	CO_2 exhaled
Acidity increases	Acidity decreases
More O_2 released from HbO_2	More O_2 bound to Hb

16.3 Hydrogen Ion Production and Control

Acid (H^+) is produced as the muscles perform work. Two products of cellular bioenergetics—carbonic acid and lactic acid—are the primary sources of this acidity. Both substances produce hydrogen ions in solution:

$$CO_2 + H_2O \rightleftharpoons H_2CO_3 \rightleftharpoons H^+ + HCO_3^- \quad (6)$$

$$\underset{\text{Lactic acid}}{CH_3CH(OH)COOH} \rightleftharpoons H^+ + \underset{\text{Lactate ion}}{CH_3CH(OH)COO^-} \quad (7)$$

To prevent a toxic buildup of acid (abnormally low pH), the excess H^+ ions must be removed from the cells. The lungs provide a short-term partial solution to the problem of increased acidity in the cells and surrounding fluid. When CO_2 is exhaled from the lungs, reaction (6) is reversed and the H^+ ion concentration is reduced in the bloodstream. During hard work, the rate of removal of carbon dioxide from the lungs is accelerated by an increase in the respiration and pulse rate. Thus, as the breathing rate increases, the blood acidity decreases.

The liver and kidneys also have an important role in controlling the pH of body fluids. The liver converts lactic acid to glucose and thereby helps to prevent toxic acid buildup. The kidneys transfer water and selected ions from the bloodstream to the urine. Hydrogen ions and bicarbonate ions are among those transferred. Because this is a relatively slow process, the kidneys are mainly concerned with the long-term maintenance of correct body fluid pH.

16.4 Metabolism

As we have seen, to do work (for example, to mow a lawn), the muscles must take in extra O_2. This oxygen reacts with nutrients such as carbohydrates or fats. Energy is released as the reduced carbons of the nutrients are converted by a series of reactions into the oxidized carbons of carbon dioxide and lactic acid. These reactions comprise an important fraction of all the chemical reactions that occur in muscle cells.

metabolism

anabolism

catabolism

The sum of all chemical reactions that occur within a living organism is defined as **metabolism**. Many hundreds of different chemical reactions occur in a typical cell. To help make sense of this myriad of reactions, biochemists have subdivided metabolism into two contrasting categories—*anabolism* and *catabolism*. **Anabolism** is the process by which simple substances are synthesized (built up) into complex substances. **Catabolism** is the process by which complex substances are broken down into simpler substances. Anabolic reactions usually involve reduction and consume cellular energy, whereas catabolic reactions usually involve oxidation and produce energy for the cell. The energy needed to mow the lawn is generated from catabolic reactions that occur within muscle cells.

16.5 Metabolism and Cell Structure

procaryote

Cells segregate many of their metabolic reactions into specific, subcellular locations. The simple, procaryotic cells (**procaryotes**)—those without internal membrane-bound bodies—have a minimum amount of spatial organization (see Figure 16.2). The anabolic processes of DNA and RNA synthesis in these cells are localized in the nuclear material, whereas most other metabolic reactions are spread throughout the cytoplasm.

eucaryote

organelle

In contrast, metabolic reactions in the cells of higher plants and animals are often segregated into specialized compartments. These cells, the **eucaryotes**, contain internal, membrane bound bodies called **organelles** (see Figure 16.2). It is within the organelles that many specific metabolic processes occur.

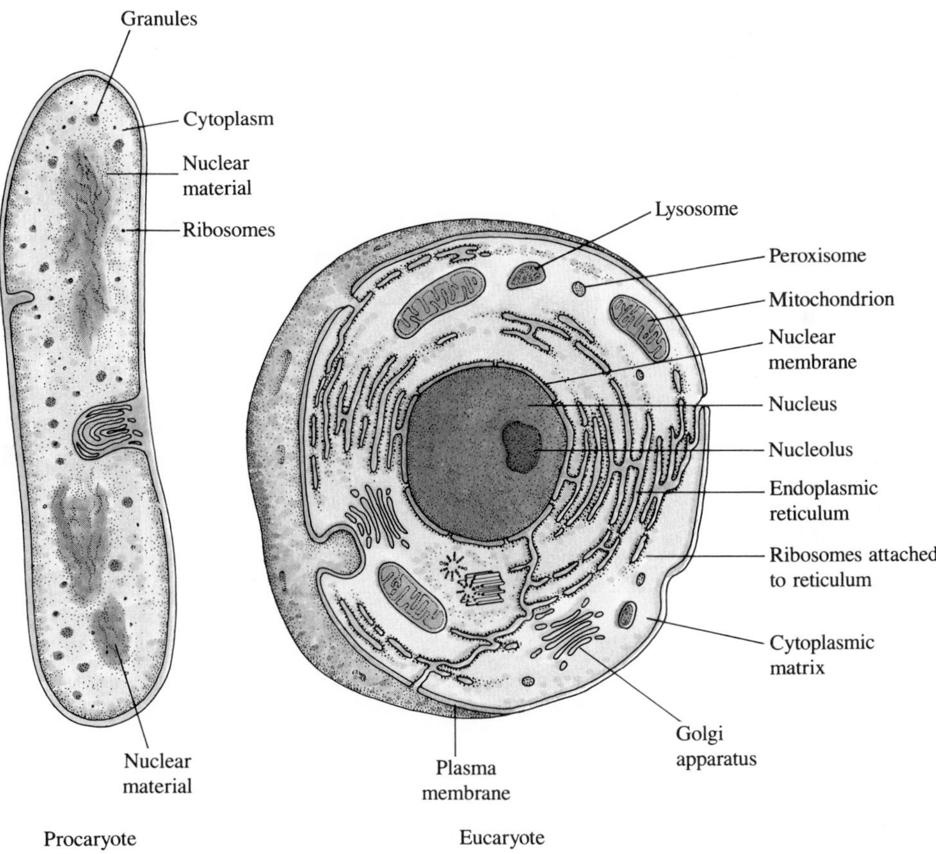

FIGURE 16.2
A schematic representation of a procaryotic and a eucaryotic cell. The procaryote lacks much of the organized structure and the numerous organelles found in the eucaryote.

In the eucaryotic cell, most of the DNA and RNA synthesis are localized in the nucleus. Anabolism of proteins takes place on the ribosomes, whereas that of carbohydrates and lipids occurs primarily in the cytoplasm.

There are a variety of specialized catabolic organelles within a eucaryotic cell. The lysosome contains the cell's digestive enzymes, and the peroxisome is the site of oxidative reactions that form hydrogen peroxide. Perhaps the most important catabolic organelle is the mitochondrion (plural, mitochondria). This membrane-bound body provides most of the energy for a typical cell. The energy is released by catabolic processes, which oxidize carbon containing nutrients. Mitochondria (1) consume most of the O_2 that is inhaled and (2) produce most of the CO_2 that is exhaled by the lungs.

16.6 Biochemical Energy Sources

The ultimate source of biological energy on earth is sunlight. Plants capture light energy and transform it to chemical energy by a process called *photosynthesis* (see Section 16.10). This chemical energy is stored in the form of reduced carbon atoms in carbohydrate molecules. It is important to understand that the energy contained in carbohydrates, lipids, and proteins originally came from

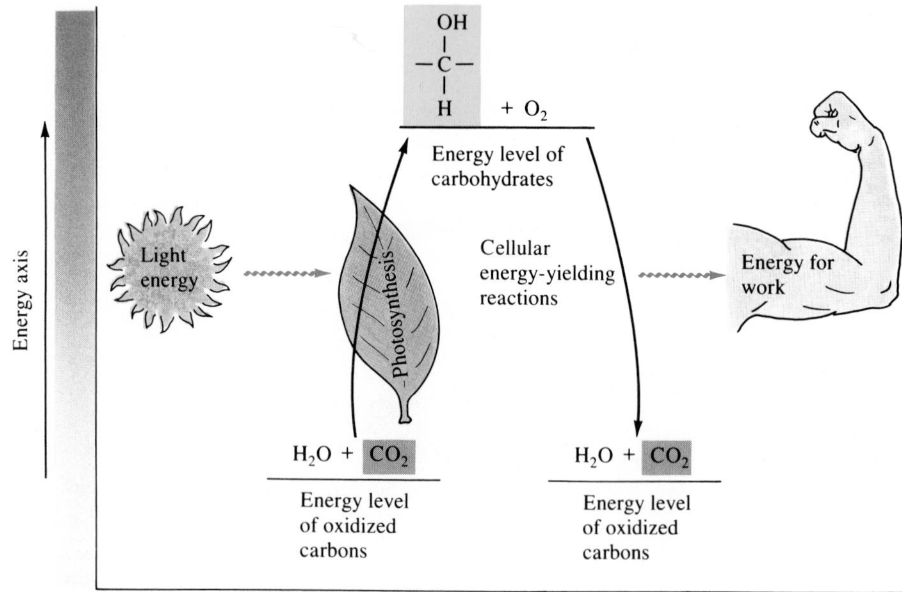

FIGURE 16.3 ▶ Energy flow through metabolism using the important energy nutrients, carbohydrates. Reduction of carbon stores energy while oxidation of carbon releases energy

sunlight. As the reduced carbon atoms are oxidized, energy is released and used by the cell.

Figure 16.3 is an energy diagram summarizing the energy flow through metabolism. Several times in this chapter an energy diagram will be used to summarize an important concept. The black arrows trace progress from one stage to the next for the specific process under consideration. Because each stage has its own special energy level, it is presented at a particular height with respect to the energy axis (the higher the level, the more energy is in a stage). When energy levels change, energy must be released or absorbed as shown by the red arrows. Thus, in Figure 16.3, photosynthesis causes oxidized carbons to move to a higher energy level as they are reduced to carbohydrate carbons. The carbohydrate carbons are then oxidized to a lower energy level with the release of energy to do work.

Humans, as well as other animals, draw most of their energy from foodstuffs that contain reduced carbons (see Chapter 15). For example, after we eat a meal, nutrients such as carbohydrates and fats are transported to our cells. The carbons in these compounds are in a reduced state and thus contain stored energy.

H | —C— | H	OH | —C— | H
Typical fatty acid carbon (oxidation number = −2)	Typical carbohydrate carbon (oxidation number = 0)

Through the cell's metabolism these reduced carbons are oxidized, step by step, and are eventually converted to carbon dioxide.

$$O{=}C{=}O$$

Carbon dioxide carbon (oxidation number = +4)

When we work at a strenuous task, the energy needed to do the work is obtained from this general catabolic process that occurs in our muscle cells. Stored nutrients, such as carbohydrates, are oxidized with the consumption of oxygen. Carbon dioxide and lactic acid are produced. To summarize, an oxidative reaction sequence releases the energy that ultimately powers muscle action.

16.7 Biological Oxidation–Reduction

Biological oxidation–reduction, as with all redox reactions, can be separated into two half-reactions. Oxidation, the loss of electrons from a reactant,

$$A \xrightarrow{\text{Oxidation}} A^+ + e^- \qquad (8)$$

is coupled with a second process, reduction, the gain of electrons by a reactant.

$$B^+ + e^- \xrightarrow{\text{Reduction}} B \qquad (9)$$

Reactions (8) and (9) can be combined to give the complete redox reaction if electron transfer is possible:

$$A + B^+ \longrightarrow A^+ + B \qquad (10)$$

Oxidation–reduction reactions are vital to cellular bioenergetics. In eucaryotic cells, specific organelles are present that specialize in redox reactions. For example, the *mitochondria* (see Figure 16.4) (often called the powerhouses of the cell) are the sites for most of the catabolic redox reactions. In the mitochondria an electron transport system completes the transfer of electrons to oxygen, forming water. *Chloroplasts* (see Figure 16.4) are organelles found in higher plants and contain an electron transport system that is responsible for the anabolic redox reactions in photosynthesis (see Section 16.10).

The cells maintain close control over these important electron transport systems by isolating them within organelles. Both the mitochondria and the chloroplasts are packed with membranes within which the electron transport systems are located. These lipid-rich membranes act as insulators and force electrons into pathways that are useful to the cell.

To move electrons from one place to another (often outside of the mitochondrion or chloroplast), the cell uses a set of oxidation–reduction coenzymes. Recall from Section 12.1 that a coenzyme is an organic compound that is used and reused to help an enzyme catalyzed reaction. The redox coenzymes facilitate reactions by acting as temporary storage places for electrons. The three most common oxidation–reduction coenzymes (nicotinamide adenine dinucleotide, NAD^+; nicotinamide adenine dinucleotide phosphate, $NADP^+$; and flavin adenine dinucleotide, FAD) are shown in Figure 16.5. Humans synthesize

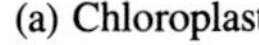

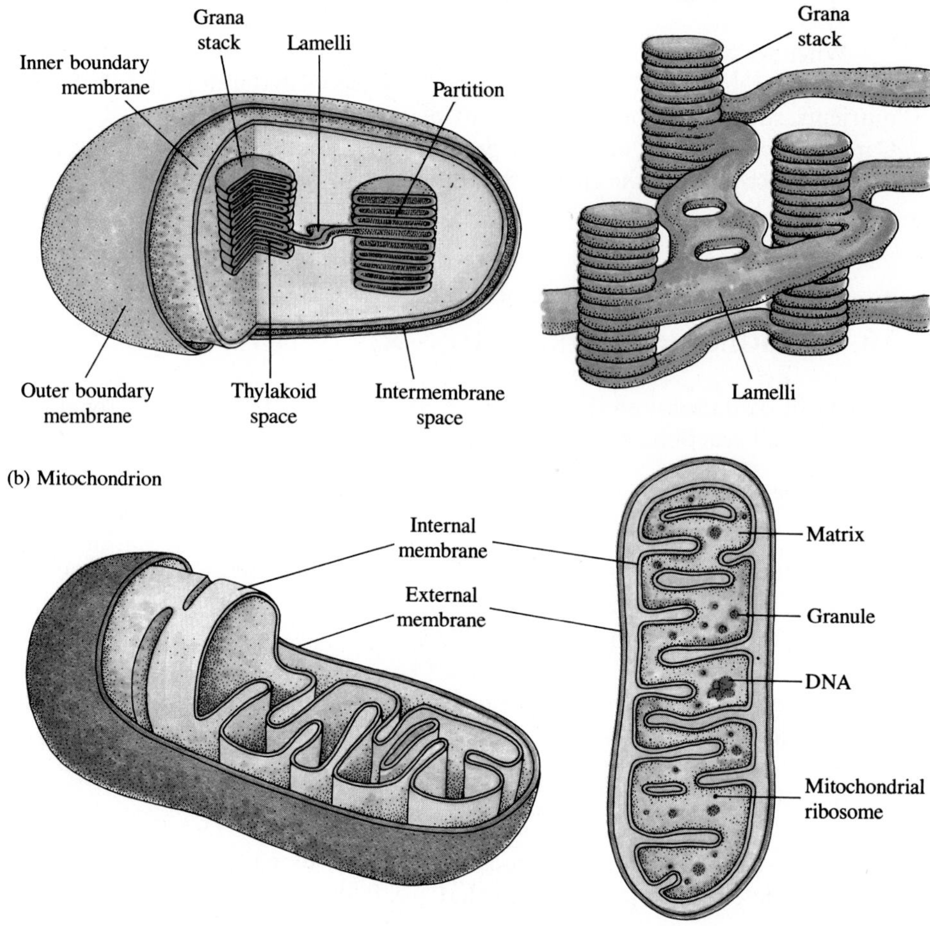

FIGURE 16.4 ► Schematic representation of (a) a chloroplast and (b) a mitochondrion.

NAD^+ and $NADP^+$ from the vitamin niacin while FAD is made from the vitamin riboflavin. In each case, the vitamin provides the reaction center of the coenzyme as defined in more detail in the next paragraph.

The addition or removal of electrons occurs in only one portion of each of these complex molecules. The nicotinamide ring is the reactive component within NAD^+ or $NADP^+$:

$$\text{(nicotinamide ring, } N^+\text{–R)–CNH}_2 + 2\,e^- + H^+ \rightleftharpoons \text{(dihydronicotinamide ring, N–R)–CNH}_2$$

NAD^+ or $NADP^+$ (oxidized form) NADH or NADPH (reduced form)

(R represents the remainder of each molecule.)

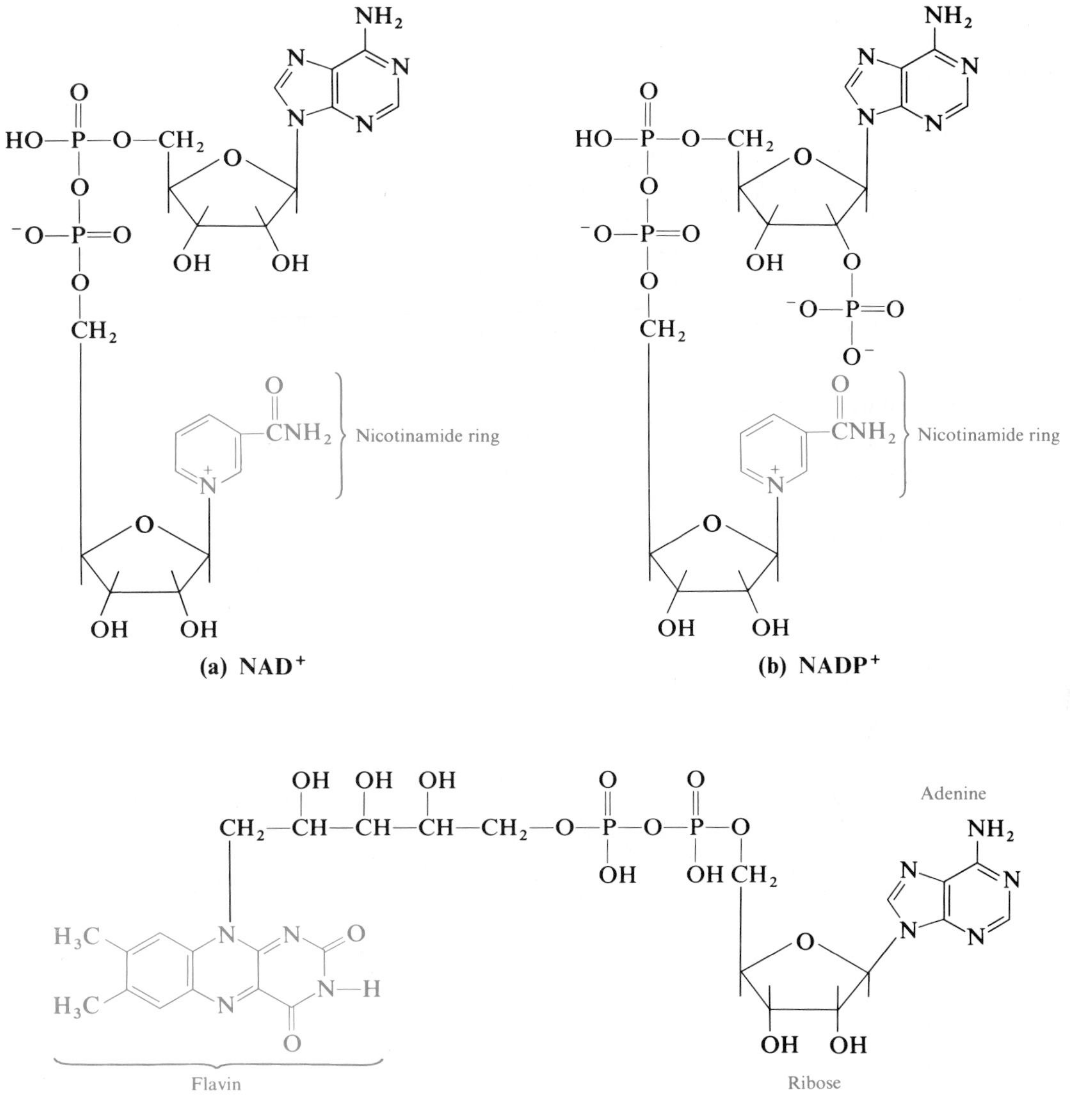

(a) NAD$^+$

(b) NADP$^+$

(c) FAD

▲
FIGURE 16.5
Structures of the oxidation–reduction coenzymes (a) nicotinamide adenine dinucleotide (NAD$^+$), (b) nicotinamide adenine dinucleotide phosphate (NADP$^+$), and (c) flavin adenine dinucleotide (FAD).

For FAD, the flavin ring is the reactive component:

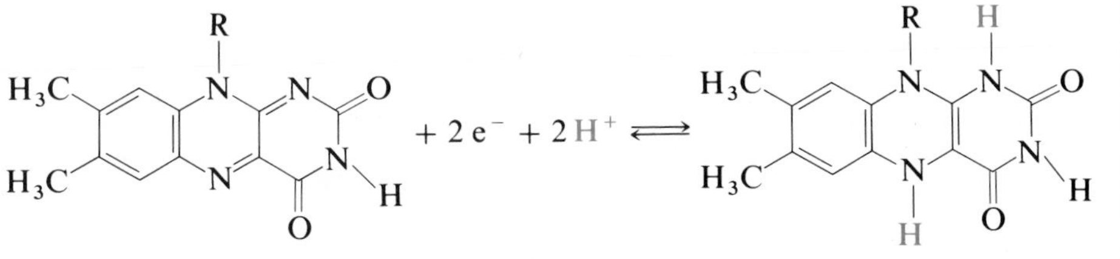

FAD (oxidized form)

FADH$_2$ (reduced form)

(R represents the remainder of each molecule.)

A very important function of these redox coenzymes is to carry electrons to the mitochondrial electron transport system. As the coenzymes are oxidized, molecular oxygen is reduced:

$$\underset{\text{Reduced coenzyme}}{2\,FADH_2} + O_2 \xrightarrow[\text{electron transport}]{\text{Mitochondrial}} \underset{\text{Oxidized coenzyme}}{2\,FAD} + 2\,H_2O$$

$$\underset{\text{Reduced coenzyme}}{2\,NADH} + 2\,H^+ + O_2 \xrightarrow[\text{electron transport}]{\text{Mitochondrial}} \underset{\text{Oxidized coenzyme}}{2\,NAD^+} + 2\,H_2O$$

With the movement of electrons, energy is released. In fact, over 85% of a typical cell's energy is derived from this redox process. (Remember the mitochondria are the powerhouses of the cell!) However, the released energy is not used immediately by the cell but stored, usually in high-energy phosphate bonds such as those in ATP.

16.8 HIGH-ENERGY PHOSPHATE BONDS

The cell needs an energy delivery system. Most cellular energy is produced in the mitochondria, but this energy must be transported throughout the cell. Such a delivery system is required to carry relatively large amounts of energy and to be easily accessible to cellular reactions. Molecules which contain high-energy phosphate bonds meet this need.

The most common high-energy phosphate bond within the cell is the phosphate anhydride bond (or phosphoanhydride bond; see Section 6.12):

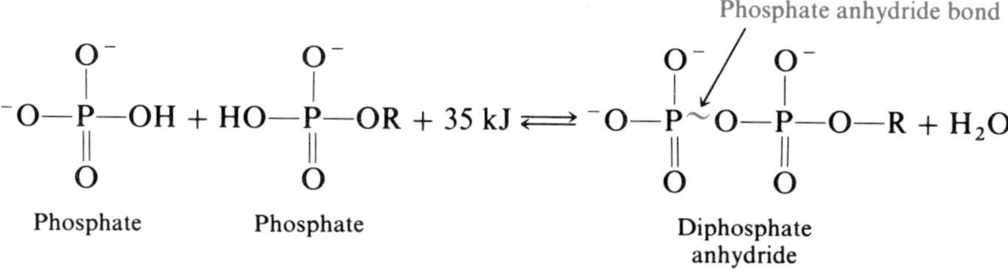

(R represents the remainder of each molecule.)

A relatively large amount of energy is required to bond together the two negatively charged phosphate groups. The repulsion between these phosphates causes the phosphate anhydride bond to behave somewhat like a coiled spring. When the bond is broken, the phosphates separate rapidly and energy is released.

The phosphate anhydride bond is an important component of the nucleotide triphosphates, the most important of which is adenosine triphosphate (ATP) (see Section 14.4):

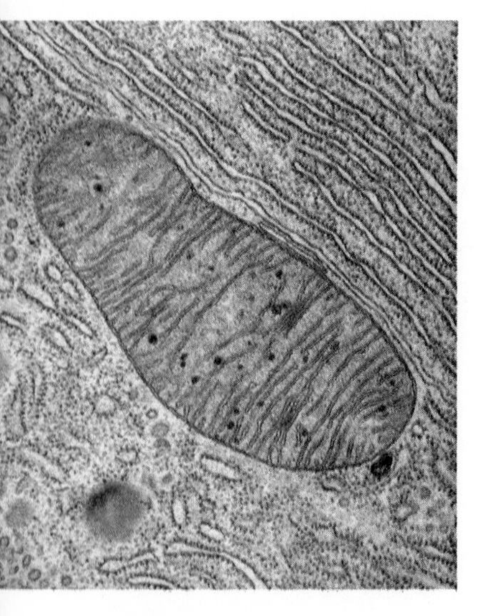

▲ **Photomicrograph of a mitochondrion.**

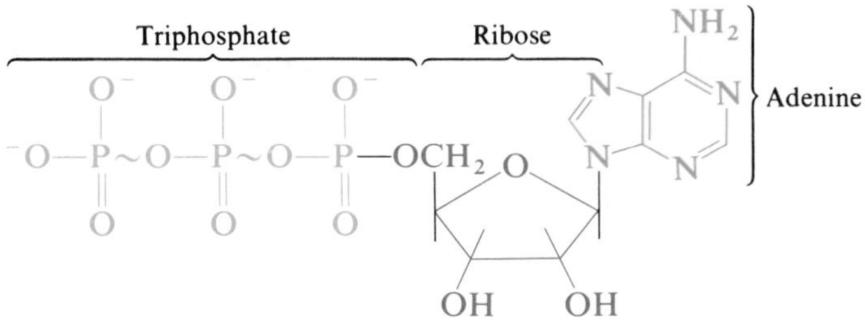

Triphosphate Ribose Adenine

Adenosine triphosphate (ATP)

Adenosine triphosphate plays an important role in all cells, from the simplest to the most complex. ATP functions by storing and transporting the energy in its high-energy phosphate bonds to the places in the cell where energy is needed. ATP is the common intermediary in energy metabolism.

The cell realizes several advantages by storing energy in ATP. First, the stored energy is easily accessible to the cell; it is readily released by a simple hydrolysis reaction yielding adenosine diphosphate (ADP) and an inorganic phosphate ion (P_i):

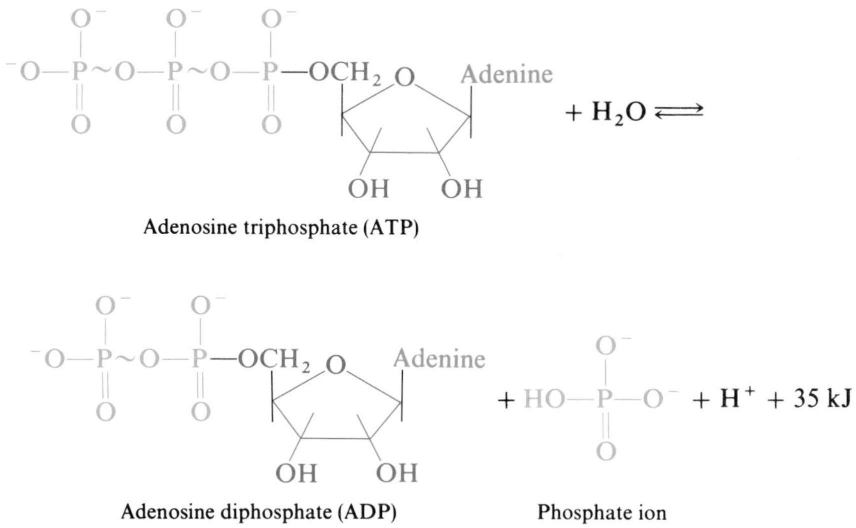

Adenosine triphosphate (ATP) $+ H_2O \rightleftharpoons$

Adenosine diphosphate (ADP) $+ HO{-}P{-}O^- + H^+ + 35\ kJ$

Phosphate ion

Second, ATP serves as the *common energy currency* for the cell. Energy from catabolism of many different kinds of molecules is stored in ATP. For example, the energy obtained from oxidation of carbohydrates, lipids, and proteins is stored in ATP. The oxidation of each of these nutrients requires many different enzyme-catalyzed reactions. To make *direct* use of this energy, the cell would need a separate series of reactions for each different energy source. Instead, the cell channels most of the energy derived from oxidation–reduction reactions into the high-energy bonds of ATP. This process is analogous to an economic system that values all goods and services in terms of a common currency, such as the dollar. Buying and selling within the system is thus greatly simplified. In the cell, energy utilization is greatly simplified by converting all stored energy to ATP, the common energy currency.

16.9 Biological Energy Transformation

To this point we have considered two forms of chemical storage of biological energy: reduced carbon atoms and high-energy phosphate bonds. It is vital that the cell be able to convert one form of stored energy to the other. These energy transformations lie at the heart of cellular metabolism.

There are many examples of energy conversion outside of biology. The chemical energy of gasoline is converted to motion (kinetic energy) of a car. The kinetic energy of a river can be converted to electrical energy. Electrical energy is converted to the heat energy that cooks a meal or heats a room. In each case we can point to a machine or process that transforms energy. For example, an automobile engine converts chemical energy to kinetic energy, and an electric stove transforms electrical energy to heat energy. Similarly, biochemists can point to cellular processes that accomplish energy transformations.

Figure 16.6 summarizes biological energy transformation. In the first process, a variety of cellular reactions oxidize the carbons of energy-supplying nutrients, converting these molecules from a high energy level to a lower energy state. The energy released (red arrow) is used to create high-energy phosphate bonds. Finally, when a cellular reaction needs energy or work must be accomplished, molecules with high-energy phosphate bonds are recycled to low-energy molecules plus inorganic phosphate.

substrate-level phosphorylation

The cell converts energy stored in reduced carbon atoms into energy stored in phosphate anhydride bonds through two biological processes—*substrate-level phosphorylation* and *oxidative phosphorylation.* **Substrate-level phosphorylation** is the process whereby energy derived from the oxidation of reduced carbon atoms is used to form high-energy phosphate bonds on various biochemical molecules (substrates) (Figure 16.7).

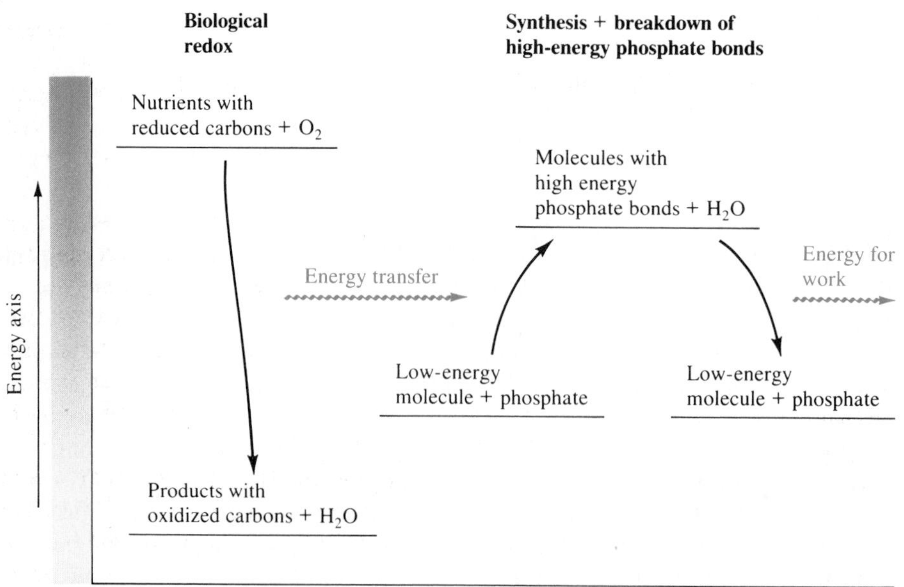

Figure 16.6 ► Energy flow from nutrients with reduced carbons (energy-yielding nutrients) to high-energy phosphate bonds that are used to do work.

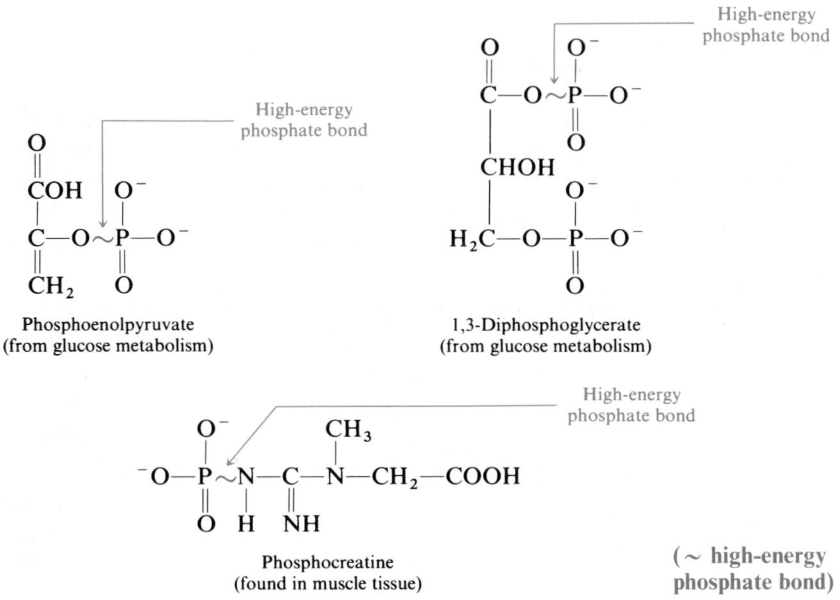

Phosphoenolpyruvate (from glucose metabolism): $CH_2=C(COOH)-O\sim PO_3^{2-}$ (High-energy phosphate bond)

1,3-Diphosphoglycerate (from glucose metabolism): $O=C(-O\sim PO_3^{2-})-CHOH-H_2C-O-PO_3^{2-}$ (High-energy phosphate bond)

Phosphocreatine (found in muscle tissue): $^{-}O-P(=O)(O^{-})\sim N(H)-C(=NH)-N(CH_3)-CH_2-COOH$ (High-energy phosphate bond)

(~ high-energy phosphate bond)

◀ **FIGURE 16.7**
Some biological molecules that contain high-energy phosphate bonds (phosphorylated substrates).

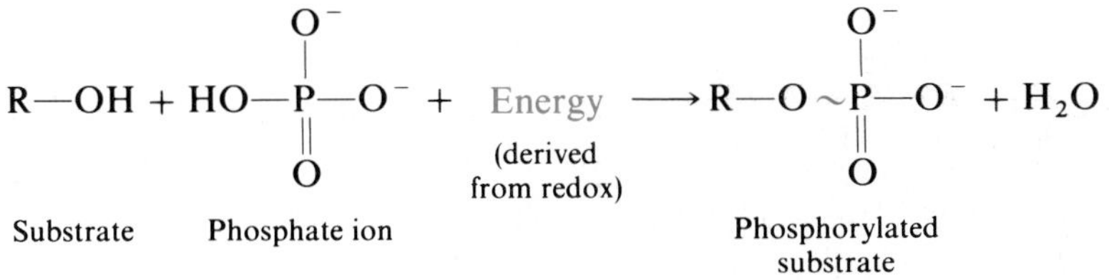

$$R{-}OH + HO{-}P(=O)(O^-){-}O^- + \text{Energy (derived from redox)} \longrightarrow R{-}O\sim P(=O)(O^-){-}O^- + H_2O$$

Substrate — Phosphate ion — Phosphorylated substrate

(R represents the remainder of the substrate molecule.)

In a succeeding reaction, the phosphorylated substrate transfers the phosphate to ADP and forms ATP.

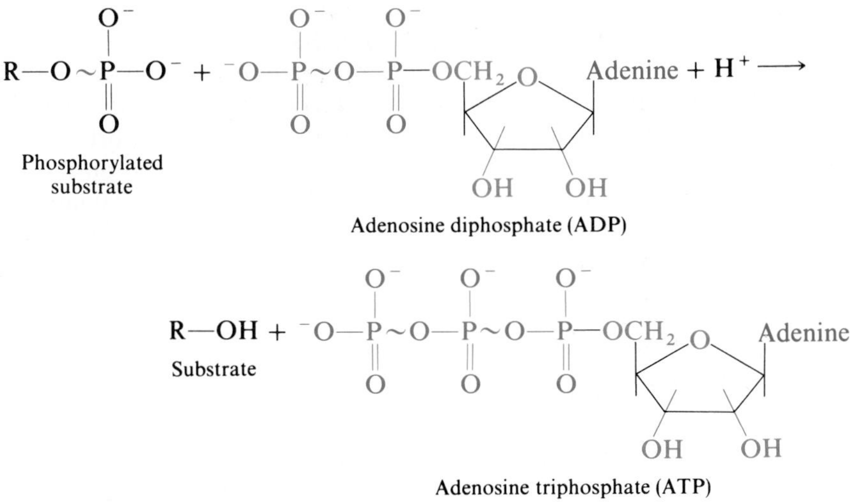

$$R{-}O\sim P(=O)(O^-){-}O^- + {}^-O{-}P(=O)(O^-)\sim O{-}P(=O)(O^-){-}OCH_2\text{-ribose(OH)(OH)-Adenine} + H^+ \longrightarrow$$

Phosphorylated substrate — Adenosine diphosphate (ADP)

$$R{-}OH + {}^-O{-}P(=O)(O^-)\sim O{-}P(=O)(O^-)\sim O{-}P(=O)(O^-){-}OCH_2\text{-ribose(OH)(OH)-Adenine}$$

Substrate — Adenosine triphosphate (ATP)

This process is called substrate level phosphorylation because ADP gains a phosphate from a cellular substrate.

Substrate level phosphorylation is found most commonly in the catabolism of carbohydrates—that is, glycolysis (see Chapter 17). This process accounts for only a minority of a resting cell's total energy production. However, this means of ATP production does not require oxygen. Under anaerobic conditions (for example, when the blood stream cannot deliver enough O_2 to hardworking muscles), substrate level phosphorylation may be the cell's principal means of forming ATP.

oxidative phosphorylation

Oxidative phosphorylation is a process that directly uses energy derived from oxidation–reduction reactions to form ATP. This process occurs in the mitochondria and depends on the mitochondrial electron transport system. The enzyme-catalyzed oxidation and phosphorylation reactions are coupled in such a way that energy released by the oxidation of the coenzyme is used to form ATP via phosphorylation. The overall process is indicated by these equations:

$$FADH_2 + \tfrac{1}{2}O_2 \xrightarrow[\text{}]{\text{Mitochondrial electron transport}} FAD + H_2O$$

$$\text{(Energy)}$$

$$2\ ADP + 2\ P_i \xrightarrow[\text{Oxidative phosphorylation}]{} 2\ ATP + 2\ H_2O$$

$$NADH + H^+ + \tfrac{1}{2}O_2 \xrightarrow{\text{Mitochondrial electron transport}} NAD^+ + H_2O$$

$$\text{(Energy)}$$

$$3\ ADP + 3\ P_i \xrightarrow[\text{Oxidative phosphorylation}]{} 3\ ATP + 3\ H_2O$$

Note that, for each $FADH_2$ oxidized, two ATPs are formed; for each NADH oxidized, three ATPs are produced. This combination of mitochondrial electron transport and oxidative phosphorylation creates most cellular ATP.

Several important reaction sequences depend on electron transport and oxidative phosphorylation to produce ATP. Cells can derive energy from fats (see Chapter 18) only when oxidative phosphorylation is functioning. The citric acid cycle (see Chapter 17), which completes oxidation of most nutrients, forms ATP using oxidative phosphorylation. Because electron transport and oxidative phosphorylation require oxygen, the processes that depend on this means of producing ATP are aerobic. Oxygen must be available during oxidative phosphorylation. Thus, the major energy-producing reaction sequences in the cell function only in the presence of oxygen.

16.10 Photosynthesis

Light from the sun is the original source of nearly all energy for biological systems. Many kinds of cells can transform chemical energy to a form useful for doing work. However, there must also be cells that can transform sunlight into

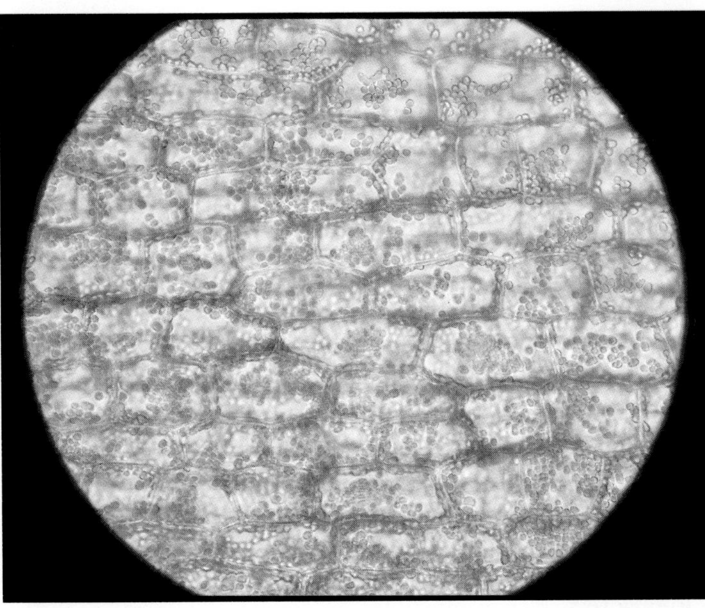

◀ **Elodea cells. The chloroplasts are visible within the cytoplasm in the cells.**

photosynthesis

chemical energy. Such cells use **photosynthesis**, a process by which energy from the sun is converted to chemical energy that is stored in chemical bonds.

Photosynthesis is performed by a wide variety of organisms, both eucaryotic and procaryotic. Besides the higher plants, photosynthetic eucaryotes include multicellular green, brown, and red algae and unicellular organisms such as euglena. Photosynthetic procaryotes include the green and purple bacteria and the blue-green algae. Although the photosynthetic importance of higher plants is usually emphasized, it has been estimated that more than half of the world's photosynthesis is carried out by unicellular organisms.

Photosynthesis in higher plants is a complex series of reactions in which carbohydrates are synthesized from atmospheric carbon dioxide and water:

$$6\,CO_2 + 6\,H_2O + 2820\text{ kJ (673 kcal)} \longrightarrow \underset{\text{Glucose}}{C_6H_{12}O_6} + 6\,O_2$$

Sunlight provides the large energy requirement for this process. An important side benefit of photosynthesis is the generation of oxygen, which is crucial to all aerobic metabolism.

The 1961 Nobel prize in chemistry was awarded to the American chemist Melvin Calvin (b. 1911), of the University of California at Berkeley, for his work on photosynthesis. Calvin and his co-workers used radioactive-carbon tracer techniques to discover the details of the complicated sequence of chemical reactions that occur in the overall process of photosynthesis.

Photosynthesis traps light energy by reducing carbons. For eucaryotes the necessary electron transfer reactions are segregated in the chloroplast (see Figure 16.4). Like the mitochondrion, the chloroplast contains an electron transport system within its internal membranes. Unlike the mitochondrial system, which oxidizes coenzymes to liberate energy, the chloroplast electron transport system reduces coenzymes with an input of energy:

$$NADP^+ + H_2O + \text{Energy} \xrightarrow[\text{electron transport}]{\text{Chloroplast}} NADPH + H^+ + \tfrac{1}{2}\,O_2$$

▲ **Melvin Calvin (1911–).**

$$\text{NADH} + \text{H}^+ + \tfrac{1}{2}\,\text{O}_2 \xrightarrow[\text{electron transport}]{\text{Mitochondrial}} \text{NAD}^+ + \text{H}_2\text{O} + \text{Energy}$$

$$\text{FADH}_2 + \tfrac{1}{2}\,\text{O}_2 \xrightarrow[\text{electron transport}]{\text{Mitochondrial}} \text{FAD} + \text{H}_2\text{O} + \text{Energy}$$

The chloroplasts capture light energy and place it in chemical storage.

The photosynthetic mechanism is complex, but it can be divided into two general components—the *dark reactions* and the *light reactions*. The dark reactions produce glucose from carbon dioxide, reduced coenzymes, and ATP. No light is needed and, in nature, these reactions continue during the night.

The light reactions of photosynthesis form the ATP and NADPH needed to produce glucose. The mechanism for capturing light energy is unique to the photosynthetic process. Although much research has been devoted to this topic, not all of the details are clear. In general, light is absorbed by colored compounds (pigments) located in· the chloroplasts. The most abundant of these pigments is chlorophyll. Once the light energy is absorbed, it is transferred to specific molecules (probably special chlorophylls) which lose electrons. These energized electrons travel through the chloroplast electron transport system as shown in Figure 16.8. Two events follow in quick succession: First, the electrons lost by these special chlorophylls are moved to higher energy levels until they can reduce molecules of the coenzyme, NADP^+. Second, the special chlorophylls that lost electrons now regain them. Water is the electron donor, giving up electrons and producing oxygen gas (and hydrogen ions) in the process. The overall oxidation–reduction reaction moves four electrons from two water molecules to produce two molecules of NADPH.

$$2\,\text{H}_2\text{O} + 2\,\text{NADP}^+ \xrightarrow{\text{Light}} 2\,\text{NADPH} + \text{O}_2 + 2\,\text{H}^+$$

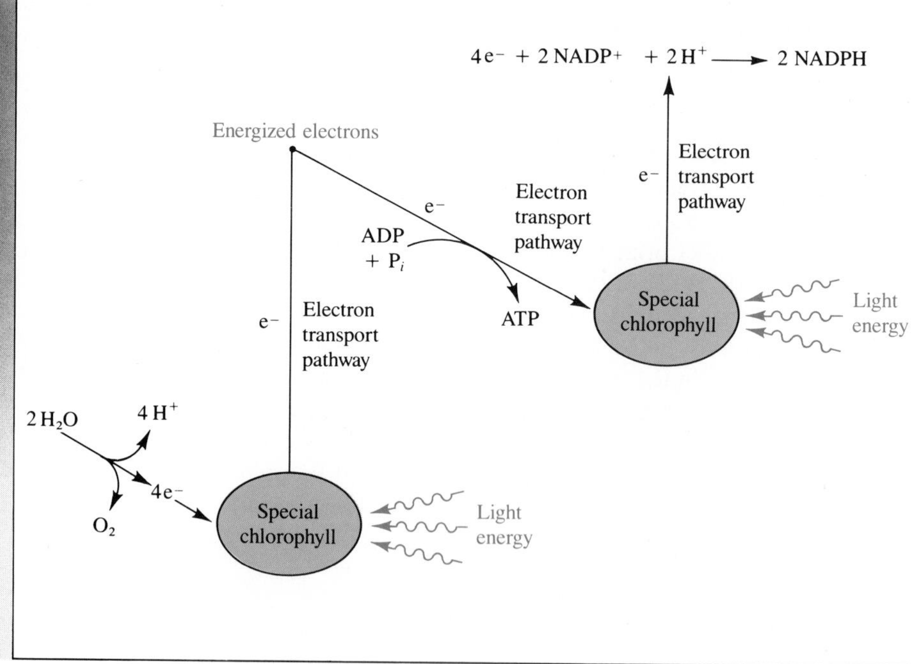

FIGURE 16.8 ▶ A schematic showing the movement of electrons from water to NADP^+ in the photosynthetic electron transport pathway: Note that light energy causes the electrons to become more energetic so that they can reduce NADP^+.

Photosynthesis uses light energy to force electrons to higher energy levels, as shown in Figure 16.8. As noted in the preceding paragraph, these energetic electrons are used to reduce $NADP^+$. But also notice that, when the electron loses energy in the middle of this electron transport process, the released energy is used to make ATP. Thus, the light reactions of photosynthesis supply both the NADPH and ATP needed to make glucose.

Concepts in Review

1. Describe the importance of hemoglobin in oxygen transport.
2. Explain how oxygen transport is coordinated with carbon dioxide production.
3. Explain how an anabolic process differs from a catabolic process.
4. List three major classes of biochemical substances that provide metabolic energy.
5. Explain how reduced carbon atoms are important in the production of cellular energy.
6. Explain the difference between a procaryote and a eucaryote.
7. List four subcellular organelles and their functions.
8. Explain the importance of membrane lipid in the mitochondrial function.
9. Define the role of the mitochondria in metabolism.
10. Briefly describe electron transport.
11. Discuss the function of NAD^+, $NADP^+$, and FAD in biological processes.
12. Explain the importance of the high-energy phosphate bond in metabolism.
13. Give two advantages for using ATP as a common energy currency for the cell.
14. Contrast substrate level phosphorylation with oxidative phosphorylation.
15. Compare the role of the mitochondrion with that of the chloroplast.
16. Outline the principal steps in the overall process of photosynthesis.

Equations in Review

Binding of Oxygen and Hydrogen Ions to Hemoglobin (Hb)

$$H^+ + HbO_2 \rightleftharpoons HbH^+ + O_2$$

Binding of Carbon Dioxide to Hemoglobin (Hb)

$$Hb{-}NH_2 + CO_2 \rightleftharpoons \underset{\text{Carbamino ion}}{Hb{-}NH{-}CO_2^-} + H^+$$

Important Hydrogen Ion-Forming Reactions in the Bloodstream

$$CO_2 + H_2O \rightleftharpoons H_2CO_3 \rightleftharpoons H^+ + HCO_3^-$$

$$\underset{\text{Lactic acid}}{CH_3CH(OH)COOH} \rightleftharpoons H^+ + \underset{\text{Lactate ion}}{CH_3CH(OH)COO^-}$$

Formation of Phosphate Anhydride Bond

$$\underset{\text{Phosphate}}{{}^-O{-}\overset{\overset{\displaystyle O^-}{|}}{\underset{\underset{\displaystyle O}{\|}}{P}}{-}OH} + \underset{\text{Phosphate}}{HO{-}\overset{\overset{\displaystyle O^-}{|}}{\underset{\underset{\displaystyle O}{\|}}{P}}{-}OR} + 35\ kJ \rightleftharpoons \underset{\text{Diphosphate anhydride}}{{}^-O{-}\overset{\overset{\displaystyle O^-}{|}}{\underset{\underset{\displaystyle O}{\|}}{P}}{\sim}O{-}\overset{\overset{\displaystyle O^-}{|}}{\underset{\underset{\displaystyle O}{\|}}{P}}{-}O{-}R} + H_2O$$

Substrate-Level Phosphorylation

$$\underset{\text{Substrate}}{R{-}OH} + \underset{\text{Phosphate ion}}{HO{-}\overset{\overset{\displaystyle O^-}{|}}{\underset{\underset{\displaystyle O}{\|}}{P}}{-}O^-} + \underset{\text{(derived from redox)}}{\text{Energy}} \longrightarrow \underset{\text{Phosphorylated substrate}}{R{-}O{-}\overset{\overset{\displaystyle O^-}{|}}{\underset{\underset{\displaystyle O}{\|}}{P}}{-}O^-} + H_2O$$

(R represents the remainder of the substrate molecule.)

Mitochondrial Electron Transport and Oxidative Phosphorylation

$$FADH_2 + \tfrac{1}{2}O_2 \xrightarrow{\text{Mitochondrial electron transport}} FAD + H_2O$$

$$\Big\downarrow \text{Energy}$$

$$2\ ADP + 2\ P_i \xrightarrow[\text{Oxidative phosphorylation}]{} 2\ ATP + 2\ H_2O$$

$$NADH + H^+ + \tfrac{1}{2}O_2 \xrightarrow{\text{Mitochondrial electron transport}} NAD^+ + H_2O$$

$$\Big\downarrow \text{Energy}$$

$$3\ ADP + 3\ P_i \xrightarrow[\text{Oxidative phosphorylation}]{} 3\ ATP + 3\ H_2O$$

Photosynthetic Electron Transport

$$2\ H_2O + 2\ NADP^+ \xrightarrow{\text{Light}} 2\ NADPH + O_2 + 2\ H^+$$

Exercises

1. Explain how increased carbon dioxide production can create a more acidic environment in muscle tissue.
2. How does rapid breathing (hyperventilation) change the blood pH? Explain.
3. Show a chemical equation for the reaction that produces a bond between hemoglobin and carbon dioxide.
4. What general characteristics are associated with a catabolic pathway? How does this process differ from an anabolic pathway?
5. Why are fats and carbohydrates good sources of cellular energy?
6. Describe the function of the mitochondria in catabolism.
7. Based on the function of the mitochondria, explain why these organelles are composed of about 90% membrane by mass.
8. Could a higher plant cell survive with chloroplasts but no mitochondria? Explain.
9. Give an example of the most common high-energy phosphate bond found in the cell. With what compound is it generally associated?
10. Why is ATP known as the "common energy currency" of the cell?
11. How much energy would be released if 3 mol of ATP was converted to 3 mol of ADP?
12. Define the term *oxidation–reduction coenzyme.*
13. Draw the ring-structure portion of NAD^+ that becomes reduced during metabolism.
14. How does oxidative phosphorylation differ from substrate-level phosphorylation?
15. In what part of the cell does oxidative phosphorylation occur?
16. How many ATPs would be formed from 2 NADH and 3 $FADH_2$ using mitochondrial electron transport and oxidative phosphorylation?
17. The following compound is formed during glucose catabolism:

```
COOH
 |      O⁻
 |      |
 C—O—P—O⁻
 ‖      ‖
CH2     O
```

Phosphoenolpyruvate

How many ATPs can be formed from one molecule of this compound during substrate level phosphorylation?

18. Compare the structural similarities between the chloroplasts and the mitochondria.
19. Explain how the function of the chloroplast differs from that of the mitochondrion.
20. What role do chloroplast pigments serve in photosynthesis?
21. Give the overall reaction for photosynthesis in higher plants.
22. In photosynthesis, electrons reduce $NADP^+$. From what compound are these electrons ultimately obtained?
23. Which of these statements are correct? Rewrite each incorrect statement to make it correct.
    (a) Slowed breathing, induced by a drug overdose, might cause the blood pH to become more acidic.
    (b) Anabolic processes are those in which complex biological substances are broken down into simpler substances.
    (c) Oxidation of reduced carbon atoms provides energy for the cell.
    (d) Typical carbohydrate carbons supply more energy to the cell than typical fatty acid carbons.
    (e) Many reduced carbons are oxidized to carbon dioxide in the mitochondria.
    (f) NAD^+ and $NADP^+$ are coenzymes that react as oxidizing agents in some metabolic processes.
    (g) Carbon dioxide provides much cellular energy.
    (h) A phosphate anhydride bond is considered to be a high-energy phosphate bond.
    (i) Mitochondrial electron transport serves to oxidize NADH.
    (j) Oxidative phosphorylation occurs in the mitochondria.
    (k) The chloroplast produces carbohydrates.
    (l) Chlorophyll absorbs light during photosynthesis.
    (m) NAD^+ is reduced during photosynthesis.

17

Carbohydrate Metabolism

◀ **CHAPTER OPENING PHOTO: An aerobics class is one way to increase the metabolism of carbohydrates.**

Have you stopped to think about why carbohydrates are a staple of our world? After all, most of the average diet is carbohydrate, much of our building material derives from this source, and most of the plant kingdom depends on carbohydrates. Yet, why is this class of molecules so prevalent? Biochemists might answer this question in a number of ways, but one of the most important answers is in the air around us. Carbohydrates can be made from carbon dioxide, water, and sunlight using a process called *photosynthesis.*

Of course, a solid carbohydrate like sugar, which is sweet to the taste, has very little in common with gaseous carbon dioxide, which is tasteless and can be hazardous in high concentrations. But a number of chemical reactions can convert carbon dioxide to sugar. Photosynthesis is an example of carbohydrate metabolism and illustrates the fact that metabolism can achieve remarkable conversions. Our world depends on such metabolic processes as photosynthesis.

17.1 METABOLIC PATHWAYS

Carbohydrates are rich sources of energy for most organisms. The energy is released when a cell subjects a carbohydrate to a series of chemical reactions, called a *metabolic pathway.* Despite the wide diversity of cell types, carbohydrate metabolic pathways vary little from cell to cell and from organism to organism.

Sunlight provides the energy that is stored in carbohydrates:

$$6\ CO_2 + 6\ H_2O + 2820\ kJ \xrightarrow[\text{Light}]{\text{Enzymes/Chlorophyll}} C_6H_{12}O_6 + 6\ O_2 \qquad (1)$$

Equation (1) summarizes the production of glucose (a carbohydrate) and oxygen by the endothermic process *photosynthesis.* Note that, in the overall transformation, carbon atoms from carbon dioxide are reduced and oxygen atoms from water are oxidized. The light energy is used to cause a net movement of electrons from water to carbon dioxide. As the carbons become more reduced, more energy is stored. Photosynthesis also supplies free oxygen to the atmosphere.

Equation (2) represents the oxidation of glucose and corresponds to the reversal of the overall photosynthesis reaction. Electrons are moved from carbohydrate carbons to oxygen. Energy stored in the reduced carbon atoms in glucose is released and can then be used by the cell to do work.

$$C_6H_{12}O_6 + 6\,O_2 \xrightarrow{\text{Enzymes}} 6\,CO_2 + 6\,H_2O + 2820\text{ kJ (673 kcal)} \qquad (2)$$

Glucose can be burned in oxygen in the laboratory to produce carbon dioxide, water, and heat. But in the living cell, the oxidation of glucose does not proceed directly to carbon dioxide and water. Instead, like photosynthesis, the overall process proceeds by a series of enzyme-catalyzed intermediate reactions. These intermediate steps channel some of the liberated energy into uses other than heat production. Specifically, a portion of the energy is stored in the chemical bonds of ATP.

17.2 Enzymes in Metabolism

Specific enzymes are required for essentially all biochemical reactions. Only when enzymes are present do the reactions of metabolic pathways proceed fast enough to keep a cell alive. In a sense, enzymes can be thought of as the valves of a large pumping plant. As long as the valves are open, metabolic chemicals can be processed. If some valves are closed, or missing, biochemicals are shunted to other reactions within the cell.

Enzymes are used to control metabolism just as valves are used to control pumping. Specific enzymes may be either created or destroyed during hormone-induced metabolic changes (see Section 17.7). For example, during a long fast our bodies must break down muscle proteins for energy. The proteins yield amino acids, which need to be converted to carbohydrates and fats by the liver. Normally this organ does not have the necessary enzyme complement to handle a large influx of amino acids. But under fasting conditions, the adrenal glands release *cortisone*. This hormone signals the liver to synthesize the extra enzymes needed to catabolize amino acids.

Metabolism is also controlled by altering the catalytic activity of enzymes. Changes in the three-dimensional structure of an enzyme can cause the rate of the reaction it catalyzes to increase or decrease (see Section 17.5). For example, calcium ions are known to initiate a process that leads to changes in the structure of the enzyme that converts glycogen to glucose. These changes activate the enzyme and increase the rate of glycogen breakdown. When muscles contract, calcium is released, and the conversion rate of glycogen to glucose is increased. Thus more glucose (and therefore energy) is provided automatically to working muscles.

17.3 Overview of Human Carbohydrate Metabolism

Glucose is the key monosaccharide in carbohydrate metabolism. Most carbohydrates that are consumed in a meal are converted to glucose in the liver. Glucose circulates in the blood, and the concentration is maintained within well defined limits in a healthy person. When blood glucose is in excess, it is converted to

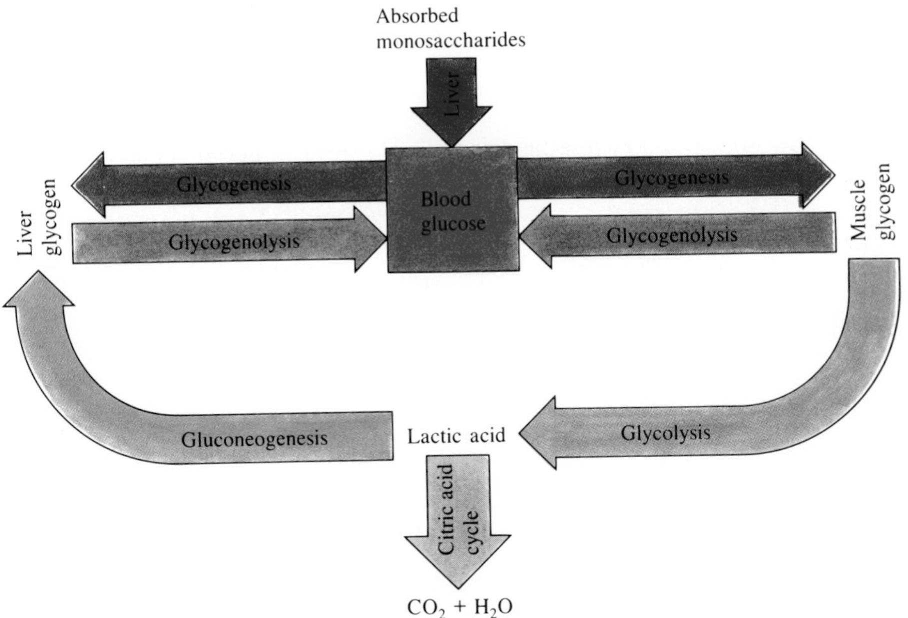

◀ **FIGURE 17.1**
Overview of carbohydrate metabolism.

glycogen in the liver and muscle tissue. Glycogen is a storage polysaccharide; it can be quickly hydrolyzed to replace depleted glucose supplies in the blood. The synthesis of glycogen from glucose is called **glycogenesis**; the hydrolysis, or breakdown, of glycogen to glucose is known as **glycogenolysis** (see Figure 17.1).

glycogenesis

glycogenolysis

Energy (stored as ATP) is obtained from glucose via several common metabolic pathways. Under *anaerobic* (oxygen not required) conditions, a general sequence of reactions known as the *Embden–Meyerhof pathway* oxidizes glucose to produce energy. When the final product of this process is lactic acid, the pathway is known as glycolysis. This reaction sequence is especially important for humans (and other animals) during strenuous activity when muscle tissue generates much lactic acid. Part of the lactic acid produced is sent to the liver and is converted to glycogen in the *gluconeogenesis* pathway (see Section 17.6). The rest is converted to carbon dioxide and water via the citric acid cycle, an *aerobic* (free or respiratory oxygen required) sequence. The *citric acid cycle*, also known as the Krebs cycle or the tricarboxylic acid cycle, is much more efficient at ATP production than is the glycolysis pathway. Consequently, the citric acid cycle is the major vehicle for obtaining metabolic energy from carbohydrates.

The diagram in Figure 17.1 presents a general overview of carbohydrate metabolism. The entire process requires specific enzymes at each reaction stage and is controlled by chemical regulatory compounds.

17.4 ANAEROBIC SEQUENCE

In the absence of oxygen, glucose in living cells can be converted to a variety of end products including lactic acid (in muscle) and alcohol (in yeast). The sequence of reactions involved is similar in different kinds of cells. At least a dozen

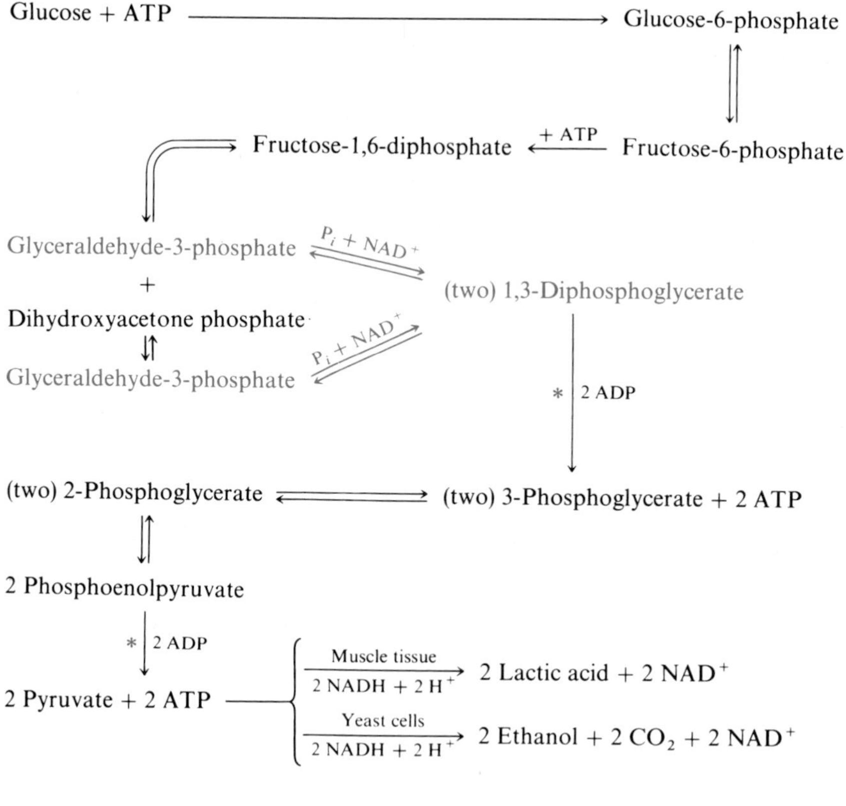

FIGURE 17.2 ▶ Conversion of glucose to pyruvate via the Embden–Meyerhof pathway (anaerobic sequence). Glycolysis proceeds further, forming lactic acid. Formation of ATP is denoted by asterisks.

reactions, many different enzymes, ATP, and inorganic phosphate (P_i) are required. Such a sequence of reactions from a particular reactant to end products is called a *metabolic pathway.*

Embden–Meyerhof pathway

The anaerobic conversion of glucose to pyruvic acid is known as the **Embden–Meyerhof pathway** (see Figure 17.2). The sequence is a catabolic one in which glucose is oxidatively degraded:

$$\underset{\substack{\text{D-Glucose} \\ \text{(sum of oxidation numbers} \\ \text{for carbon} = 0)}}{C_6H_{12}O_6} \xrightarrow{\text{Embden–Meyerhof pathway}} \underset{\substack{\text{Pyruvic acid} \\ \text{(sum of oxidation numbers} \\ \text{for carbon} = +4)}}{2\ CH_3\overset{\overset{\displaystyle O}{\|}}{C}{-}COOH}$$

In glucose the sum of the oxidation numbers of the six carbon atoms is zero. After processing one molecule of glucose to two molecules of pyruvic acid by the pathway, the sum of the oxidation numbers of the six carbon atoms is +4. This makes it evident that an overall oxidation of carbon must occur in the Embden–Meyerhof pathway.

As with most catabolic processes, the Embden–Meyerhof pathway produces energy for the cell. Carbon atoms are oxidized; energy is released and stored in the form of ATP. The pathway uses the process of *substrate-level phosphorylation* (see Section 16.9)—the energy released from carbon oxidation is used to form a high-energy substrate–phosphate bond, which in turn is used to form ATP. It is interesting to note that there is only one oxidation–reduction reaction in the Embden–Meyerhof pathway—the conversion of glyceraldehyde-3-phosphate to 1,3-diphosphoglycerate (marked in red on Figure 17.2):

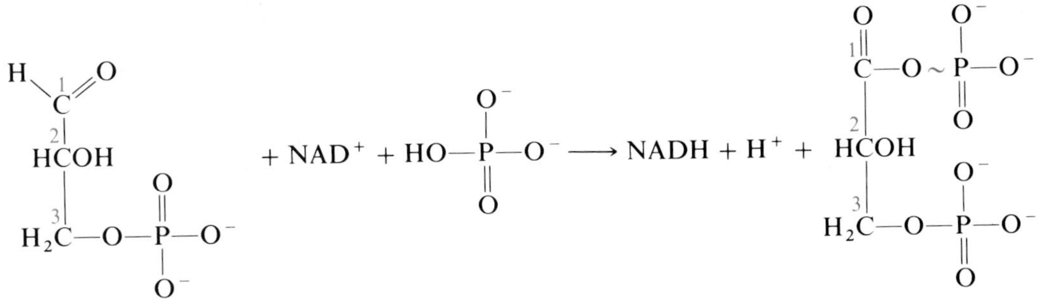

$$\text{Glyceraldehyde-3-phosphate} + NAD^+ + HO\text{—}PO_3^{2-} \longrightarrow NADH + H^+ + \text{1,3-Diphosphoglycerate}$$

Glyceraldehyde-3-phosphate

1,3-Diphosphoglycerate

Carbon 1 is oxidized from the aldehyde to the carboxylate oxidation state. Simultaneously, the oxidation–reduction coenzyme, NAD^+, is reduced. This single oxidation–reduction supplies most of the energy that is generated by the Embden–Meyerhof pathway. This energy is used to make the following two different high-energy phosphate bonds:

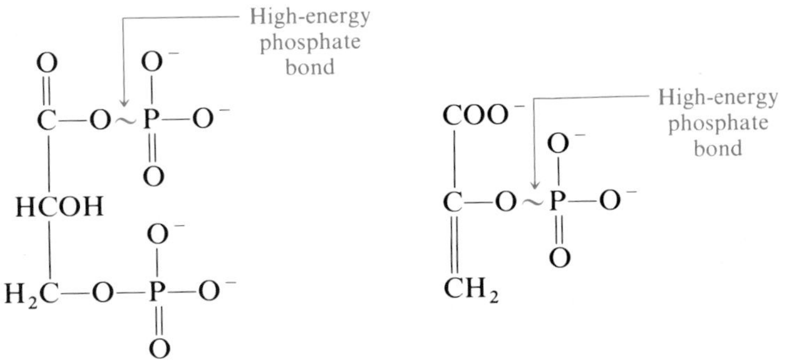

High-energy phosphate bond

1,3-Diphosphoglycerate

High-energy phosphate bond

Phosphoenolpyruvate

These high-energy bonds are found on intermediate compounds or *pathway substrates*. Substrate-level phosphorylation is complete when these substrates transfer their high-energy phosphate bonds to ADP, forming ATP (the reactions marked with an asterisk on Figure 17.2).

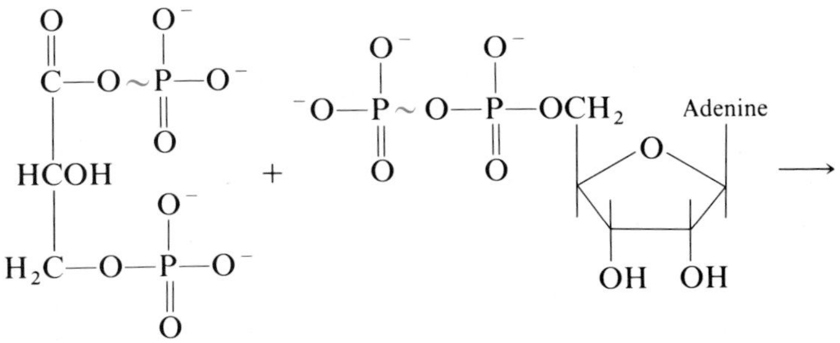

Adenine

1,3-Diphosphoglycerate + Adenosine diphosphate (ADP) ⟶

1,3-Diphosphoglycerate

Adenosine diphosphate (ADP)

$$ {}^{-}O-\overset{\overset{\large O^-}{|}}{\underset{\underset{\large O}{\|}}{P}}\sim O-\overset{\overset{\large O^-}{|}}{\underset{\underset{\large O}{\|}}{P}}\sim O-\overset{\overset{\large O^-}{|}}{\underset{\underset{\large O}{\|}}{P}}-OCH_2(\text{ribose, OH OH})\text{–Adenine} \quad + \quad COO^-\text{–}HCOH\text{–}H_2C-O-\overset{\overset{\large O^-}{|}}{\underset{\underset{\large O}{\|}}{P}}-O^- $$

Adenosine triphosphate (ATP) 3-Phosphoglycerate

$$ H^+ + \overset{\overset{\large COO^-}{|}}{\underset{\underset{\large CH_2}{\|}}{C}}-O\sim\overset{\overset{\large O^-}{|}}{\underset{\underset{\large O}{\|}}{P}}-O^- + {}^{-}O-\overset{\overset{\large O^-}{|}}{\underset{\underset{\large O}{\|}}{P}}\sim O-\overset{\overset{\large O^-}{|}}{\underset{\underset{\large O}{\|}}{P}}-OCH_2(\text{ribose, OH OH})\text{–Adenine} \longrightarrow $$

Phosphoenolpyruvate Adenosine diphosphate (ADP)

$$ {}^{-}O-\overset{\overset{\large O^-}{|}}{\underset{\underset{\large O}{\|}}{P}}\sim O-\overset{\overset{\large O^-}{|}}{\underset{\underset{\large O}{\|}}{P}}\sim O-\overset{\overset{\large O^-}{|}}{\underset{\underset{\large O}{\|}}{P}}-OCH_2(\text{ribose, OH OH})\text{–Adenine} + \overset{\overset{\large COO^-}{|}}{\underset{\underset{\large CH_3}{|}}{C}}=O $$

Adenosine triphosphate (ATP) Pyruvate

It is important to note that the Embden–Meyerhof pathway oxidizes carbon and produces ATP in the absence of molecular oxygen. This pathway provides for *anaerobic* energy production. In order for this reaction sequence to continue, the coenzyme NADH must be recycled back to NAD^+; that is, an additional oxidation–reduction reaction is needed to remove electrons from NADH. In the absence of oxygen, pyruvate is used as an electron acceptor. In human muscle cells pyruvate is reduced directly to lactic acid:

$$ CH_3\underset{\underset{\large O}{\|}}{C}COO^- + NADH + H^+ \rightleftharpoons CH_3\underset{\underset{\large OH}{|}}{C}HCOO^- + NAD^+ $$

Pyruvate Lactate

In yeast cells, pyruvate is converted to acetaldehyde, which is then reduced to ethanol:

$$ CH_3\underset{\underset{\large O}{\|}}{C}COO^- + H^+ \longrightarrow CH_3\overset{\overset{\large O}{\|}}{C}-H + CO_2 $$

Pyruvate Acetaldehyde

$$\underset{\text{Acetaldehyde}}{CH_3\overset{\overset{\Large O}{\|}}{C}-H} + NADH + H^+ \rightleftharpoons \underset{\text{Ethanol}}{CH_3CH_2OH} + NAD^+$$

In each case NADH is reoxidized to NAD^+, and a carbon atom from pyruvate is reduced. When lactic acid is the final product of anaerobic glucose catabolism, the pathway is termed **glycolysis**. As the Embden–Meyerhof pathway produces equal amounts of pyruvate and NADH, there is just enough pyruvate to recycle all the NADH. This is a good example of an important general characteristic of metabolism: Chemical reactions in the cell are precisely balanced so that there is never a large surplus or a large deficit of any metabolic product. If such a situation does occur, the cell may die.

glycolysis

What glycolysis does for the cell can be summarized with the following net chemical equation:

$$C_6H_{12}O_6 + 2\text{ ADP} + 2\text{ P}_i \longrightarrow 2\text{ CH}_3\text{CH(OH)COOH} + 2\text{ ATP} + (150\text{ kJ or }36\text{ kcal})$$

This anaerobic process produces cellular energy. However, it is not very efficient because only two moles of ATP are formed per mole of glucose. In fact, if the energy stored in the two ATPs is summed with the energy released as heat during the Embden–Meyerhof pathway, a total of only about 209 kJ/mol (50 kcal/mol) is found to have been removed from glucose. Compare this result with the complete oxidation of glucose:

$$C_6H_{12}O_6 + 6\text{ O}_2 \longrightarrow 6\text{ CO}_2 + 6\text{ H}_2\text{O} + (2820\text{ kJ or }673\text{ kcal})$$

We see that the Embden–Meyerhof pathway releases less than one-tenth of the total energy available in glucose. Thus, lactic acid must still contain much energy in its reduced carbon atoms.

17.5 Citric Acid Cycle (Aerobic Sequence)

As discussed previously, only a small fraction of the energy that is potentially available from glucose is liberated during the anaerobic conversion to lactic acid (glycolysis). Consequently, this acid remains valuable to the cells because of its stored energy. The lactic acid formed may be (1) circulated back to the liver and converted to glycogen at the expense of some ATP or (2) converted back to pyruvic acid in order to enter the citric acid cycle.

$$\underset{\text{Lactic acid}}{CH_3\overset{\overset{\Large OH}{|}}{C}HCOOH} + NAD^+ \rightleftharpoons \underset{\text{Pyruvic acid}}{CH_3\overset{\overset{\Large O}{\|}}{C}COOH} + NADH + H^+$$

Pyruvic acid is the link between the anaerobic sequence (Embden–Meyerhof pathway) and the aerobic sequence (citric acid cycle). Pyruvic acid itself does not enter into the citric acid cycle. It is converted to acetyl coenzyme A (acetyl-CoA), a complex substance that like ATP is of great importance in metabolism:

$$\mathrm{CH_3\overset{\overset{\large O}{\|}}{C}{-}COOH + CoASH + NAD^+ \longrightarrow CH_3\overset{\overset{\large O}{\|}}{C}{-}SCoA + NADH + H^+ + CO_2}$$

(Coenzyme A) Acetyl-CoA

This important reaction depends on the availability of several vitamins. In addition to niacin (needed for synthesis of NAD^+), the enzyme that catalyzes this reaction requires riboflavin and thiamine. This is one of the few metabolic reactions that requires thiamine, but because this reaction is key to obtaining large amounts of energy from carbohydrate, thiamine is a vitamin of major importance. Also, our bodies need the vitamin pantothenic acid to synthesize coenzyme A.

Acetyl coenzyme A consists of an acetyl group bonded to a coenzyme A group. Coenzyme A contains the following units: adenine, ribose, diphosphate, pantothenic acid, and thioethanolamine. Coenzyme A is abbreviated as CoASH or CoA. Acetyl coenzyme A is abbreviated as acetyl-CoA or acetyl-SCoA.

Acetyl — Thioethanolamine — Pantothenic acid — Diphosphate — Ribose — Adenine

Acetyl-CoA

The acetyl group is the group that is actually oxidized in the citric acid cycle. This group is attached to the large carrier molecule as a thio ester—that is, by an ester linkage in which oxygen is replaced by sulfur:

$$\mathrm{CH_3{-}\overset{\overset{\large O}{\|}}{C}{-}S{-}CoA}$$

Acetyl group; Thioester linkage; Carrier group

Acetyl-CoA not only is a key component of carbohydrate metabolism but also, as we shall see in Chapter 18, serves to tie the metabolism of fats and that of certain amino acids to the citric acid cycle.

The citric acid cycle was elucidated by Hans A. Krebs (1900–1981), a British biochemist; thus it is also called the Krebs cycle. For his studies in intermediary metabolism, Krebs shared the 1953 Nobel prize in medicine and physiology with Fritz A. Lipmann (1899–1986), an American biochemist who discovered coenzyme A.

▲ **Hans Krebs (1900–1981).**

Krebs showed the citric acid cycle to be a series of eight reactions in which the acetyl group of acetyl-CoA is oxidized to carbon dioxide and water, and where many reduced coenzymes (both NADH and $FADH_2$) are formed. These reduced coenzymes then pass electrons through the electron transport system and, in the process, ATP is produced. The citric acid cycle is found in the mitochondria, which are the primary sites for the production of cellular energy.

The sequence of reactions involved in the citric acid cycle is shown in Figure 17.3. It is important to note that this cycle produces little usable cellular energy directly (only one GTP, or guanosine triphosphate, convertible to ATP). However, many ATPs are produced from the oxidation of acetyl-CoA (or from pyruvic acid) because of two other processes—*electron transport* and *oxidative phosphorylation* (see Section 16.9). Electron transport recycles the large number

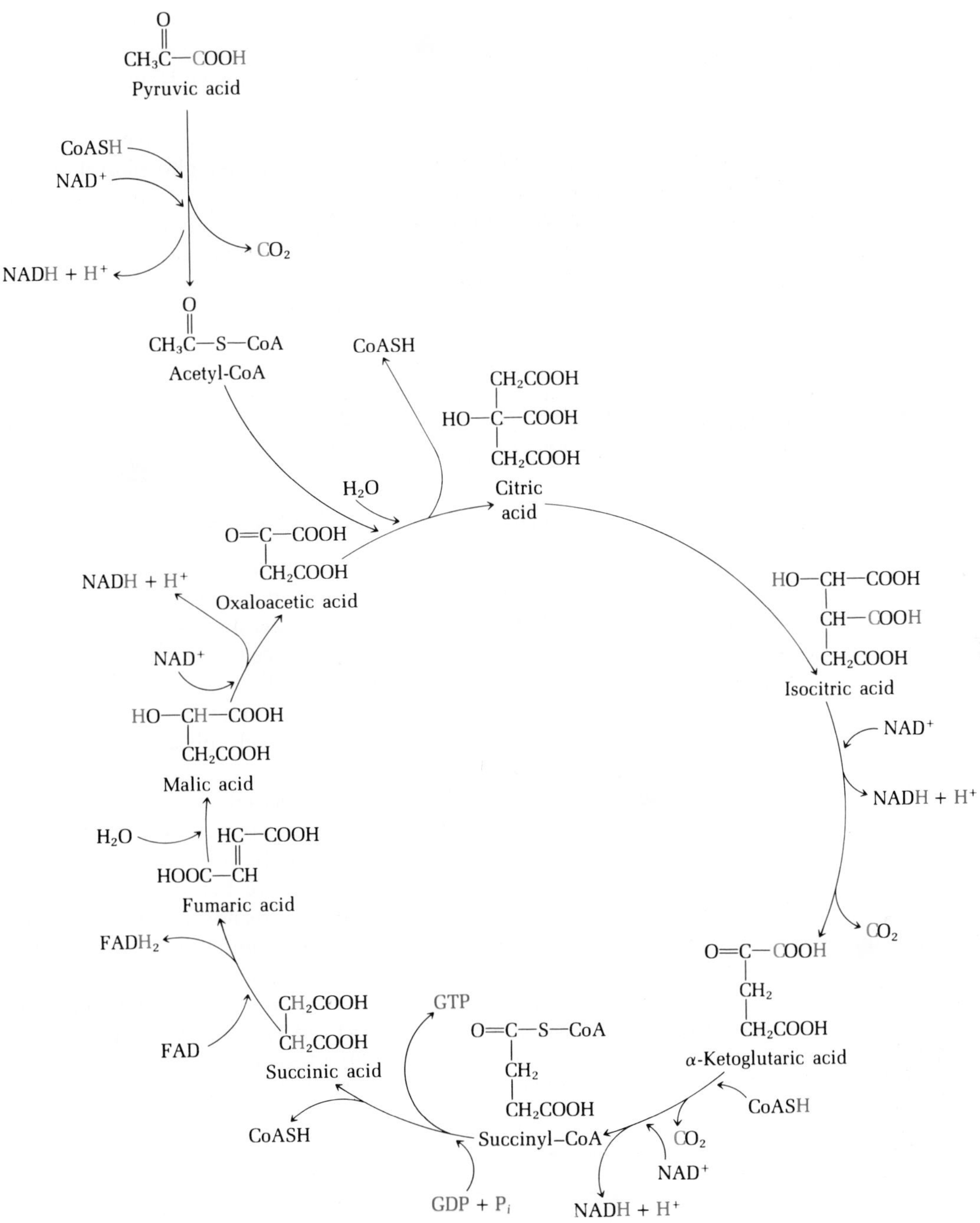

▲
FIGURE 17.3
The citric acid cycle (Krebs cycle).

of reduced coenzymes formed by the citric acid cycle. As a consequence, oxidative phosphorylation can produce ATP from ADP and phosphate. Because electron transport requires oxygen and the citric acid cycle depends upon electron transport, the citric acid cycle is termed *aerobic.*

All three processes—the citric acid cycle (plus the initial conversion of pyruvic acid to acetyl-CoA), electron transport, and oxidative phosphorylation—team up to produce energy for the cell. All three take place in the mitochondria. Overall, these three processes result in the oxidation of one pyruvic acid molecule to three carbon dioxide molecules and the formation of about 15 ATP molecules.

$$CH_3\overset{\overset{\displaystyle O}{\|}}{C}—COOH \longrightarrow 3\ CO_2$$

A large quantity of energy (1260 kJ; about 300 kcal) becomes available for the cell when these three carbon atoms are fully oxidized. Most of this energy is used to reduce coenzymes:

$$4\ NAD^+ + FAD + 10\ H \longrightarrow 4\ NADH + 4\ H^+ + FADH_2$$

These coenzymes, in turn, yield a total of 14 ATP molecules via mitochondrial electron transport and oxidative phosphorylation. Each mole of ATP stores approximately 35 kJ (8 kcal) of energy. If we include the single GTP (convertible to ATP) that is formed in the citric acid cycle, the cell obtains about 462 kJ (110 kcal) from each mole of pyruvic acid that is oxidized. By using an aerobic process, the cell can produce about 30 ATP molecules from two lactic acids after gaining only two ATPs using the anaerobic pathway, glycolysis. The presence of oxygen yields a large energy bonus for the cell.

Myocardial infarction and stroke are two injuries that are especially serious because they deprive rapidly metabolizing tissue of oxygen. When the heart muscle loses at least part of its normal blood supply, myocardial infarction results; a similar occurrence in the brain results in a stroke. In both cases, a lack of blood circulation means at least part of the tissue loses its normal oxygen supply. Suddenly these cells lose most of their capacity to generate ATP; from a glucose molecule these cells can only gain two ATPs where previously they could garner over thirty. Because the heart and brain are very active tissues, the anaerobic process of glycolysis cannot support continued cell viability. Permanent tissue damage results from only minutes of oxygen deprivation.

17.6 GLUCONEOGENESIS

A continuous supply of glucose is needed by the body, especially for the brain and the nervous system. But the amount of glucose and glycogen present in the body is sufficient to last for only about 4 hours at normal metabolic rates. Thus, there is a metabolic need for a pathway that produces glucose from noncarbohydrate sources. The formation of glucose from noncarbohydrate sources is called **gluconeogenesis**.

gluconeogenesis

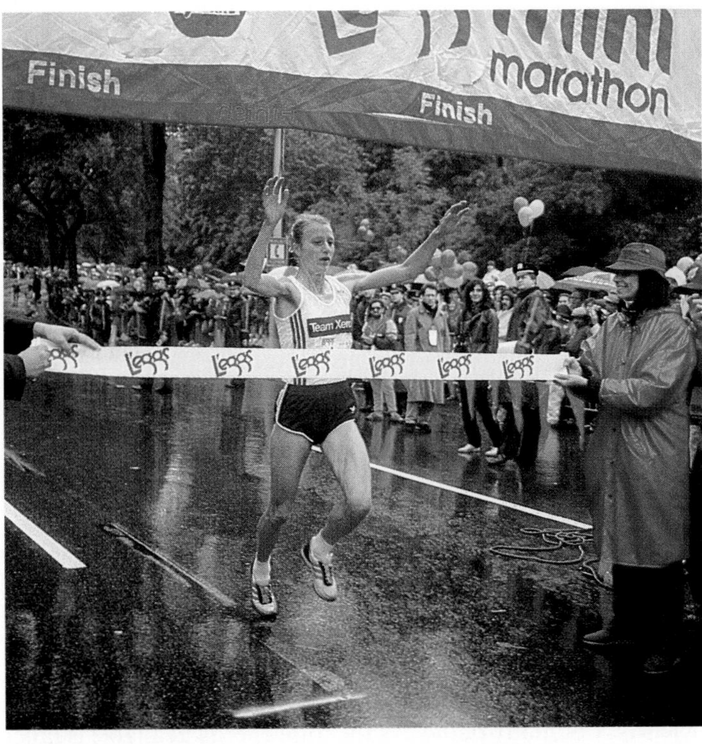

◄ **Grete Waitz winning the New York City Marathon. Long distance runners use gluconeogenesis to provide a source of glucose when more readily available supplies are exhausted.**

Most of the glucose formed during gluconeogenesis comes from lactic acid, certain amino acids, and the glycerol of fats. In each case, these molecules are converted to Embden–Meyerhof pathway intermediates (see Figure 17.2). As shown previously, lactic acid is converted to pyruvic acid. Amino acids first undergo *deamination* (loss of amino groups) and then are converted to phosphoenolpyruvic acid. Glycerol is converted to glyceraldehyde-3-phosphate (see Figure 17.4). Most of the steps in the Embden–Meyerhof pathway are reversed to transform these pathway intermediates into glucose.

Gluconeogenesis takes place primarily in the liver and also in the kidneys. These organs have the enzymes that catalyze reversal of the Embden–Meyerhof pathway. Because of this capability the liver is the organ primarily responsible for maintaining normal blood-sugar levels.

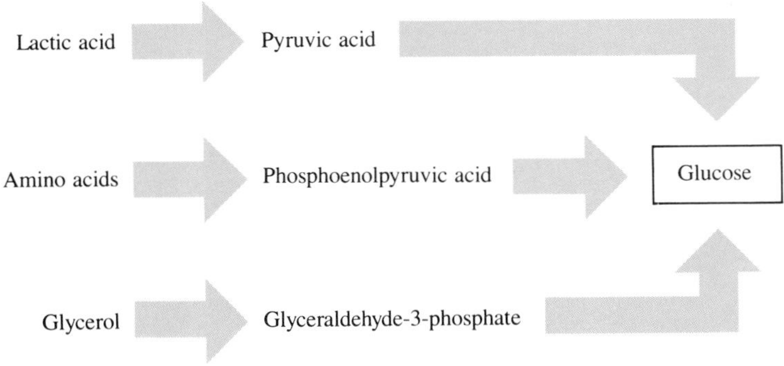

◄ **FIGURE 17.4**
An overview of gluconeogenesis. All transformations except lactic acid to pyruvic acid require several reactions.

17.7 Overview of Complex Metabolic Pathways

When we examine a metabolic pathway such as the Embden–Meyerhof pathway (Figure 17.2) or the citric acid cycle (Figure 17.3), the sheer complexity may be puzzling and overwhelming. We are tempted to ask why so many reactions are used by a cell to achieve its goal. This is a question that biochemists have asked for many years. It appears that a physiological design that includes a number of reactions per pathway achieves several vital objectives for the cell.

First, many of the chemicals that are formed in the middle of a pathway, *pathway intermediates*, are used in other metabolic processes within the cell.

$$A \rightleftharpoons B \rightleftharpoons C \rightleftharpoons D$$ Pathway I (B, C = pathway intermediates)

$$B \rightleftharpoons X \rightleftharpoons Y \rightleftharpoons Z$$ Pathway II

$$C \rightleftharpoons I \rightleftharpoons J \rightleftharpoons K$$ Pathway III

These intermediates are like interchangeable machine parts. Once such machine parts are made, they can be used in more than one machine. And once pathway intermediates are formed, they can be used in several pathways and serve a variety of metabolic functions in the cell.

Second, having multiple-step pathways helps the cell to handle metabolic energy efficiently. For many pathways the total energy available is much greater than the cell can handle in a single reaction. As an example, a one-step complete oxidation of glucose yields enough energy to cook a cell, figuratively speaking. To avoid such disasters the cell extracts only a little energy from glucose at each chemical reaction (Figure 17.5). The quantity of energy released in each step is small enough to be handled by the cell. Thus, in order for a cell to extract the maximum energy, a metabolic pathway must have a number of steps.

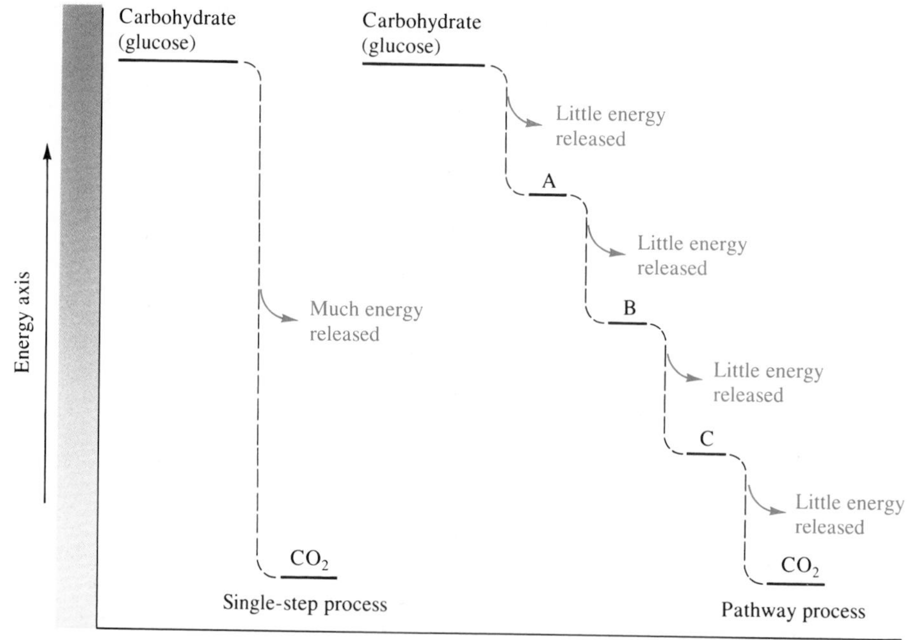

FIGURE 17.5 ▶ A single-step oxidation process compared with a multiple-step process: In the pathway, A, B, and C represent hypothetical pathway intermediates.

Metabolic reaction sequences seem needlessly complex because we see only a small part of the total cellular function. Although the processes must be studied separately, it is important to remember that they are all interrelated.

17.8 Hormones

hormones

Hormones are chemical substances that act as control agents in the body, often regulating metabolic pathways. They help to adjust physiological processes such as digestion, metabolism, growth, and reproduction. For example, the concentration of glucose in the blood is maintained within definite limits by the actions of hormones. Hormones are secreted by the endocrine, or ductless, glands directly into the bloodstream and are transported to various parts of the body to exert specific control functions. The endocrine glands include the thyroid, parathyroid, pancreas, adrenal, pituitary, ovaries, testes, placenta, and certain portions of the gastrointestinal tract. A hormone produced by one species is usually active in some other species. For example, the insulin used to treat diabetes mellitus in humans may be obtained from the pancreas of animals slaughtered in meat packing plants.

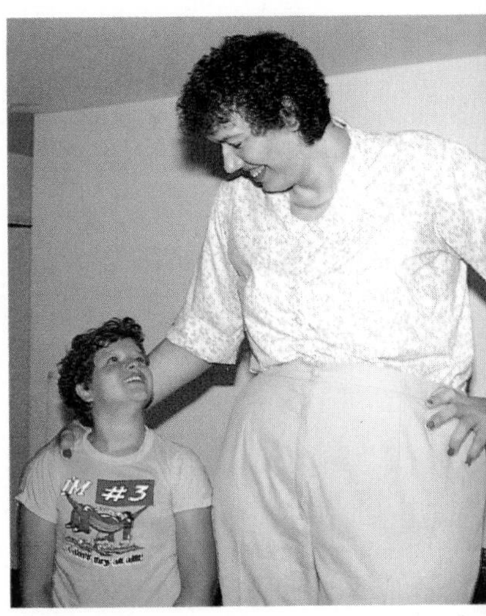

▲ **The height of this woman (7 feet, 7 inches) is due in large part to a constant hypersecretion of the growth hormone during the formative years.**

Hormones are often referred to as the chemical messengers of the body. They do not fit into any single chemical structural classification. Many are proteins or polypeptides, some are steroids, others are phenol or amino acid derivatives; examples are shown in Figure 17.6. Because a lack of any hormone can produce serious physiological disorders, many hormones are produced synthetically or are extracted from their natural sources and made available for medical use.

Like the vitamins, hormones are generally needed in only minute amounts. Concentrations range from 10^{-6} *M* to 10^{-12} *M*. Unlike vitamins, which must be supplied in the diet, the necessary hormones are produced in the body of a healthy person. A number of hormones and their functions are listed in Table 17.1.

HO–(ring with I, I)–O–(ring with I, I)–$CH_2CHCOOH$ with NH_2

Thyroxin

Cys-Tyr-Ile-Gln-Asn-Cys-Pro-Leu-Gly-NH_2 (S—S bridge between the two Cys)

Oxytocin

1 10 15
His-Ser-Gln-Gly-Thr-Phe-Thr-Ser-Asp-Tyr-Ser-Lys-Tyr-Leu-Asp-Ser-Arg-Arg-
20 29
Ala-Gln-Asp-Phe-Val-Gln-Tyr-Leu-Met-Asn-Thr

Glucagon

CH_3 OH, CH_3, O

Testosterone

CH_3 OH, HO

Estradiol (Estrogen)

OH, OH, $HOCHCH_2NHCH_3$

Epinephrine (Adrenalin)

◀ **Figure 17.6** **Structure of selected hormones. Thyroxin is produced in the thyroid gland; oxytocin is a polypeptide produced in the posterior lobe of the pituitary gland; glucagon is a polypeptide produced in the pancreas; testosterone and estradiol are steroid hormones produced in the testes and the ovaries, respectively; epinephrine is produced in the adrenal glands.**

TABLE 17.1 Selected Hormones and Their Functions

Hormone	Source	Principal functions
Insulin	Pancreas	Controls blood-sugar level and storage of glycogen
Glucagon	Pancreas	Stimulates conversion of glycogen to glucose; raises blood-sugar level
Oxytocin	Pituitary gland	Stimulates contraction of the uterine muscles and secretion of milk by the mammary glands
Vasopressin	Pituitary gland	Controls water excretion by the kidneys; stimulates constriction of the blood vessels
Growth hormone	Pituitary gland	Stimulates growth
Adrenocorticotrophic hormone (ACTH)	Pituitary gland	Stimulates the adrenal cortex, which, in turn, releases several steroid hormones
Prolactin	Pituitary gland	Stimulates milk production by mammary glands after birth of a baby
Epinephrine (adrenalin)	Adrenal glands	Stimulates rise in blood pressure, acceleration of heartbeat, decreased secretion of insulin, and increased blood sugar
Cortisone	Adrenal glands	Helps control carbohydrate metabolism, salt and water balance, formation and storage of glycogen
Thyroxine and triiodothyronine	Thyroid gland	Increases the metabolic rate of carbohydrates and proteins
Calcitonin	Thyroid gland	Prevents the rise of calcium in the blood above the required level
Parathyroid hormone	Parathyroid gland	Regulates the metabolism of calcium and phosphate in the body
Gastrin	Stomach	Stimulates secretion of gastric juices
Secretin	Duodenum	Stimulates secretion of pancreatic juice
Estrogen	Ovaries	Stimulates development and maintenance of female sexual characteristics
Progesterone	Ovaries	Stimulates female sexual characteristics and maintains pregnancy
Testosterone	Testes	Stimulates development and maintenance of male sexual characteristics

CHEMISTRY IN ACTION

GLUCOSE CONCENTRATION IN THE BLOOD

An adequate blood-glucose level must be maintained to ensure good health. To achieve this goal, hormones regulate and coordinate metabolism in specific organs. The hormones control selected enzymes, which, in turn, regulate the rates of reaction with the appropriate metabolic pathways. In the following paragraphs, we will examine some of the physiological mechanisms that maintain proper blood-sugar levels.

Glucose concentrations average about 70 to 90 mg/100 mL of blood under normal fasting conditions—that is, when no nourishment has been taken for several hours. Most people are in a normal fasting condition before eating breakfast. After the ingestion of carbohydrates, the glucose concentration rises above the normal level, and a condition of *hyperglycemia* exists. If the concentration of glucose rises still further, the renal threshold for glucose is eventually reached. The *renal threshold* is the concentration of a substance in the blood above which the kidneys begin to excrete that substance into the urine. The renal threshold for glucose is about 140 to 170 mg/100 mL of blood. Glucose excreted by the kidneys can be detected in the urine by a test for reducing sugars (for example, the Benedict test; see Section 10.12). When the glucose concentration of the blood is below the normal fasting level, *hypoglycemia* exists (see figure).

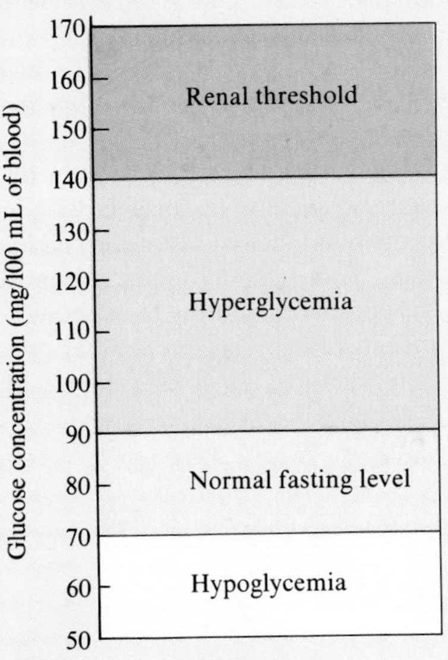

▲ **Conditions related to concentration of glucose in the blood.**

Glucose concentration in the blood is under the control of various hormones. These hormones act as checks on one another and establish an equilibrium condition called *homeostasis*—that is, self-regulated equilibrium. Three hormones—insulin, epinephrine (adrenalin), and glucagon—are of special significance in maintaining glucose concentration within the proper limits. Insulin, secreted by the islets of Langerhans in the pancreas, acts to reduce blood-glucose levels by increasing the rate of glycogen formation. Epinephrine from the adrenal glands and glucagon from the pancreas increase the rate of glycogen breakdown (glycogenolysis) and thereby increase blood-glucose levels. These opposing effects are summarized as follows:

$$\text{Blood glucose} \underset{\text{Glycogenolysis}}{\overset{\text{Glycogenesis}}{\rightleftharpoons}} \text{Glycogen}$$

Glycogenesis: Stimulated by insulin
Glycogenolysis: Stimulated by epinephrine and glucagon

During the digestion of a meal rich in carbohydrates, the blood-glucose level of a healthy person rises into the hyperglycemic range. This stimulates insulin secretion, and the excess glucose is converted to glycogen, thereby returning the glucose level to normal. A large amount of ingested carbohydrates can overstimulate insulin production and thereby produce a condition of mild hypoglycemia. This in turn triggers the secretion of additional epinephrine and glucagon, and the blood-glucose levels are again restored to normal. The body is able to maintain the normal fasting level of blood glucose for long periods of time without food by drawing on liver glycogen, muscle glycogen, and finally on body fat as glucose replacement sources. Thus, in a normal person neither hyperglycemia nor mild hypoglycemia has serious consequences, since the body is able to correct these conditions. However, either condition, if not corrected, can have very serious consequences. Since the brain is heavily dependent on blood glucose for energy, hypoglycemia affects the brain and the central nervous system. Mild hypoglycemia may result in impaired vision, dizziness, and fainting spells. Severe hypoglycemia produces convulsions and unconsciousness; if prolonged, it may result in permanent brain damage and death.

Hyperglycemia may be induced by fear or anger, because the rate

(*continued*)

(continued)

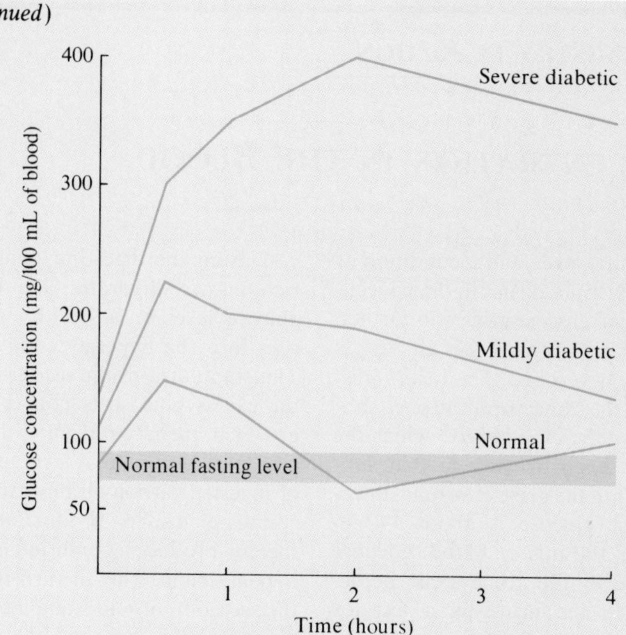

Typical responses to a glucose-tolerance test.

of epinephrine secretion is increased under emotional stress. Glycogen hydrolysis is thereby speeded up and glucose concentration levels rise sharply. This whole sequence readies the individual for the strenuous effort to either fighting or fleeing as the situation demands.

Diabetes mellitus is a serious metabolic disorder characterized by hyperglycemia, glycosuria (glucose in the urine), frequent urination, thirst, weakness and loss of weight. Prior to 1921 diabetes often resulted in death. In that year Frederick Banting and Charles Best, working at the University of Toronto, discovered insulin and devised methods for extracting the hormone from animal pancreases. For his work on insulin, Banting, with J. J. MacLeod, received the Nobel prize in medicine and physiology in 1923. Insulin is very effective in controlling diabetes. It must be given by injection, because, like any other protein, it would be hydrolyzed to amino acids in the gastrointestinal tract.

People with mild or borderline diabetes may show normal fasting blood glucose levels, but they are unable to produce sufficient insulin for prompt control of ingested carbohydrates. As a result, their blood glucose rises to an abnormally high level and does not return to normal for a long period of time. Such a person has a decreased tolerance for glucose, which may be diagnosed by a glucose tolerance test. After fasting for at least 12 hours blood and urine specimens are taken to establish a beginning reference level. The person then drinks a solution containing 100 g of glucose (amount for adults). Blood and urine specimens are then collected at 0.5, 1, 2, and 3 hour intervals and tested for glucose content. In a normal situation the blood glucose level returns to normal after about 3 hours. Individuals with mild diabetes show a slower drop in glucose levels, but the glucose level in a severe diabetic remains high for the entire 3 hours. Responses to a glucose tolerance test are shown in the diagram.

The chemical structure of insulin has been determined and biologically active insulin has been synthesized in the laboratory. In 1978 scientists at the City of Hope Medical Center in Duarte, California, announced the production of insulin identical in structure to that made in the human pancreas. Genes containing the codons required to produce the A and B polypeptide chains of insulin were made and attached to the bacteria *Escherichia coli*, which then synthesized the two chains. The A and B chains were extracted and brought together; insulin was formed when the two chains linked together through the two disulfide groups.

In 1982, this insulin became the first genetically engineered human protein to receive FDA approval for sale. Today many diabetics have the option of choosing to use human insulin rather than the animal protein obtained as a by-product of meat packing.

Concepts in Review

1. Briefly explain why carbohydrates are known as energy-storage molecules.
2. List two general ways that hormones can control metabolic pathways.
3. Briefly explain why enzymes are of vital importance in metabolism.
4. Explain why the Embden–Meyerhof pathway is catabolic.
5. State the purpose of the final reactions in anaerobic glucose catabolism.
6. Explain why the Embden–Meyerhof pathway is termed anaerobic.
7. Explain the role of glycogen in maintenance of blood-glucose levels.
8. Explain the role of epinephrine, insulin, and glucagon in the control of blood-glucose concentration.
9. Briefly describe how substrate level phosphorylation is involved in the Embden–Meyerhof pathway.
10. Give an overall description of the Embden–Meyerhof pathway (anaerobic) for metabolism of glucose.
11. Give an overall description of the citric acid cycle (aerobic).
12. Discuss the relationship between electron transport, oxidative phosphorylation, and the citric acid cycle.
13. Compare the amounts of energy formed in the anaerobic and aerobic metabolic pathways of glucose.
14. Describe the function of acetyl-CoA in carbohydrate metabolism.
15. Describe the formation of glucose by gluconeogenesis.
16. Explain the function of hormones in the body.
17. List the blood glucose levels that are considered to be normal, hyperglycemic, and hypoglycemic.
18. Explain the renal threshold.
19. Predict what might happen to the blood glucose level if a large overdose of insulin is taken.
20. Describe the glucose tolerance test and how it ties in with the condition of diabetes mellitus.

EQUATIONS IN REVIEW

Interconversion of Glycogen and Glucose

$$\text{Glycogen} \underset{\text{Glycogenesis}}{\overset{\text{Glycogenolysis}}{\rightleftharpoons}} \text{Glucose}$$

Embden–Meyerhof Pathway

$$C_6H_{12}O_6 + 2\,NAD^+ + 2\,ADP + 2\,P_i \longrightarrow 2\,CH_3\overset{\overset{\displaystyle O}{\|}}{C}{-}COOH + 2\,ATP + 2\,NADH + 2\,H^+$$

Citric Acid Cycle

$$CH_3{-}\overset{\overset{\displaystyle O}{\|}}{C}{-}S{-}CoA + FAD + 2\,H_2O + 3\,NAD^+ + GDP + P_i \longrightarrow 2\,CO_2 + FADH_2 + 3\,NADH + 3\,H^+ + GTP + CoASH$$

EXERCISES

1. Why are carbohydrates considered to be energy storage molecules?
2. List two general ways in which glucose catabolism differs from photosynthesis.
3. How much energy would be released if three moles of glucose was converted to carbon dioxide?
4. Why are enzymes important in metabolism?
5. What major storage carbohydrate is found in the liver?
6. Draw the structure of the carbohydrate that is produced during glycogenolysis.
7. Define the type of ATP production that occurs in the Embden–Meyerhof pathway.
8. Explain why the Embden–Meyerhof pathway is considered to be anaerobic even though the oxidation of glucose occurs.
9. What are the end products of the anaerobic catabolism of glucose in (a) muscle tissue and (b) yeast cells?
10. What is the purpose of the final reactions in anaerobic glucose catabolism?
11. Explain why the Embden–Meyerhof pathway is considered to be catabolic.
12. How many ATPs would be produced if three glucose molecules were processed through the Embden–Meyerhof pathway?
13. Write the structure of lactic acid. Would you predict that this molecule could provide cellular energy? Briefly explain.
14. How many high-energy phosphate bonds are directly formed in the citric acid cycle? List the number and types of reduced coenzymes that are produced in this cycle.
15. Why are electron transport and oxidative phosphorylation needed when the cell uses the citric acid cycle to produce energy?
16. Compare the amounts of metabolic energy (in the form of ATP) produced per glucose unit via the anaerobic sequence and via the aerobic sequence.
17. Why was the citric acid cycle not involved in the metabolism of life forms that existed before the evolution of photosynthesis?
18. What is acetyl-CoA and what is its function in metabolism?
19. What are the functions of hormones and where are they produced?

20. How does the function of hormones in the body differ from that of enzymes?
21. (a) What is the range of glucose concentration in blood under normal fasting conditions?
    (b) What blood-glucose concentrations are considered to be hyperglycemic? Hypoglycemic?
22. What is meant by the renal threshold?
23. What is meant by normal fasting blood sugar level?
24. Does the presence of glucose in the urine establish that the condition of diabetes mellitus is present? Explain.
25. Explain how the body maintains blood-glucose concentrations within certain definite limits despite wide variations in the rates of glucose intake and utilization.
26. Why is epinephrine sometimes called the emergency or crisis hormone?
27. Explain how epinephrine and insulin maintain blood glucose within a definite concentration range.
28. Predict what might happen to blood glucose concentrations if a large overdose of insulin were taken by accident.
29. Why is insulin not effective when taken orally?
30. Describe the glucose tolerance test.
31. Which of these statements are correct? Rewrite each incorrect statement to make it correct.
    (a) Carbon dioxide is a final product of glucose catabolism.
    (b) In general, only very few metabolic reactions require enzymes.
    (c) Hormonal control often changes an enzyme's function.
    (d) Glycolysis refers to the process of forming glycogen.
    (e) The Embden–Meyerhof pathway uses oxidative phosphorylation to form ATP.
    (f) Lactic acid is one product of gluconeogenesis.
    (g) ATP is produced directly in the citric acid cycle.
    (h) The Embden–Meyerhof metabolic pathway is an anaerobic sequence of reactions.
    (i) In the Embden–Meyerhof metabolic pathway, one mole of glucose is converted to two moles of lactic acid in muscle tissue.
    (j) The citric acid cycle is much more efficient in energy production than is the Embden–Meyerhof pathway.
    (k) Hormones are regulatory agents that are secreted into the stomach and intestine to control metabolism.
    (l) A person with diabetes mellitus suffers from hypoglycemia.
    (m) Hypoglycemia can affect the brain due to low blood sugar level.
    (n) When the blood glucose level exceeds the renal threshold, glucose is eliminated through the kidneys into the urine.

18

Metabolism of Lipids and Proteins

18.1 Metabolic Energy Sources

18.2 Fatty Acid Oxidation (Beta Oxidation)

18.3 Fat Storage and Utilization

18.4 Biosynthesis of Fatty Acids (Lipogenesis)

18.5 Amino Acid Metabolism

18.6 Metabolic Nitrogen Acquisition

18.7 Amino Acid Utilization

18.8 Nitrogen Excretion and the Urea Cycle

18.9 Acetyl-CoA, a Central Molecule in Metabolism

◀ **Chapter Opening Photo: These New York Marathon runners will metabolize lipids and proteins as well as carbohydrates by the end of the race.**

One of the world's most pervasive nutritional problems is protein deficiency, known as kwashiorkor. It especially afflicts children and, when untreated, has a mortality rate of between 30 and 90 percent. These young people suffer from growth retardation, anemia, liver damage, and often appear bloated because of excess water absorption.

In more affluent societies, nutritional problems are often associated with a high intake of saturated fat—stroke and heart disease are closely correlated to lipid intake.

These disparate nutritional problems point toward an important similarity between protein and lipid metabolism. Our biochemical processes have needs for specific amino acids (proteins) and lipids. No matter how much food is available for our diet, we must also be concerned with meeting requirements for selected nutrients.

18.1 Metabolic Energy Sources

The ability to produce cellular energy is a vital characteristic of every cell's metabolism. As we have seen, carbohydrates are one of the major sources of cellular energy. The other two are lipids and proteins.

Of all the lipids, fatty acids are the most commonly used for cellular energy. Each fatty acid contains a long chain of reduced carbon atoms that can be oxidized to yield energy.

$$CH_3CH_2CH_2CH_2CH_2CH_2CH_2CH_2CH_2CH_2CH_2CH_2CH_2CH_2CH_2COOH$$

Palmitic acid

The average oxidation number of the carbon atoms in fatty acids is about -2 compared with 0 in carbohydrates. Thus, when catabolized (oxidized), fatty acids yield more energy per carbon atom than do carbohydrates.

Proteins (amino acids) are also a source of reduced carbon atoms that can be catabolized to provide cellular energy. In addition, amino acids provide the major pool of usable nitrogen for cells. Proteins and amino acids also perform diverse other functions. Some of these functions will be considered later in this chapter.

18.2 FATTY ACID OXIDATION (BETA OXIDATION)

Fats are the most energy rich class of nutrients. Most of the energy from fats is derived from their constituent fatty acids. Palmitic acid derived from fat yields 39.1 kJ (9.36 kcal) per gram when burned to form carbon dioxide and water. By contrast, glucose yields only 15.6 kJ (3.74 kcal) per gram. Of course, fats are not actually burned in the body simply to produce heat. They are broken down in a series of enzyme catalyzed reactions that also produce useful potential chemical energy in the form of ATP. In complete biochemical oxidation, the carbon and hydrogen of a fat ultimately are combined with oxygen (from respiration) to form carbon dioxide and water.

In 1904 Franz Knoop, a German biochemist, established that the catabolism of fatty acids involved a process whereby their carbon chains are shortened by two carbon atoms at a time. Knoop knew that animals do not metabolize benzene groups to carbon dioxide and water. Instead the benzene nucleus remains attached to at least one carbon atom and is eliminated in the urine as a derivative of either benzoic acid or phenylacetic acid.

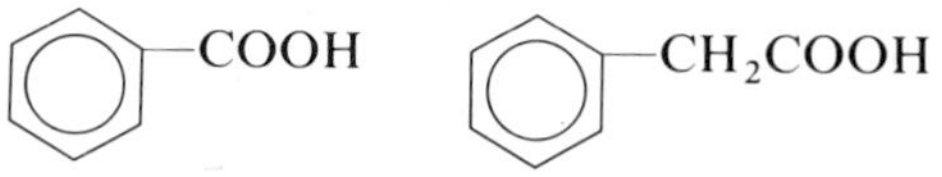

C_6H_5—COOH C_6H_5—CH_2COOH

Benzoic acid   Phenylacetic acid

Accordingly Knoop prepared a homologous series of straight-chain fatty acids with a phenyl group at one end and a carboxyl group at the other end. He then fed these benzene-tagged acids to test animals. Phenylaceturic acid was identified in the urine of the animals that had eaten acids with an even number of carbon atoms; hippuric acid was present in the urine of the animals that had consumed acids with an odd number of carbon atoms:

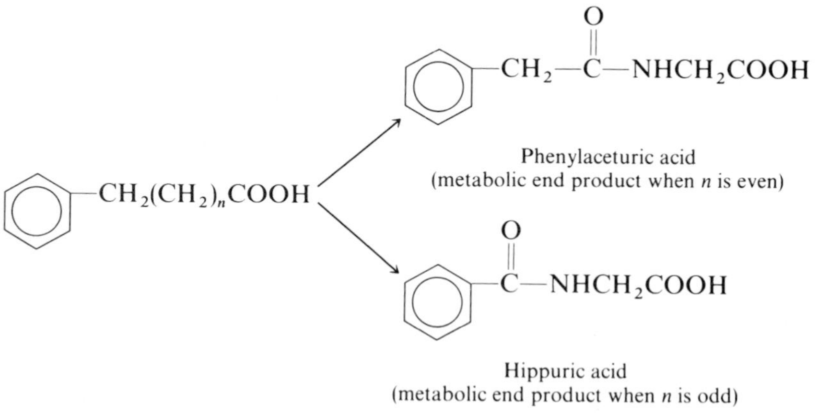

$$C_6H_5\text{—}CH_2(CH_2)_nCOOH \rightarrow C_6H_5\text{—}CH_2\text{—}\overset{\overset{\displaystyle O}{\|}}{C}\text{—}NHCH_2COOH$$

Phenylaceturic acid
(metabolic end product when n is even)

$$C_6H_5\text{—}CH_2(CH_2)_nCOOH \rightarrow C_6H_5\text{—}\overset{\overset{\displaystyle O}{\|}}{C}\text{—}NHCH_2COOH$$

Hippuric acid
(metabolic end product when n is odd)

These results indicated a metabolic pathway for fatty acids in which the carbon chain is shortened by two carbon atoms at each stage.

Knoop's experiments were remarkable for their time. They involved the use of tagged molecules and served as prototypes for modern research that utilizes isotopes to tag molecules.

Knoop postulated that the carbon chain of a fatty acid is shortened by successive removals of acetic acid units. The process involves the oxidation of the beta-carbon atom and cleavage of the chain between the alpha and beta carbons. A six-carbon fatty acid would produce three molecules of acetic acid, thus:

First reaction sequence

$$\underset{\text{Caproic acid}}{CH_3CH_2CH_2\overset{\beta}{C}H_2\overset{\alpha}{C}H_2COOH} \longrightarrow \underset{\text{Butyric acid}}{CH_3CH_2CH_2COOH} + \underset{\text{Acetic acid}}{CH_3COOH}$$

(This C is oxidized: the β carbon. Chain is cleaved here: between the β and α carbons.)

Second reaction sequence

$$CH_3\overset{\beta}{C}H_2\overset{\alpha}{C}H_2COOH \longrightarrow CH_3COOH + CH_3COOH$$

(This C is oxidized: the β carbon. Chain is cleaved here: between the β and α carbons.)

The general validity of Knoop's theory of beta-carbon atom oxidation has been confirmed. However, the detailed pathway for fatty acid oxidation was not established until about 50 years after his original work. The sequence of reactions involved, like those of the Embden–Meyerhof and citric acid pathways, is another fundamental metabolic pathway. Beta oxidation, or the *two-carbon chop*, is accomplished in a series of reactions whereby the first two carbon atoms of the fatty acid chain become the acetyl group in a molecule of acetyl-CoA.

The catabolism proceeds in this manner: A fatty acid reacts with coenzyme A (CoASH) to form an activated thioester. The energy needed for this step of the catabolism is obtained from ATP.

Step 1 Activation: Formation of thioester with CoA

$$\underset{\text{Fatty acid}}{RCH_2CH_2CH_2\overset{O}{\overset{\|}{C}}OH} + CoASH + ATP \longrightarrow$$

$$\underset{\text{CoA thioester of a fatty acid}}{RCH_2CH_2CH_2\overset{O}{\overset{\|}{C}}{-}SCoA} + AMP + \underset{\text{Inorganic phosphate}}{2\ P_i}$$

The activated thioester next undergoes four more steps in the reaction sequence involving *oxidation*, *hydration*, *oxidation*, and *cleavage* to produce acetyl-CoA and an activated thioester shortened by two carbon atoms. The cleavage reaction requires an additional molecule of CoA.

Step 2 Oxidation: Dehydrogenation at carbons 2 and 3 (alpha and beta carbons)

$$RCH_2CH_2CH_2\overset{O}{\overset{\|}{C}}{-}SCoA + FAD \longrightarrow RCH_2CH{=}CH\overset{O}{\overset{\|}{C}}{-}SCoA + FADH_2$$

Step 3 Hydration: Conversion to secondary alcohol

$$\mathrm{RCH_2CH{=}CH\overset{O}{\overset{\|}{C}}{-}SCoA + H_2O \longrightarrow RCH_2\overset{OH}{\overset{|}{C}}HCH_2\overset{O}{\overset{\|}{C}}{-}SCoA}$$

Step 4 Oxidation: Dehydrogenation of carbon 3 (beta carbon) to a keto group

$$\mathrm{RCH_2\overset{OH}{\overset{|}{C}}HCH_2\overset{O}{\overset{\|}{C}}{-}SCoA + NAD^+ \longrightarrow RCH_2\overset{O}{\overset{\|}{C}}CH_2\overset{O}{\overset{\|}{C}}{-}SCoA + NADH + H^+}$$

Step 5 Carbon-chain cleavage: Reaction with CoA to produce acetyl-CoA and activated thioester of a fatty acid shortened by two carbons

$$\mathrm{RCH_2\overset{O}{\overset{\|}{C}}CH_2\overset{O}{\overset{\|}{C}}{-}SCoA + CoASH \longrightarrow RCH_2\overset{O}{\overset{\|}{C}}{-}SCoA + \underset{\text{Acetyl-CoA}}{CH_3\overset{O}{\overset{\|}{C}}{-}SCoA}}$$

The shortened chain thioester repeats the reaction sequence of oxidation, hydration, oxidation, and cleavage to shorten the carbon chain further and produce another molecule of acetyl-CoA. Thus, for example, eight molecules of acetyl-CoA can be produced from one molecule of palmitic acid.

As in the metabolic pathways for glucose, each reaction in the fatty acid oxidation pathway is enzyme catalyzed. No ATP is directly produced during fatty acid catabolism. Instead, ATP is formed when the reduced coenzymes, $FADH_2$ and NADH, are oxidized by the mitochondrial electron transport system in concert with oxidative phosphorylation. Fatty acid oxidation is aerobic because the products, $FADH_2$ and NADH, can only be reoxidized when oxygen is present.

In general, fatty acid catabolism yields more energy than can be derived from the breakdown of glucose. For example, the reduced coenzymes derived from palmitic acid will yield 123 ATP via electron transport and oxidative phosphorylation. Eight additional ATPs can be obtained from the eight GTPs formed in the citric acid cycle while one ATP is used to start the beta oxidation process. Thus, the 16 carbons of palmitic acid yield a total of 130 ATP or about 8.1 ATP per carbon atom. In contrast, glucose can yield between 36 and 38 ATPs as its six carbons are completely oxidized to carbon dioxide. About six ATPs per carbon atom are gained from glucose as compared with about eight ATPs per carbon atom from a fatty acid. Because fatty acid carbons are, in general, more reduced than glucose carbons, fatty acids are a more potent source of energy and yield more ATP molecules during metabolism.

Not surprisingly, the energy storage molecule of choice in the human body is the fatty acid. On the average, a 70-kg male adult carries about 15 kg of fat (as triacylglycerols) but only about 0.22 kg of carbohydrate (as glycogen). Fat is such a good energy storage that many obese people could exist for about one year without food. Unfortunately, fat is not the best energy supply molecule for all tissues. For example, the brain normally derives all of its energy needs from glucose, using about 60% of all glucose metabolized by an adult at rest. Thus, fatty acids are not a universal energy source although they are our most concentrated supply of energy.

18.3 Fat Storage and Utilization

Fats (triacylglycerols) are stored primarily in adipose tissue, which is widely distributed in the body. Fat tends to accumulate under the skin (subcutaneous fat), in the abdominal region, and around some internal organs, especially the kidneys. Fat is deposited around internal organs as a shock absorber, or cushion. Subcutaneous fat acts as an insulating blanket. It is developed to an extreme degree in mammals such as seals, walruses, and whales that live in cold water.

Fat is the major reserve of potential energy. It is metabolized continuously. Stored fat does not remain in the body unchanged; there is a rapid exchange between the triacylglycerols of the plasma lipoproteins and the triacylglycerols in the adipose tissue. The plasma lipoprotein–bound triacylglycerols are broken down by an enzyme (lipoprotein lipase) that is found on the walls of all capillaries, and the resulting free fatty acids are transported into the adipose cells. When the body needs energy from fat, adipose cell enzymes hydrolyze triacylglycerols and the fatty acids are exported to other body tissues. This vital process is under careful hormonal control. For example, a part of the "fight or flight" response caused by the hormone epinephrine (adrenalin) is an increased fatty acid output from the adipose tissue. Conversely, when there is more energy available in the diet than the body needs, the excess energy is used to make body fat. Continued eating of more food than the body can use results in obesity.

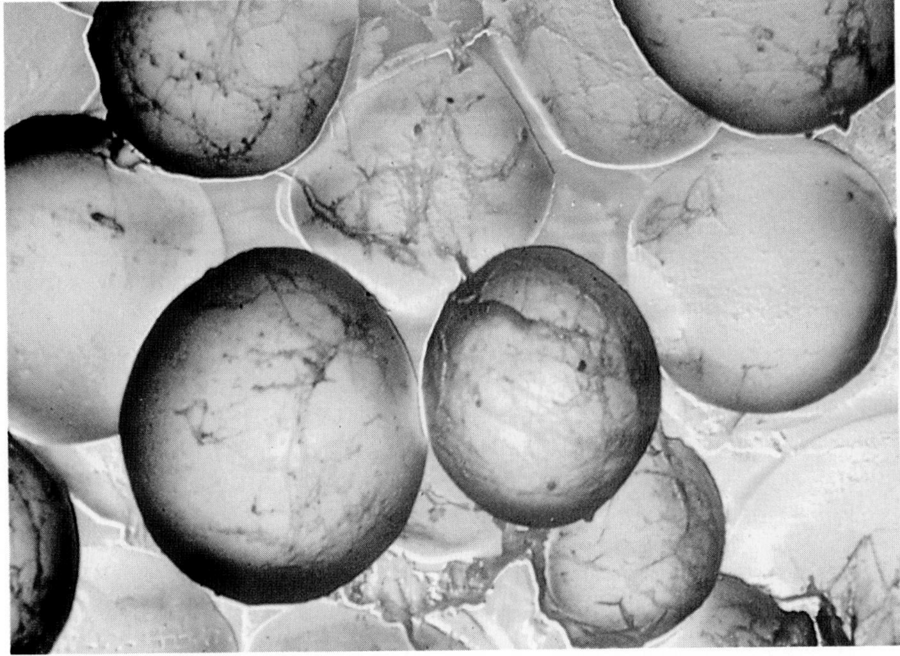

◀ **Photomicrograph of fat cells. These fat cells provide a major reserve of potential energy.**

18.4 Biosynthesis of Fatty Acids (Lipogenesis)

lipogenesis

The biosynthesis of fatty acids from acetyl-CoA is called **lipogenesis**. Acetyl-CoA may be obtained from the catabolism of carbohydrates, fats, or proteins. Fatty acids, in turn, may be combined with glycerol to form triacylglycerols, which are stored in adipose tissue. Consequently, lipogenesis is the pathway by which all three of the major classes of nutrients may ultimately be converted to body fat.

Is lipogenesis just the reverse of fatty acid oxidation (beta oxidation)? By analogy with carbohydrate metabolism (compare glycolysis with gluconeogenesis, see Chapter 17), we might expect this to be the case. However, fatty acid biosynthesis is not simply a reversal of fatty acid oxidation. The following are the major differences between the two pathways:

1. Fatty acid catabolism occurs in the mitochondria, but fatty acid anabolism (lipogenesis) occurs in the cytoplasm.
2. Lipogenesis requires a set of enzymes that are different from the enzymes used in the catabolism.
3. In the anabolic pathway (lipogenesis), the growing fatty acid chain is linked to a special acyl carrier protein (ACP—SH). ACP—SH acts as a handle to transfer the growing chain from one enzyme to another through the series of enzyme-catalyzed reactions in the pathway. Coenzyme A is the carrier in fatty acid catabolism.
4. A preliminary set of reactions, involving malonyl-CoA, occurs for each two-carbon addition cycle in the synthesis. Malonyl is a three-carbon group and has no counterpart in the catabolic pathway. Malonyl-CoA is synthesized from acetyl-CoA and carbon dioxide in the presence of the enzyme acetyl-CoA carboxylase, ATP, and the vitamin biotin.

$$\underset{\text{Acetyl-CoA}}{CH_3\overset{\overset{\displaystyle O}{\|}}{C}\text{—SCoA}} + CO_2 \xrightarrow[\text{Acetyl-CoA carboxylase}]{\text{ATP, biotin}} \underset{\text{Malonyl-CoA}}{HO\overset{\overset{\displaystyle O}{\|}}{C}CH_2\overset{\overset{\displaystyle O}{\|}}{C}\text{—SCoA}}$$

The biosynthesis of a fatty acid occurs by addition of successive two-carbon-atom increments to a lengthening chain starting with acetyl-CoA. Each incremental addition follows this five-step pathway or reaction sequence.

Step 1 Acetyl-CoA and malonyl-CoA are linked to separate acyl carrier proteins:

$$\underset{\text{Acetyl-CoA}}{CH_3\overset{\overset{\displaystyle O}{\|}}{C}\text{—SCoA}} + \underset{\text{Malonyl-CoA}}{HO\overset{\overset{\displaystyle O}{\|}}{C}CH_2\overset{\overset{\displaystyle O}{\|}}{C}\text{—SCoA}} + 2\ \underset{\text{Acyl protein carrier}}{\text{ACP—SH}} \longrightarrow$$

$$\underset{\text{Acetyl-ACP}}{CH_3\overset{\overset{\displaystyle O}{\|}}{C}\text{—SACP}} + \underset{\text{Malonyl-ACP}}{HO\overset{\overset{\displaystyle O}{\|}}{C}CH_2\overset{\overset{\displaystyle O}{\|}}{C}\text{—SACP}} + 2\ \text{CoASH}$$

Step 2 Acetyl-ACP and malonyl-ACP condense, with loss of carbon dioxide (decarboxylation):

$$\underset{\text{Acetyl-ACP}}{CH_3\overset{O}{\overset{\|}{C}}-SACP} + \underset{\text{Malonyl-ACP}}{HO\overset{O}{\overset{\|}{C}}CH_2\overset{O}{\overset{\|}{C}}-SACP} \longrightarrow \underset{\text{Acetoacetyl-ACP}}{CH_3\overset{O}{\overset{\|}{C}}CH_2\overset{O}{\overset{\|}{C}}-SACP} + CO_2 + ACP-SH$$

The three steps that follow are approximate reversals of three steps in fatty acid beta oxidation (Section 17.2).

Step 3 Reduction: Hydrogenation of carbon 3 (β-keto group)

$$CH_3\overset{O}{\overset{\|}{C}}CH_2\overset{O}{\overset{\|}{C}}-SACP + NADPH + H^+ \longrightarrow \underset{\beta\text{-Hydroxybutyryl-ACP}}{CH_3\overset{OH}{\overset{|}{C}}HCH_2\overset{O}{\overset{\|}{C}}-SACP} + NADP^+$$

Step 4 Dehydration: Formation of a double bond between carbons 2 and 3

$$CH_3\overset{OH}{\overset{|}{C}}HCH_2\overset{O}{\overset{\|}{C}}-SACP \longrightarrow \underset{\text{Crotonyl-ACP}}{CH_3CH{=}CH\overset{O}{\overset{\|}{C}}-SACP} + H_2O$$

Step 5 Reduction: Hydrogenation of carbons 2 and 3

$$CH_3CH{=}CH\overset{O}{\overset{\|}{C}}-SACP + NADPH + H^+ \longrightarrow \underset{\text{Butyryl-ACP}}{CH_3CH_2CH_2\overset{O}{\overset{\|}{C}}-SACP} + NADP^+$$

This completes the first cycle of the synthesis; the chain has been lengthened by two carbon atoms. Biosynthesis of longer-chain fatty acids proceeds by a series of such cycles, each lengthening the carbon chain by an increment of two carbon atoms. The next cycle would begin with the reaction of butyryl-ACP and malonyl-ACP, leading to a six-carbon chain, and so on. This synthesis commonly produces palmitic acid (16 carbons) as its end product. The synthesis of palmitic acid from acetyl-CoA and malonyl-CoA requires cycling through the series of steps seven times. The condensed equation for the formation of palmitic acid is

$$\underset{\text{Acetyl-CoA}}{CH_3\overset{\overset{O}{\parallel}}{C}\text{—SCoA}} + 7\ \underset{\text{Malonyl-CoA}}{HO\overset{\overset{O}{\parallel}}{C}CH_2\overset{\overset{O}{\parallel}}{C}\text{—SCoA}} + 14\ NADPH + 14\ H^+ \longrightarrow$$

$$\underset{\text{Palmitic acid}}{CH_3(CH_2)_{14}COOH} + 7\ CO_2 + 6\ H_2O + 8\ CoASH + 14\ NADP^+$$

Nearly all naturally occurring fatty acids have even numbers of carbon atoms. A sound reason for this fact is that both the catabolism and the synthesis proceed by two-carbon increments.

In conclusion, it should be noted that the metabolism of fats has some features in common with that of carbohydrates. The acetyl-CoA produced in the catabolism of both carbohydrates and fatty acids can be used as a raw material for making other substances and as an energy source. When acetyl-CoA is oxidized via the citric acid cycle, more potential energy can be trapped in ATP. The ATP in turn serves as the source of energy needed for the production of other substances, including the synthesis of carbohydrates and fats.

18.5 Amino Acid Metabolism

Amino acids serve an important and unique role in cellular metabolism; they are the building blocks of proteins and also provide most of the nitrogen for other nitrogen containing compounds.

Amino acid metabolism differs markedly from the biochemistry of carbohydrates or fatty acids. Amino acids always contain nitrogen, and the chemistry of this element presents unique problems for the cell. In addition, there is no structure common to all the carbon skeletons of amino acids. The carbohydrates can share a common metabolic pathway, as can fatty acids, because they share common structures. But the carbon skeletons of amino acids vary widely, and the cell must use a different metabolic pathway for almost every amino acid. Thus the metabolism of the carbon structures of amino acids is complex. In the sections that follow, a brief overview of amino acid metabolism will be presented together with a more detailed examination of nitrogen metabolism.

18.6 Metabolic Nitrogen Acquisition

Nitrogen is an important component of many biochemicals. In addition to being a component of amino acids, nitrogen is found in nucleic acids, hemoglobin, and many vitamins. Every cell must have a continuous nitrogen supply. This supply might seem easy to obtain because the atmosphere contains about 78% free (elemental) nitrogen. Unfortunately, most cells cannot use elemental nitrogen.

Most higher plant and animal cells require nitrogen that is bonded to other elements before it is biochemically useful. However, most nitrogen on earth exists as N_2 molecules, the two atoms being bonded together by a strong and unreactive triple bond. On an industrial scale, high temperature (400–500°C), high pressure (several hundred atmospheres), and a catalyst are required to react nitrogen gas with the reducing agent, hydrogen, to form ammonia. In the biosphere only a few organisms have the metabolic machinery necessary to use the abundant atmospheric nitrogen. These are procaryotes including *Azobacter* species, *Clostridium pasteurianum*, and *Rhizobium* species. By converting nitrogen gas to compounds, these organisms make nitrogen available to the rest of the biological world.

nitrogen fixation

The conversion of diatomic nitrogen to a biochemically useful form is termed **nitrogen fixation**. Nitrogen is fixed by several methods, including (1) soil bacteria, (2) lightning, (3) Haber synthesis of ammonia, and (4) high-temperature processes such as combustion reactions. Of the procaryotes that are able to catalyze nitrogen fixation, *Rhizobium* bacteria deserve special attention. These bacteria flourish on the roots of legumes, such as clover and soybeans, in a symbiotic relationship. The bacteria have degenerated essentially into nitrogen fixing machines that are maintained by the plants in root nodules. The legumes even provide a special hemoglobin protein to assist the bacteria in their task.

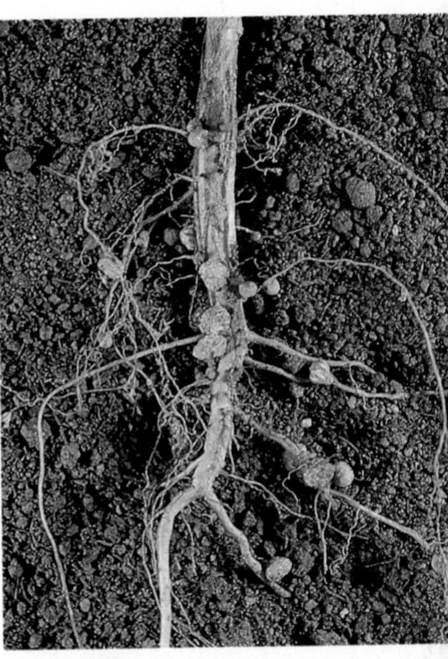

▲ **Soybean root nodules containing nitrogen-fixing bacteria.**

Currently, in many university and industrial genetic-engineering laboratories, scientists are attempting to transfer the nitrogen fixation capability of procaryotes to higher plants. To accomplish this transfer, the appropriate genes must be removed from procaryotic cells and spliced into the DNA of higher plants (see Chemistry in Action, Chapter 14). This research is particularly challenging and, if successful, would have potentially great rewards. Success would mean that grains and other commercially important crops could be grown in poor soils using little or no nitrogen fertilizer. This achievement would create a vast increase in the world's food production capability.

Higher plants use nitrogen compounds primarily to produce proteins, which, in turn, enter the animal food chain. Both plant and animal proteins are important human nutrients.

Protein is digested and absorbed to provide the amino acid dietary requirements (see Chapter 15). Once absorbed, an amino acid can be used in one of the following ways:

1. Be incorporated into a protein
2. Be utilized in the synthesis of other nitrogenous compounds such as nucleic acids
3. Be deaminated to a keto acid, which either can be used to synthesize other compounds or can be oxidized to carbon dioxide and water to provide energy

amino acid pool

Absorbed amino acids enter the amino acid pool. The **amino acid pool** is the total supply of amino acids available for use throughout the body. The amount of amino acids in the pool is maintained in balance with other cellular nitrogen pools (see Figure 18.1).

One particularly important nitrogen pool is composed of the proteins in all the body's tissues. Amino acids continually move back and forth between the amino acid pool and the tissue proteins. In other words, our body proteins are constantly being broken down and resynthesized. The rate of turnover varies

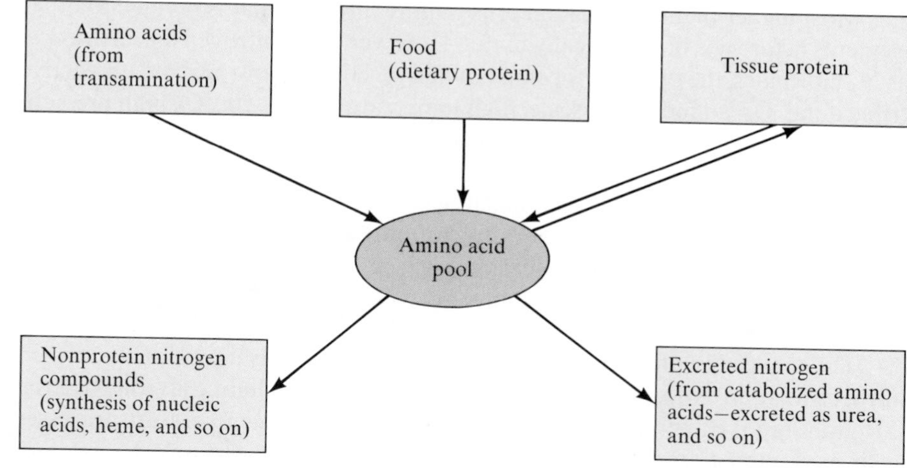

FIGURE 18.1 ▶ Major biological nitrogen pools showing the central amino acid pool.

with different proteins, but research with tagged (isotopically labeled) amino acids has shown that some proteins from liver and other active tissues have a half-life of less than a week, whereas the half-life of some muscle proteins is about six months.

When there is a dietary deficiency of protein (or amino acids), the tissue protein acts as an emergency source to maintain the amino acid pool. For example, one symptom of chronic undernourishment is a wasting of muscle tissue protein. The tissue protein is broken down to yield amino acids. The amino acids may then be used to supply other nitrogen pools or simply may be converted to cellular energy.

nitrogen balance

positive nitrogen balance

negative nitrogen balance

In a healthy, well-nourished adult, the amount of nitrogen excreted is equal to the amount of nitrogen ingested. Such a person is said to be in nitrogen equilibrium, or **nitrogen balance**. In a growing child, the amount of nitrogen excreted is less than that consumed, and the child is in **positive nitrogen balance**. A fasting or starving person or one suffering from certain diseases excretes more nitrogen than is ingested; such a person is in **negative nitrogen balance**. A person on a diet that lacks one or more essential amino acids is in negative nitrogen balance. Tissue proteins can be broken down, but resynthesis is blocked if an amino acid that the body cannot synthesize is missing from the diet. More nitrogen is then excreted than consumed, because the body cannot synthesize specific tissue proteins. The nitrogen balance depends on both the amount and the nature of the nitrogen in the diet.

18.7 AMINO ACID UTILIZATION

Amino acids are important in metabolism as carriers of usable nitrogen. If an amino acid is not directly incorporated into tissue proteins, its nitrogen may be incorporated into a variety of other molecules such as amino acids, nucleic acid bases, the heme of hemoglobin, and some lipids. In general, when an amino acid is to be used for some purpose other than protein synthesis, the amino acid carbon skeleton is separated from the amino acid nitrogen.

transamination

A process called transamination is responsible for most of the nitrogen transfer to and from amino acids. **Transamination** is the exchange of an oxygen atom for an amino group between an α-keto acid and an α-amino acid:

$$\underset{\alpha\text{-Amino acid}}{R\underset{NH_2}{\underset{|}{C}}H-COOH} + \underset{\alpha\text{-Keto acid}}{R'\overset{O}{\overset{\|}{C}}-COOH} \rightleftharpoons R\overset{O}{\overset{\|}{C}}-COOH + R'\underset{NH_2}{\underset{|}{C}}H-COOH$$

Transamination may involve many different molecules, with each different transamination requiring a different enzyme (transaminase). For example, one enzyme (glutamic-pyruvic transaminase) catalyzes the conversion of pyruvic acid to L-alanine:

$$\underset{\text{Pyruvic acid}}{CH_3\overset{O}{\overset{\|}{C}}-COOH} + \underset{\text{L-Glutamic acid}}{NH_2-CH(CH_2CH_2COOH)-COOH} \rightleftharpoons \underset{\text{L-Alanine}}{CH_3\underset{NH_2}{\underset{|}{C}}H-COOH} + \underset{\alpha\text{-Ketoglutaric acid}}{O=C(CH_2CH_2COOH)-COOH}$$

A different enzyme catalyzes the production of L-aspartic acid from oxaloacetic acid:

$$\underset{\text{Oxaloacetic acid}}{O=C(CH_2COOH)-COOH} + \underset{\text{L-Glutamic acid}}{NH_2-CH(CH_2CH_2COOH)COOH} \rightleftharpoons \underset{\text{L-Aspartic acid}}{NH_2-CH(CH_2COOH)COOH} + \underset{\alpha\text{-Ketoglutaric acid}}{O=C(CH_2CH_2COOH)-COOH}$$

Note that both of these reactions involve the conversion of L-glutamic acid to α-ketoglutaric acid. In fact, most transaminations use L-glutamic acid. Thus, this amino acid plays a central role in cellular nitrogen transfer.

glucogenic amino acids

ketogenic amino acids

Transamination is the first step in the conversion of the carbon skeletons of amino acids to energy-storage compounds. Amino acids that are used to produce glucose and glycogen are termed **glucogenic amino acids**. Most amino acids are glucogenic (see Table 18.1). But some amino acids are converted to acetyl-CoA. When fed to starving animals, these amino acids cause an increase in the rate of ketone-body formation and are, therefore, called **ketogenic amino acids** (see Section 18.10). Only leucine is completely ketogenic, but a few amino acids can be converted to either glucose or acetyl-CoA and are both ketogenic and glucogenic.

TABLE 18.1 Classification of Amino Acids as Sources of Energy-Storage Molecules

Glucogenic	Ketogenic and glucogenic	Ketogenic
Alanine	Isoleucine	Leucine
Arginine	Lysine	
Aspartic acid	Phenylalanine	
Asparagine	Tyrosine	
Cysteine		
Glutamic acid		
Glutamine		
Glycine		
Histidine		
Methionine		
Proline		
Serine		
Threonine		
Tryptophan		
Valine		

The amino acid pool of Figure 18.1 can now be described in more detail. At the center of this pool is L-glutamic acid, and other amino acids can either add or remove nitrogen from this central compound. Given the important role of L-glutamic acid, it is not surprising that there are other cellular reactions by which nitrogen is interchanged with this amino acid. L-Glutamic acid can accept a second nitrogen atom and form L-glutamine:

$$NH_3 + \underset{\text{L-Glutamic acid}}{NH_2\text{—}CH(CH_2CH_2COOH)COOH} \rightleftharpoons \underset{\text{L-Glutamine}}{NH_2\text{—}CH(CH_2CH_2CONH_2)COOH} + H_2O$$

Although this reaction can be considered as the simple addition of ammonia to yield an amide, the actual cellular reactions are more complex. The product, L-glutamine, also serves in biological nitrogen transfer, the amide nitrogen being transferable in a number of cellular reactions.

It is worthwhile to consider the synthesis of L-glutamine in more detail. Ammonia is a base and therefore is toxic to the cell. When ammonia forms an amide bond to L-glutamic acid, the nitrogen becomes less basic and also nontoxic. Thus L-glutamine serves as a safe package for transporting nitrogen. In the human body, L-glutamine is the major compound for transferring nitrogen from one cell to another via the bloodstream.

18.8 Nitrogen Excretion and the Urea Cycle

Nitrogen—unlike carbon, hydrogen, and oxygen—is often conserved for reuse by the cell. But the cell excretes nitrogen when it has an excess of this element or when the carbon skeletons of nitrogen containing compounds are needed for other purposes. Two examples from human nutrition arise: (1) when we consume more protein than is needed (an excess of nitrogen containing molecules) or (2) when we experience starvation (protein is destroyed to provide reduced carbons for energy). Under normal conditions, adult humans excrete about 20 g of urea nitrogen per day.

The nitrogen elimination process poses a major problem for the cell. The simplest excretion product is ammonia, but ammonia is basic and, therefore, toxic to the cell. Fish can excrete ammonia through their gills because ammonia is soluble and is swept away by water passing through the gills. Land animals and birds excrete nitrogen in less toxic forms. Birds and reptiles excrete nitrogen as the white solid uric acid, a derivative of the purine bases. Mammals excrete the water-soluble compound urea. Both of these compounds contain a high percentage of nitrogen in a nontoxic form.

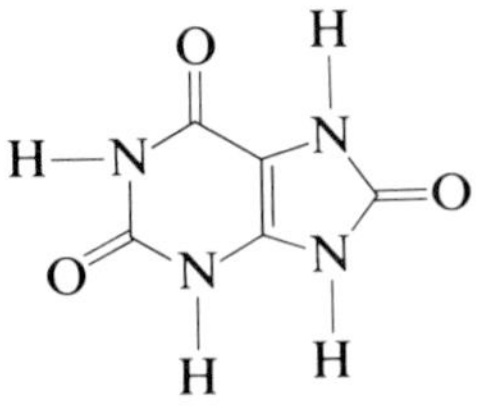

Uric acid

$$H_2N\overset{\overset{\large O}{\|}}{C}NH_2$$

Urea

Urea synthesis in mammals follows a pathway called the urea cycle (Figure 18.2), which takes place in the liver. Ammonia is first produced from L-glutamic acid in an oxidation–reduction reaction:

$$\underset{\text{L-Glutamic acid}}{NH_2\text{—}CH(CH_2CH_2COOH)COOH} + NAD^+ + H_2O \rightleftharpoons \underset{\alpha\text{-Ketoglutaric acid}}{O\text{=}C(CH_2CH_2COOH)\text{—}COOH} + NADH + H^+ + NH_3$$

The ammonia quickly reacts with bicarbonate and ATP to form carbamoyl phosphate:

$$NH_3 + HCO_3^- + 2\,ATP \rightleftharpoons \underset{\text{Carbamoyl phosphate}}{NH_2\text{—}\overset{\overset{O}{\|}}{C}\text{—}O\text{—}\overset{\overset{O^-}{|}}{\underset{\underset{O}{\|}}{P}}\text{—}O^-} + 2\,ADP + P_i$$

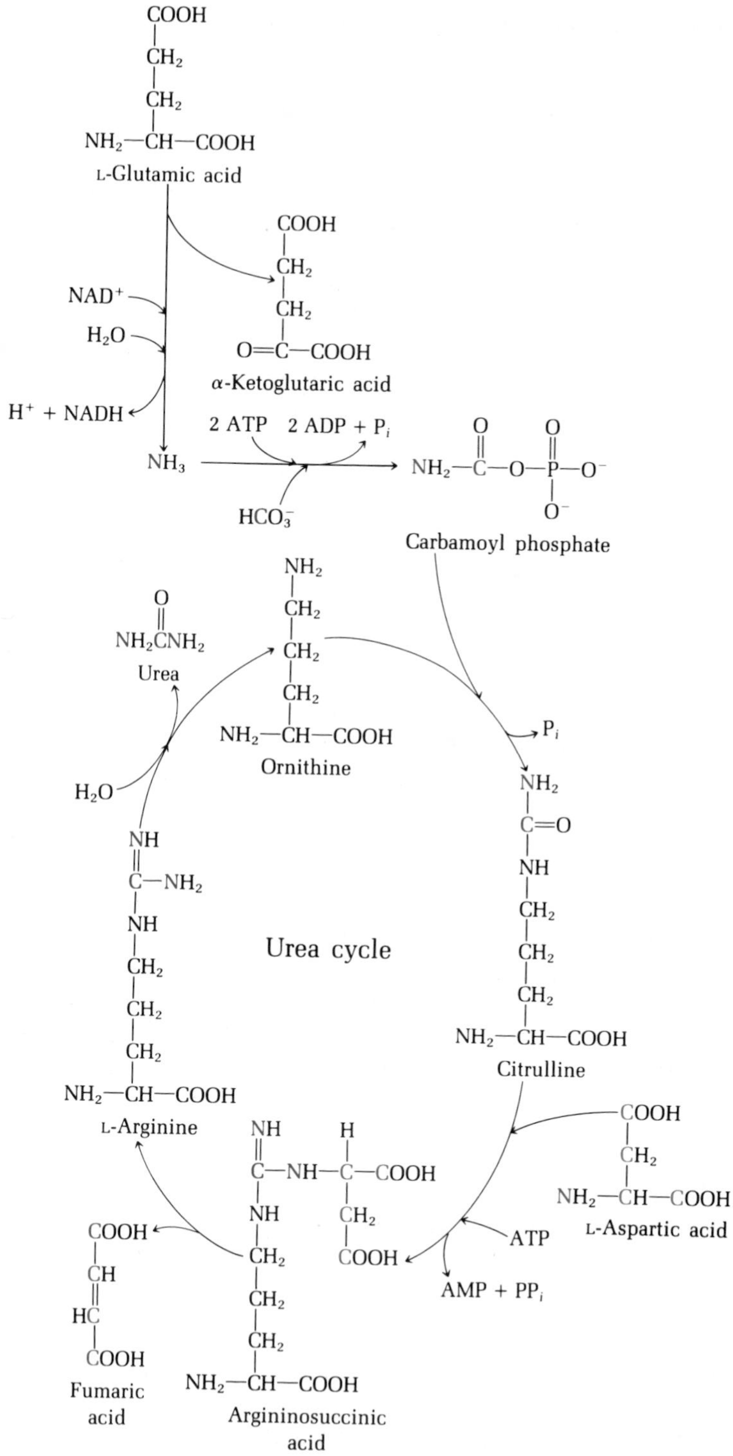

FIGURE 18.2 ▶ Urea cycle.

COOH
CH_2
CH_2
NH_2—CH—COOH
L-Glutamic acid

NAD^+
H_2O
H^+ + NADH

COOH
CH_2
CH_2
O=C—COOH
α-Ketoglutaric acid

NH_3
2 ATP 2 ADP + P_i
HCO_3^-

NH_2—C(=O)—O—P(=O)(O$^-$)—O$^-$
Carbamoyl phosphate

NH_2CNH_2 (C=O)
Urea

NH_2
CH_2
CH_2
CH_2
NH_2—CH—COOH
Ornithine

P_i

NH_2
C=O
NH
CH_2
CH_2
CH_2
NH_2—CH—COOH
Citrulline

Urea cycle

H_2O

NH
C—NH_2
NH
CH_2
CH_2
CH_2
NH_2—CH—COOH
L-Arginine

COOH
CH_2
NH_2—CH—COOH
L-Aspartic acid

ATP
AMP + PP_i

NH H
C—NH—C—COOH
NH CH_2
CH_2 COOH
CH_2
CH_2
NH_2—CH—COOH
Argininosuccinic acid

COOH
CH
HC
COOH
Fumaric acid

Finally, carbamoyl phosphate enters the urea cycle:

$$\underset{\text{Carbamoyl phosphate}}{NH_2-\overset{\overset{\displaystyle O}{\|}}{C}-O-\overset{\overset{\displaystyle O^-}{|}}{\underset{\underset{\displaystyle O}{\|}}{P}}-O^-} + \underset{\text{L-Aspartic acid}}{NH_2-\overset{\overset{\displaystyle COOH}{|}}{\overset{\displaystyle CH_2}{|}}\!\!\!\!\!\!\underset{\underset{\displaystyle H}{|}}{C}-COOH} + ATP \xrightarrow[\text{cycle}]{\text{Urea}}$$

$$\underset{\text{Urea}}{NH_2-\overset{\overset{\displaystyle O}{\|}}{C}-NH_2} + \underset{\text{Fumaric acid}}{\begin{matrix} COOH \\ | \\ CH \\ \| \\ HC \\ | \\ COOH \end{matrix}} + 3\ P_i + AMP$$

Like the intermediate compounds of the citric acid cycle, the compounds intermediate in the urea cycle do not appear in the overall reactions and serve only a catalytic function in the production of urea. Note that the urea cycle intermediates are α-amino acids. These are amino acids that are rarely used in protein synthesis. Their primary role is in the formation of urea.

Also it is important to recognize that the cell must expend energy, ATP, to produce urea. Formation of a nontoxic nitrogen excretion product is essential. In fact, impairment of the urea cycle is one of the major problems of liver cirrhosis caused by alcoholism. As liver function is impaired, more nitrogen is excreted as ammonia, leading to toxic effects.

Finally, let us look at the sources of the nitrogen that is excreted as urea. One nitrogen atom in each urea molecule comes from L-glutamic acid. The other nitrogen atom comes from L-aspartic acid, which may have gained its nitrogen from L-glutamic acid by transamination. Thus, the amino acid that is central to nitrogen transfer reactions is also the major contributor to nitrogen excretion.

18.9 Acetyl-CoA, a Central Molecule in Metabolism

As we think back through metabolism, we can identify some especially important compounds, molecules that are central to that portion of biochemistry. For example, glucose is the central compound in carbohydrate metabolism; glutamic acid is central in amino acid metabolism. There is one compound that is at the hub of all common metabolic processes; acetyl-CoA is central in the metabolism of carbon compounds (Figure 18.3). This molecule is a critical intermediate in the processes that form and break down both fats and amino acids. In addition, essentially all compounds that enter the citric acid cycle first must be catabolized

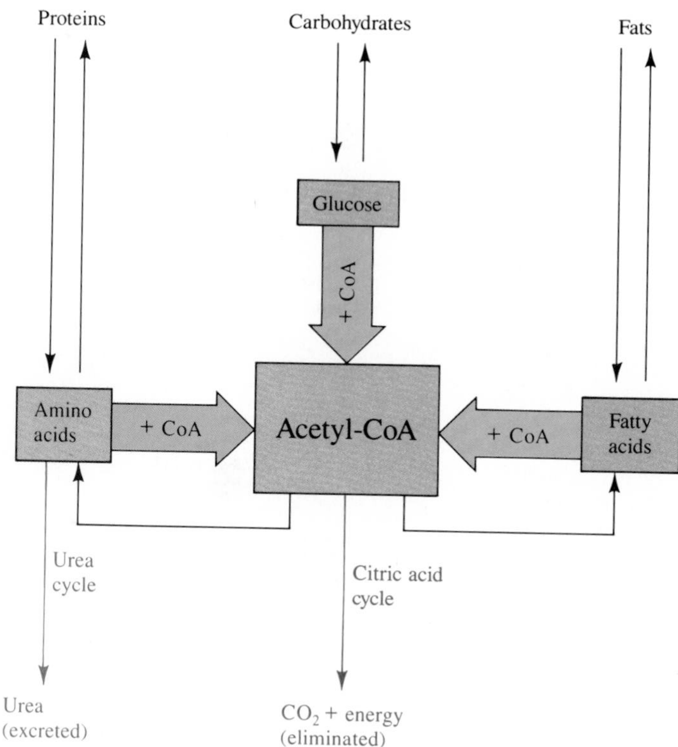

FIGURE 18.3 ► Simplified diagram showing acetyl-CoA at the hub of protein, carbohydrate, and fat metabolism.

to acetyl-CoA. This section will examine the characteristics of acetyl-CoA that make it a central metabolic compound and the advantages of a centralized metabolism for the cell.

Recall that acetyl-CoA consists of a small two-carbon unit (acetyl group) bonded by thioester linkage to a large organic coenzyme molecule, coenzyme A (CoA):

$$\underbrace{\mathrm{CH_3{-}\overset{\overset{\displaystyle O}{\|}}{C}}}_{\text{Acetyl group}}{-}\underset{\uparrow\ \text{Thioester linkage}}{\mathrm{S}}{-}\boxed{\text{Coenzyme A}}$$

This structure makes for an almost ideal central metabolic molecule with the following major advantages:

1. *Potential Use in a Wide Variety of Syntheses.* The small size and simple structure of the two-carbon acetyl fragment enables this molecule to be used to build a variety of diverse structures. Complex molecules with very different shapes and functions such as long chain fatty acids, amino acids, and steroid hormones are synthesized from acetyl-CoA.
2. *Special Reactivity of Bonds.* The thioester causes both carbons in the acetyl fragment to be specially reactive. These carbons are "primed" to form new bonds as the acetyl-CoA enters various metabolic pathways.

Chemistry in Action

Ketone Bodies—A Stress Response

Extreme circumstances such as long-term, continuous exercise, starvation, and untreated diabetes mellitus cause a change in metabolism. In such cases the energy obtainable from glucose is severely limited. In response the body produces small molecules from fatty acids, called *ketone bodies*, as glucose substitutes. These molecules include acetoacetic acid and two of its derivatives, β-hydroxybutyric acid and acetone.

$$CH_3\overset{\overset{O}{\|}}{C}CH_2COOH$$

Acetoacetic acid

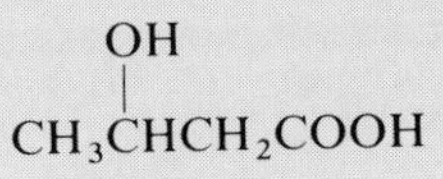

$$CH_3\overset{\overset{OH}{|}}{C}HCH_2COOH$$

β-Hydroxybutyric acid

$$CH_3\overset{\overset{O}{\|}}{C}CH_3$$

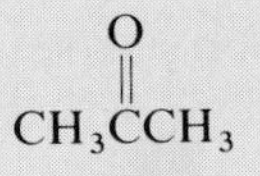

Acetone

Ketone bodies are highly soluble in blood and are able to provide cellular energy via beta oxidation and the citric acid cycle. When blood glucose becomes less available, some body tissues can adapt to using ketone bodies as substitute energy-supply molecules. For example, the brain, which depends upon glucose more than other human tissues, shifts its metabolism to use about 70% ketone bodies after 40 days of minimal food intake.

An increase in ketone-body concentration is an emergency response to an extreme circumstance. This response can have dangerous side effects. For example, most ketone bodies are carboxylic acids. When their concentration increases in the blood, the acidity rises, causing a condition called *ketosis*, or *ketoacidosis*. Ketosis can affect respiration and cause a general deterioration of normal body function.

3. *Structure That Is Recognizable by a Wide Variety of Enzymes.* Coenzyme A (CoA) acts as a kind of handle for the various enzymes that catalyze reactions of the acetyl group. Because many enzymes bind tightly to CoA, the acetyl group of acetyl-CoA can be involved in a great number of diverse reactions.

Acetyl-CoA can be compared with ATP as a central metabolic molecule. Remember that ATP (1) has a potential use in a wide variety of syntheses, (2) has a special reactivity in its phosphate anhydride bonds, and (3) has a structure that is recognizable and used by a wide variety of enzymes. For these important reasons, ATP serves as the "common energy currency" for the cell. In analogous fashion, acetyl-CoA might be termed the "common carbon currency" for the cell.

A consideration of these central metabolic compounds raises an important question: How does centralization aid the cell? We have seen numerous examples of centralization in biochemistry. Not only are there important central metabolites such as ATP and acetyl-CoA, but pathways such as the citric acid cycle centralize the cellular metabolic machinery. A general answer to this question is that centralization improves the efficiency of metabolism and ensures that biochemistry can be under careful metabolic control.

Greater efficiency results from designing central metabolic pathways to handle a variety of different nutrients. For example, the citric acid cycle completes carbon-oxidation for all energy supplying nutrients that are first converted to the central metabolite, acetyl-CoA.

Greater control results from the dependence of many "feeder" pathways on a single central process. Control of a central path like the citric acid cycle will affect in a coordinated way the metabolism of a variety of nutrients. As scientists have learned more about metabolism it has become clear that centralization is an important attribute of the chemistry of life.

CONCEPTS IN REVIEW

1. Briefly explain what characteristic of fatty acids allows them to provide large amounts of metabolic energy.
2. Briefly describe Knoop's experiments on fatty acid oxidation and degradation and the conclusions derived from them.
3. Explain what is meant by beta oxidation and beta cleavage in relation to the metabolism of fatty acids.
4. Tell the purpose of ketone-body production and indicate a dangerous side effect.
5. Briefly describe the biosynthesis of fatty acids using palmitic acid as an example.
6. List three major differences between beta oxidation and fatty acid synthesis.
7. Briefly describe how amino acid metabolism differs from carbohydrate and fatty acid metabolism.
8. List the possible metabolic fates of amino acids in humans.
9. Describe the major purpose of transamination.
10. Briefly explain the importance of L-glutamic acid and L-glutamine in nitrogen metabolism.
11. Explain how metabolism of proteins (amino acids) is tied into that of carbohydrates and fats.
12. Explain how a lack of essential amino acids in the diet affects the nitrogen balance.
13. Explain the purpose of the urea cycle.
14. Summarize the importance of acetyl-CoA in metabolism.
15. Discuss the major advantages of a centralized metabolism.

EQUATIONS IN REVIEW

One Cycle of Beta Oxidation

$$RCH_2CH_2CH_2\overset{\overset{\displaystyle O}{\|}}{C}{-}SCoA + FAD + NAD^+ + H_2O + CoASH \longrightarrow$$

$$RCH_2\overset{\overset{\displaystyle O}{\|}}{C}{-}SCoA + FADH_2 + NADH + H^+ + CH_3\overset{\overset{\displaystyle O}{\|}}{C}{-}SCoA$$

One Cycle of Fatty Acid Synthesis

$$CH_3\overset{\overset{O}{\|}}{C}{-}SCoA + HO\overset{\overset{O}{\|}}{C}CH_2\overset{\overset{O}{\|}}{C}{-}SCoA + 2\ NADPH + 2\ H^+ + ACP{-}SH \longrightarrow$$

$$CH_3CH_2CH_2\overset{\overset{O}{\|}}{C}{-}SACP + 2\ NADP^+ + H_2O + 2\ CoASH + CO_2$$

Transamination

$$\underset{\substack{\alpha\text{-Amino} \\ \text{acid}}}{\underset{NH_2}{\underset{|}{RCH}}{-}COOH} + \underset{\substack{\alpha\text{-Keto} \\ \text{acid}}}{R'\overset{\overset{O}{\|}}{C}{-}COOH} \rightleftharpoons \underset{\substack{\alpha\text{-Amino} \\ \text{acid}}}{R\overset{\overset{O}{\|}}{C}{-}COOH} + \underset{\substack{\alpha\text{-Keto} \\ \text{acid}}}{R'\underset{NH_2}{\underset{|}{CH}}{-}COOH}$$

Urea Cycle (overall reaction)

$$HOOC\underset{NH_2}{\underset{|}{C}}HCH_2COOH + ATP + H_2O + NH_2{-}\overset{\overset{O}{\|}}{C}{-}O{-}\underset{O^-}{\underset{|}{\overset{\overset{O}{\|}}{P}}}{-}O^- \longrightarrow$$

$$HOOCCH{=}CHCOOH + P_i + PP_i + AMP + NH_2\overset{\overset{O}{\|}}{C}NH_2$$

EXERCISES

1. What major characteristic of a fatty acid allows it to serve as an energy storage molecule?
2. How is it possible to become obese even though very little fat is included in the diet?
3. Briefly describe Knoop's experiment on fatty acid oxidation and catabolism.
4. What is meant by beta oxidation and beta cleavage in relation to the biochemistry of fatty acids?
5. By means of a diagram, outline how caproic acid is catabolized to butyric acid.
6. Why is the acyl carrier protein (ACP) of importance in fatty acid synthesis?
7. Aside from being the source of certain fatty acids, are fats essential in our diet? Explain your answer.
8. Beta oxidation is used by the cell to produce energy, yet no ATPs are formed in this pathway. Can you explain this seeming contradiction?
9. Give the name and structure of a ketone body that does *not* contain a ketone functional group.
10. How are ketone bodies important in energy metabolism?
11. Define *ketosis*.
12. Is fatty acid synthesis simply the reverse of beta oxidation? Briefly explain.
13. Aside from being a food reserve, what are the two principal functions of body fat?
14. In what way is the citric acid cycle involved in obtaining energy from fats?
15. Why is the ATP yield from a six-carbon fatty acid greater than the ATP yield from a six-carbon hexose (glucose)?
16. Outline the parts played by malonyl-CoA and acetyl-CoA in the biosynthesis of fatty acids.
17. List several reasons why acetyl-CoA is considered to be an important, central intermediate in metabolism.
18. Prepare a diagram showing the principal steps in the conversion of starch to body fat.

19. Briefly describe why soybeans are a crop that enriches the soil.
20. What are the possible metabolic fates of amino acids?
21. How might a low-protein diet cause a negative nitrogen balance?
22. Give an example of a reaction that is central to metabolic nitrogen transfer.
23. Briefly describe why L-glutamic acid is considered to be the central amino acid of the amino acid pool.
24. Why is L-glutamine a better nitrogen transport molecule than ammonia?
25. Is L-aspartic acid a ketogenic amino acid? Explain.
26. Write the structural formulas of the compounds produced by transamination of the following acids:
    (a) L-Alanine (c) L-Phenylalanine
    (b) L-Aspartic acid (d) L-Serine
27. Give the structure of urea.
28. How many ATPs are used to produce urea? Why is the production of urea of metabolic importance?
29. Draw the structures of the two common amino acids that contribute nitrogen to the urea cycle.
30. Which of these statements are correct? Rewrite each incorrect statement to make it correct.
    (a) The average carbon in palmitic acid is relatively oxidized, and, thus, this fatty acid contains little stored metabolic energy.
    (b) Carbohydrates provide more metabolic energy than fatty acids on a per-gram basis.
    (c) Based on his experiments, Knoop postulated that fatty acids are broken down via beta oxidation—that is, by a "two-carbon chop."
    (d) Fatty acid oxidation is an anaerobic reaction sequence.
    (e) The beta oxidation pathway directly produces 38 ATPs.
    (f) Acetyl-CoA is a very important product of beta oxidation.
    (g) When energy from glucose is severely limited, the body produces and uses ketone bodies to provide cellular energy.
    (h) Triacylglycerols stored in adipose tissue are continuously exchanged with triacylglycerols of the plasma lipoproteins.
    (i) The catabolism of fatty acids is known as lipogenesis.
    (j) Fatty acid anabolism occurs in the cytoplasm.
    (k) An acyl carrier protein is used in both beta oxidation and fatty acid synthesis.
    (l) Malonyl-CoA is synthesized from acetyl-CoA.
    (m) The biosynthesis of fatty acids occurs by successive additions of two-carbon increments.
    (n) During a dietary deficiency of protein, tissue protein acts as an emergency source to maintain a balanced amino acid pool.
    (o) Most amino acids are glucogenic.
    (p) Nitrogen fixation occurs in higher plants.
    (q) A positive nitrogen balance means more nitrogen is excreted than is consumed.
    (r) A ketogenic amino acid can cause an increase in the rate of ketone body formation.
    (s) Transamination allows formation of amino acids from α-keto acids.
    (t) Acetyl-CoA can be produced from carbohydrates, fatty acids, and proteins.
    (u) Acetyl-CoA consists of an acetyl group and a coenzyme A molecule linked through a phosphate ester bond.
    (v) Mammals excrete nitrogen in the form of urea.
    (w) Compared with other nitrogen excretion compounds, urea is especially toxic.

INDEX/GLOSSARY

Entries and page numbers that are in boldface type refer to definitions of key terms in the text.

Photo Credits

This page is an extension of the copyright page.

Chapter 1

Page 1: NASA; Page 9: Rita Amaya; Page 13: NASA; Page 15: Michael Melford/Tony Stone Worldwide.

Chapter 2

Page 16: Marcella Pedone/The Image Bank; Page35: Alan Carey/ The Image Works; Page 38: Kirby Harrison/The Image Works; Page 43: Russell Wood/Taurus Photos.

Chapter 3

Page 46: John Yurka/The Picture Cube; Page 64: Ralph Eagle, Jr./ Photo Researchers; Page 67: Michael Nelson/FPG International.

Chapter 4

Page 83: Leslye Borden/Photo Edit; Page 101: Visuals Unlimited; Page 106: SIU/Photo Researchers.

Chapter 5

Page 113: Comstock; Page 125: Robert Brenner/PhotoEdit; Page 127: David Wells/The Image Works; Page 129: Bonnie Kamin.

Chapter 6

Page 135: W. Marc Bernsau/The Image Works; Page 137: Hans Pfletschinger/Peter Arnold; Page 141: Hanson Carroll/FPG International; Page 149: Holt Studios Limited/Earth Scenes/ Animals Animals; Page 153: Sara Hunsaker; Page 157: Robert S. Arnold, Old SturbridgeVillage; Page 162: Sara Hunsaker.

Chapter 7

Page 169: Todd Powell/ProFiles West; Page 174: Sara Hunsaker; Page 175: Gary Bumgarner/Tony Stone Worldwide;Page 178: G. L. Twiest/Visuals Unlimited; Page 181: Sara Hunsaker.

Chapter 8

Page188: Wiley Wales/ProFiles West; Page 194: Thomas Zimmermann/FPG International; Page 197: Custom Medical Stock Photo; Page 198: Peter A. Simon/Phototake; Page 201: NCI/ Science Source/Photo Researchers.

Chapter 9

Page 205: Dennis Kunkel/Phototake NYC; Page 207: Rita Amaya; Page 210: Runk/Schoenberger/Grant Heilman; Pages 212 and Pages 213: Sara Hunsaker.

Chapter 10

Page 225: Comstock; Page 232: Scott Camazine/Photo Researchers; Page 242: ProPix/Monkmeyer Press; Page 243: Brady/ Monkmeyer Press; Page 249: James Webb/Phototake; Page 253: Eric V. Gravè/Photo Researchers; Page 256: Science Source/Photo Researchers; Page 257: Visuals Unlimited.

Chapter 11

Page 263: Ocean Images/The Image Bank; Page 273: Liane Enkelis/Stock Boston; Page 277: Donna Jernigan/Monkmeyer Press; Page 279: Alfred Pasieka/Peter Arnold; Page 282: D. W. Fawcett/Photo Researchers.

Chapter 12

Page 286: Bob Daemmrich/The Image Works; Page 290: Manfred Kage/Peter Arnold; Page 301: AP/Wide World Photos; Page 308: Stanley Flegler/Visuals Unlimited; Page 317: James Holmes/ Science Photo Library/Photo Researchers.

Chapter 13

Page 321: Simon Yea/Tony Stone Worldwide; Page 323: Rita Amaya; Page 336: Sunkist Corporation.

Chapter 14

Pages 339 : Character House/Photo Researchers; 347: Photo Researchers; Page 353: David Scharf/Peter Arnold; Page 358: Science Source/Photo Researchers; Page 363: Science Photo Library/Photo Researchers.

Chapter 15

Page 367: Jeffrey W. Myers/Stock Boston; Page 369: Comstock; Page 370: Art Attack/Monkmeyer Press; Page 380: Paul Conklin/ Monkmeyer Press; Page 383: (3 photos) Sara Hunsaker; Page 388: Fawcett/Hirokawa/Henses/Science Source/Photo Researchers.

Chapter 16

Page 393: John Lawlor/TSN-Click/Chicago Limited; Page 395: Comstock; Page 404: K. R. Porter/Photo Researchers; Page 409: (top) Runk/Schoenberger/Grant Heilman, (bottom) Lawrence Berkeley Laboratory/University of California.

Chapter 17

Page 414: Steve Dunwell/The Image Bank; Page 422: AP/ WideWorld Photos Page 425: Ken Levinson/Monkmeyer Press; Page 427: Bettina Cirone/Photo Researchers.

Chapter 18

Page 434: Allen Russell/ProFiles West; Page 439: CNRI/Phototake.

Table of Atomic Masses (Weights) Based on Carbon-12

Name	Symbol	Atomic No.	Atomic Mass
Actinium	**Ac**	89	(227)[a]
Aluminum	**Al**	13	26.98154
Americium	**Am**	95	(243)[a]
Antimony	**Sb**	51	121.75
Argon	**Ar**	18	39.948
Arsenic	**As**	33	74.9216
Astatine	**At**	85	(210)[a]
Barium	**Ba**	56	137.34
Berkelium	**Bk**	97	(247)[a]
Beryllium	**Be**	4	9.01218
Bismuth	**Bi**	83	208.9804
Boron	**B**	5	10.81
Bromine	**Br**	35	79.904
Cadmium	**Cd**	48	112.40
Calcium	**Ca**	20	40.08
Californium	**Cf**	98	(251)[a]
Carbon	**C**	6	12.011
Cerium	**Ce**	58	140.12
Cesium	**Cs**	55	132.9054
Chlorine	**Cl**	17	35.453
Chromium	**Cr**	24	51.996
Cobalt	**Co**	27	58.9332
Copper	**Cu**	29	63.546
Curium	**Cm**	96	(247)[a]
Dysprosium	**Dy**	66	162.50
Einsteinium	**Es**	99	(252)[a]
Erbium	**Er**	68	167.26
Europium	**Eu**	63	151.96
Fermium	**Fm**	100	(257)[a]
Fluorine	**F**	9	18.99840
Francium	**Fr**	87	(223)[a]
Gadolinium	**Gd**	64	157.25
Gallium	**Ga**	31	69.72
Germanium	**Ge**	32	72.59
Gold	**Au**	79	196.9665
Hafnium	**Hf**	72	178.49
Helium	**He**	2	4.00260
Holmium	**Ho**	67	164.9304
Hydrogen	**H**	1	1.0079
Indium	**In**	49	114.82
Iodine	**I**	53	126.9045
Iridium	**Ir**	77	192.22
Iron	**Fe**	26	55.847
Krypton	**Kr**	36	83.80
Lanthanum	**La**	57	138.9055
Lawrencium	**Lr**	103	(260)[a]
Lead	**Pb**	82	207.2
Lithium	**Li**	3	6.941
Lutetium	**Lu**	71	174.97
Magnesium	**Mg**	12	24.305
Manganese	**Mn**	25	54.9380
Mendelevium	**Md**	101	(258)[a]
Mercury	**Hg**	80	200.59
Molybdenum	**Mo**	42	95.94
Neodymium	**Nd**	60	144.24
Neon	**Ne**	10	20.179
Neptunium	**Np**	93	237.0482[b]
Nickel	**Ni**	28	58.71
Niobium	**Nb**	41	92.9064
Nitrogen	**N**	7	14.0067
Nobelium	**No**	102	(259)[a]
Osmium	**Os**	76	190.2
Oxygen	**O**	8	15.9994
Palladium	**Pd**	46	106.4
Phosphorus	**P**	15	30.97376
Platinum	**Pt**	78	195.09
Plutonium	**Pu**	94	(244)[a]
Polonium	**Po**	84	(210)[a]
Potassium	**K**	19	39.098
Praseodymium	**Pr**	59	140.9077
Promethium	**Pm**	61	(145)[a]
Protactinium	**Pa**	91	231.0359[b]
Radium	**Ra**	88	226.0254[b]
Radon	**Rn**	86	(222)[a]
Rhenium	**Re**	75	186.2
Rhodium	**Rh**	45	102.9055
Rubidium	**Rb**	37	85.4678
Ruthenium	**Ru**	44	101.07
Samarium	**Sm**	62	150.4
Scandium	**Sc**	21	44.9559
Selenium	**Se**	34	78.96
Silicon	**Si**	14	28.086
Silver	**Ag**	47	107.868
Sodium	**Na**	11	22.98977
Strontium	**Sr**	38	87.62
Sulfur	**S**	16	32.06
Tantalum	**Ta**	73	180.9479
Technetium	**Tc**	43	98.9062[b]
Tellurium	**Te**	52	127.60
Terbium	**Tb**	65	158.9254
Thallium	**Tl**	81	204.37
Thorium	**Th**	90	232.0381[b]
Thulium	**Tm**	69	168.9342
Tin	**Sn**	50	118.69
Titanium	**Ti**	22	47.90
Tungsten	**W**	74	183.85
Unnilhexium	**Unh**	106	(263)[a]
Unnilpentium	**Unp**	105	(262)[a]
Unnilquadium	**Unq**	104	(261)[a]
Uranium	**U**	92	238.029
Vanadium	**V**	23	50.9414
Xenon	**Xe**	54	131.30
Ytterbium	**Yb**	70	173.04
Yttrium	**Y**	39	88.9059
Zinc	**Zn**	30	65.38
Zirconium	**Zr**	40	91.22

[a]Mass number of most stable or best-known isotope

[b]Mass number of the isotope of longest half-life